THE KINGFISHER
NATURAL
HISTORY
OF BRITAIN
& EUROPE

THE KINGFISHER
NATURAL
HISTORY
OF BRITAIN
& EUROPE

Consultant Editor

MICHAEL CHINERY

Kingfisher Books

CONSULTANT EDITOR
Michael Chinery

SENIOR EDITOR
Stuart Cooper

ASSISTANT EDITORS
John Birdsall
Neil Harris
Nina Hathway
Andrea Moran
Rick Morris

DESIGN
Peter Bridgewater
Heather Gough
Louise Jervis
Annie Moss
Michael Rand
Terry Woodley

PICTURE RESEARCH
Sue Alexander
Elaine Willis

Kingfisher Books, Grisewood & Dempsey Ltd,
Elsley House, 24–30 Great Titchfield Street,
London W1P 7AD

First published in 1992 by Kingfisher Books
2 4 6 8 10 9 7 5 3 1

BRITISH LIBRARY CATALOGUING IN PUBLICATION DATA
A catalogue record for this book is available
from the British Library.

ISBN 0 86272 774 X

Phototypeset by Tradespools Ltd, Frome, Somerset
Printed in Spain

CONTENTS

HABITAT ESSAYS

INTRODUCTION

Europe stretches from the Arctic environment of the North Cape to the heat of the Mediterranean, and from Iceland to the Ural Mountains. The Urals are regarded as Europe's official eastern boundary, but for the purposes of this book the boundary runs from the North Cape to the western shores of the Black Sea and Istanbul, roughly following the 30° East line of longitude.

LEFT: The upland hay meadows are among Europe's richest habitats for flowering plants. This one in the Italian Dolomites is dominated by Meadow Crane's-bill.

Europe's Habitat Zones

Packed into Europe's 10,500,000 square kilometres is an amazingly wide variety of habitats and a wealth of beautiful and fascinating wildlife. There are no tropical forests and no typical deserts, although parts of Spain verge on a true desert climate. The tundra of Iceland and Lapland is also a dry habitat and is often described as a cold desert. Extensive coniferous forests, collectively known as the taiga, stretch across many northern areas, and further south are numerous deciduous woodlands. Grasslands cover much of central Europe, while to the south there are fragments of forest and scrub whose plants are adapted to the hot, dry summers of the Mediterranean region. Superimposed on these major life-zones are the rivers and coastlines and the mountains. Short essays, scattered through this book, describe the essential features of each habitat and its characteristic plant and animal life.

VEGETATION ZONES

- Tundra
- Taiga
- Deciduous forest
- Steppe grassland
- Mediterranean
- Montane

The map shows the distribution of the major types of vegetation in Europe. Montane vegetation includes the mountain forests as well as the true alpine vegetation that occurs above the tree line.

Oxford Ragwort has spread rapidly along Britain's roadsides during the last 150 years and has invaded all kinds of waste ground.

Scope of this Book

One of the aims of this book is to help you to identify some of the rich variety of European wildlife. It includes a wide range of plants and animals, from all the major habitats. The mammals and birds are covered in full, but the other groups are represented only by the most common or conspicuous members of each group. As well as helping with identification, this book explains how the species fit into their environments – why they live where they do and what they do during their daily lives.

You don't have to go to wild or remote places to find wildlife. Plants and animals are everywhere and there are many opportunities to enjoy nature in your garden or in the town park. Gardens are, in fact, among the most important habitats today, for while woods and heaths are disappearing under the plough or under bricks and mortar, gardens are increasing rapidly as we build more and more houses. The growing tendency to make gardens attractive to wildlife adds to their importance as habitats. Naturalists often curse new roads and the havoc they cause in the countryside, but roads do have some benefit. They allow us to get out into the countryside and see wildlife, and the roadsides themselves can actually play a part in conserving wildlife. Motorway verges, for example, are rarely-disturbed areas of grassland and scrub and they provide homes for a wide range of plants and animals.

Classification and Names

For ease of reference, the flowering plants included in this book have been placed in two separate chapters – Wild Flowers and Trees and Shrubs – but the rest of the plants and animals are arranged in chapters in accordance with their scientific classification.

The Animal Kingdom is split into about 30 major groups known as phyla (singular: phylum). The members of each phylum all share a similar body plan. All the vertebrates (animals with backbones), for example, belong to the Phylum Chordata, with the mammals, birds, reptiles, amphibians, and fishes forming various classes of this phylum. The other phyla in the Animal Kingdom, which include all the invertebrates (animals without backbones), are similarly divided into classes. The classes are divided into orders, and the orders are divided into families. Animal family names all end in -idae. Each of the families contains one or more genera (singular: genus), and each genus contains one or more species. The classification of plants is runs on similar lines, although the family names all end in -aceae.

CLASSIFCATION OF THE RED FOX	
Kingdom	Animalia
Phylum	Chordata
Class	Mammalia
Order	Carnivora
Family	Canidae
Genus	Vulpes
Species	Vulpes vulpes

Most species in this book have an English name and a scientific name, the latter consisting of two parts and usually printed in italics. The first part is the generic name (the name of the genus) and is often shared by several closely related species. The second part is the specific name. Scientific names are understood all over the world, but they are not entirely stable and you might find different names in different books. Such changes occur when biologists make new discoveries about the relationships of species. Many invertebrates and flowerless plants have no English names.

Look after Wildlife

Wild plants and animals are becoming less common every year as woods and hedgerows are ripped out, grassland is ploughed up, and marshland is drained. Conservation organisations are doing sterling work to halt the decline in wildlife in many countries, but it is up to all of us to do our bit. Never pick large numbers of flowers – and certainly never dig up wild plants for your garden. Rare flowers should never be picked. Take your field guide to the flower, and then you won't need to pick it for identification. Small insects may have to be caught for accurate identification, but they should be released afterwards. Several countries now have laws protecting many of their plants and animals and forbidding collection.

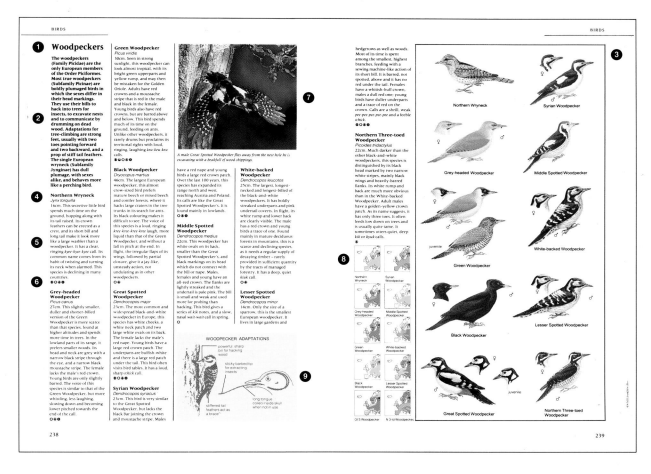

HOW TO USE THIS BOOK

1 Within each chapter, most of the plants and animals are arranged in their families, although larger groupings – such as orders and classes – are used for the flowerless plants and for some of the invertebrates.

2 A short introduction gives the main characteristics of the family or larger group.

3 Accurate illustrations help with identification. The sex is indicated if males ♂ and females ♀ are significantly different.

4 Each species is given its English name (if there is one), its scientific name (in italics), and its family name. If no family name is given it may be assumed that the species belongs to the same family as the preceding one.

5 A text describes a species' behaviour, as well as indicating size, distribution, and time of appearance. Where no distribution is given it may be assumed that the species occurs in suitable habitats throughout Europe. If no times of appearance are given it may be assumed that the species can be found throughout the year.

6 Symbols (explained right) show at a glance the main habitats of each species, whether it occurs in the British Isles, and whether it is in danger of extinction. The symbols for the tundra and for the Mediterranean indicate that the species is characteristic of the region although not necessarily confined to it.

7 Colour photographs show animals and plants in their natural environments.

8 Distribution maps are provided for birds and mammals, the distributions of which are better known than those of other groups of animals or plants.

9 Additional information on many species appears in accompanying charts or diagrams.

KEY TO SYMBOLS

Ⓑ Found in Britain

◔ Mediterranean

◓ Tundra

◭ Mountains

◒ Heaths and moors

◯ Deciduous woodland

♣ Coniferous woodland

◉ Freshwater

✖ Man-made habitats

◒ The coast

⬤ Grasslands

⊗ In danger of extinction

WILD FLOWERS

Flowering plants belong to the most advanced group of plants, known as the Angiosperms. The group contains all of the flower-bearing plants, including trees and shrubs as well as plants usually thought of as wild flowers that are generally herbaceous, with most or all of the plant composed of non-woody tissue. Trees and large shrubs are covered in a separate chapter of this book, but spreading or dwarf shrubs that are not obviously different from perennial wild flowers are included in this section.

Some wild flowers are evergreen but most species die back to become invisible for at least one season – usually the harshest – of the year.

Flowering Plant Groups

Flowering plants are divided into two classes – the monocotyledons and the dicotyledons. This division is based on whether the germinating seed produces one or two cotyledons or seed-leaves.

Dicotyledons have two seed-leaves. They have a primary root that may develop as a tap-root, with smaller roots arising from it. The stem's transport system consists of regularly arranged bundles of vascular tissue. The leaves have a network of veins and a strong mid-rib. They may have stipules. The flowers have floral parts in fours or fives.

Monocotyledons have one seed-leaf. They have a tap-root that is soon replaced by adventitious roots growing from the stem base. The transport system consists of bundles of vascular tissue scattered irregularly throughout the stem. The leaves are parallel-veined, without a clear mid-rib. They are rarely stalked and lack stipules. The flowers have floral parts in threes or sixes.

Within these two groups, flowering plants are divided into families.

ABOVE: *One of many dwarf shrubs, Shrubby Milkwort is rarely more than a few centimetres high.*

BELOW: *An example of a dicotyledon (Charlock) and monocotyledon (Bee Orchid).*

The Families of Flowering Plants

The number of flowering plant families is held to be between 250 and 350. The most primitive flowers are those with many parts, of indefinite number, such as the flowers of the water-lilies. Sepals, petals, stamens and carpels are all present, but the sepals and petals are arranged in whorls and not united. The flower is regularly symmetrical. Gradually, primitive flowers have become modified, with floral parts decreasing to a definite number. Fusion of sepals and petals may occur, producing a calyx tube and a corolla tube. Sepals and petals may even be absent. The flower may be male ♂ or female ♀, rather than hermaphrodite ☿. Advanced pollination methods may also bring about change. The flower may become irregularly symmetrical. Alternatively, instead of being large and single, the flowers may become small and crowded together in heads, as in the Daisy Family.

Charlock

Bee Orchid

Plant Life Cycles

Wild flowers show three distinct life cycles: annual, biennial and perennial. Annuals go through their cycle from germination to seed setting in a single season. The plant survives the inclement season as a resistant seed.

Biennials go through their cycle in two years. In the first year, the plant produces leaves, and forms food-storage organs to survive the hard season. In the second year it produces flowers, then seeds, and then it dies.

Perennials live for several years. Most survive the hard season either as dormant buds or as underground storage organs.

Leaf shape is very useful for identifying plants. The pinnate (compound) leaf is divided into separate leaflets.

LEAF SHAPES

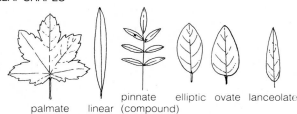

palmate   linear   pinnate   elliptic   ovate   lanceolate
                    (compound)

Habitats

Some plants are confined to only one or two habitats, while others are more far-ranging. An adaptable species, such as the Daisy, is found from the Arctic tundra to the Mediterranean, whereas Edelweiss is restricted to alpine rocks. The flora of each habitat is made up of a few characteristic species and a larger number of less choosy species. Extreme habitats such as high mountain areas show little variation in their flora from place to place. Heaths and moors, freshwater and coastal habitats, show more variation, and less demanding habitats such as woodland and grassland are still richer in species and vary greatly from area to area.

The Parts of a Plant

Roots Roots are of two types. The first is the single tap-root found in many perennials. The second type, known as adventitious roots, are found in all annuals and many perennials. They arise in unusual positions (not from the initial root of the seedling) and form a branching network. The functions of the roots are to absorb water and salts from the soil, and to anchor the plant.

Stem The stem's function is to hold the leaves and flowers in an optimum arrangement to absorb sunlight and attract pollinating insects.

Leaves The leaves are where sugars are synthesized from carbon dioxide and water, utilizing light energy via the green pigment chlorophyll. The leaf shape gives clues to identity, and six basic forms are shown above. In some species the leaves are veined or hairy. Leaves may be stalked or unstalked, and where they join the stem there may be a small, leaf-like stipule.

Bracts Bracts are leaf-like organs found at the base of the flower stalk.

Flowers The flowers are the plant's organs of sexual reproduction, and they lead to the formation of the seed.

The Parts of a Flower

Sepals Sepals are usually green, and form the protective bud over the flower. Together they form the calyx.

Petals Petals are often large and brightly coloured, often with markings to guide insects into the middle of the flower. Together they form the corolla.

Stamens Stamens consist of the filament and the anthers. They are the male parts of the flower. Pollen grains are produced in the anthers and the male gametes develop in the pollen grains.

Carpels Carpels contain the ovules, which enclose the female gametes. Pollen falls on the stigmas, and sends a tube through the style to the ovule. The male gamete passes down this tube and fertilizes the female gamete. Once fertilized, the ovule becomes a seed and the whole structure surrounding it develops as a fruit. By examining the number and structure of their floral parts, you can readily allot wild flowers to their families.

The Buttercup shows all the major parts of a typical flowering plant.

flower

flower stalk

bract

leaf

leaf stalk (petiole)

leaf axil

stipule

A TYPICAL FLOWERING PLANT

stem

root

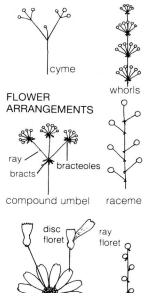

cyme

whorls

FLOWER ARRANGEMENTS

ray bracts   bracteoles

compound umbel   raceme

disc floret   ray floret

composite flower head   spike

LEFT: *Six basic types of floral arrangement, or inflorescence, and the terms used to describe them.*

RIGHT: *All the specialized floral structures can be seen in this section through a typical flower.*

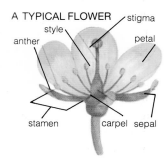

A TYPICAL FLOWER   stigma
style   petal
anther

stamen   carpel   sepal

Flowering Times

The charts on the following pages give the
average flowering times for each species, but it
should be remembered that plants growing in
northern latitudes may flower several weeks later
than the same species growing in warmer regions.
Flowering times also vary with the local weather
conditions and a cold snap in the spring can delay
flowering for several weeks.

Pollination

The most common method of pollination used by
wild flowers involves insects, and many species
have developed special techniques to entice them
such as offering nectar as a reward. Colour helps

to advertise the flowers to potential insect visitors, and many flowers bear
special markings to guide the insects to the nectar. While visiting a flower, an
insect becomes dusted with pollen, which is later transferred to the stigma of
another flower to effect cross-pollination. Shape may also be important in
attracting or repelling visitors. Primitive blossoms, such as buttercups, are
open to many pollinators. More specialized flowers, such as toadflaxes,
conceal their nectar in a long spur, to exclude all but long-tongued insects.

Many plants use wind and water to carry their pollen. In these cases the
flower is simplified, as showy petals are not required. All that are needed are
large amounts of pollen that will float in air or on water, and a stigma that is
designed to waylay the passing pollen grains.

ABOVE: *The Wild Rose is
pollinated by insects such as
the beetle* Strangalia
maculata.

creeping,
rooting stem
(Wild Thyme)

LEFT: *The long, creeping
stems of Wild Thyme root at
intervals and quickly form
extensive mats.*

RIGHT: *Star-of-Bethlehem
increases rapidly through the
production of many small
bulbs at the base of
the parent bulb.*

bulb
(Star-of-
Bethlehem)

Grasses are the best known of the wind-pollinated plants and their flowers
are built in a rather different way from the typical flowers just described.
Each flower consists of a single carpel and three stamens, without sepals or
petals. The flowers are enclosed in spikelets, which consist of two outer scales
called glumes and a number of smaller inner scales. One or more of these
scales may bear a bristle called an awn, and if these are long they give the
flower heads a bristly appearance. The number of flowers in a spikelet varies
from one to many, and the spikelets may be grouped in dense spikes (ears)
or in loose, spreading heads called panicles.

Many plants also have another technique. If not rapidly insect-pollinated,
they automatically self-pollinate. This fail-safe mechanism guarantees 100
per cent seed production, albeit at the expense of genetic variations.

Some perennial plants are also able to reproduce vegetatively; that is, from
parts other than seeds and without the need for any form of sexual
reproduction. Common methods of vegetative reproduction include rooting
from creeping overground stems (stolons and runners), regeneration from
fragments of underground stems (rhizomes) and the production of small
bulbs as offsets from the parent bulb. In such cases the plant can spread
rapidly to form large colonies.

13

Dicotyledons

WILLOW FAMILY

Although almost all willows (Salicaceae) are trees or shrubs, a few arctic and alpine species are so dwarfed that they do not produce even a short trunk but only a creeping, underground stem with extremely short aerial branches. A dwarf habit is a typical survival strategy in harsh habitats, reducing the adverse effects of the cold and the wind in exposed situations.

Least Willow
Salix herbacea
Up to 3cm high. This is a prostrate, mat-forming, deciduous dwarf shrub. It has slender stems bearing small, round, shiny green leaves, toothed at the margins. Its flowers are borne in short catkins, appearing after the leaves and with males and females on separate plants, the females later releasing tiny seeds with fluffy, white hairs. It is found in arctic tundra and the mountains of northern and central Europe, growing in damp grassland and among rocks up to 2800m. Its dwarf habit and seeds, which are dispersed by winds, are adaptions to open, treeless conditions.
Ⓑ◒◓

RAFFLESIA FAMILY

The plants of this family (Rafflesiaceae) chiefly come from the tropics and subtropics, where they are total parasites, obtaining all their nutrients and water from a host plant. They do not need roots, stems or green leaves of their own and consist only of a web-like system spread through the host's tissues. The flowers burst through the roots or stems of the host to allow pollination and dispersal of the seeds. They include some of the largest known flowers which are up to a metre across. In order to attract the flies which pollinate them, the fleshy flowers of many species produce a strong odour of rotting meat. They may also be blotched and livid coloured to resemble carrion. The fruits of these species may also be fleshy and they contain numerous seeds.

Cytinus hypocistis
Up to 4cm high. This extraordinary plant has no English name. Completely lacking green chlorophyll, it grows as a parasite attached to the roots of *Cistus* bushes. Its visible part comprises a fleshy, waxy-textured, globular head of tubular, bright yellow flowers, each surrounded by orange-red bracts. The central flowers are male, the outer ones female. Its underground part is a fleshy, horn-shaped stem, narrowed at the base and closely covered with orange-red scales. It is widespread in the Mediterranean region in scrubland. *C. ruber*, found in south-eastern Europe, has pink and white flowers.
◒

MISTLETOE FAMILY

Most of the 1500 or so species in this family (Loranthaceae) are semi-parasites. They contain chlorophyll and so can manufacture some food, but rely on their hosts

Tiny male catkins of the Least Willow are cradled in the ground-hugging leaves on the windswept northern tundra.

for water and minerals. These are obtained via specialized roots which invade the host's roots or stem. The majority of species are small, brittle shrubs growing on the branches of other trees. The family is spread throughout the southern hemisphere and milder parts of the northern hemisphere.

Mistletoe
Viscum album
This small shrub is parasitic on the branches of trees. Its specialized roots (haustoria) invade the tissues of the host, drawing off water and nutrients. Regularly forked, green stems bear opposite pairs of leathery leaves and small, yellowish flowers, with males and females on separate plants. Translucent white berries with sticky juice ripen after about nine months. The plant is dispersed by birds which wipe the seeds from their beaks after eating the berries. The common European form of mistletoe grows on a large range of deciduous trees, especially apples and poplars, but two southern and central European forms occur only on conifers.
Ⓑ◒◓◔

HOP FAMILY

This tiny family (Cannabidaceae) contains only three species. One is cannabis, an erect, perennial herb no longer found truly wild but cultivated widely as a source of fibre, birdseed, and oil for soap and food, as well as for drugs. The other two members are hops: climbing plants with twining stems. The leaves are bristly with gland-bearing hairs. Wind-pollinated, the male and female flowers are borne on separate plants. The fruit is a very small nut.

Hop
Humulus lupulus
Up to 6m. This climbing, perennial herb has slender, four-sided, bristly stems which twine clockwise. Its leaves are broad and deeply cut into three or five lobes with toothed margins. The male flowers are borne in open, much-branched clusters. The dense heads of small, green, female flowers are followed by oval fruiting heads with overlapping, leaf-like bracts giving a cone-like appearance. Widespread in

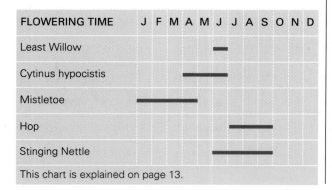

FLOWERING TIME	J	F	M	A	M	J	J	A	S	O	N	D
Least Willow						▬						
Cytinus hypocistis				▬▬▬								
Mistletoe		▬▬▬										
Hop							▬▬▬					
Stinging Nettle							▬▬▬					

This chart is explained on page 13.

Europe, it is commonly found in woods, hedges and among scrub. Cultivars of this species are grown commercially for their fruiting heads which give ale its bitter flavour. Pillows stuffed with hops have also been used to relieve nervous ailments and insomnia.

Ⓑ ◐ ✿

NETTLE FAMILY

Many of the thousand or so species in this widespread family (Urticaceae) are armed with stinging hairs which act as a protection against grazing animals – though not against the various caterpillars for which it is a food plant. The hairs contain formic acid, which causes the stinging sensation and an allergic rash when the plant is touched. The family includes trees, shrubs and vines, but all European species are herbaceous. The male and female flowers are green but tend to be inconspicuous, lacking petals. The stamens of male flowers in this family are violently flicked out as the flower opens, expelling clouds of pollen.

Stinging Nettle
Urtica dioica
Up to 150cm. This perennial herb has erect stems and opposite pairs of heart-shaped, serrated leaves all covered with bristly, stinging hairs. These function as hypodermic needles which pierce the skin and break open to release formic acid from the cavity within. Its flowers are small and green, and carried on branched catkin-like shoots which droop on female plants and spread outwards on male plants. It is found throughout Europe in various habitats, but prefers rich soils where it often forms dense patches. The young shoots are rich in Vitamin C and are edible. They can be cooked in exactly the same way as spinach. The similar Small Nettle (*U. urens*) is an annual with the flowers of both sexes borne on the same plant.

Ⓑ ◐ ✿

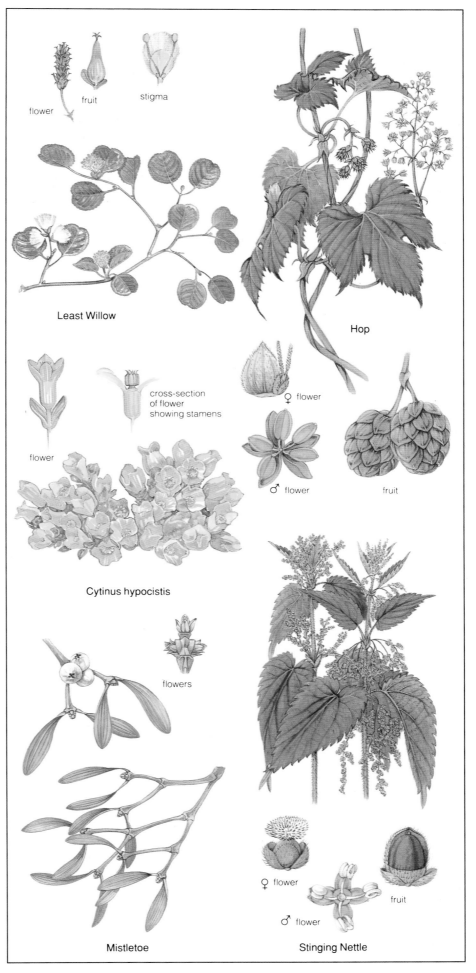

flower fruit stigma

Least Willow

Hop

cross-section of flower showing stamens

flower

♀ flower

♂ flower

fruit

Cytinus hypocistis

flowers

Mistletoe

♀ flower

♂ flower

fruit

Stinging Nettle

DOCK FAMILY

Most members of this large, abundant family (Polygonaceae) are from the northern temperate regions. They include trees, shrubs and climbers as well as herbaceous plants. Many are found in arid zones; others are invasive weeds of farm land. There are also useful species including buckwheat and rhubarb. The leaves have a characteristic papery sheath, called an ochrea, encircling the stem at the leaf-base. The fruit is a small nut enclosed by the persistent flower.

Amphibious bistort
Polygonum amphibium
This creeping perennial has reddish stems up to 70cm long, bearing oval to narrowly oblong leaves. Two distinct forms exist: one floats in water, and has smooth leaves on long stalks, the other grows on adjacent damp ground and is almost upright with slightly hairy leaves on shorter stalks. Small, pink flowers are borne in dense spikes at tips of stems. It is found widely in Europe.
Ⓑ☻

Redshank
Polygonum persicaria
Up to 80cm. This branched annual has sprawling reddish stems which are swollen at the leaf-joints where fringed, brownish scales (ochreae) are attached. Its leaves are spear-shaped, and often bear dark blotches. The small, pink flowers are densely crowded into short spikes borne at the tips of stems. It is widespread

in Europe often growing on disturbed soil in waste ground. It is also a common weed found in arable fields and gardens.
Ⓑ☻✪

Knotgrass
Polygonum aviculare
This annual usually forms low mats which may reach 100cm across. Its stems are slender and branched, and bear small, narrowly elliptical to spear-shaped leaves. Tiny white or pink flowers are borne in angles between the leaf-stalks and stem. Widespread throughout most of Europe, it grows in waste areas, on seashores and disturbed soil. Its seeds may lie dormant for years before they germinate.
Ⓑ✪☻

Sheep's Sorrel
Rumex acetosella
Up to 30cm. A perennial herb, it has an upright, branching habit. The lower leaves each have a pair of prominent basal lobes, while those above are few and unlobed. The small, reddish flowers are male or female, borne on separate plants and arranged in circular clusters surrounding shoots at regular intervals. It is widespread throughout Europe in open, dry places on sandy, acidic soils, heathlands and shingle. The leaves taste sour as they contain calcium oxalate.
Ⓑ☻☻⚀

Broad-leaved Dock
Rumex obtusifolia
Up to 120cm. A perennial, with deep tap-roots and upright, branching stems, its leaves are broad and oblong low down but become narrower higher up the plant. The small, green flowers

Hottentot Fig, seen here in Jersey, clothes many coastal cliffs with its bright pink, daisy-like flowers throughout the summer.

occur in circular groups around the stems and have three toothed sepal-like petals which enlarge after pollination to enclose fruits. It is widespread in Europe and is commonly found beside woods, fields, roads and in waste areas, especially on disturbed ground. It was once used medicinally for skin complaints and its leaves are still rubbed on to nettle stings to alleviate pain.
Ⓑ◐✪

MESEMBRYAN-THEMUM FAMILY

Containing over 2000 species, most members of this family (Aizoaceae) are found in South Africa, with only a few widespread species occurring elsewhere. All are adapted to desert conditions and have fleshy leaves to store water. The daisy-like flowers have numerous petals. The family includes the so-called 'living stones', which are plant mimics having a single pair of glossy, swollen leaves coloured and patterned to match precisely the different rocks among which each species grows.

Hottentot Fig
Carpobrotus edulis
A very fleshy, succulent plant, it forms coarse mats of trailing stems. Its upwardly curving, three-sided leaves are often reddish at the tip. The flowers have numerous yellow or magenta petals and open completely only in full sun. Its large fruit, crowned with persistent sepals, is fleshy and edible. Native to South Africa,

it has been introduced to many parts of Europe both to stabilize sandy soils and as a decorative plant. It now flourishes on beaches, dunes and cliffs in mild areas as far north as Britain but always near the sea.
Ⓑ◐☻

PURSLANE FAMILY

Many of the 500 species of this common family (Portulacaceae) are found in South Africa and South America but a few occur in colder regions of the world. Most are fleshy-leaved annuals or herbaceous perennials. The flowers have two sepals and usually five petals; the fruit is a capsule. Various species are grown as garden flowers and several others are used as either salad plants or root vegetables.

Spring Beauty
Montia perfoliata
Up to 30cm. This annual has several rather fleshy upright stems and opposite pairs of upper leaves, fused at the base and encircling the stem to form a round, green cup, above which are clustered the white-petalled flowers. The basal leaves, in contrast, are very long-stalked. Its fruits are small capsules, enclosed by the sepals. A plant introduced from North America, it is now found scattered on waste and cultivated ground, in western Europe where it prefers light sandy soils. Pink Purslane (*M. sibirica*) has larger, pink flowers and the stem leaves are not joined at the base.
Ⓑ✪

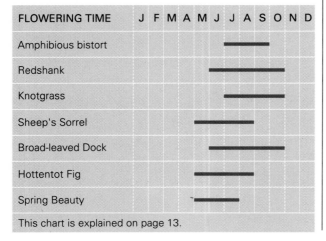

FLOWERING TIME	J F M A M J J A S O N D
Amphibious bistort	— — —
Redshank	— — — —
Knotgrass	— — — —
Sheep's Sorrel	— — —
Broad-leaved Dock	— — —
Hottentot Fig	— — —
Spring Beauty	—
This chart is explained on page 13.	

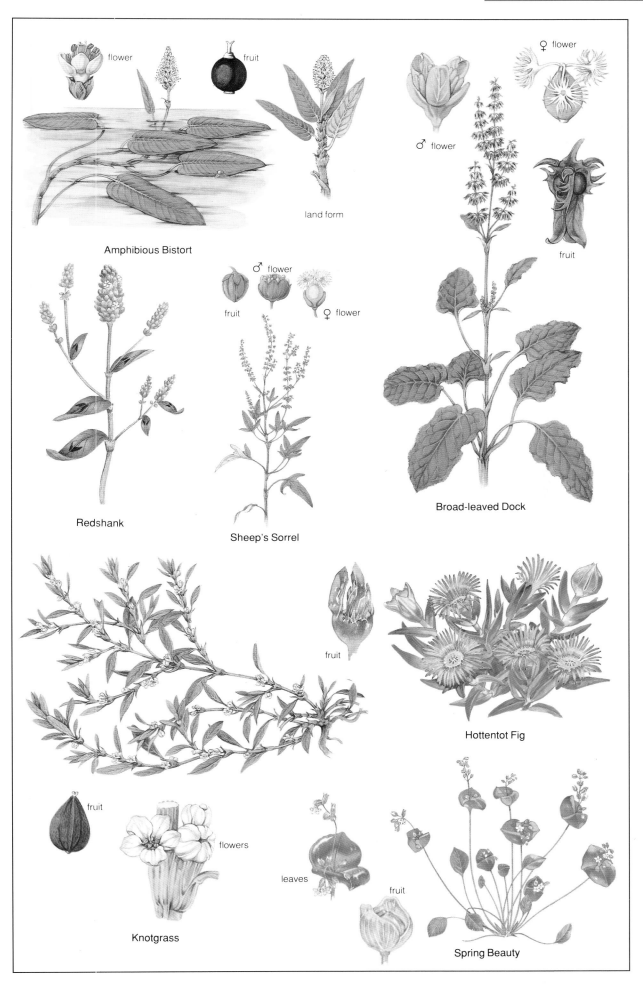

flower

fruit

♂ flower

♀ flower

land form

fruit

Amphibious Bistort

Redshank

fruit   ♂ flower

♀ flower

Sheep's Sorrel

Broad-leaved Dock

fruit

Hottentot Fig

fruit

flowers

leaves

fruit

Knotgrass

Spring Beauty

GOOSEFOOT FAMILY

Some 1500 species make up this family (Chenopodiaceae) of salt-tolerant plants which includes vegetables such as beetroot and spinach. Most grow in coastal habitats or in desert regions. These plants typically have extensive root systems and lobed or spiny leaves. Some species have no leaves and resemble tiny cacti.

Fat-hen
Chenopodium album
Up to 150cm. This much-branched annual has upright stems. Its lower leaves are diamond-shaped, shallowly toothed and densely covered with whitish meal. The tiny, green flowers are crowded into densely branched clusters. A widespread weed in Europe, it is commonly found in disturbed soil and on cultivated ground. If boiled, it can be eaten like spinach.
Ⓑ ✿

Common Orache
Atriplex patula
Up to 150cm. A much-branched annual similar to Fat-hen, this plant has upright, often reddish stems. Its lower leaves are diamond-shaped with forward-pointing lobes on their margins and covered with a whitish, mealy coating. Its unisexual flowers are tiny and green, and borne in short, terminal spikes. Each flower is enclosed by a pair of small, triangular structures (bracteoles). Widespread in Europe, it grows in waste areas, salt-marshes and on beaches. It was once grown as a spinach-like vegetable.
Ⓑ ✿ 🌊

Sea-purslane
Halimione portulacoides
Up to 80cm, rarely to 150cm. This much-branched, rather sprawling, shrubby perennial bears elliptical leaves with a silvery-mealy coating of microscopic, papery hairs. Its flowers are borne in dense, yellowish, terminal spikes. Widespread on European coasts, it grows in muddy salt-marshes. The mealy coating on its leaves provides protection from the drying effects of salty water.
Ⓑ 🌊

Glasswort
Salicornia europaea
Up to 40cm. This is a very fleshy annual with jointed, usually branched stems often flushed reddish or yellowish. Its leaves are reduced to fleshy, translucent scales in opposite pairs fused together and completely surrounding the stem. Tiny greenish flowers are borne near the stem tip. Widespread on European coasts, it grows in the mud of salt-marshes, and occasionally in saline places inland. Its young shoots may be eaten lightly boiled or pickled in vinegar.
Ⓑ 🌊

Annual Sea-blite
Suaeda maritima
Up to 60cm, rarely to 1m. This branching, often reddish-flushed annual has prostrate to upright stems bearing narrow, fleshy leaves, each with a flat upper surface and a pointed tip. Its flowers are small and greenish, carried in axils of leaves and stems. Widespread on European coasts, it grows in sandy parts of salt-marshes and on beaches. This plant was once burned to produce ashes rich in soda for glass-making.
Ⓑ 🌊

FLOWERING TIME	J	F	M	A	M	J	J	A	S	O	N	D
Fat-hen						▬	▬	▬	▬			
Common Orache						▬	▬	▬				
Sea-purslane						▬	▬	▬				
Glasswort							▬					
Annual Sea-blite						▬	▬	▬	▬			
Common Poppy						▬	▬	▬				
Yellow Horned-poppy						▬	▬	▬				
Greater Celandine					▬	▬	▬	▬	▬			
Common Fumitory				▬	▬	▬	▬	▬	▬			

This chart is explained on page 13.

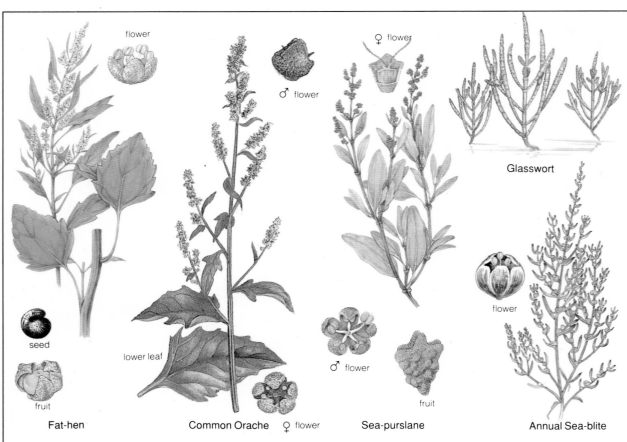

flower

♂ flower

♀ flower

seed

lower leaf

fruit

Fat-hen

Common Orache   ♀ flower

♂ flower

fruit

Sea-purslane

Glasswort

flower

Annual Sea-blite

Field Poppies still produce brilliant splashes of colour on roadsides and field margins, despite the use of weedkillers.

POPPY FAMILY

The 200 or so species of this varied family (Papaveraceae) include many flowers and weeds found in northern, temperate areas. The family can be divided into two distinct groups. The poppies (genus *Papaver*) produce milky or coloured sap. Their flowers are bowl-shaped and the fruit is a capsule. The fumitories (genus *Fumaria*) are generally sprawling plants with watery sap. They have narrow, almost tubular flowers with a short, rounded spur and the fruit is a nut.

Common Poppy
Papaver rhoeas
Up to 60cm. This annual has stiffly hairy, branched upright stems containing a sticky white latex. Its pinnately lobed leaves are deeply divided into narrow, pointed and toothed lobes. The scarlet flowers are up to 10cm across and often have a dark blotch at the base of each petal. The fruit is a smooth, globular capsule with a ring of small pores at the top to release the seeds. Although becoming less common because of improvements in agriculture, it is still a frequent weed of cultivated ground, with seeds that can remain viable in the soil for many years.
Ⓑ Ⓧ Ⓦ

Yellow Horned-poppy
Glaucium flavum
Up to 1m. This erect biennial or perennial of coastal areas has branched stems and pinnately lobed leaves which are bluish green and rough. The lower leaves are deeply cut into toothed lobes, the upper ones less lobed and clasping the stem at the base. The large pale or golden-yellow flowers are up to 9cm across. The distinctive fruits are long and curved, the two sides splitting almost to the base when mature, the seeds remaining embedded in the dividing wall. This plant is characteristic of maritime shingle, but sometimes may also be found inland.
Ⓑ ☻

Greater Celandine
Chelidonium majus
Up to 90cm. This perennial herb contains a poisonous orange sap. Its soft-textured, pinnate leaves are a bluish-green beneath. The flowers are golden yellow. The fruits are narrow, and the black seeds have an oily white outgrowth that is attractive to ants, who collect the seeds and help in their dispersal. The Greater Celandine is common in Europe, and is usually found near human habitation.
Ⓑ Ⓧ

Common Fumitory
Fumaria officinalis
Up to 70cm. This upright or scrambling annual plant has slender, finely cut stems and bluish-green leaves. Each flower has four pink petals with blackish-purple tips, the upper one hooded and prolonged into a short spur. The fruits are small nutlets, each with a single seed. It is a common weed found on cultivated ground.
Ⓑ Ⓧ

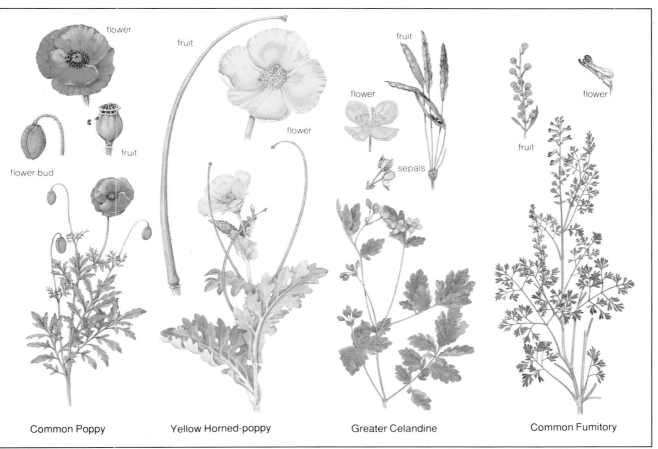

Common Poppy   Yellow Horned-poppy   Greater Celandine   Common Fumitory

STITCHWORT FAMILY

The 2000 species of this world-wide family (Caryophyllaceae) include many well-known wild flowers such as campions and stitchworts as well as garden flowers including pinks and carnations. They are annuals or herbaceous perennials with swollen nodes bearing opposite leaves. The flowers have four or five sepals, either separate or fused into a tube. The four or five petals are often deeply notched or fringed and there are two to five styles. Some species have flowers which open or emit scent only at night to attract moths for pollination. The fruit is a toothed capsule.

Greater Stitchwort
Stellaria holostea
Up to 60cm. A straggling perennial with very thin, brittle stems, it has narrow, rather stiff leaves which are very rough on the margins and below on the midrib. Its white flowers are visited by many different insects including flies, bees, and beetles. The fruit is a globular capsule containing numerous kidney-shaped seeds. A common plant of woods and hedgerows, it is found throughout Europe but occurs infrequently in the Mediterranean region. It was once used to treat a stitch or pains in the side.
Ⓑ Ⓞ 🏵

Common Chickweed
Stellaria media
This low-growing, sprawling annual has weak, much-branched stems up to 15cm long, with a single line of hairs running down their length. Its leaves are oval and pointed and only the lower ones are stalked. It is a prolific, widespread weed, flowering more or less all year round and readily producing seed. The flowers have deeply lobed petals, about the same length as the sepals. A variable and cosmopolitan species, it is most often found on arable and waste ground.
Ⓑ Ⓧ 🏵

Sand Spurrey
Spergularia rubra
Up to 30cm. This sprawling annual or perennial has conspicuous silvery stipules with ragged tips and narrow, pointed leaves. The pink petals are slightly shorter than the sepals. Its fruit is a capsule which opens by three valves. Common throughout Europe, it grows on sandy and gravelly open ground.
Ⓑ Ⓧ 🏵

Moss Campion
Silene acaulis
Up to 10cm. This low-growing perennial forms tufted, moss-like cushions. Bright green, narrow, pointed leaves occur in dense rosettes. Its solitary flowers vary in colour from reddish pink to white. This is a plant of damp rocks, cliffs and short turf, and it is found in northern and mountainous areas.
Ⓑ ◐ ◑

The fragrant flowers of Bladder Campion are pollinated largely by long-tongued, night-flying moths.

Red Campion
Silene dioica
Up to 90cm. This biennial or perennial plant is rather similar in habit to the White Campion, but with more short, sterile shoots at the base. Its male and female flowers are borne on separate plants; bright pink or rarely white, they are unscented and open during the day when they are usually pollinated by long-tongued bees or hoverflies. The fruit is a capsule opening by ten teeth. Found beside woodlands and hedgerows, mainly on lime-rich soils, it grows in both lowland and mountainous areas.
Ⓑ ◑ Ⓞ Ⓧ 🏵

White Campion
Silene alba
Up to 1m. This upright annual or perennial has softly hairy flowering stems which are slightly sticky above, and much shorter, sterile shoots. Its leaves are oval or lance-shaped. Night-flying moths are attracted to the delicately scented, white-petalled flowers that open in the evening. The male and female flowers are found on separate plants. It is common on arable and waste ground, along roadsides, hedgerows and in most grassy areas.
Ⓑ Ⓞ Ⓧ 🏵

Bladder Campion
Silene vulgaris subsp. vulgaris
Up to 90cm. A variable perennial with erect stems arising from a rather woody base. Its leaves are broadly lance-shaped, bluish-green and slightly waxy. The white-petalled flowers may be male, female or bisexual and are large and drooping, with an inflated calyx, the sepals joined to form a tube, and a distinct network of veins. The fruit is a globular capsule opening by six teeth. It is found throughout most of Europe on arable and waste land, roadsides and along hedgerows.
Ⓑ Ⓞ Ⓧ 🏵

Soapwort
Saponaria officinalis
Up to 90cm. A perennial herb with numerous stout upright stems, its broad, oval or elliptical, hairless leaves have three to five prominent veins. The flowers form dense clusters at the tips of the stems, with pink, often shallowly notched petals, and are usually pollinated by hawkmoths. The sepals are fused together to form a smooth, green tube and the fruit is an oblong capsule. It is usually found by streams, hedgebanks, roadsides and in damp woods, often in the vicinity of houses.
Ⓑ Ⓞ Ⓧ

Rock Soapwort
Saponaria ocymoides
This perennial, mat-forming plant has much-branched, sprawling stems up to 30cm long. Its leaves are elliptical or spoon-shaped. Conspicuous bright pink or purplish flowers are borne in loose clusters on glandular, hairy stalks. Its fruit is a capsule opening by four teeth. This mountain plant grows in stony places and by the side of tracks in central and south-western Europe. It sometimes can become established outside its native region.
Ⓧ

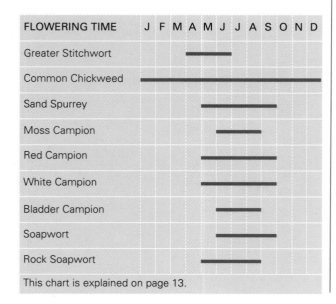

FLOWERING TIME	J	F	M	A	M	J	J	A	S	O	N	D
Greater Stitchwort				▬▬▬								
Common Chickweed	▬▬▬▬▬▬▬▬▬▬▬▬											
Sand Spurrey					▬▬▬▬▬▬							
Moss Campion					▬▬▬▬							
Red Campion					▬▬▬▬▬▬							
White Campion					▬▬▬▬▬▬							
Bladder Campion					▬▬▬▬▬▬							
Soapwort						▬▬▬▬▬						
Rock Soapwort					▬▬▬							

This chart is explained on page 13.

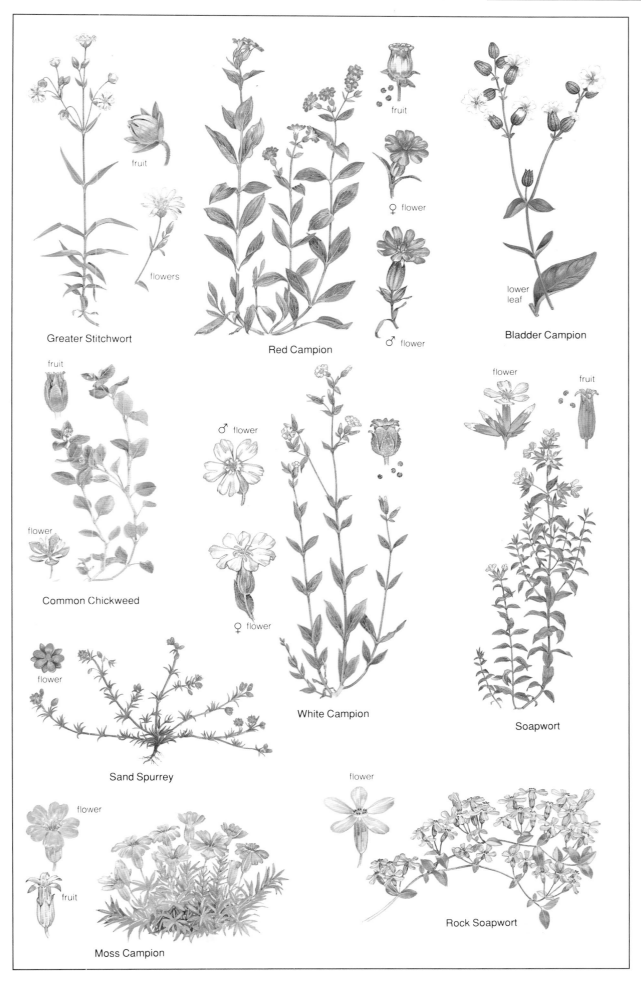

fruit

Greater Stitchwort

flowers

Red Campion

fruit

♀ flower

♂ flower

fruit

♀ flower

lower
leaf

Bladder Campion

fruit

flower

Common Chickweed

♂ flower

♀ flower

White Campion

flower   fruit

Soapwort

flower

Sand Spurrey

flower

fruit

Moss Campion

flower

Rock Soapwort

21

WATER-LILY FAMILY

This is a world-wide family (Nymphaeaceae), of some 60 species of aquatic plants. They grow in still or slow-moving water with their roots and stout rhizomes buried in mud. Their leaves and flowers grow on long stalks, often floating on the surface and covering large areas. The flowers have many stamens and no specialized pollination mechanisms. The seeds often contain air to help them float to new areas of lakes and rivers.

Yellow Water-lily
Nuphar lutea
This aquatic perennial has very large oval, thick and leathery leaves, deeply notched at the base, which float on the water surface, and thin, translucent, round leaves which remain submerged. The yellow flowers which smell of alcohol and attract small flies are held above the water surface. The fruit is flask-shaped. It is found in both still and flowing waters in most of Europe.
Ⓑ ☻

BUTTERCUP FAMILY

The 1800 species of this family (Ranunculaceae) are distributed world-wide but are especially common in cooler regions. Most are annual or perennial herbs and many are well-known garden ornamentals. The leaves are usually alternate but vary in shape and division. The flowers, which are regarded as primitive, may be regular or bilaterally symmetrical. There are usually five sepals, often petal-like and indistinguishable from true petals, which may be absent. Their stamens and carpels are numerous, the carpels each forming a single-seeded fruit. Many species are poisonous.

Common Water-crowfoot
Ranunculus aquatilis
Height very variable. This annual or perennial aquatic plant has underwater stems bearing two very different types of leaves: submerged leaves are finely divided with thread-like segments, the floating leaves are broader, deeply-lobed and with wedge-shaped segments. The flowers are white with a yellow centre, borne singly and held above the water surface. It grows in ponds and ditches, often in masses, and in slow-moving streams.
Ⓑ ☻

Glacier Crowfoot
Ranunculus glacialis
This low perennial, 4–25cm high, has rather fleshy, dark metallic-looking leaves. The lower ones have three lobes, toothed with short stalks. Its flowers are 2–3cm across and have five white, pink or purplish petals which persist after the fruits ripen. A

Lesser Celandines are among the earliest flowers to show themselves in the woods and hedgerows in the spring.

mountain species, it is often found near patches of snow. It has the highest recorded altitude (4275m) of any European flowering plant.
☻

Pyrenean Buttercup
Ranunculus pyrenaeus
Up to 20cm. This small perennial has bluish-green leaves. Those at the base are narrow, tapering at both ends, and stalkless. Its white flowers, 2–3cm across, are usually solitary. The sepals are whitish and hairless. It is found mainly on limestone soils at altitudes of 1700–3500m in the mountains of western and central Europe, in damp meadows and on slopes. It sometimes hybridizes with other white-flowered species of buttercup.
☻ ⓜ

Meadow Buttercup
Ranunculus acris
Up to 1m. A variable perennial with erect, branched stems. Its lower leaves are palmately lobed with each lobe stalkless. Several similar species have a middle lobe with a short stalk. The flowers are shining yellow. The small fruits, with short, hooked beaks, are held in rounded heads. This species is most commonly found in damp meadows and grassy places, on chalky or neutral soils.
Ⓑ ☻ ⓜ

Lesser Celandine
Ranunculus ficaria
Up to 25cm. A compact, low-growing perennial, this plant has distinctive heart-shaped, dark green, glossy leaves. Its flowers each have three sepals and eight to twelve shining yellow petals. They attract many spring-flying insects. The plant overwinters by means of small tubers, and may develop bulblets. It is commonly found in woods, along hedgerows, and in damp, shady places.
Ⓑ ☻ ⓜ

Lesser Spearwort
Ranunculus flammula
Up to 50cm. This perennial has hollow, upright or creeping stems, rooting from the nodes near the base. The lower leaves are distinctly stalked and broader than those above. Its few, glossy, yellow flowers range from 7–20cm across. Common in wet places, its acrid sap is poisonous to livestock.
Ⓑ ☻ ⓜ

Stinking Hellebore
Helleborus foetida
Up to 80cm. An unpleasant-smelling, evergreen perennial, this plant has palmate divided leaves. The flowers have green petal-like segments bordered with reddish-purple. The seeds are dispersed by ants. A poisonous plant of woods and scrub in western Europe, it is sometimes cultivated in gardens as an ornamental.
Ⓑ ☻

Marsh-marigold
Caltha palustris
Up to 30cm. This hollow-stemmed perennial has dark green, shiny leaves, more or less kidney-shaped, with toothed margins. The golden-yellow petals and sepals are both petal-like and not readily distinguishable. A variable, early-flowering plant, it flourishes in damp partially shaded places.
Ⓑ ☻ ☻

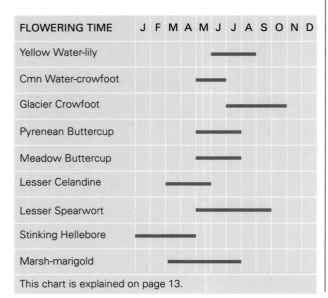

FLOWERING TIME	J	F	M	A	M	J	J	A	S	O	N	D
Yellow Water-lily						▬▬▬▬▬						
Cmn Water-crowfoot					▬▬▬							
Glacier Crowfoot							▬▬▬▬					
Pyrenean Buttercup					▬▬▬							
Meadow Buttercup					▬▬▬							
Lesser Celandine			▬▬▬									
Lesser Spearwort					▬▬▬▬▬▬							
Stinking Hellebore		▬▬▬▬										
Marsh-marigold			▬▬▬									

This chart is explained on page 13.

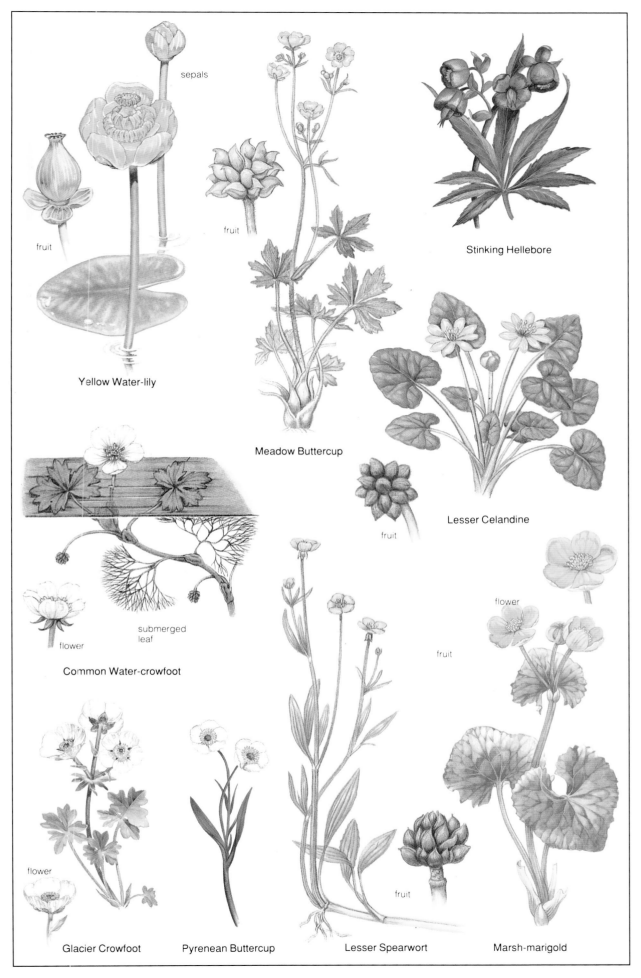

sepals

fruit

fruit

Stinking Hellebore

Yellow Water-lily

Meadow Buttercup

Lesser Celandine

fruit

submerged
leaf

flower

flower

Common Water-crowfoot

flower

fruit

flower

fruit

Glacier Crowfoot   Pyrenean Buttercup   Lesser Spearwort   Marsh-marigold

Globeflower
Trollius europaeus

Up to 70cm. This perennial has erect, leafy stems and dark green basal leaves which are palmately cut into lobes that are further lobed or toothed. The large, usually solitary flowers are nearly spherical with long stalks and broad, overlapping, pale yellow petaloid sepals curving in at the top and hiding the yellow petals. This poisonous plant is widespread in damp mountain pastures and open woods of Europe.
Ⓑ🌸Ⓞ🝔

Wood Anemone
Anemone nemorosa

Up to 30cm. This delicate, early spring-flowering plant has a creeping underground rhizome giving rise to an erect, unbranched flowering stem bearing three palmately-lobed leaves and a solitary white flower. Its long-stalked basal leaves appear after the flowers have gone. It is commonly found in deciduous woodland.
ⒷⓄ

Pasqueflower
Pulsatilla vulgaris

Up to 30cm. This is a low perennial with feathery, silkily hairy leaves which become almost hairless. Its erect, dark to pale purple, bell-shaped flowers droop as they begin to fade. The style remains attached to the fruit, forming a long feathery plume which aids wind dispersal. It is found on chalk grassland in central and north-western Europe.
Ⓑ🝔

Traveller's-joy
Clematis vitalba

Up to 30m. This perennial climbing plant has woody, stems. The deciduous leaves are divided into stalked, oval leaflets, with both the leaf and leaflet-stalks twining around twigs and branches of other plants for support. Its fragrant, greenish-white flowers have four, spreading, petal-like segments that are densely hairy below. The clusters of nut-like fruits have long, feathery styles attached which aid wind dispersal. Widespread in most of Europe as far north as southern Britain, it grows in woods, hedgerows, and thickets.
ⒷⓄ🝔

Common Columbine
Aquilegia vulgaris

Up to 1m. This slender perennial has erect stems which become branched in the upper part. It has long-stalked, bluish-green leaves low down that are divided into irregularly three-lobed leaflets. The flowers are drooping, usually blue, but sometimes pink or white, with distinctive long hollow spurs containing nectar. The dry fruits are many-seeded. A plant of woods, fens and damp meadows, it prefers lime-rich soils. Rare in Britain, it is more frequently found in southern and central Europe although various cultivars are grown as garden flowers. Larkspur (*Consolidata ambigua*) has one spur and one pod-like fruit. Forking Larkspur (*C. regalis*) has shorter fruit.
ⒷⓄ🝔

The Pasque Flower is so named because it often flowers at Easter – 'pasque' being a corruption of the French 'Pâques', meaning Easter.

CABBAGE FAMILY

This large and important family (Cruciferae) contains many vegetable crops and ornamental flowers as well as various weeds among its 3000 species. Plants in this family have very characteristic flowers. They have four sepals and four petals which are arranged in the form of a cross – giving the family its Latin name. The fruits, too, are characteristic. They are basically slender capsules with two chambers separated by a thin, papery wall which persists after the seeds have been shed.

Garlic Mustard
Alliaria petiolata

Up to 120cm. This erect biennial has pale green leaves which give off a strong smell of garlic when crushed. They are heart-shaped with a toothed margin, the basal ones arranged in a rosette. Despite their unpleasant smell, the clusters of white flowers attract midges and other small insects, but are often self-pollinated. It is a widespread plant of shady wood margins, hedgerows and walls.
ⒷⓄ✿

Water-cress
Nasturtium officinale

Up to 60cm. This perennial water plant has hairless, hollow and rather weak stems which root at the nodes. Its shining, dark green and slightly fleshy leaves are divided into several pairs of oval leaflets. The flowers in spike-like heads are white-petalled. The fruit is a capsule of two rows of seeds. Common in lowland areas, it prefers running to stagnant water. It is widespread in Europe where it is cultivated as a salad plant.
Ⓑ🥗

Hedge Mustard
Sisymbrium officinale

Up to 90cm. This erect annual or biennial has bristly haired stems with stiff, widely-spreading branches. The pinnate leaves are cut into toothed lobes with a broader lobe at the tip. The tiny pale yellow flowers are little visited by insects, and so are usually self-pollinated. The hairy fruit capsules are held upright, pressed closely against the stem. Native throughout Europe, it commonly grows in waste places, arable land and along hedgebanks.
Ⓑ✿

Cuckoo Flower
Cardamine pratensis

Up to 60cm. This perennial plant, has a basal rosette of pinnate leaves, each divided into several pairs of oval or rounded leaflets. The stem leaves are much smaller with narrow leaflets. The clusters of flowers are pink, purplish or white. The capsules open explosively when mature and may eject the seeds up to a distance of 2m. This plant is widespread in Europe in damp habitats such as meadows and by streams, usually on acid soils.
Ⓑ🌸✿🝔

FLOWERING TIME	J	F	M	A	M	J	J	A	S	O	N	D
Globeflower					█	█						
Wood Anemone			█	█	█							
Pasqueflower			█	█	█							
Traveller's-joy							█	█	█			
Common Columbine					█	█	█					
Garlic Mustard				█	█	█						
Water-cress					█	█	█	█	█			
Hedge Mustard					█	█	█	█				
Cuckoo Flower				█	█							

This chart is explained on page 13.

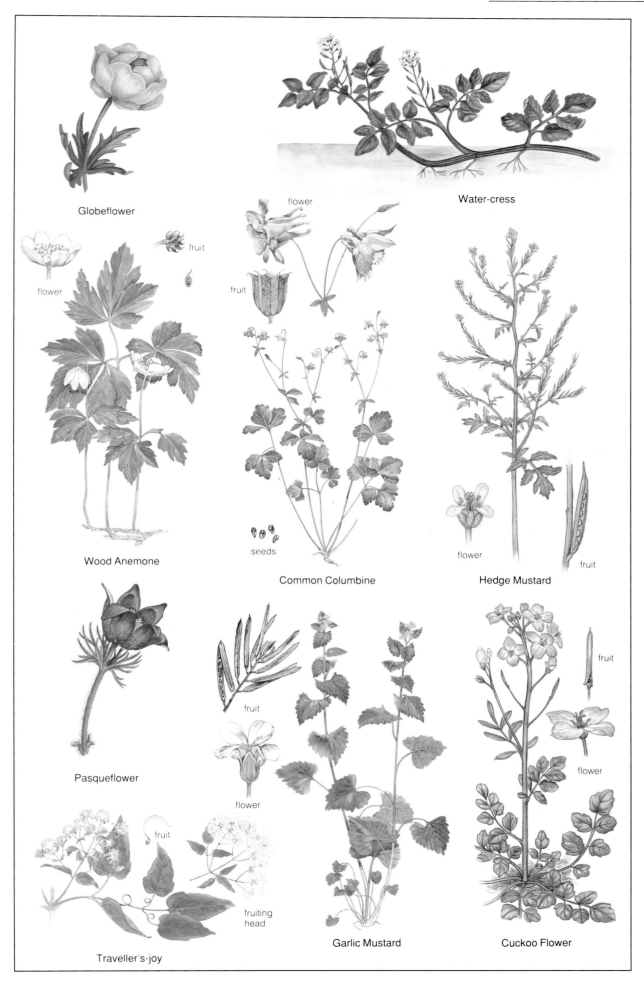

Globeflower

Water-cress

flower

fruit

flower

fruit

flower

Wood Anemone

seeds

Common Columbine

flower

fruit

Hedge Mustard

Pasqueflower

fruit

flower

fruit

flower

fruit

fruiting
head

Traveller's-joy

Garlic Mustard

Cuckoo Flower

Common Scurvygrass
Cochlearia officinalis
Up to 50cm. This rather spreading, fleshy biennial or perennial has a rosette of long-stalked, heart or kidney-shaped leaves at the base. The upper leaves clasp the stem and are coarsely toothed or lobed. The flowers are white or, very rarely, lilac and the fruit is a conspicuously veined rounded capsule. This variable species grows on coastal rocks, cliffs and some salt-marshes.
Ⓑ☻☺

Horse-radish
Armoracia rusticana
Up to 125cm. This robust perennial has long fleshy roots. Its basal leaves are very large and oval with toothed margins. The smaller stem leaves may be deeply lobed. The numerous white flowers of this plant are sweetly-scented. In some countries, including Britain, the many-seeded fruit only rarely ripens. A native of south-eastern Europe and western Asia, a condiment is often made from its roots.
Ⓑ✪

Shepherd's-purse
Capsella bursa-pastoris
Up to 40cm. This annual or biennial has a basal rosette of deeply-lobed leaves and an erect stem with clasping leaves that are arrow-shaped at the base. Its small white flowers are usually self-pollinated. The fruits, which are heart-shaped or triangular and notched at the tip, are several-seeded.
Ⓑ☻✪

Sea Rocket
Cakile maritima
This low-growing coastal annual has branched stems 15–45cm long, and very variable, fleshy leaves, undivided or deeply lobed. The one-seeded upper section of the fruit becomes detached when ripe from the lower seedless section which stays on the plant. The seeds are dispersed in the sea. It is widespread in Europe.
Ⓑ☺

Charlock
Sinapis arvensis
Up to 80cm. This annual has an upright, usually stiffly hairy stem. Its leaves are roughly hairy, the lower ones lobed and the upper ones stalkless and coarsely toothed. Its distinctive capsules have a long, conical beak. It is a serious weed of arable land throughout Europe, where its seeds remain viable in the soil for up to 50 years.
Ⓑ✪

SUNDEW FAMILY

All 85 species of this family (Droseraceae) are carnivorous, trapping various types of insects. Specialized leaves in basal rosettes bear the traps which range from sticky hairs which move when touched, to jaw-like traps which snap shut on the victim as in the Venus Fly-trap. Once the insect is caught, the plant releases enzymes to digest it and absorbs the products.

Sea Rocket grows on sand and shingle all round Europe's coastline. Its seeds are unaffected by the salt water which transports them.

Round-leaved Sundew
Drosera rotundifolia
4–8cm. This delicate perennial has leaves fringed with long, reddish, glistening, glandular hairs. They are attractive to insects which are trapped by the sticky secretions and enclosed by the curling leaf. This Sundew was once valued for its medicinal uses. It is found on acid soils of bogs, moorland and heaths, often growing with the moss Sphagnum.
Ⓑ☻

STONECROP FAMILY

The 1300 or so species of the family Crassulaceae are succulents – that is, their stems and leaves are fleshy and swollen with water-storing tissue. They can withstand prolonged drought and are typical of mountain slopes and other dry habitats such as walls, shingle and stony places but also occur in wetter sites. Most of the species are rosette-forming perennials with showy flower heads. Several species are grown in gardens, others are well-known indoor plants.

Mountain Houseleek
Sempervivum montanum
5–15cm. This very fleshy plant has leaf rosettes, forming low mats or tufts. They vary in size from 1–5cm across and the resin-scented leaves have a glandular hairy, sticky surface. Erect stems bear small clusters of star-like flowers with 11–13 reddish purple, or more rarely

yellowish, petals. It is an alpine plant of acid rocks and screes, found at altitudes of between 1500–2800m.
☻

Biting Stonecrop
Sedum acre
Up to 10cm. This perennial has creeping, mat-forming stems. Its small, overlapping, bright green leaves are often tinged with crimson when young; and they are hot and acrid-tasting. The bright yellow, five-petalled flowers are star-like. This widespread plant thrives in dry, sunny places, and may be found at altitudes up to 2300m.
Ⓑ☻✪☺

SAXIFRAGE FAMILY

This widespread family (Saxifragaceae) contains about 450 species of mostly perennials with basal rosettes of leaves. In most cases, the unspecialized flowers have five sepals and petals and 10 or more stamens. The fruit is a capsule. This family is common in montane habitats. Many species and their hybrids are grown as ornamentals.

Meadow Saxifrage
Saxifraga granulata
Up to 50cm. This erect perennial plant overwinters by means of a mass of small, brown bulb-like buds produced near the base of the lower leaves. Showy, large flowers, borne in a lax cluster attract different insects. A plant of acidic grassland, it also occurs on wood margins.
Ⓑ☻ⓜ

FLOWERING TIME	J	F	M	A	M	J	J	A	S	O	N	D
Common Scurvygrass					▬	▬	▬					
Horse-radish					▬							
Shepherd's-purse	▬	▬	▬	▬	▬	▬	▬	▬	▬	▬	▬	▬
Sea Rocket						▬	▬					
Charlock					▬	▬						
Round-leaved Sundew							▬					
Mountain Houseleek							▬					
Biting Stonecrop						▬	▬					
Meadow Saxifrage				▬	▬							

This chart is explained on page 13.

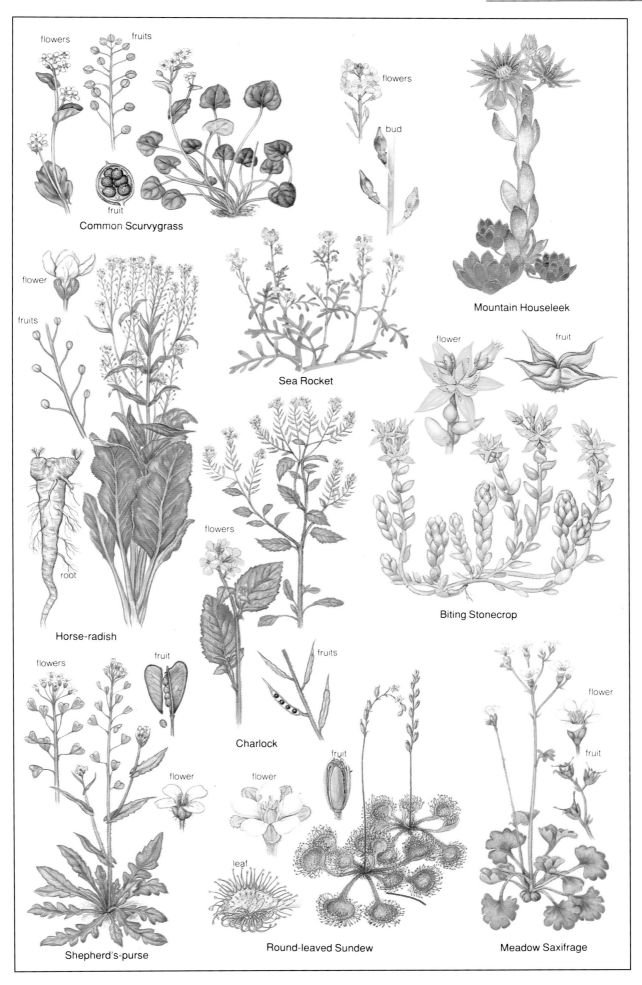

flowers
fruits
fruit
Common Scurvygrass

flowers
bud

Mountain Houseleek

flower
fruits
root
Horse-radish

Sea Rocket

flower
fruit

flowers

Biting Stonecrop

flowers
fruit

flowers

Charlock

flowers
flower

leaf

fruits

fruit

flower

Shepherd's-purse

flower

Round-leaved Sundew

flower
fruit
Meadow Saxifrage

ROSE FAMILY

This large family (Rosaceae) contains over 3000 species of herbs, trees, shrubs and climbers distributed world-wide. As well as roses themselves, the family contains numerous other garden ornamentals. Many of the garden plants are complicated hybrids now greatly altered from their wild ancestors. The regular, unspecialized flowers are frequently showy, with a wide range of colours. They have equal numbers of petals and sepals, and often an additional whorl of sepal-like segments called the epicalyx immediately below the true sepals. The stamens are numerous and the fruits are very varied, ranging from dry capsules to juicy berries.

Meadowsweet
Filipendula ulmaria
Up to 120cm. This perennial of wet places has tall, erect stems. Its leaves are pinnately divided with large, toothed leaflets interspersed with pairs of very small leaflets, all dark green above and usually white-haired below. Small, creamy white and sweetly scented flowers are five or six-petalled. The fruits are spirally twisted. Common in damp meadows, it is also found in marshes, wet woods, ditches, and by rivers.
Ⓑ ⊞

Stone Bramble
Rubus saxatilis
Up to 40cm. This plant has erect, annual flowering stems and long, perennial, vegetative stolons, creeping above the ground and rooting at the tips. Its leaves are divided into three, oval, coarsely toothed leaflets. The white petals are narrow and held upright. Its edible fruits, scarlet when ripe, have a few large, fleshy segments. It occurs mainly in damp, upland habitats.
Ⓑ ⊙ ○

Bramble
Rubus fruticosus agg
This very variable perennial has long, prickly, woody stems, arching and often rooting at the tips. Its leaves are pinnately divided into five to seven leaflets. The flowers may be white or pink. Often forming tangled masses, it grows in woods, hedgerows, scrub, heaths, and often on waste ground.
Ⓑ ○ ❀

Dog-rose
Rosa canina
One of the most common wild roses, this deciduous shrubby plant has prickly stems up to 3m long. Its leaves are pinnately divided with two to three pairs of oval and toothed leaflets. The pink or white flowers, 3–5cm across, are scentless. The berry-like fruits, called hips, are a rich source of vitamin C. A very variable species it is common in Europe, except the far north, growing in woodland and hedgerows.
Ⓑ ○

Meadowsweet, seen here with Great Willowherb, dominates many river banks and other damp habitats up to altitudes of 1000 metres.

Burnet Rose
Rosa pimpinellifolia
10–100cm. This low, deciduous shrub suckers freely to cover large areas. It is easily recognized by the dense covering of straight prickles interspersed with stiff bristles on the stems. The small, globular fruits, unlike other wild roses, turn black when ripe. It is most commonly found near the sea, on sand dunes, rocks, and sandy heaths.
Ⓑ ⊙ ⊛

Agrimony
Agrimonia eupatoria
Up to 60cm. This erect perennial has leaves divided into large, toothed leaflets with smaller leaflets between. The cone-shaped fruit has a covering of hooked spines around the top which catch in the fur of animals. Widespread in Europe, it grows in hedgebanks, and many grassy places, and can be used to produce a strong yellow dye.
Ⓑ ⊞

Salad Burnet
Sanguisorba minor
15–80cm. This tufted perennial has erect stems and pinnately divided leaves that are mostly basal, with four to 12 pairs of rounded, toothed, greyish-green leaflets. The tiny, greenish, petalless flowers, tinged crimson, are

carried in dense, rounded heads. It grows in dry grassland, especially on chalky and limestone soils. When crushed, the leaves and shoots smell similar to cucumber, and are edible when young.
Ⓑ ⊙ ⊞

Great Burnet
Sanguisorba officinalis
Up to 100cm. This tall perennial has erect stems, branched above and leaves pinnately divided with bluish-green leaflets. It is generally similar to Salad Burnet, but distinguished by its oval, rather than rounded, flower heads. The flowers produce abundant nectar and so attract insects. Widespread in most of Europe, it grows in damp grassy habitats, and hilly areas up to 2300m.
Ⓑ ⊙ ⊞

Wood Avens
Geum urbanum
Up to 60cm. This erect perennial has rather brittle stems and pinnately divided leaves. Its pale yellow flowers are few, long-stalked and held upright. The fruits are oblong and have hooked tips which readily catch on to fur or clothing and are dispersed by animals. A common plant of damp, rich soils, woodland and hedgerows, it prefers shady places.
Ⓑ ○

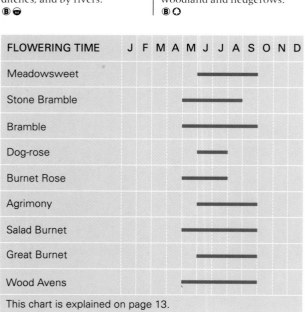

FLOWERING TIME	J	F	M	A	M	J	J	A	S	O	N	D
Meadowsweet							▬	▬	▬			
Stone Bramble						▬	▬	▬				
Bramble						▬	▬	▬				
Dog-rose						▬						
Burnet Rose					▬	▬						
Agrimony						▬	▬	▬				
Salad Burnet					▬	▬	▬					
Great Burnet						▬	▬	▬				
Wood Avens					▬	▬	▬	▬				

This chart is explained on page 13.

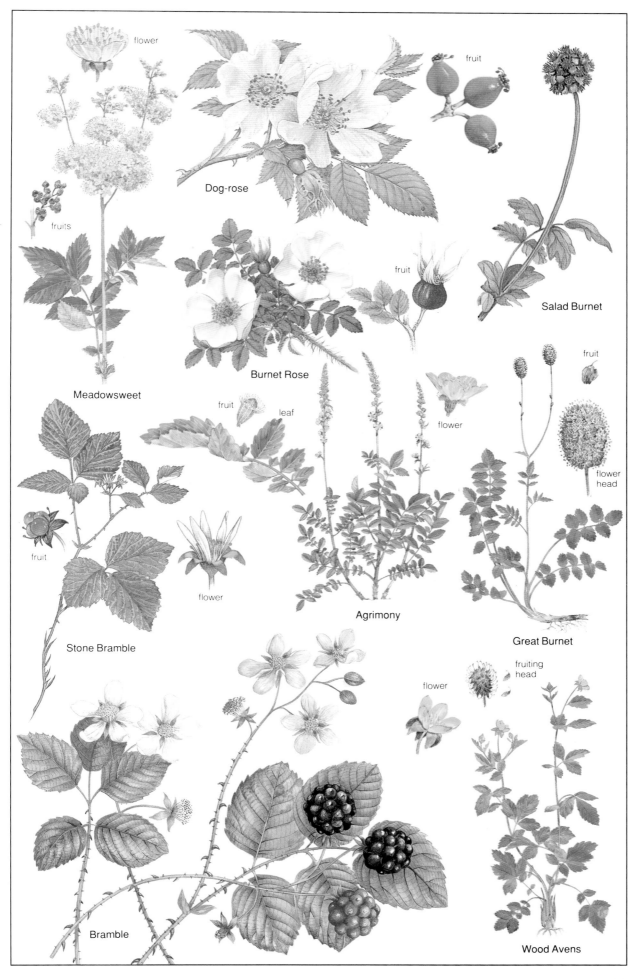

flower

fruit

Dog-rose

fruits

Salad Burnet

fruit

Burnet Rose

Meadowsweet

fruit   leaf

flower

fruit

flower
head

flower

fruit

flower

Agrimony

Great Burnet

Stone Bramble

flower   fruiting
head

flower

Bramble

Wood Avens

29

Water Avens
Geum rivale

Up to 60cm. This hairy perennial of damp places has erect, little-branched stems and lower leaves pinnately divided with three to six pairs of unequal leaflets. It may be distinguished from Wood Avens by its larger flowers, nodding rather than erect, its orange-pink petals and long, reddish-purple sepals. However, it frequently hybridizes with the Wood Avens when the two are found growing nearby. It is widespread in much of Europe, but in Britain is very rarely found in the south. It grows in marshes, damp meadows, and beside streams, often in shady places.
Ⓑ⊕

Silverweed
Potentilla anserina

This low perennial sends out creeping runners up to 80cm long which root at the nodes and form new plants. The leaves, which form a central rosette, are pinnately lobed with six to 12 pairs of oblong leaflets which have saw-toothed margins. They alternate with much smaller leaflets, and all have a distinctive covering of silvery, silky hairs sometimes above but always below. The solitary, long-stalked flowers are five-petalled and bright yellow. A common and widespread plant, it grows in damp grassy areas, dunes, along roadsides and in other waste places where it is immediately recognizable by its silvery appearance.
Ⓑ⊕⊕

Tormentil
Potentilla erecta

This slender, downy-haired perennial has creeping stems up to 50cm long, often forming patches. Its leaves usually have three, but occasionally four to five leaflets, and are silvery below, with margins toothed towards the tip. The stem leaves are stalkless, and the rosette of basal leaves withers before flowering. It is most easily distinguished from other, similar species by the lax clusters of bright yellow flowers which are mostly four-petalled, and only rarely have five petals. A common plant of grassy places such as heaths and garden lawns, it is widely distributed on cultivated land, occurring on most types of soil except chalk, and is found at altitudes up to 2500m.
Ⓑ⊕⊕⊕

Silverweed, an abundant roadside weed named for the silvery hairs on its leaves, spreads rapidly by means of creeping runners.

Wild Strawberry
Fragaria vesca

This low perennial spreads by sending out long, arching runners over the ground which root at the nodes and form new plants. The leaves have three coarsely toothed leaflets which are bright green above, and much paler and silky-haired beneath. After flowering, the tip of the flower stalk (receptacle) becomes enlarged, bright red, and fleshy while small, dry and seed-like 'pips' – the true fruits – project from its surface. Widespread in woodland, hedgebanks and grassland, especially on chalky soils, its edible 'fruits' can be used for making jam. The similar Barren Strawberry (*Potentilla sterilis*) has bluish-green leaves and produces small, dry 'fruits' with brownish pips.
Ⓑ⊕⊕⊕

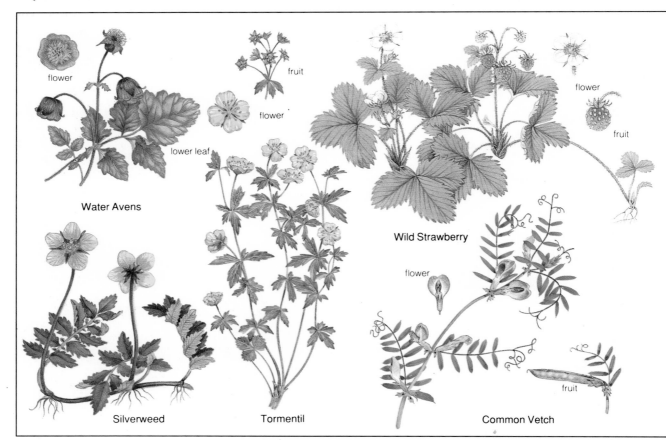

flower

fruit

flower

lower leaf

Water Avens

Silverweed

Tormentil

Wild Strawberry

flower

flower

fruit

Common Vetch

PEA FAMILY

Distributed world-wide, with nearly 16,500 species, this family (Leguminosae) contains herbs, trees, shrubs and climbers, many of them important food crops. The distinctive flowers are characteristic of the whole family. The leaves are usually trifoliate or pinnate and may end in a tendril. The fruit is always a pod containing a row of seeds. All species form root nodules containing nitrogen-fixing bacteria which act as a fertilizer.

Common Vetch
Vicia sativa
20–120cm long. This variable annual is frequently seen clambering up surrounding vegetation. Its leaves have three to eight pairs of narrow or oval leaflets, with a branched tendril at the tip. The red-purple flowers bloom from May to September and are up to 3cm long, borne singly or in pairs in the leaf-axils. It is now a plant of grassland and waste places throughout Europe, but was formerly widely cultivated.
Ⓑ🔴🔟

Tufted Vetch
Vicia cracca
60–200cm long. This handsome, far-scrambling perennial has leaves with six to 15 pairs of narrow leaflets, which end with a branched tendril. The flower spike is up to 10cm long, on a stalk of equal length. It is distinctly one-sided and contains up to 40 blue-purple, drooping flowers, which open from the bottom of the spike upwards. It is a common plant of bushy or grassy areas and is found more or less throughout the whole of Europe.
Ⓑ🔟

Bush Vetch
Vicia sepium
Up to 100cm long. This virtually hairless perennial has leaves of five to nine pairs of leaflets and a branched tendril at the tip. The short-stalked flower-heads have up to six blue-purple flowers, 12–15mm long, on a short stalk. The pod is black when ripe. It is widespread in Europe occurring in hedgerows, grassland and as a weed on cultivated ground. Like many peaflowers, it is often grown for fodder. The Wood Vetch (*V. sylvatica*) has larger flowers.
Ⓑ🔴🔟

Meadow Vetchling
Lathyrus pratensis
Up to 120cm. This scrambling downy perennial has spindly stems which grow more or less upright in the surrounding vegetation. Its leaves have one or two pairs of narrow leaflets, with a forked tendril at the tip. The yellow flowers are borne in clusters of five to twelve, on a stalk longer than the leaves. This species occurs in grassy places and hedgerows, and is found throughout Europe.
Ⓑ🔴🔟

Common Restharrow
Ononis repens
Up to 40cm long. A hairy, often spiny perennial, its leaves have three oval, toothed leaflets. The pink flowers, 10–15mm long, are borne in leaf-axils. The pod is up to four-seeded and hidden by a calyx which enlarges after flowering. A common plant of dry, grassy areas, especially on chalk, it is absent from parts of the far north of Europe as well as the Mediterranean islands.
Ⓑ🔟

FLOWERING TIME	J	F	M	A	M	J	J	A	S	O	N	D
Water Avens						▬▬▬						
Silverweed						▬▬▬						
Tormentil						▬▬▬▬▬						
Wild Strawberry					▬▬							
Common Vetch					▬▬▬▬▬							
Tufted Vetch						▬▬▬						
Bush Vetch				▬▬▬▬▬▬▬								
Meadow Vetchling					▬▬▬							
Common Restharrow						▬▬▬						

This chart is explained on page 13.

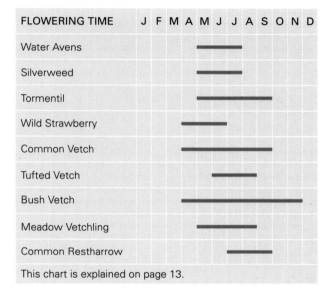

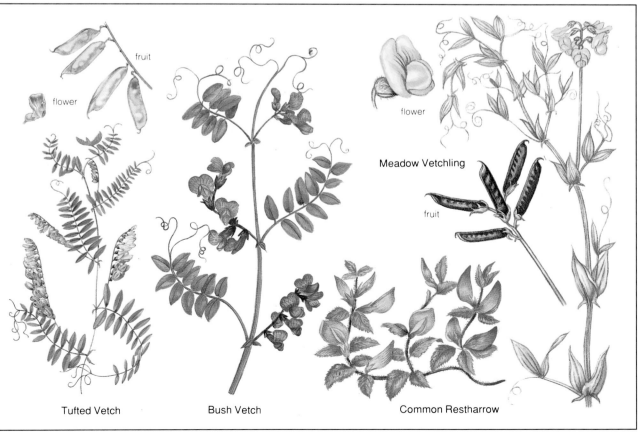

flower

fruit

Meadow Vetchling

flower

fruit

Tufted Vetch

Bush Vetch

Common Restharrow

Lucerne
Medicago sativa
Up to 90cm. This plant has several distinct subspecies in Europe but only two of them are widespread throughout the region. Both of the common subspecies are upright, hairless perennials with leaves consisting of three oval leaflets and flowers 8mm long, in a spike of 20 or more. Its seed-pods vary from being sickle-like to spiral in shape. The flowers are purple or violet in one subspecies, yellow in the other. Both hybridize readily, giving progeny with flower colours ranging from yellow to almost black. The yellow subspecies grows in grassy places; the purple is the common fodder crop alfalfa.
Ⓑ ✿ ⏶

Black Medick
Medicago lupulina
15–50 cm long. This low-growing annual, or occasionally, perennial, bears leaves with three rounded leaflets, each with a tiny point at the top. The yellow flowers are about 3mm long, and as many as 50 merge together into dense globular heads. The pods are small, black when ripe, and coiled into an almost complete circle. A common plant of waste or grassy areas throughout Europe, it is often grown as a fodder crop, and utilized for its nitrogen-fixing abilities. It is also one of the plants worn as shamrock on St. Patrick's Day in Ireland.
Ⓑ ✿ ⏶

Hop Trefoil
Trifolium campestre
35–50cm long. Very similar to Black Medick, this low-growing, slightly hairy annual has the three leaflets nearly oval, without a point at the tip. Each flower head has 25–40 yellow flowers, each about 5mm long. The small pods are covered by the dead brown flowers, which makes it resemble a small hop fruit. It grows in dry, grassy places throughout most of Europe.
Ⓑ ✿ ⏶

Hare's-foot Clover
Trifolium arvense
Up to 40cm. This attractive, softly hairy annual has spreading branches and leaves with three leaflets, each long-stalked and narrowly oval. The small pink or white flowers are packed into a dense cylindrical head. This head is softly hairy, giving it a fanciful resemblance to a hare's foot. The head elongates after flowering. A plant of grassy areas, it often grows on cultivated ground. It is found throughout most of Europe.
Ⓑ ✿ ⏶

Red Clover
Trifolium pratense
Up to 60cm. This upright, downy perennial, has three elliptical or oval leaflets, usually with a white V-shaped band about halfway along each one. The round flowerheads are about 4cm across, with up to 50 small pinkish-purple flowers. The dead flowers persist, covering the developing pods. This is a widely-distributed plant of grassy places absent only from the extreme north and south of Europe. It is often grown as a fodder crop.
Ⓑ ✿ ⏶

White Clover
Trifolium repens
Very often the curse of lawn fanatics, the creeping, hairless stems root regularly and form dense patches up to 50cm across. Its leaves are borne on long stalks, usually with a white band at the base of each of the three leaflets. The flower-heads arise from leaf axils. They are up to 35mm across, with many small white, or rose-pink flowers. The dead flowers are persistent, and cover the seed-pods. A common plant of grassy places throughout Europe, it is an invaluable source of nectar for hive bees.
Ⓑ ✿ ⏶

Common Bird's-foot Trefoil
Lotus corniculatus
Up to 30cm. This is a scrambling, many-stemmed, usually hairless perennial. Its leaves have five leaflets, with the lower pair bent back, so that only three leaflets are obvious. The flowers are 10–16mm long, yellow, often streaked with red, and two to seven are grouped together in a stalked head. Its name derives from the mature seed heads which resemble a bird's foot. This common plant of grassy places has many other popular names ranging from 'bacon-and-eggs' – due to its red and yellow streaks – to 'crow toes' from the shape of the seed pods.
Ⓑ ✿ ⏶

Kidney Vetch, also known as Ladies' Fingers, covers large areas of coastal dunes but is equally well at home on chalk and limestone.

Horseshoe Vetch
Hippocrepis comosa
Up to 40cm. This straggling perennial has leaves of up to seven pairs of leaflets, with a single leaflet at the tip. The yellow flowers, each 6–10mm long, are grouped in loose heads of five to 12. The seed-pods break up into horseshoe-shaped sections, This is a locally common plant of dry, grassy areas and an indicator of a chalky soil. It is found in Europe, north to England and Germany.
Ⓑ ⚘ ⏶

Kidney Vetch
Anthyllis vulneraria
Up to 60cm. This silky-haired herb has pinnate leaves with a large terminal leaflet. The yellow flowers are clustered in a long-stalked head which has leafy bracts immediately beneath it. Densely hairy, inflated calyces give the heads a characteristic woolly appearance. It was once believed to cure kidney complaints. It is found on both coasts and inland rocks, often in calcareous areas.
Ⓑ ✿ ⚘ ⏶

Sainfoin
Onobrychis viciifolia
Up to 30–60cm. This upright downy perennial has leaves composed of 6–12 pairs of narrow oval leaflets. The flowers vary from pink to red, and are about 12mm long, The warty pods are single-seeded. Although possibly native to parts of Europe on chalk grassland, it has long been cultivated elsewhere as a fodder crop and is widely naturalized. The name is derived from the French for 'wholesome hay'.
Ⓑ ✿ ⏶

FLOWERING TIME	J	F	M	A	M	J	J	A	S	O	N	D
Lucerne						—	—	—	—			
Black Medick				—	—	—	—	—	—			
Hop Trefoil						—	—	—	—			
Hare's-foot Clover						—	—	—	—			
Red Clover					—	—	—	—	—			
White Clover					—	—	—	—	—			
Cmn Bird's-foot Trefoil					—	—	—	—	—			
Horseshoe Vetch					—	—	—					
Kidney-vetch						—	—	—	—			
Sainfoin						—	—	—				

This chart is explained on page 13.

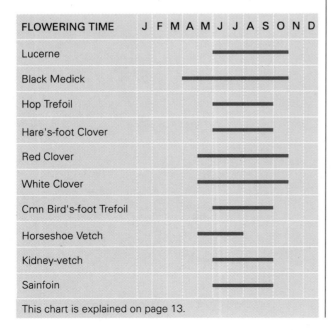

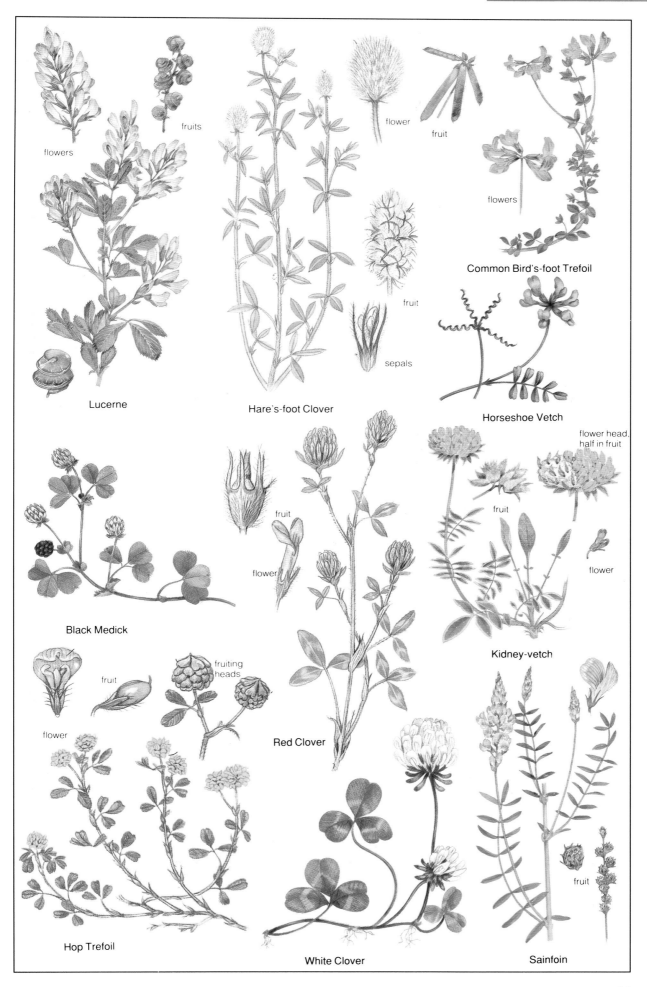

flowers

fruits

Lucerne

flower

fruit

fruit

sepals

Hare's-foot Clover

flowers

Common Bird's-foot Trefoil

Horseshoe Vetch

flower head,
half in fruit

fruit

flower

Kidney-vetch

fruit

flower

Black Medick

flower

fruit

fruiting
heads

flower

Red Clover

Hop Trefoil

White Clover

fruit

Sainfoin

Wood Sorrel, one of the candidates for Ireland's elusive national emblem the Shamrock, grows well on mossy banks.

WOOD-SORREL FAMILY

The 575 species in this family (Oxalidaceae) are mainly found in warm and tropical regions. In the genus *Oxalis* the leaves are usually trifoliate with leaflets that fold down at night and in cold weather. The flowers have five petals and 10 stamens. In some species the ripe seeds are shot out from the capsule to disperse them well away from the parent. Although they can become invasive weeds, some *Oxalis* species are grown as garden ornamentals and a few have edible tubers or pleasantly bitter-tasting leaves.

Wood-sorrel
Oxalis acetosella
Up to 15cm. This delicate plant has tufts of long-stalked leaves, each with three yellowish-green, wedge-shaped leaflets. Its solitary, white-petalled flowers are usually distinctly veined with lilac. They produce much nectar to attract bees and other insects, but it is the petalless flowers formed close to the ground later in the year, which never open and always self-pollinate, that produce most of the plant's seed. Commonly found in deciduous woodland and other shady places, its trailing stems may form extensive carpets in the spring.
Ⓑ Ⓞ

CRANE'S-BILL FAMILY

The 730 or so species of this family (Geraniaceae) are found in cool and subtropical regions. Garden geraniums belong to the subtropical genus *Pelargonium* and should not be confused with the related genus *Geranium*. The crane's-bills (genus *Geranium*) and their relatives are usually covered with soft hairs which in many species are glandular. The flowers are often large and showy, with five brightly coloured petals. The fruit of crane's-bills and stork's-bills (genus *Erodium*) is arranged around the base of the stiff and persistent style and resembles the beak of a bird before splitting into five one-seeded segments.

Common Stork's-bill
Erodium cicutarium
Up to 60cm long. This variable annual, sometimes stickily hairy, has upright or trailing stems. Its petals are typically purplish-pink, the upper two often with a blackish basal spot. The long beak of the fruit splits from the base, each portion twisting spirally with a one-seeded segment attached at the base. Movements in this corkscrew-like structure, brought about by changes in humidity, help to bury the seed in the ground. It grows on dunes, cultivated or waste ground, and dry grassland, especially on sandy soils.
Ⓑ Ⓞ Ⓧ Ⓦ

Herb Robert
Geranium robertianum
Up to 50cm. This annual or biennial, usually reddish-tinged plant has a strong, rather unpleasant smell. Its fragile stems bear bright green, palmately divided leaves, often tinged with red. The flowers are usually bright pink, but plants with white-petalled flowers may be locally common. It is widespread in woodland, hedgebanks, and on walls, preferring shady places; it also grows among rocks up to altitudes of 2000m. A maritime form, generally rather smaller than typical plants, is found on shingle beaches, with its stems lying along the ground. It is often distinguished as a separate subspecies.
Ⓑ Ⓞ Ⓧ Ⓦ

Meadow Crane's-bill
Geranium pratense
Up to 80cm. This erect, softly hairy perennial has long-stalked, five to seven-lobed leaves at the base and smaller, three-lobed leaves above. Its petals are bright bluish-violet or rarely white. The fruit is beaked, splitting when mature, each strip curling upwards with a one-seeded segment attached. A summer-flowering plant of meadows and grassy places, it is also often grown as an ornamental in gardens, particularly in its double-flowered form. Bloody Crane's-bill (*G. sanguineum*) is a creeping plant with reddish-purple flowers. Dusky Crane's-bill (*G. phaeum*) has blackish-purple petals with pointed tips.
Ⓑ Ⓦ

Wood Crane's-bill
Geranium sylvaticum
Up to 80cm. This hairy perennial is generally similar to Meadow Crane's-bill, but may be distinguished by its less deeply cut leaves with broader lobes, and by its flower stalks which always remain erect after flowering. The flowers are also rather smaller, and the rounded petals very variable in colour, ranging from reddish-purple to blue, but often whitish towards the base. It is found in meadows, woods, hedgebanks, and rocky places, usually on chalky soils. This species is widespread in much of Europe, but in the south it only occurs in the mountains.
Ⓑ Ⓞ Ⓞ Ⓦ

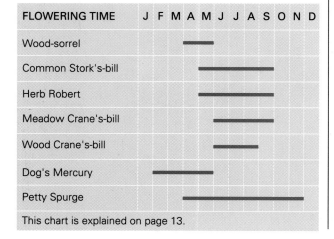

FLOWERING TIME	J	F	M	A	M	J	J	A	S	O	N	D
Wood-sorrel				▬	▬							
Common Stork's-bill					▬	▬	▬	▬	▬			
Herb Robert					▬	▬	▬	▬	▬			
Meadow Crane's-bill						▬	▬	▬	▬			
Wood Crane's-bill						▬	▬	▬				
Dog's Mercury		▬	▬	▬	▬							
Petty Spurge				▬	▬	▬	▬	▬	▬	▬		

This chart is explained on page 13.

34

SPURGE FAMILY

This very large family (Euphorbiaceae) contains 7750 species. It includes many fleshy and succulent desert plants which resemble cacti, as well as trees and shrubs, but all the European species are herbaceous or shrubby. All members of the family produce a milky, poisonous sap. The flowers of spurges are specialized inflorescences called cyathia and consist of a little cup in which there are several minute male flowers and a single female flower. Nectar-secreting glands around the edges of the cup attract pollinating insects. The flowers of this family do not have petals and sepals but the cyathia itself may be surrounded by large, colourful bracts.

Dog's Mercury
Mercurialis perennis
Up to 40cm. This hairy perennial has upright leafy stems arising from creeping underground rhizomes. Its oval or elliptical leaves are shortly stalked, in opposite pairs up the stems; the margins are saw-toothed. The tiny, greenish male and female flowers are borne on different plants – the clusters of male flowers in erect, slender spikes, the females in small, long-stemmed clusters. The fruit is two-lobed and stiffly hairy. A poisonous plant, it is found in woods and other shady places, and also among mountain rocks, at altitudes up to 1800m.
Ⓑ◑◯

Petty Spurge
Euphorbia peplus
Up to 30cm. This hairless, erect annual plant is branched above and its shortly-stalked leaves are broadly oval, blunt and green. Four to five conspicuous glands, half moon-shaped with long slender horns, are borne on the edge of each cyathium. The fruit is a capsule with three narrow two-winged segments. It is commonly found throughout Europe on waste and cultivated ground, and in fields and gardens.
Ⓑ✸

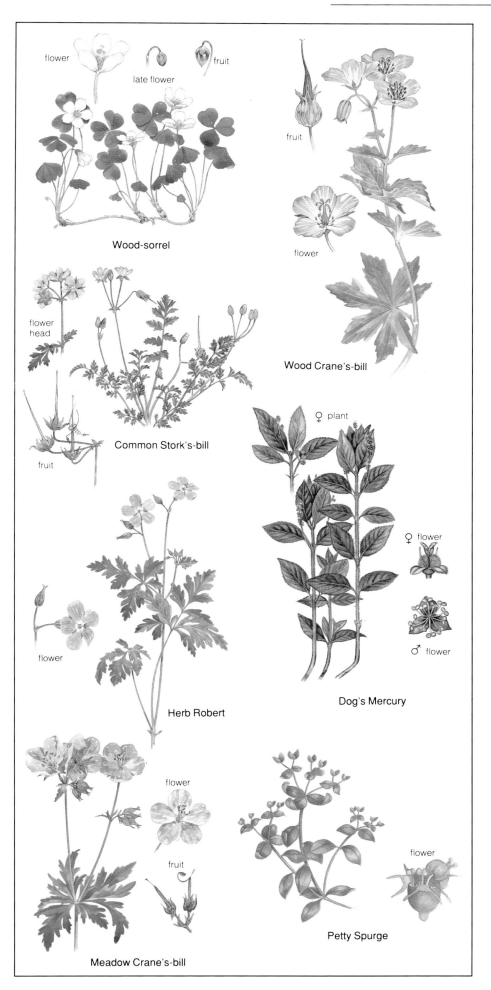

flower   late flower   fruit

Wood-sorrel

fruit

fruit

flower

Wood Crane's-bill

flower head

fruit

Common Stork's-bill

♀ plant

♀ flower

♂ flower

Dog's Mercury

flower

Herb Robert

flower

fruit

flower

flower

Meadow Crane's-bill

Petty Spurge

MILKWORT FAMILY

There are about 1000 species in this very widespread family (Polygalaceae). The European species are all small shrubs or herbs, usually found growing in short grassland. The flowers are easily mistaken for those of the unrelated Pea Family. Two of the five sepals are large and petal-like, enclosing the three true petals. The stamens form a tube around the ovary. The fruit of the family is a pod-like capsule.

Common Milkwort
Polygala vulgaris
Up to 30cm. This perennial plant has much-branched stems which are woody at the base. Its narrowly lance-shaped leaves are scattered alternately up the stem, with those near the top being longer than those below. The flowers have five overlapping sepals; the three outer ones are small and green, and two inner are brightly coloured and petal-like. Three narrow petals are blue, purplish-pink or white. The fruit is a flat, heart-shaped capsule, which remains hidden by the sepals. A grassland plant, it also grows on heaths and dunes.
Ⓑ◗🌰

BALSAM FAMILY

All but one of the 850 species in this family (Balsaminaceae) belong to the genus *Impatiens*; most species are tropical. The irregular flowers have five petals forming a broad lip and a hood; there is also a curved, nectar-filled spur. Only one species is native to Europe but a few others have been introduced and rapidly become common. Others are grown in gardens and as house plants.

Indian Balsam
Impatiens glandulifera
Up to 200cm. This robust annual has thick, often reddish stems and lance-shaped or elliptical leaves which are opposite or in whorls of three. Large purplish pink or rarely white flowers borne in long-stemmed clusters are pollinated by bumble-bees. The narrow pear-shaped fruit has elastic walls which coil back spirally when touched, shooting out seeds. A native of the Himalayas, it has been widely introduced in Europe as an ornamental, where it thrives on damp soils. It has also become well established on some river banks.
Ⓑ◗🌰

ST JOHNS'S-WORT FAMILY

This family (Guttiferae) of around 1300 species contains drug, dye and food plants as well as a number of ornamental plants. The species found in Europe are all herbaceous plants or small shrubs belonging to the genus *Hypericum*. Glands, appearing as black or transluscent dots on the plants, are characteristic of the family. The leaves are opposite or in whorls. There are five petals and the numerous stamens are joined at their bases in bundles. The fruit is a berry or a capsule.

Dog Violets have nothing to do with dogs – in this context 'dog' means inferior, implying that they are not as good as the Sweet Violets.

Perforate St John's-wort
Hypericum perforatum
Up to 100cm. This erect hairless perennial has stems which are woody at the base and with two raised lines along their length. Its stalkless leaves grow in opposite pairs on the stem and have numerous translucent glandular dots, which become visible if held against the light. The numerous flowers are borne in branched clusters, the five golden yellow petals dotted black at the edge. The fruit is a capsule. Widespread in Europe, this plant grows in grassland, along hedgebanks and in open woods, mainly on chalky soils.
Ⓑ○🌰

VIOLET FAMILY

With 500 species, *Viola* is by far the largest genus of the family (Violaceae), and the only one found in Europe. The five-petalled flowers are markedly irregular; the lowest petal is extended backwards into a nectar-filled spur. The five sepals are also prolonged at the base into backward-pointing flaps. Lines on the petals guide insects towards the mouth of the spur. After producing normal flowers in spring, many violets produce late-season, self-fertilizing flowers which never open. The fruit is a small capsule which splits open in three parts. Many violets are grown in gardens, including the hybrid garden pansies.

Sweet Violet
Viola odorata
This low perennial plant has creeping stolons which root at the tips. Its leaves all arise from the base of the plant. The stipules at the base of each leaf-stalk are toothed with glandular hairs. The solitary bluish-violet or white flowers are sweetly scented. Its fruit is a globular, hairy capsule which splits to release the seeds after it has fallen to the ground. This plant is commonly found in hedges and woods, and usually prefers chalky soils.
Ⓑ○🌰

Common Dog-violet
Viola riviniana
Up to 40cm. This low tufted perennial has short leafy stems but lacks stolons. The basal leaves form rosettes. The stipules at the base of each leaf-stalk have fringed margins. Its blue-violet flowers have a thick, much paler spur, and are unscented. The three-angled, hairless capsule splits while still attached to the plant. It is widespread in dry woods, heaths and mountain rocks.
Ⓑ◗◗○🌰

Wild Pansy
Viola tricolor tricolor
Up to 50cm. This annual, biennial, or perennial plant has tufted, ascending or upright stems. Its leaves are very variable, heart-shaped to lance-shaped, with deeply-lobed, leaf-like stipules at the base of the stalk. The unscented flowers are often three-coloured, with yellow, white, and violet. Often known as Heartsease, it is widespread but found mainly on lime-free soils.
Ⓑ✿🌰

FLOWERING TIME	J	F	M	A	M	J	J	A	S	O	N	D
Common Milkwort					▬	▬	▬	▬				
Indian Balsam						▬	▬	▬	▬			
Perforate St J's-wort					▬	▬	▬	▬				
Sweet Violet			▬	▬	▬							
Common Dog-violet				▬	▬	▬						
Wild Pansy			▬	▬	▬	▬	▬	▬				

This chart is explained on page 13.

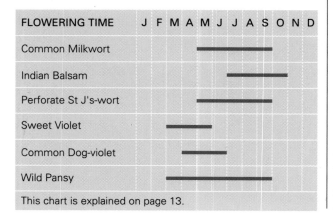

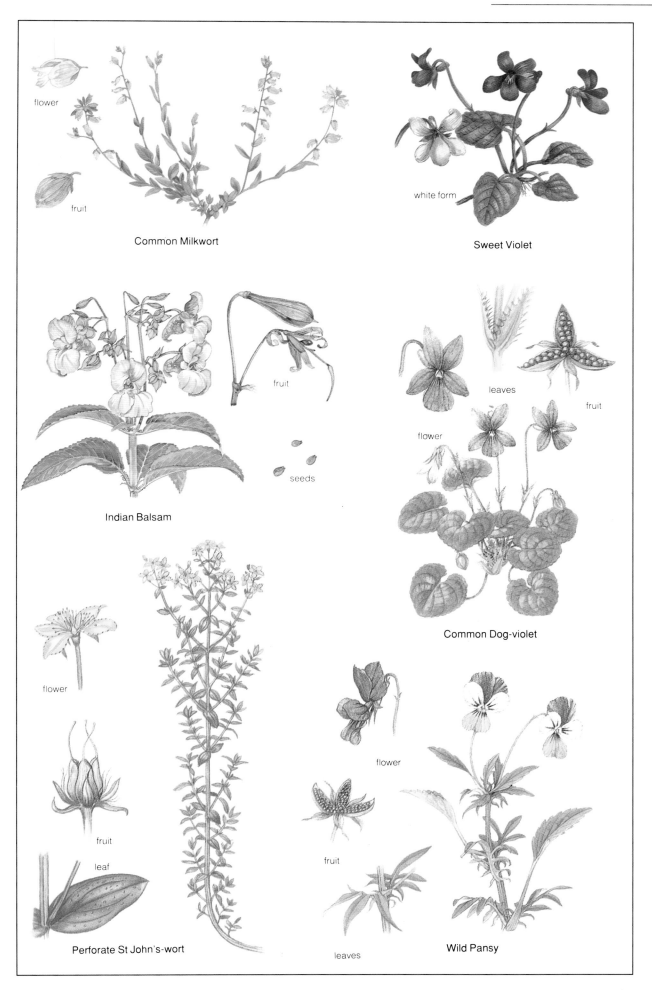

flower

fruit

Common Milkwort

white form

Sweet Violet

fruit

seeds

Indian Balsam

leaves

fruit

flower

Common Dog-violet

flower

fruit

leaf

Perforate St John's-wort

flower

fruit

leaves

Wild Pansy

MALLOW FAMILY

This cosmopolitan family (Malvaceae) of herbs, shrubs and trees contains many tropical species. Their flowers are five-petalled, often large and showy, with numerous stamens joined into a tubular column. Nectar, secreted deep within the flower and guarded by hairs, is available only to long-tongued insects. Dark veins or patches on the petals act as way markers to feeding insects. There is often an extra whorl of segments (the epicalyx) beneath the calyx. The fruit is a capsule or breaks into segments like wedges of cheese. In some species the fruits are edible but very slimy. The family contains familiar ornamentals such as Hollyhock and Hibiscus, and important fibre plants such as Cotton.

Common Mallow
Malva sylvestris
Up to 90cm. This perennial plant has a sparsely hairy, erect, ascending stem which bears almost circular, shallowly-lobed leaves at the base and more deeply-lobed leaves higher up. Clusters of large rose-purple flowers appear in the axils of the upper leaves, and the petals are veined with dark purple and notched at the tip. The round fruit consists of several one-seeded, brownish green nutlets. It is a common plant found in waste places and by roadsides throughout Europe. The young leaves and shoots have been used as a vegetable. Dwarf Mallow (*M. neglecta*) is a low-growing annual plant that has smaller, paler flowers.
Ⓑ Ⓞ

ROCK-ROSE FAMILY

Most of the 160 or so species in this essentially Mediterranean family (Cistaceae) are shrubs, some very low and creeping. Most grow in dry, rocky areas. The leaves are opposite, frequently very hairy and covered with oil glands. The flowers are showy with five sepals, of which two are very small, and five often crumpled petals and numerous stamens. Many species are grown as ornamentals.

Common Rock-rose
Helianthemum nummularium
Up to 50cm. This low-growing, spreading, wiry-stemmed dwarf shrub sports paired leaves, which are oblong or oval, green above, and densely white hairy below. Its flowers are 2–3cm in diameter, borne in lax, one-sided clusters. The two outer sepals are narrower and much smaller than the three oval and prominently veined, inner sepals. The petals are usually bright yellow, but cream, white or orange forms occur, while many more colour variations have been produced in the large number of cultivated forms. A plant found on grassland and scrub, it prefers lime-rich soils.
Ⓑ Ⓞ Ⓜ

GOURD FAMILY

The Gourd Family (Cucurbitaceae) is found mainly in the tropics and includes melons, marrows and cucumbers. Some species are typical of dry, semi-desert regions and a few extend into northern Europe. The majority of species

White Bryony berries decorate hedgerows everywhere in the autumn. Blackbirds enjoy them, but they are poisonous to humans.

are vines, climbing by means of spring-like tendrils or trailing along the ground. The unisexual flowers are yellow or white, with five sepals and five petals which form a funnel-shaped corolla. The fruit is usually a berry, often with a thick skin as in melons.

White Bryony
Bryonia cretica subsp. *dioica*
Up to 4m. This climbing plant attaches itself to other vegetation for support by means of long, spirally coiled tendrils that wrap around twigs and stalks. The stems are brittle and rough to the touch, and arise from a massive swollen stock. The bristly leaves usually have five wavy-toothed lobes. Male and female flowers are borne on separate plants. A poisonous plant, the toxic berries are conspicuous in autumn, when they hang in clusters. They ripen from green to bright red. This plant is commonly found in hedgerows and woods and prefers well-drained soils.
Ⓑ Ⓞ Ⓜ

LOOSESTRIFE FAMILY

This is a small family (Lythraceae) of mainly tropical plants. The species found in temperate regions are mostly herbaceous plants which prefer damp habitats. The leaves are opposite or in whorls. The flowers are grouped in clusters or heads, and have four to six petals which are crumpled in bud. There are two whorls of stamens which may be at any of three different levels within the flower. The family contains a number of ornamental species but is best known as a source of dyes, the most famous of which is henna.

Purple-loosestrife
Lythrum salicaria
Up to 200cm. This tall perennial has erect, usually unbranched stems. The lance-shaped, pointed leaves are stalkless and arranged in pairs or threes. The rose-purple flowers are borne in long, dense spikes. Three different sorts of flower occur, which

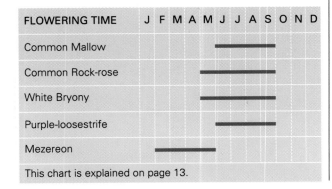

FLOWERING TIME	J	F	M	A	M	J	J	A	S	O	N	D
Common Mallow						▬	▬	▬				
Common Rock-rose					▬	▬	▬					
White Bryony					▬	▬	▬					
Purple-loosestrife						▬	▬	▬				
Mezereon		▬	▬	▬								
This chart is explained on page 13.												

vary in the lengths of the style and stamens, although each plant bears one type of flower only. These differences ensure that pollen is transferred to a flower of a different plant. A wetland species, it is found in fens and marshes and also by the edges of lakes, ponds and streams. The closely related Grass-poly (*L. hyssopifolia*) is an annual plant with inconspicuous flowers and oblong leaves. Ⓑ ☻

DAPHNE FAMILY

This is a small family (Thymelaeaceae) which consists mostly of low-growing shrubs and is best represented in Africa. European species frequently occur in woods, thickets and scrub in dry habitats or on chalky soils. Some are grown as garden ornamentals. Many produce toxins which are used in Mediterranean lands as fish poisons. The flowers are grouped in clusters or short spikes and consist of a tubular and often brightly coloured receptacle with four or five petal-like sepals around the rim. There may be a similar number of tiny scale-like petals and twice as many stamens. The fruit varies from dry to fleshy or berry-like.

Mezereon

Daphne mezereum
Up to 100cm. This small deciduous shrub bears a few, erect branches with short-stalked leaves, bright green above and pale green below, clustered at the ends. Small clusters of two to four pinkish purple, or rarely white, flowers bloom early in the year before the leaves have appeared. They are very sweetly scented and attract butterflies and long-tongued bees. The fruits are shiny scarlet-red and fleshy. A poisonous plant, it is found throughout most of Europe in woodland, usually on limestone. It has become scattered and rare in many areas because gardeners have collected it. Ⓑ ○

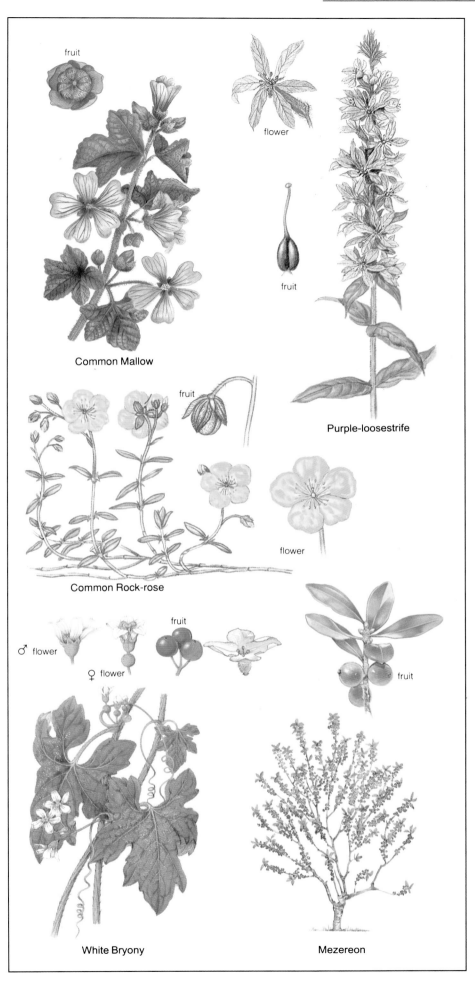

fruit

flower

fruit

Common Mallow

Purple-loosestrife

fruit

flower

Common Rock-rose

♂ flower

♀ flower

fruit

fruit

White Bryony

Mezereon

WILLOWHERB FAMILY

This widespread family (Onagraceae) includes shrubs, and water and garden plants as well as the familiar willowherbs which spring up on roadsides and waste ground. The flowers usually have four sepals and four petals (though enchanter's nightshades have only two of each). The flower tube contains nectar and attracts bees and moths. There are commonly eight stamens and the stigma is often four-lobed. The fruit is usually a long slender capsule, which opens by four longitudinal slits to release large numbers of plumed seeds that are scattered by the wind.

Enchanter's-nightshade
Circaea lutetiana
Up to 60cm. This slender perennial sports long, creeping, underground stems and oval, dull green leaves in opposite pairs. Its white or pinkish flowers form a loose spike and are pollinated by small flies. The two petals are deeply lobed. The club-shaped fruits are covered with stiff, whitish, hooked bristles, and are dispersed by animals. A common woodland plant, it is also found in other shady places on damp, fertile soils.
Ⓑ Ⓞ ✿

Large-flowered Evening-primrose
Oenothera erythrosepala
Up to 180cm. This robust biennial has erect, red-spotted, stiffly hairy stems, the hairs with distinctive expanded red bases. Its large,

pale yellow flowers, 5–8cm across, are borne in long, leafy spikes. They open rapidly in the early evening and become scented, attracting night-flying moths. Thought to be of garden origin, it is naturalized in western and central Europe where it is becoming more common at roadsides.
Ⓑ ✿

Broad-leaved Willowherb
Epilobium montanum
Up to 60cm. This sparsely hairy perennial herb has reddish stems and oval, toothed leaves which are mostly arranged in opposite pairs. Its small flowers, with pale pink, deeply notched petals, are drooping in bud and often self-pollinated. The fruit is a downy-haired capsule about 4–8cm long. A common, widespread species, it grows in woods and hedgerows, on walls and waste ground and is often a troublesome weed.
Ⓑ Ⓞ ✿

Great Willowherb
Epilobium hirsutum
Up to 150cm. This tall perennial herb has erect, glandular stems and large, oblong to lance-shaped leaves. Its purplish rose flowers are borne in terminal, leafy clusters and are pollinated by bees and flies. The petals are notched at the top and the stigma is four-lobed. The fruit is a long slender capsule that contains numerous seeds, each with a long plume of hairs attached. It is common in wet places such as the margins of ponds and rivers, and often forms colonies in sunny locations.
Ⓑ 🐝

Ivy is one of the last plants to bloom in the autumn. Its flowers provide valuable nectar for insects about to enter hibernation.

Rosebay Willowherb
Chamaenerion angustifolium
Up to 150cm. This tall, robust perennial typically forms large clumps, its long roots spreading horizontally and sending up new shoots. Its conspicuous, rose-purple flowers, 2–3cm across, are numerous in long, leafless spikes with narrow, dark purple sepals and petals that are sometimes slightly notched. Once a much rarer plant, it is now widespread and common, perhaps due to an increase in suitable habitats. It grows in wood margins and clearings, on rocky slopes, and waste ground such as railway embankments and disused building sites.
Ⓑ Ⓞ ✿

IVY FAMILY

This family (Araliaceae) of 800 trees, shrubs and climbers is almost entirely tropical. The only European species are the ivies, woody climbers which cling to tree trunks and walls by means of small aerial roots. The flowers are green or white, and arranged in umbels with the stalks arising from the same point.

Ivy
Hedera helix
This evergreen, woody plant develops stems up to 30m long. These may be either climbing, by attaching to a substrate with tufts of brown, clinging roots, or creeping, when they spread over the ground. The glossy, dark green leaves are very variable, mostly with three to five triangular lobes, but some are

also oval to heart-shaped and unlobed on mature flowering branches. The yellowish-green flowers are rather insignificant, but produce copious nectar at a time when little else is in flower and so are visited by large numbers of insects, particularly wasps and hornets. Ivy is common in woodland, along hedgerows and is also found on rocks and old walls.
Ⓑ Ⓞ ✿

MILFOIL FAMILY

This is a small family (Haloragidaceae) of aquatic and damp habitat plants. They range from stout, terrestrial perennials with leaves up to 6m in circumference to delicate free-floating plants with air-chambers in their stems. The aquatic species have feathery, submerged leaves. The individual flowers are inconspicuous but may be massed into dense spikes. They are wind-pollinated.

Spiked Water-milfoil
Myriophyllum spicatum
This submerged aquatic perennial has flexible, leafy stems up to 250cm long and finely divided leaves in whorls of four. Its minute reddish flowers are inconspicuous and borne above the water surface in slender spikes. The lower whorls of flowers are female and the upper ones are male. The fruit is rounded and four-lobed. This plant is widespread in Europe and occurs in freshwater ponds, lakes and ditches.
Ⓑ 🐝

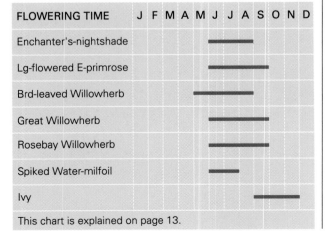

FLOWERING TIME	J	F	M	A	M	J	J	A	S	O	N	D
Enchanter's-nightshade						▬	▬	▬				
Lg-flowered E-primrose						▬	▬	▬	▬			
Brd-leaved Willowherb					▬	▬	▬	▬				
Great Willowherb						▬	▬	▬				
Rosebay Willowherb						▬	▬	▬				
Spiked Water-milfoil						▬	▬					
Ivy									▬	▬		

This chart is explained on page 13.

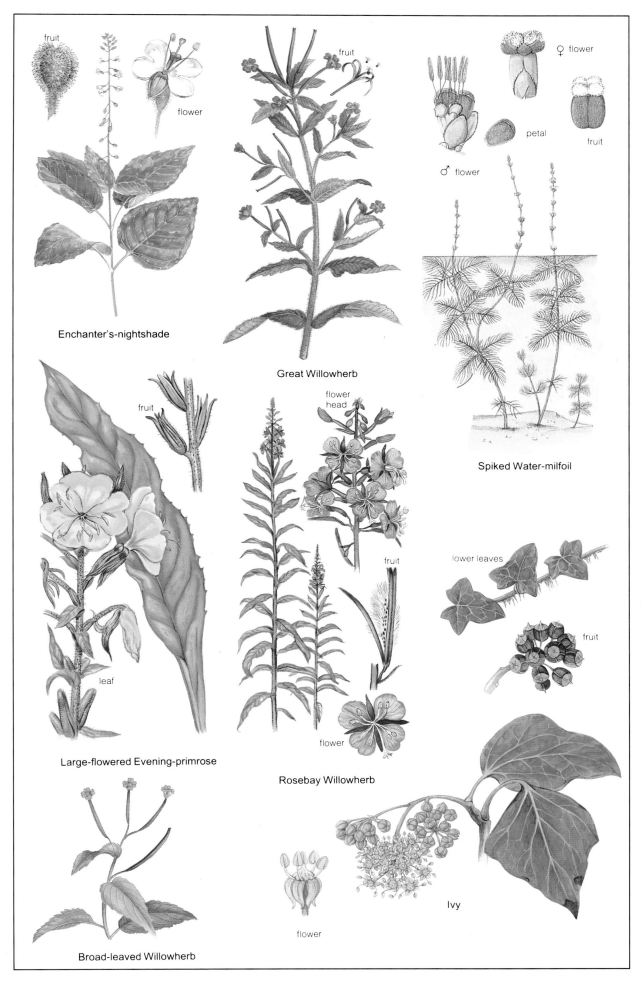

fruit

flower

Enchanter's-nightshade

fruit

Great Willowherb

♀ flower

petal

fruit

♂ flower

Spiked Water-milfoil

fruit

flower head

fruit

lower leaves

fruit

leaf

Large-flowered Evening-primrose

flower

Rosebay Willowherb

Ivy

flower

Broad-leaved Willowherb

CARROT FAMILY

Many herbs and spices including angelica, dill, fennel and parsley belong to this family (Umbelliferae) of over 3000 plants. Among the most easily recognizable features of the family is the arrangement of the tiny flowers into umbels. These are flat-topped clusters of flowers, with the bases of the stalks (rays) all arising from one point. Most species have compound umbels. These are umbels formed, in turn, of smaller umbels. This clustering of the tiny flowers makes them more visible and attractive to pollinating insects. Each flower has five petals; those of flowers on the rim of the umbel are often markedly different in size and the sepals are often absent. The fruits are variously decorated with ridges, furrows, hooks and spines, depending on how they are dispersed. They always split into two one-seeded segments when ripe. The fruits are very important for identification.

Sanicle
Sanicula europaea
Up to 60cm. This hairless perennial has little-branched stems and glossy, dark green leaves, which are deeply lobed and long-stalked, mostly in a loose basal rosette. White or pale, the small pink rounded heads, have a central cluster of bisexual flowers surrounded by short-stalked male flowers. The fruits are covered with hooked bristles. Widely distributed, but particularly frequent in beech and oak woods, this plant prefers chalky soils.
Ⓑ ✿

Sea-holly
Eryngium maritimum
Up to 60cm. This striking maritime plant sports blue stems and leaves. Its stalked, three-lobed basal leaves are thick and spiny-toothed, with prominent white veins. The bluish-white flowers in compact, almost globular heads are surrounded by spiny bracts, very similar to the leaves. It is found on sand and, less frequently, shingle beaches around the coasts of many European countries, growing just above the high-tide mark. It is sometimes cultivated as an ornamental in gardens.
Ⓑ 🦋

The lacy white flowers of Cow Parsley, also known as Queen Anne's Lace, line thousands of miles of country lanes in the spring.

Cow Parsley
Anthriscus sylvestris
Up to 150cm. This common biennial or perennial plant is one of the earliest umbellifers to flower each year. Its erect stems are hollow and furrowed, bearing finely divided, fern-like leaves. The creamy white flowers are 3–4mm across with minute sepals and shallowly notched petals. The dry, oblong-oval fruits are smooth and shortly beaked, brown or blackish when ripe. A widespread plant of hedgerows, it is also found on the edges of woods, waste ground and in grassy places. The related Bur Chervil (*A. caucalis*) is an annual which has egg-shaped fruits covered with hooked spines.
Ⓑ ✿ ⓜ

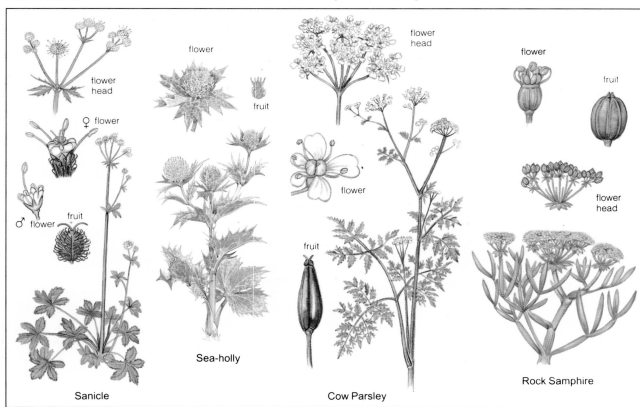

flower

flower head

♀ flower

fruit

♂ flower   fruit

Sanicle

flower

fruit

Sea-holly

flower head

flower

fruit

Cow Parsley

flower

fruit

flower head

Rock Samphire

Rock Samphire
Crithmum maritimum
Up to 45cm. This is a fleshy perennial with densely branched stems and is very characteristic of maritime areas. Its bluish-green leaves are divided into oblong lobes, which are circular in cross-section, and membranous leaf stalks form a sheath around the stem. The tiny, yellowish green flowers are borne in flattened heads. The fruits are oval and corky and, able to survive immersion in salt water, they may float in the sea to reach new sites. It is found on sea-cliffs and rocks and, less commonly, on coastal shingle or sand. In Britain, it is most frequent in the south and west. The leaves give off a strong smell and were formerly popular as a pickled delicacy.
Ⓑ 😋

Burnet-saxifrage
Pimpinella saxifraga
Up to 100cm. This slender perennial of dry, grassy places has upright, slightly ridged stems. Its lower leaves have two rows of oval, toothed leaflets, while the upper stem leaves have much narrower leaflets that are further subdivided. The flowers with five white petals, but no sepals, are arranged in flat-topped heads and usually bloom during late summer. Preferring limestone and chalk soils, it is widespread throughout most of Europe, but in Britain it occurs less frequently in the north and west. Greater Burnet-saxifrage (*P. major*) is a larger plant which is found in more shady habitats.
Ⓑ 🌰

Ground-elder
Aegopodium podagraria
This perennial has far-creeping underground stems, which send up new shoots some distance from the parent plant. It is readily distinguished by the leaves which are divided into groups of three oval, toothed leaflets. The flowers are white, with the outer petals slightly longer, and lack sepals. The egg-shaped fruit has slender ridges. It is widespread throughout most of Europe but is thought to have been introduced to Britain as a cultivated pot-herb. It grows in woodland, along roadsides and on waste ground, preferring shade, and often becomes a persistent weed in gardens. The leaflets of the similar Fool's Water-cress (*A. nodiflorum*) are not grouped in threes and the Lesser Marshwort (*A. inundatum*) has narrow-lobed, lower leaves.
Ⓑ ☉ ✿

Hemlock
Conium maculatum
Up to 200cm. This tall hairless biennial has hollow greyish stems, furrowed above and usually spotted with purple. Its large leaves are finely divided into toothed leaflets. The flowers are small, with white petals and no sepals. All parts of the plant contain the poison coniine; the highest concentrations are found in the seeds. It is commonly found in damp places, along roadsides and on waste ground, where it may be easily recognized by its purple-mottled stems and strong mousey smell.
Ⓑ ✿ ☠

Wild Parsnip
Pastinaca sativa
Up to 150cm. This erect, hairy and strong-smelling biennial has furrowed, angled and often hollow stems and pale yellowish-green leaves, which are divided into oval, lobed and toothed leaflets. Cultivated forms are often grown for the sweet-tasting tap roots eaten as a vegetable. In contrast, wild plants have slender, often woody roots which are bitter-tasting and inedible. Common in grassy places, by roadsides and on waste ground throughout most of Europe, it has been widely introduced elsewhere.
Ⓑ ☠ 🌰

FLOWERING TIME	J	F	M	A	M	J	J	A	S	O	N	D
Sanicle						▬	▬	▬				
Sea-holly							▬	▬	▬			
Cow Parsley					▬	▬						
Rock Samphire							▬	▬	▬			
Burnet-saxifrage							▬	▬				
Ground-elder					▬	▬	▬	▬				
Hemlock						▬	▬	▬				
Wild Parsnip							▬	▬				

This chart is explained on page 13.

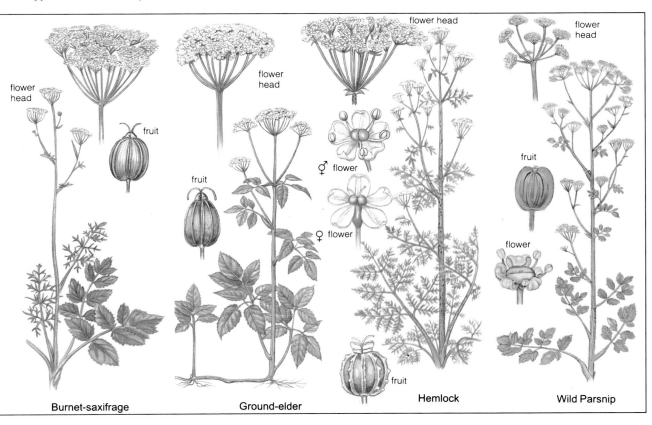

flower head — flower head — flower head — flower head

flower head — flower head

fruit — fruit — ♂ flower — ♀ flower — fruit

fruit — fruit — flower

Burnet-saxifrage — Ground-elder — Hemlock — Wild Parsnip

Hogweed
Heracleum sphondylium
Up to 200cm. This very variable, robust biennial has erect, ribbed and stiffly hairy stems and large, coarse leaves divided into irregularly lobed and toothed leaflets. Its white or pinkish flowers are arranged in large, almost flat-topped heads up to 15cm across and attract many different insects, including beetles. The petals are notched at the top, with those of the outer flowers of unequal size. A very common plant, it is widely distributed, growing in grassy places, hedgerows, roads and alongside open woods.
Ⓑ◑❸❻⊕

Fool's Parsley
Aethusa cynapium
This hairless, leafy poisonous plant has hollow, finely ridged stems and dark green, pinnately lobed leaves with oval, lobed leaflets. It is easily recognized by its long, hanging bracteoles below the white-petalled flowers. Two different forms may be recognized; one, a small plant less than 20cm high, is found mainly on arable land, and, two, a taller plant up to 80cm, occurs as a weed in gardens and along roadsides.
Ⓑ❸⊕

Wild Carrot
Daucus carota subsp. *carota*
Up to 100cm. This erect hairy biennial has leaves two to three times divided into slender, lobed segments. Its umbrella-shaped flower heads are composed of numerous white flowers, except for the central one which is usually dark purple. The oval fruits have alternate spiny and hairy ribs. They are densely packed in the umbel as the rays all curve in towards the centre as the fruits ripen. The root is tough and not at all fleshy, unlike the cultivated carrot which belongs to a different subspecies. Common in grassy places, especially on chalky soils, it is often found near the sea.
Ⓑ☻⊕

HEATH FAMILY

The majority of the 3350 species in this family (Ericaceae) are shrubs, either low-growing like heather or large like rhododendrons. A few species make small trees. The leaves are evergreen and often tiny and needle-like. The flowers are characteristically urn-shaped and frequently white, pink or reddish and waxy-looking. The fruit is a capsule or a berry. The family is distributed mainly in temperate regions and is almost exclusively confined to acid soils.

Cassiope
Cassiope hypnoides
Up to 10cm. This very low-growing, evergreen, mat-forming undershrub has tiny, very narrow leaves arranged alternately on the stem, giving the plant the appearance of a large moss. The white, bell-shaped flowers are borne at the ends of branches, singly or in pairs, on long pink stalks. This is a plant of mossy tundra, not thriving much south of the Arctic Circle, but common on Icelandic mountains.
☻

Heather
Calluna vulgaris
Up to 100cm. This evergreen shrub has many stems and short branches, which become more spreading as the plant ages. The small unstalked leaves are in opposite rows, flattened against the stem. The flowers are in leaf axils, giving a spike up to 15cm long. A common plant of acid heath, it often becomes the dominant plant. The small size and structure of the leaves helps retain water, essential on soils which are rapidly draining. It is widespread in Europe though rare in Mediterranean regions. Many varieties are grown as garden plants.
Ⓑ☙

Cross-leaved Heath
Erica tetralix
Up to 60cm. This is a sprawling, many-stemmed, greyish-downy evergreen shrub, the branches often rooting. The leaves are in whorls of four, each 4mm long, narrow, with the margins rolled up to the middle of the leaf. The flowers are in compact clusters at the ends of stems. Its flowers are oval, rose-pink and about 6mm long. A plant of boggy areas, and wet heathlands in western and northern Europe, it rarely spreads on to drier areas, although several garden varieties exist.
Ⓑ☙

Heather, seen here growing on the Yorkshire Moors in England, dominates the heaths and moors of western Europe, from southern Norway to the coasts of northern Spain.

Bell Heather
Erica cinerea
Up to 60cm. The stem of this evergreen shrub bears numerous clusters of very short leafy branches. Each leaf is hairless, narrow, with the margin rolled over. The pink flowers are markedly bell-shaped. This is a plant of dry heath and moorland areas. It has a western European distribution.
Ⓑ☙

Bilberry
Vaccinium myrtillus
To 60cm. This hairless, much branched deciduous shrub has bright green oval leaves which are pointed, with a toothed margin, and very pronounced veins. The pink globular flowers are borne singly or in pairs in the axils of leaves. Each one has short, slightly turned-back lobes. The fruit is a black berry, rich in both vitamin C and D. This is a plant of heath, moorland and open woods.
Ⓑ☙◑❹

Cranberry
Vaccinium oxycoccus
10–30cm long. This creeping evergreen has long, slender stems which root at the nodes. Its leaves are oval, pointed, dark green above and grey-green below, with the margins rolled under. The flowers are borne one to four together, on long stalks at the end of branches. They are pink, with four spreading or bent back lobes, and prominent stamens. The red, roundish, edible berries are up to 8mm across. This plant grows in boggy areas in northern Europe.
Ⓑ☙

FLOWERING TIME	J	F	M	A	M	J	J	A	S	O	N	D
Hogweed							▬	▬				
Wild Carrot						▬	▬	▬	▬			
Fool's Parsley						▬	▬	▬				
Cassiope						▬	▬					
Heather							▬	▬	▬			
Cross-leaved Heath							▬	▬	▬			
Bell Heather							▬	▬	▬			
Bilberry				▬	▬	▬						
Cranberry						▬	▬	▬				

This chart is explained on page 13.

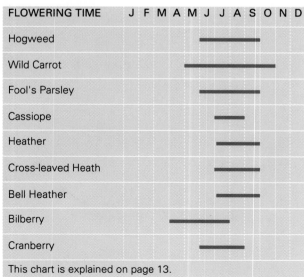

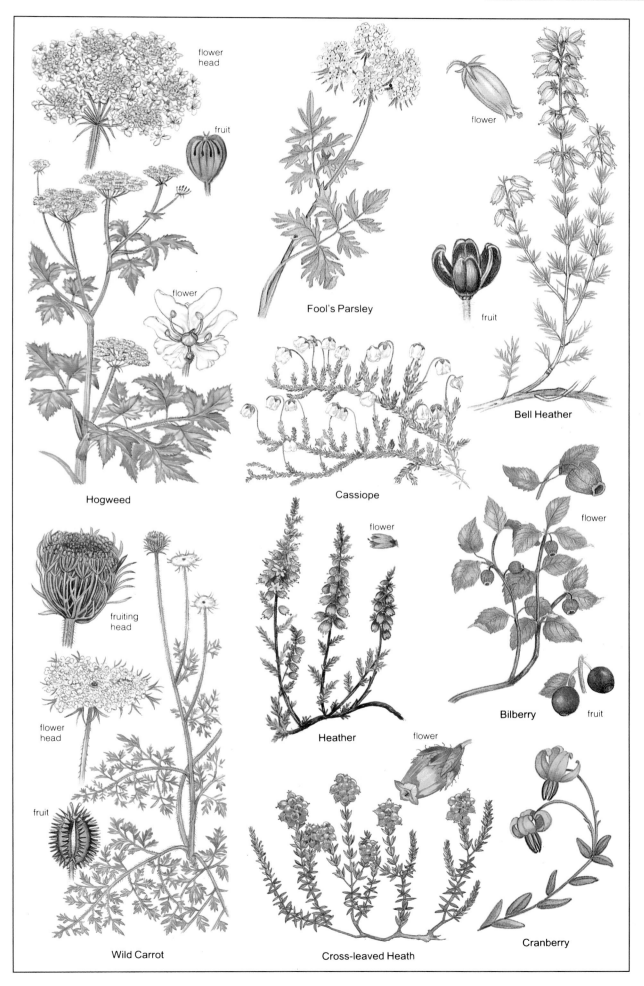

flower head

fruit

flower

Fool's Parsley

flower

fruit

Bell Heather

Hogweed

Cassiope

flower

Bilberry   fruit

fruiting head

flower head

fruit

Heather

flower

flower

Wild Carrot

Cross-leaved Heath

Cranberry

45

HEATHS and MOORS

Heathland and moorland are both open habitats dominated by Heather. Typical heathland occurs in dry lowland areas and moorland is characteristic of the wet uplands, but the two communities grade into each other and it is impossible to make a clear and concise distinction between them. Some ecologists now refer to all heather-dominated communities as heathlands.

The Lowland Heath

Lowland heaths are scattered along the western edge of Europe, from southern Scandinavia to Portugal, and are rarely more than about 300km from the coast. They develop on poor, sandy soils. Some coastal heathlands may be natural, but pollen deposits indicate that most of today's heathlands were originally covered with trees. The land was cleared for farming, but the poor soils could not sustain crops and it was abandoned to the Heather, which thrives on the acidic sands thanks to the mycorrhizal fungi (see p. 141) in its roots. But the plant needs plenty of moisture and it cannot tolerate severe cold – hence the limitation of heathland to the Atlantic region.

In addition to Heather, many heathlands carry one or more species of gorse, which survives well on the poor soil due to the nourishment provided by the nitrogen bacteria in its root nodules. Broom takes its place on the German heathland. Bracken is abundant in some regions, and grasses grow on the more open areas. Lichens are common on the ground and on old heather stems. Cross-leaved Heath and sundews grow in poorly drained low-lying areas, and if the ground is very wet the sphagnum mosses may take over and create small patches of peat bog.

Few insect species feed on the tough heathland plants, but those that do exist in huge numbers and support a wealth of predatory insects and spiders. Solitary wasps are common and so are mining bees, which make full use of the heather pollen and nectar. Few of the vertebrates are restricted to heathland habitats. The Sand Lizard and the Smooth Snake are more or less confined to heathland in England, but both species are found in a number of other habitats on the continent. Herds of sheep used to graze the heathlands, but there is now little grazing other than by

ABOVE: *During the autumn rut each Red Deer stag rounds up as many hinds as he can defend against other stags.*
RIGHT: *The Red Grouse occurs only in the British Isles, where it inhabits huge tracts of specially managed moorland.*

Rabbits, and many former heathlands are rapidly returning to forest. Birch is usually the first invader and it actually improves the sandy soil, making it more suitable for the pines and other trees that follow. Many heathlands have been taken over for forestry and also for housing. About 75 per cent of the English heathlands have been lost during the last 150 years.

Moorland

Moorlands develop in cool areas with high rainfall. They are characteristic of upland Britain and cover about 65 per cent of Scotland. Heather dominates in all but the wettest areas and is often joined by Bilberry and various grasses.

The driest moors resemble the lowland heaths, but most moorlands sit on a layer of peat which may be several metres thick. Decay is almost non-existent in the cold, wet conditions and the peat is formed from the accumulated remains of the plants. Bog mosses thrive, and in the wettest areas they cover almost everything. This squelchy community, in which cotton grasses and sundews are common, covers thousands of square kilometres and is known as blanket bog. Heather flourishes only on the drier hummocks. Millions of midges breed in the surface layers. Pollen deposits suggest that the most northerly moors

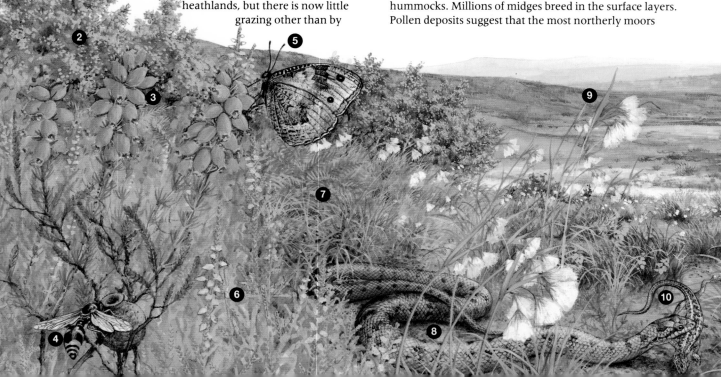

ABOVE: *Fir Clubmoss is common on dry moors. Spore capsules grow near the tips of the stems, which resemble dwarf conifers.*
LEFT: *Grazing has a marked effect on this moor. Heather dominates the lightly grazed upper regions, while heavily grazed areas are grassy.*

have never been anything else, but tree stumps buried in the peat elsewhere show that most moorlands were once forests. Human activity led to the destruction of the forests in the drier parts, but elsewhere the conversion from forest to moorland was caused by the wetter climate which came in about 4000 years ago. The leaching of the soil and the spread of the bog mosses and their peat made tree growth impossible and led to the development of moorland.

The Grouse Moor

Moorlands support even fewer animals than the lowland heaths, although many areas are grazed by Rabbits, deer, sheep and cattle. Where grazing is heavy the grasses take over from the heather to form grass moors. Many birds, such as the Stone Curlew, nest on the moors, but the best known moorland birds are the grouse. Huge tracts of moorland are devoted to rearing – and shooting – them. They feed mainly on heather shoots, and to maintain the supply of young shoots the landowners periodically set fire to the moors. This both encourages the heather to shoot from the base and promotes seed germination.

Wildlife of the Lowland Heath
1 Stonechat
2 Gorse
3 Bell Heather
4 Potter Wasp
5 Grayling
6 Heather
7 Bracken
8 Smooth Snake
9 Cotton Grass
10 Sand Lizard
11 Bog Asphodel
12 Four-spotted Chaser
13 Round-leaved Sundew
14 Broom
15 Stone Curlew
16 Wavy Hair-grass
17 Cross-leaved Heath
18 Emperor Moth

PRIMROSE FAMILY

Cyclamens, pimpernels and primroses, including the garden polyanthus, all belong to this family (Primulaceae). There are some 800 species in all, most of them north temperate, as well as many garden hybrids. They occur in a wide range of habitats, including woods, meadows, on high mountains and even in fresh water. Most species are perennials with rhizomes or tubers but a few are sub-shrubs. Many species lack stems and have all the leaves grouped into a basal rosette. The flowers have three to nine, but usually five, petals which are joined in a tube. A considerable number of species have two kinds of flowers: pin-eyed, in which the stigma shows in the throat of the tube with the stamens far below it, and thrum-eyed, with the stamens in the throat and the stigma below them. This type of arrangement encourages cross-pollination.

FLOWERING TIME	J	F	M	A	M	J	J	A	S	O	N	D
Primrose			▬	▬	▬							
Cowslip				▬	▬							
Alpine Snowbell				▬	▬	▬	▬					
Yellow Pimpernel					▬	▬	▬	▬	▬			
Yellow Loosestrife						▬	▬	▬				
Scarlet Pimpernel					▬	▬	▬	▬	▬			
Bog Pimpernel						▬	▬	▬	▬			
Water Violet					▬	▬						

This chart is explained on page 13.

Primrose
Primula vulgaris
Up to 20cm. This downy plant sports a basal rosette of oval, toothed leaves, which are widest above the middle, narrowing to the base. The flowers, borne singly on long stalks, each have a four to six toothed calyx, and the five-lobed corolla, up to 30mm in diameter, is usually the characteristic primrose yellow, although pink flowers are occasionally found (probably the result of hybridizing with cultivated forms). Typically a plant of grassy banks, hedgerows and woodlands, but it also grows on mountains throughout most of Europe. It is becoming rare in places, due to over-picking of the flowers and collectors digging up this lovely plant.
Ⓑ Ⓞ ⊞

Cowslip
Primula veris
Up to 30cm. This downy short-lived perennial has a rosette of oval, toothed leaves, each up to 20cm long and narrowing abruptly at the base. There are up to 30 flowers in a drooping, slightly one-sided cluster, on a downy flowering shoot. Each flower is short stalked and 10–15mm in diameter, narrowing down to a tube surrounded by a five-lobed calyx about 15mm long. The corolla is deep yellow, with five notched lobes, each with an orange spot at the base. A plant of grass and scrub-land, and open woods, it prefers chalky soils. It occurs throughout Europe except in the extreme north.
Ⓑ Ⓞ ⊞

Yellow Pimpernel
Lysimachia nemorum
Up to 40cm. This slender-stemmed, hairless perennial normally grows along the ground. The oval leaves are bright green, up to 4cm long on short stalks. The flowers are borne in the leaf axils on thin stalks as long as the leaves. They are yellow, up to 12mm across, with 5mm long, narrow calyx-teeth. It is a plant of damp, shady woods and hedgebanks which occurs throughout Europe, decreasing eastwards.
Ⓑ Ⓞ

Alpine Snowbell
Soldanella alpina
Up to 8cm. This low-growing plant often forms mats. Its leaves, borne on the long stems in a rosette, are dark green and oval or kidney-

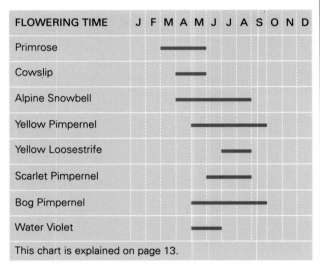

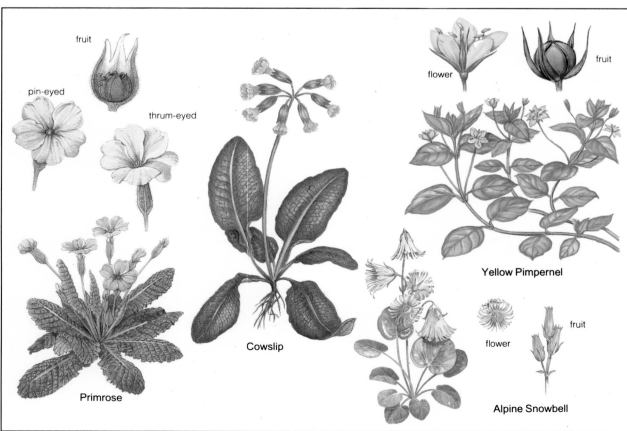

fruit

pin-eyed

thrum-eyed

flower

fruit

Cowslip

Yellow Pimpernel

Primrose

flower

fruit

Alpine Snowbell

The delicate flowers of Bog Pimpernel are inconspicuous in the dense vegetation of the heath.

shaped, with a heart-shaped base. One to four flowers are carried together on a long stalk, each 2cm across, bell-shaped, deeply fringed around the edges and mauve or blue-violet, with crimson streaks on the inside. It grows on wet grassland and rocky areas, particularly on limestone and up to altitudes of 3000m in the major mountain ranges of Europe, where the flowers often push up through late lying snow. The beauty of this small plant makes it much prized by Alpine plant growers, and has put it at risk from collectors. The smaller Dwarf Snowbell (*S. pusilla*) grows on non-calcareous soils.

Yellow Loosestrife
Lysimachia vulgaris
Up to 150cm. This upright perennial creeps by means of rhizomes. Its leaves are up to 12cm long, either opposite, or in whorls of three or four together, broadly lance-shaped and short stalked. They are often dotted with small black or orange glands. The flowers are borne in a cluster, at the ends of branches. They are on short slender stalks, and are up to 20mm across, more or less bell-shaped and glossy yellow. Bees are attracted by the abundant pollen. This plant grows in boggy areas, and beside fresh water, across all regions of Europe.

Scarlet Pimpernel
Anagallis arvensis
Up to 30cm. This scrambling or semi-upright, hairless annual, or short-lived perennial, has square stems. Its leaves are opposite, up to 25cm long, oval, pointed, dotted underneath with black glands. The solitary flowers are borne in the leaf axils, and are on long stalks. Each is about 15mm in diameter, with a five-lobed calyx, and five-lobed corolla, which is usually red, but can be pink, lilac or blue. The petals open only in sunshine, hence its alternative country name of 'Poor man's weather-glass'. A common weed of disturbed ground throughout Europe.

Bog Pimpernel
Anagallis tenella
Up to 15cm across. This narrow-stemmed, creeping, hairless perennial roots at regular intervals. The opposite leaves are oval and about 5mm across. The flowers are solitary and borne in the leaf axils on long thin stalks. The pink corolla is up to 15mm in diameter and funnel-shaped. It opens in full sun. A plant of damp, peaty, boggy or marshy places, it is found throughout Europe from the British Isles southwards.

Water Violet
Hottonia palustris
Up to 45cm. This pale green, aquatic plant has floating and rooting stems. The leaves, up to 10cm long, are submerged, arranged in whorls and finely divided, with narrow lobes. The flowers are also formed in whorls, three to eight together. They are up to 25mm in diameter, pale lilac with a yellow centre, on a 1–2cm long stalk. It is found throughout most of Europe, but is not common.

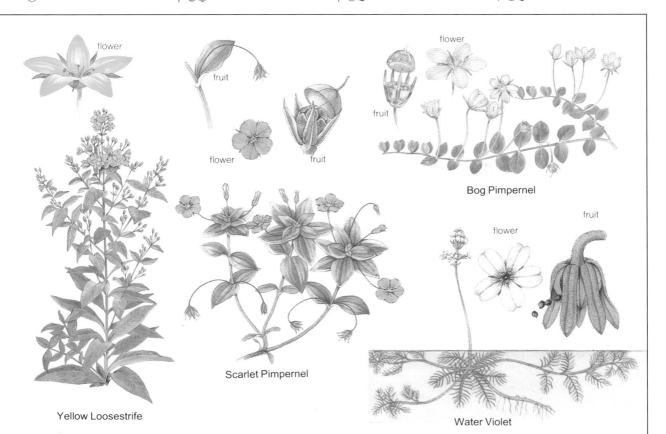

Yellow Loosestrife

flower

fruit

flower

fruit

fruit

flower

fruit

Scarlet Pimpernel

flower

Bog Pimpernel

flower

fruit

Water Violet

The Yellow Gentian, found in the alpine meadows, is protected for its use in the manufacture of liqueurs and aperitifs.

THRIFT FAMILY

Some 440 herbs, mainly perennials and shrubs make up this family (Plumbaginaceae). The majority of species are salt-tolerant and are conspicuous on sea coasts, salt-marshes and salt steppes. The leaves are arranged in a basal rosette or alternately along the stem. They have specialized chalk glands which eliminate excess water and calcium salts. The flowers have a large, five-toothed, membranous calyx and the five petals are often fused below into a tube. The characteristic papery calyces persist on the plant and enclose the ripe fruit.

Thrift
Armeria maritima
Up to 30cm. This perennial is low-growing with narrow, fleshy leaves up to 15cm long. As the plant ages, it comes to consist of many leaf rosettes and acquires a compact, domed appearance. Each long-stalked flower head is about 25mm across, and consists of many small rose-pink flowers, which are about 8mm in diameter. An inhabitant of salt-marshes and sea cliffs, it is also found less commonly inland, and on mountains. This species has a distinct western European distribution.
Ⓑ ☻ ☻

Common Sea-lavender
Limonium vulgare
Up to 40cm. This is a perennial which often forms carpets. The leaves are in a basal rosette, each up to 25cm long, leathery, dull green above and greyish-green below. They are often elliptical, narrowing to a long stalk. The flowering stem is branched, the branches with upward-facing flat-topped clusters of small bluish-purple flowers, each of which is about 8mm in diameter. A plant of coastal salt-marshes, it occurs mainly in western Europe.
Ⓑ ☻

GENTIAN FAMILY

About 1200 species belong to this family, (Gentianaceae), of which many are Arctic or mountain plants. Most species are herbaceous perennials with opposite leaves. The erect flowers have a tubular calyx and funnel-shaped corolla. Their colours range from rose and yellow to vibrant blue. Many species are prized as ornamental flowers; most also accumulate bitter substances which are important in various medicines.

Common Centaury
Centaurium erythraea
2–50cm. This very variable, greyish-green annual has a basal rosette of leaves which are up to 5cm long, oval, and with three to seven veins. The stem leaves are shorter and more elliptical. The flowering stems are usually single, with the flowers forming a dense cluster at the ends of branches. Each flower is up to 12mm across, five-petalled and pink. A plant of grassland and coastal sand dunes, it occurs throughout Europe.
Ⓑ ☻ ☻

Field Gentian
Gentianella campestris
Up to 30cm. This variable annual or biennial has blunt basal leaves up to 25mm, while those on the stems are up to 30mm, narrower and more pointed. The flowers, up to 30mm long, are bluish-lilac with a fringe of hairs inside the flower-tube and are readily distinguished from other similar gentians by having only four lobes. It grows on grassland and dunes throughout northern Europe.
Ⓑ ☻ ☻

Spring Gentian
Gentiana verna
Up to 6cm. This low-growing perennial eventually forms a dense cushion. The rosette leaves are up to 15mm long, oval and bright green, while those on the flowering stems are smaller and elliptical. The flowers are a deep gentian blue, borne singly at the end of flowering shoots, and up to 25mm across, five-lobed and narrowing into a tube. A plant of grassland and rocks, at altitudes up to 3000m, it occurs from England and Ireland southward, but in the south of Europe it is found only on mountains.
Ⓑ ☻

Yellow Gentian
Gentiana lutea
Up to 175mm. This tall perennial has blue-green leaves up to 30cm long, oval, pointed and strongly ribbed. Each flower is up to 3cm across, with five to nine petals. It occurs in grassland, marshy areas and rocks up to 2500m in the mountains of southern and central Europe.
☻ ☻

PERIWINKLE FAMILY

Members of this large family (Apocynaceae) are mainly tall rainforest trees of the tropics. The rest are shrubs or woody climbers and in northern Europe they are herbaceous perennials.

Lesser Periwinkle
Vinca minor
30–60cm long. This trailing evergreen plant has stems which root at intervals to form tangled mats. The leaves are opposite, more or less elliptical and shiny green. The single flowers are up to 30mm across and have five lobes. It grows in woodland, hedgebanks and rocky areas throughout Europe.
Ⓑ Ⓞ ✿

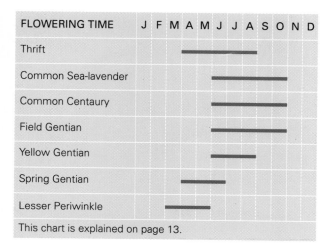

FLOWERING TIME	J F M A M J J A S O N D
Thrift	▬▬▬▬
Common Sea-lavender	▬▬▬▬
Common Centaury	▬▬▬▬
Field Gentian	▬▬▬▬
Yellow Gentian	▬▬▬
Spring Gentian	▬▬▬
Lesser Periwinkle	▬▬▬▬

This chart is explained on page 13.

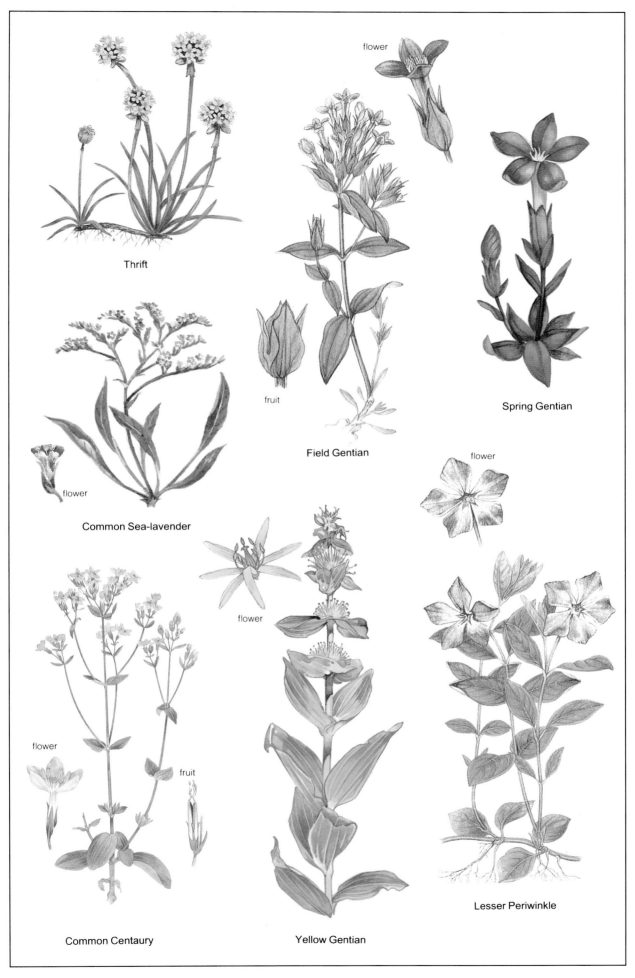

Thrift

flower

Spring Gentian

Common Sea-lavender

flower

fruit

Field Gentian

flower

flower

Common Centaury

flower

fruit

flower

Yellow Gentian

Lesser Periwinkle

BEDSTRAW FAMILY

This is a large, world-wide family (Rubiaceae) of 10,700 species, most of them trees or shrubs. The European members are all small herbs, often scrambling or climbing by means of tiny hooks on the leaves and stems. The flowers have four or five petals and are always small.

Cleavers
Galium aparine
Up to 120cm. This annual plant has long, weak, square stems. The four angles have stiff, downward-pointing prickles, enabling them to cling to other vegetation. Its flowers are inconspicuous and little visited by insects. The fruits have two rounded lobes, covered with hooked bristles, and are dispersed by animals. A common species, it has been introduced to many parts of the world where it thrives in lowland habitats, such as hedgerows and shingle beaches.
Ⓑ◒❶❄

Lady's Bedstraw
Galium verum
Up to 100cm. This slender perennial has four-angled stems with upright branches. Its dark green, shiny leaves have inrolled margins. The bright yellow flowers are borne in loose, branched, leafy clusters and are visited by insects. Fruits are two one-seeded nuts. Widespread throughout most of Europe, it grows in meadows, hedgebanks, along roadside verges, and on dunes. It is sometimes collected for its roots which yield a red dye.
Ⓑ❶●

BINDWEED FAMILY

This large and widely distributed family (Convolvulaceae) contains 1600 woody and herbaceous plants. Many species are climbers with stems that always twine to the right. The flowers are funnel-shaped, the five petals completely fused together. The dodders (*Cuscuta* species) are parasitic.

Hedge Bindweed
Calystegia sepium
This perennial has slender, twining stems which may extend 300cm or more and bear heart-shaped leaves. The large, trumpet-shaped flowers are pure white, only rarely pink, with two oval, leaf-like structures (bracteoles) enveloping the base of the tube. Widespread in Europe, it grows along woodland margins, in hedges, waste ground and gardens.
Ⓑ◒❶

Sea Bindweed
Calystegia soldanella
This perennial has creeping, non-twining stems up to 50cm long which are subterranean and leafless for most of their length. The leaves are kidney-shaped, rather fleshy and borne crowded onto short stem-tips protruding above ground-surface. The large funnel-shaped flowers are bright pink with a contrasting star-shaped pattern of five white lines radiating from the tube. Sea Bindweed is widespread on European coasts, except in the far north, it grows in open areas of sand and shingle, and is common on dunes.
Ⓑ❄

Field Bindweed, also known as Cornbine, seen here smothering wheat stems, is a serious problem for both farmer and gardener.

Field Bindweed
Convolvulus arvensis
This perennial has slender stems trailing or twining up to 200cm long and bearing leaves shaped like arrow-heads, with two basal spreading lobes. Its flowers are funnel-shaped, white to pink, often with contrasting lines radiating from their tube. Widespread in Europe, it grows in hedges, on coastal grassland and waste areas. It can become an extremely troublesome weed.
Ⓑ❶●

Dodder
Cuscuta epithymum
Up to 150cm. This leafless parasite, has thread-like, twining, yellowish or reddish stems completely lacking green chlorophyll. Its seedlings quickly attach themselves to host plants by means of specialized roots (haustoria), which invade tissues to gain water and nutrients. The parasite's root then withers away. Its flowers are tiny and pink and borne in dense, globular clusters, which are conspicuous on the otherwise bare stems. It is found almost throughout Europe, growing on Heather, Gorse, and other species of dwarf shrubs.
Ⓑ❄●

STARWORT FAMILY

This very small family (Callitrichaceae) contains just 17 species of small, slender water plants. Some grow completely submerged and are water pollinated; others can grow beside water or on wet ground and are pollinated by the wind. The unisexual flowers are minute and lack both sepals and petals.

Common Water-starwort
Callitriche stagnalis
Up to 60cm. This perennial grows in water or on damp mud, forming lush, masses of slender, branching stems with leaves in opposite pairs. The aquatic form is rooted in mud and has ascending stems with roots emerging at the joints. The leaves at the stem-tips are broad, almost round and are crowded into flat rosettes floating on the surface. The fruit has four lobes. The terrestrial form is more compact, reaching only 15cm high. Found throughout most of Europe it grows in ponds, springs, streams and other shallow, fresh water. It also occurs on damp ground such as woodland tracks.
Ⓑ◒❶❄

FLOWERING TIME	J	F	M	A	M	J	J	A	S	O	N	D
Cleavers						▬	▬	▬				
Lady's Bedstraw						▬	▬	▬				
Hedge Bindweed							▬	▬				
Sea Bindweed						▬	▬					
Field Bindweed						▬	▬	▬				
Dodder							▬	▬				
Cmn Water-starwort						▬	▬	▬				
This chart is explained on page 13.												

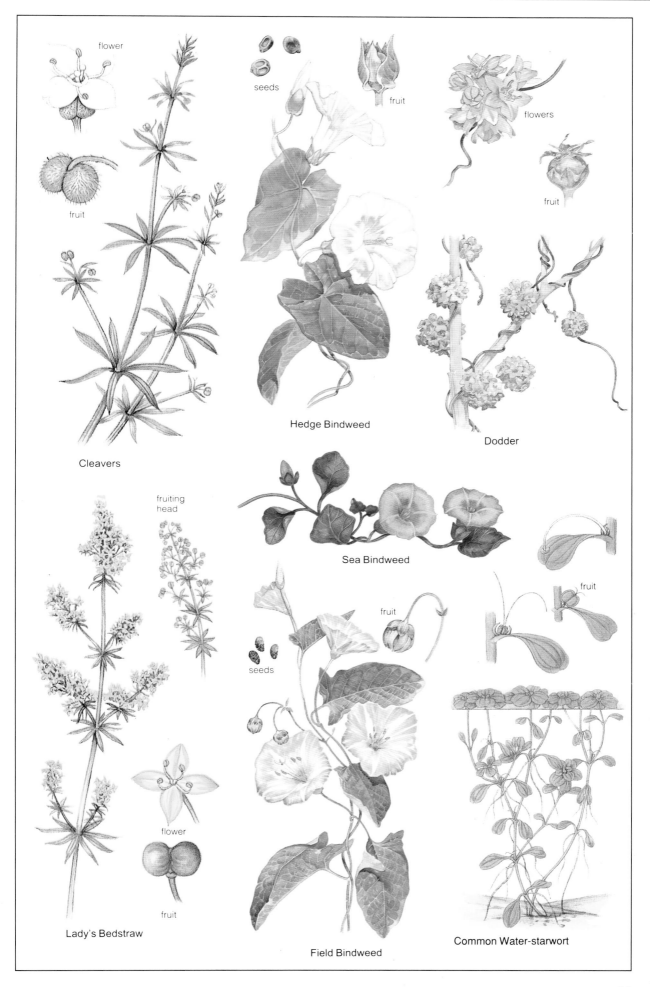

flower

seeds

fruit

flowers

fruit

fruit

Hedge Bindweed

Dodder

Cleavers

fruiting
head

Sea Bindweed

fruit

fruit

seeds

flower

fruit

Lady's Bedstraw

Field Bindweed

Common Water-starwort

MARE'S-TAIL FAMILY

There is only one species in this aquatic family (Hippuridaceae). It is sometimes mistaken for a horsetail (p. 134), but it has pink flowers.

Mare's-tail
Hippuris vulgaris
Up to 75cm. This perennial has unbranched, spongy-textured stems either growing upright and rising above the water's surface or trailing and remaining submerged. Its rather short, strap-shaped leaves are arranged in regularly spaced whorls along the stem. Emergent shoots have tiny, unisexual flowers borne at the joints between leaves and stem. Found almost throughout Europe but rare in the Mediterranean region, it grows in ponds, shallow lakes and other still or slow-moving bodies of fresh water.
Ⓑ☻

FORGET-ME-NOT FAMILY

The members of this family (Boraginaceae) are almost always covered with stiff hairs. They are easily recognized by the flowerheads which consist of tightly coiled, one-sided sprays that uncurl as the flowers open. The flowers themselves have five petals which may be joined into a tube. They are often purplish or blue, starting pink in the bud before darkening as they open. Those of some species are pendulous and pollinated by bees. The fruit always consists of four small nutlets. The 2500 species include the dye plant Alkanet, and herbs such as Borage and Comfrey.

Common Comfrey
Symphytum officinale
Up to 100cm. This robust perennial has upright stems bearing large spear-shaped, bristly leaves. Its tubular flowers are carried in terminal clusters and may be white, pink or purple, but are only one colour on any individual plant. It is widespread in Europe, except for the Mediterranean region, growing on river-banks and in marshes and damp grassland. The leaves are rich in vitamins and may be eaten boiled in the same way as spinach. Its pulped roots were once greatly valued by herbalists for helping to heal broken bones and other injuries. Not surprisingly, one of its old folk-names was 'Knitbone'.
Ⓑ☻🐛

Water Forget-me-not
Myosotis scorpioides
Up to 100cm. This hairy perennial has creeping rhizomes and runners. Ascending, branching flowering stems bear oblong leaves and terminate in long sprays of small, bright blue flowers, each with five petal-like lobes surrounding a yellow eye. Widespread in northern and central Europe, it grows in swamps, marshes, by ponds, streams and other fresh water. The scientific name means scorpion-like and refers to the plant's tail-like, curling flower-sprays.
Ⓑ☻

Viper's-bugloss
Echium vulgare
Up to 90cm. This rough, bristly biennial has strap-shaped leaves arranged in a basal rosette. A tall, spire-shaped flowering stem is produced in the second year, carrying funnel-shaped flowers along much of its length. Pink in bud, these change to bright blue as they open. They attract many insects. Widespread in Europe, it grows in dry grassland, bare areas on limestone and chalk, on sand-dunes and shingly beaches. Herbalists once used the plant as a cure for snake-bite.
Ⓑ☻🐛

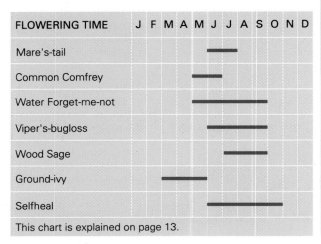

FLOWERING TIME	J	F	M	A	M	J	J	A	S	O	N	D
Mare's-tail						▬	▬					
Common Comfrey					▬	▬						
Water Forget-me-not					▬	▬	▬	▬	▬			
Viper's-bugloss						▬	▬	▬				
Wood Sage							▬	▬				
Ground-ivy				▬	▬							
Selfheal						▬	▬	▬	▬			

This chart is explained on page 13.

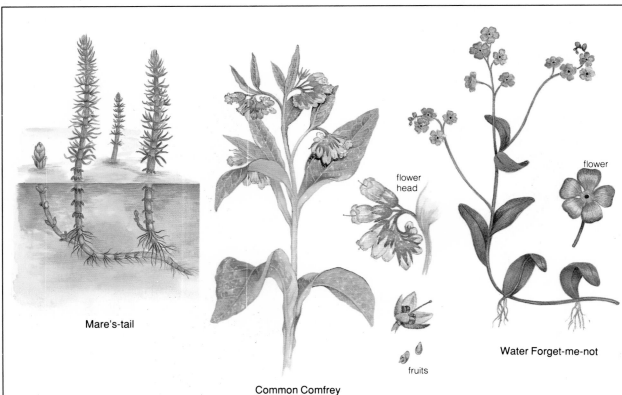

Mare's-tail

Common Comfrey

flower head

fruits

Water Forget-me-not

flower

Powdered roots of Common Comfrey make good plaster for setting broken bones – hence the plant's other name of Knitback. The leaves can be eaten, boiled or fried in batter.

MINT FAMILY

This fairly large family (Labiatae) has about 5600 species distributed world-wide but is especially numerous in the Mediterranean region. It is one of the most easily recognized of the flowering plant families. All members have stems which are square in cross-section and bear leaves in opposite pairs. Most species, especially those from warm, dry climates, have leaves dotted with numerous oil glands which give off an aromatic scent. The flowers are borne in whorls around the stem and the whorls are frequently grouped into spikes. The flowers are usually two-lipped, the upper lip often hooded and covering the four stamens and single style, the lower lip spreading and forming a landing platform for pollinating insects. The ovary is four-lobed, ripening to give four small nutlets. The family contains annuals, perennials and small shrubs. It also includes a substantial number of culinary herbs such as the ever-popular Mint, Oregano, Sage and Thyme.

Wood Sage
Teucrium scorodonia
Up to 60cm. This aromatic perennial has upright, branching stems bearing oval leaves that are wrinkled in texture and covered with downy hairs. Its stems terminate in spires of small, creamy-white flowers, each with a prominent lower lip but no upper lip. Widespread in central and southern Europe, it is found in dry woodland, grassland, on heaths and sand-dunes. This species prefers light, free-draining soils. It was formerly used for flavouring ale due to its rather bitter taste. An infusion of the leaves has also been used to help combat the disease of rheumatism. Wall Germander (*T. chamaedrys*) has similar purple flowers.
ⓑ🍃Ⓞ④🔟

Ground-ivy
Glechoma hederacea
Up to 50cm. This softly hairy perennial has slender stems rooting as they creep across the soil to form low, dense mats. Its leaves are kidney-shaped with rounded teeth at the margins, often bronze tinged and giving off a garlic-like odour when crushed. Small groups of pale violet flowers all face the same way. Widespread through most of Europe, it grows in a variety of habitats, preferring rather damp soils. It was used for clearing and flavouring ale and for coughs.
ⓑⓄ🌀🔟

Selfheal
Prunella vulgaris
Up to 50cm. This perennial has creeping, rooting stems which carpet the ground. Its upright flowering shoots bear opposite pairs of oval leaves and terminate in a dense, oblong head of violet-blue, two-lipped flowers, each one emerging from a purple-flushed, tubular calyx. Forms with white or pink flowers also rarely occur. Widespread in Europe, it grows in woodland clearings, grassland and waste areas. It was widely used in former times for treating wounds, hence its common name.
ⓑⓄ🌀🔟

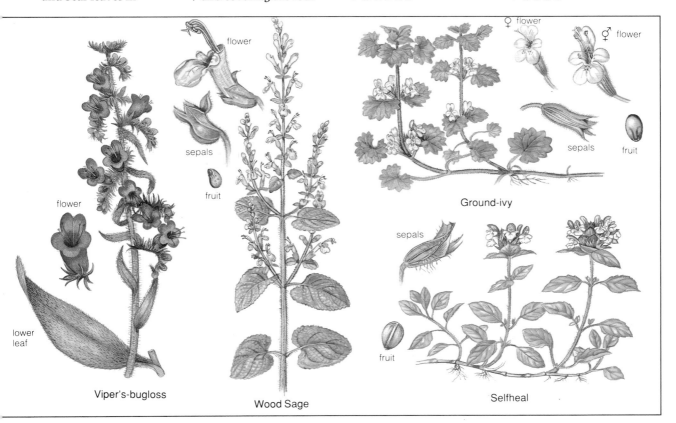

Viper's-bugloss

Wood Sage

Ground-ivy

Selfheal

White Dead-nettle
Lamium album
Up to 80cm. Appearing distinctly nettle-like when not in flower, this dead-nettle has opposite pairs of oval, pointed leaves serrated at the margins. However, the soft hairs do not sting. It is a perennial plant with upright stems carrying whorls of rather large, two-lipped, white flowers. Widespread in Europe, but rare in the Mediterranean region, it grows in hedges, on waste areas and roadsides.
Ⓑ◐❊

Red Dead-nettle
Lamium purpureum
Up to 40cm. This quick-growing, often purplish-tinged annual has branching stems bearing oval to heart-shaped leaves bluntly toothed at the margins. Its flowers are small and pinkish-purple and carried towards the stem-tips. It is widespread in Europe, growing in waste areas and disturbed ground. Its short life cycle enables it to rapidly invade bare soil and it can sometimes become a pest.
Ⓑ❊

Hedge Woundwort
Stachys sylvatica
Up to 100cm. This tall, hairy perennial has oval, pointed leaves which are serrated at the margins. Forming large patches by means of its creeping rhizomes, the plant has spires of deep reddish-purple flowers arranged in whorls. It is often mistaken for the stinging nettle when not in flower. Widespread in Europe, it grows in woodland, hedges and other shady places. Formerly used for healing wounds, hence the common name; now modern science has confirmed that the plant's oil possesses antiseptic properties.
Ⓑ◐ⓜ

Water Mint
Mentha aquatica
Up to 90cm. This aromatic perennial has upright flowering stems and creeping shoots which cling to the ground or grow beneath the soil. Its leaves are oval with toothed margins and give off a strong, minty scent when disturbed, perfuming the air where it grows in quantity. The tiny, pink flowers are densely packed into whorls which are themselves grouped into rounded heads at the stem-tips. It is found almost throughout Europe, growing in marshes, fens, wet woodland, as well as by ponds and streams.
Ⓑ◐◉

Marjoram
Origanum vulgare
Up to 90cm. This erect, much-branched perennial has oval leaves and many terminal clusters of small, pinkish flowers and small leaf-like, purple-flushed bracts. The whole plant has a strong, Thyme-like aroma when rubbed. Widespread in Europe, this species grows in woodland clearings, scrub, hedges and grassland on lime-rich soils. It was formerly utilized for its sweet scent, supposed healing properties, and for dying wool purple.
Ⓑ◐ⓜ

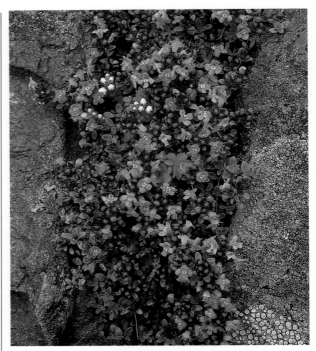

Wild Thyme is seen at its best among upland rocks. Elsewhere it is often swamped by other plants.

Wild Thyme
Thymus praecox arcticus
Up to 8cm. This low-growing perennial has sprawling stems forming close mats. Its leaves are small and oval and have a tangy aroma, like that of the culinary herb. The tiny, pink flowers are grouped into compact heads at the stem-tips. Found in western Europe, it grows in dry grassland, on heaths, sand-dunes and rocks, preferring lime-rich soils.
Ⓑ☙ⓜ

French Lavender
Lavandula stoechas
Up to 100cm. This much-branched, highly aromatic shrub bears narrow, grey leaves. Its compact, terminal spikes are very distinctive, with small, blackish-purple flowers and a few large, blue-to-violet, petal-like bracts emerging from the tips. Characteristic of the Mediterranean region, it grows in scrub, usually away from limestone soils. It has been used for its perfume.
🌢

POTATO FAMILY

About 50 of the 2600 species in this family (Solanaceae) are found in Europe and some of them are very common. The family provides many edible fruits, such as tomatoes as well as tubers, but most species also contain toxic chemicals called alkaloids. Species such as Deadly Nightshade are highly poisonous.

Bittersweet
Solanum dulcamara
Up to 200cm. This vigorous, woody-stemmed perennial generally scrambles over other plants. Its oval, pointed leaves, often have small, lateral lobes or leaflets. The flowers have narrow, backward-curved, violet petals. Small, egg-shaped berries follow, ripening bright, shiny red. It is found almost throughout Europe, growing in woodland, scrub, hedges and waste areas. This species is also known as Woody Nightshade.
Ⓑ◐❊☙ⓜ

Deadly Nightshade
Atropa belladonna
Up to 150cm. This stout, perennial herb has large, oval leaves. Brownish-purple or greenish bell-shaped flowers are followed by large, black, shiny berries backed by green, persistent sepals. Widespread in Europe, it grows in woodland and scrub, often on lime-rich soils. The whole plant is extremely poisonous, containing alkaloids which attack the nervous system, and can even cause death.
Ⓑ◐

FLOWERING TIME	J	F	M	A	M	J	J	A	S	O	N	D
White Dead-nettle					▬	▬	▬	▬	▬	▬		
Red Dead-nettle			▬	▬	▬							
Hedge Woundwort							▬	▬				
Water Mint							▬	▬	▬			
Marjoram							▬	▬				
Wild Thyme					▬	▬	▬					
French Lavender			▬	▬	▬							
Bittersweet						▬	▬	▬				
Deadly Nightshade						▬	▬	▬				

This chart is explained on page 13.

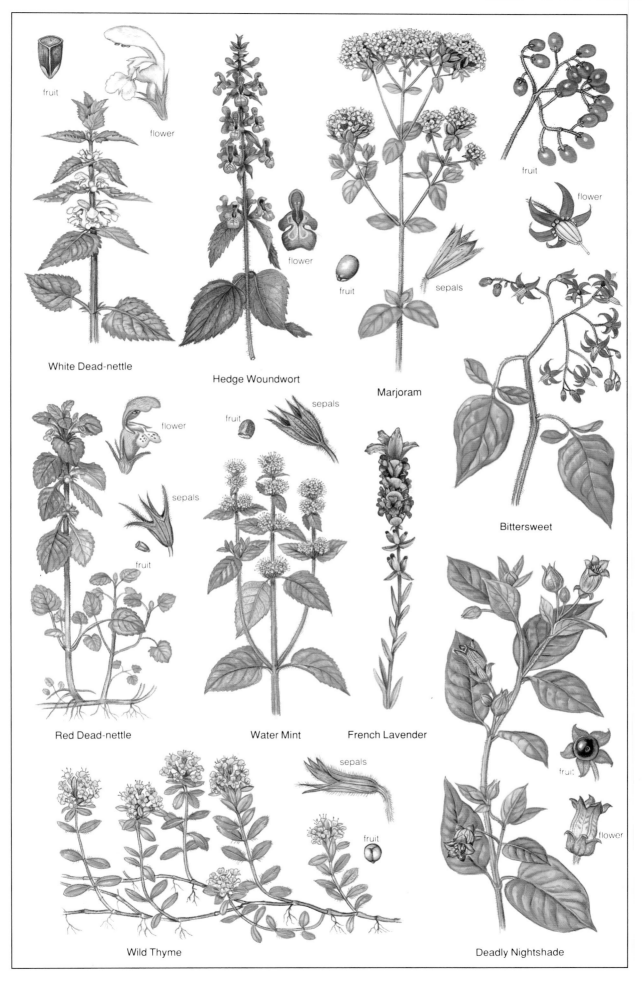

fruit

flower

White Dead-nettle

flower

flower

Hedge Woundwort

fruit

sepals

Marjoram

fruit

flower

Bittersweet

flower

sepals

fruit

sepals

Red Dead-nettle

fruit

sepals

Water Mint

French Lavender

fruit

sepals

fruit

flower

Wild Thyme

Deadly Nightshade

57

FIGWORT FAMILY

Around 4500 species belong to this family (Scrophulariaceae). Most are herbs, a few are shrubs or even large trees. Some groups, for example eyebrights (*Euphrasia* species), are semi-parasitic on the roots of other plants. The family also contains many ornamental garden plants. The leaves are arranged alternately or, sometimes, in opposite pairs. The flowers are two-lipped, the lips sometimes closing completely over the mouth of the flower so that only strong or heavy insects can part them to reach the nectar within. A nectar-filled spur may also be present. Some species, resemble members of the Mint Family but can be distinguished by their fruits which are always many-seeded capsules, not clusters of four nutlets as in the mints.

Great Mullein
Verbascum thapsus
Up to 200cm. This densely white-woolly biennial forms a large rosette of broad leaves and, in the second year, a stout, erect, leafy stem terminating in a long, dense spike of yellow flowers. It is found through most of Europe, except the far north and Balkan peninsula, growing in woodland clearings, dry hedges and waste areas, usually on soil which has been disturbed. In the past, the woolly coating of leaves and stems was used to make candlewicks. White Mullein (*V. lychnitis*) has whitish, smaller flowers and hairy stamens.
Ⓑ ☉ ✿

Ivy-leaved Toadflax
Cymbalaria muralis
This creeping, mat-forming perennial has wiry stems up to 60cm long. Its small, rather fleshy leaves are shallowly five-lobed and similar in shape to those of Ivy, hence the name. The two-lipped flowers are borne singly from the axils between leaves and stems and range in colour from lilac to violet, with the upper part of the lower lip yellow and closing the flower. White forms rarely occur. It is native to central-southern Europe, but naturalized over a much wider area, growing mainly on rocks and walls.
Ⓑ ✿

Common Toadflax
Linaria vulgaris
Up to 80cm. This perennial has creeping roots producing upright stems which bear many narrow, grey-green leaves and terminal, spike-like heads of two-lipped, bright yellow flowers. Each has an orange upper portion of the lower lip which closes the mouth of the flower and a long, downward-pointing spur which contains nectar at its tip. Widespread through most of Europe, except the far north and Mediterranean region, it grows in grassland, waste areas, on roadsides, cultivated ground and along railways. It may form large, colourful patches under suitable conditions.
Ⓑ ✿ ⊕

Speedwells are so-named because their flowers fall off when picked – 'speed-well' is an old form of 'good-bye'. This is Germander Speedwell.

Monkeyflower
Mimulus guttatus
Up to 50cm. This creeping perennial produces upright flowering stems bearing opposite pairs of oval leaves toothed at the margins. Very showy, bright yellow, two-lipped flowers are carried singly on slender stalks. The lips are lobed, the lower one larger with two hairy, red-spotted bulges blocking the entrance to the flower-tube. Native to western North America it is now widely naturalized in Europe, where it grows in wet meadows, marshes and besides streams. A garden escape, it is still grown for ornament.
Ⓑ ☻ ⊕

Foxglove
Digitalis purpurea
Up to 180cm. Usually biennial, this plant initially forms a large rosette of broadly spear-shaped, crinkly leaves. The erect, leafy stem ends in a spire of large, drooping, tubular, purple flowers, each with a mottled pattern within. Sometimes pale or white forms occur. Widespread in western Europe, it grows in woods, hedges and on rocky ground, preferring acidic soils. It is also grown for ornament in gardens. The whole plant is very poisonous, containing digitalin, which is used as a drug in treating heart illnesses by speeding and strengthening the heart-beat.
Ⓑ ☉ ✿

Germander Speedwell
Veronica chamaedrys
Up to 25cm. This creeping and ascending perennial has slender stems with two rows of white hairs on opposite sides, and oval leaves toothed at the margins. Sprays carry pale blue, four-petalled flowers which are followed by heart-shaped fruits. Widespread in Europe, except for some Mediterranean islands, this species grows in woodland, hedges and grassland. The plant was once used for various medicinal purposes.
Ⓑ ☉ ✿ ⊕

Brooklime
Veronica beccabunga
Up to 30cm. This fleshy-stemmed perennial creeps along the ground to form large patches. Its upright shoots bear hairless, oval leaves and short, spike-like sprays of blue flowers. It grows in wet and muddy places such as marshes, meadows, ponds and streams throughout Europe. The stems may root into the mud as they creep along or float in shallow water. Both the Latin and common names derive from the plant's wet habitat. The leaves are edible and had medicinal uses in the past.
Ⓑ ☻ ⊕

Common Eyebright
Euphrasia nemorosa
Up to 35cm. This branching semi-parasitic annual gains water and nutrients by normal means as well as via root-attachments to other plants such as clovers and plantains. The upright stems bear sharply toothed, oval leaves and small, two-lipped, white flowers streaked purple and with a yellow patch on the lower lip. Found in northern and central Europe, it grows in open woodland, grassland and on heaths, moors and mountains, up to altitudes of 2300m.
Ⓑ ☉ ☻ ☉ ✿

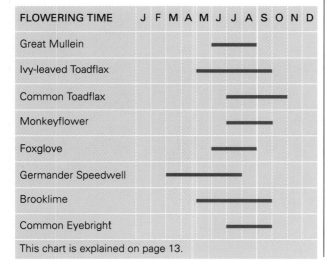

FLOWERING TIME	J	F	M	A	M	J	J	A	S	O	N	D
Great Mullein							▬	▬				
Ivy-leaved Toadflax					▬	▬	▬	▬				
Common Toadflax						▬	▬	▬	▬			
Monkeyflower						▬	▬	▬	▬			
Foxglove						▬	▬	▬				
Germander Speedwell			▬	▬	▬	▬						
Brooklime					▬	▬	▬					
Common Eyebright						▬	▬	▬	▬			

This chart is explained on page 13.

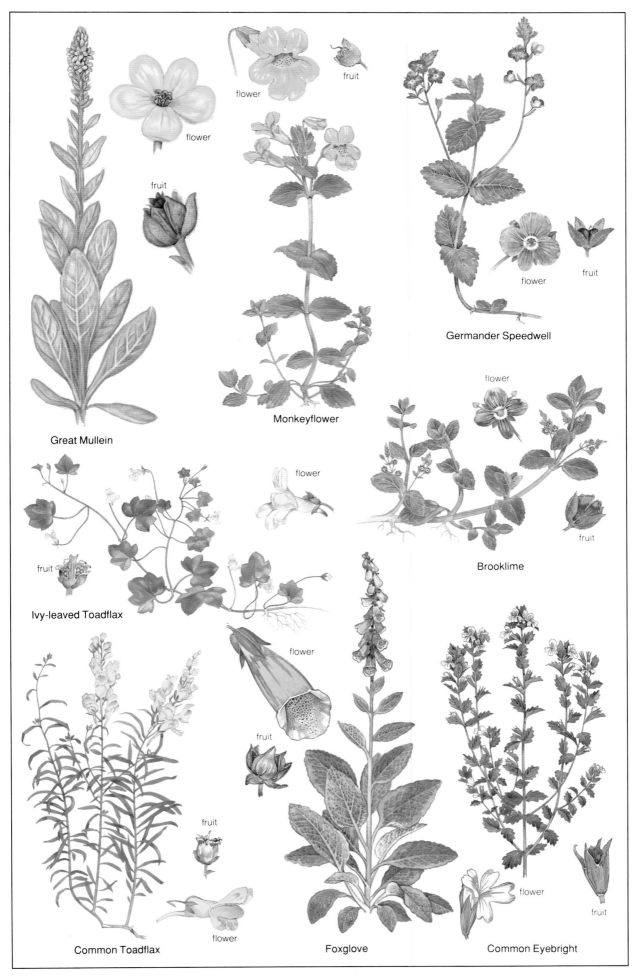

flower

fruit

flower

fruit

Germander Speedwell

flower

fruit

Great Mullein

Monkeyflower

flower

flower

fruit

Brooklime

flower

fruit

Ivy-leaved Toadflax

flower

fruit

fruit

fruit

flower

Common Toadflax

flower

Foxglove

flower

fruit

Common Eyebright

59

The flowers of the Ribwort Plantain open from the bottom up, so the ring of white anthers appears to move up the spike.

Red Bartsia
Odontites verna
Up to 50cm. This erect, branching, semi-parasitic annual gains some of its water and nutrients via root-attachments to various grasses. Its pale-hairy, spear-shaped leaves often have a strong, reddish tinge. The numerous, two-lipped, pink flowers all face in one direction. Found throughout most of Europe, it grows in grassland, waste areas, on roadsides and arable ground.
Ⓑ🟠🔵

Yellow-rattle
Rhinanthus minor
Up to 50cm. This upright, semi-parasitic annual obtains its water and nutrients partly via root-attachments to grasses. Each yellow flower is partially enclosed by a pale green, bladder-like calyx. These persist after flowering, enveloping capsules which rattle with loose seeds when ripe, hence the name. Widespread in Europe, it grows in grassland and on sand dunes.
Ⓑ😊🔵

Common Cow-wheat
Melampyrum pratense
Up to 60cm. This annual is semi-parasitic on the roots of grasses. Its stems bear spear-shaped leaves drawn out into a point. The pale yellow, two-lipped flowers are carried in pairs and face in one direction. Found throughout most of Europe, it grows in woodland, hedges, bogs and on heaths and moorland.
Ⓑ🟤🟢🟣

BUTTERWORT FAMILY

This small family (Lentibulariaceae) of small carnivorous plants can be divided into two groups. The terrestrial butterworts have a rosette of sticky leaves to trap insects. The aquatic bladderworts have many-branched, submerged stems bearing tiny, bladder-like suction traps which catch minute water animals.

Common Butterwort
Pinguicula vulgaris
5–15cm. This small plant forms a flat, star-shaped rosette of greasy, yellowish-green leaves which are rolled inwards at the margins. Its pale violet flowers, with five lobes and a spur at the rear, are solitary and borne on slender, erect stems. Widespread in northern and central Europe, it is found on bogs, wet heaths and wet rocks where nutrient levels, especially of nitrogen, are often low. It overcomes this problem by secreting enzymes and digesting tiny insects trapped on the sticky surfaces of its leaves.
Ⓑ😊🟤🟢😀😊

Greater Bladderwort
Utricularia vulgaris
15–45cm. The branching, rootless stems of this plant float just below the water's surface, reaching 100cm long and bearing leaves divided into thread-like segments. Its showy, yellow, two-lipped flowers are carried on erect, emergent stems. Small bladders carried on the leaves trap and digest tiny, aquatic organisms. The bladders have low internal pressure and when an organism brushes the bristles near the mouth, a flap opens and the victim is sucked inside. This species is found throughout most of Europe and grows in still, fresh waters.
Ⓑ😀

PLANTAIN FAMILY

Nearly all the 250 or so species in this family (Plantaginaceae) belong to the plantain genus *Plantago*. The small flowers are clustered tightly into spikes on stalks growing from a rosette of leaves. They are mainly wind-pollinated and produce large amounts of pollen. Together with the grasses, plantains are a major cause of hay-fever.

Several species of plantain are stubborn weeds, although the Ribwort is quite nutritious and therefore a useful component of pasture land.

Ribwort
Plantago lanceolata
Up to 45cm. This rosette-forming perennial bears prostrate or ascending, spear-shaped leaves with three to five prominent rib-like veins, hence the common name. The tiny, brownish flowers have creamy-white anthers. The latter form a conspicuous ring as the flowers progressively open and wither from the bottom of the head upwards. Widespread in Europe, this species grows abundantly in grassland, waste areas, along roadsides and paths.
Ⓑ🟠🔵

Greater Plantain
Plantago major
Up to 30cm. This perennial forms a flat rosette of long-stalked, broadly oval, almost hairless leaves. Its upright stems end in tail-like, narrowly cylindrical, green spikes bearing tiny, whitish flowers. Widespread in Europe, it grows abundantly on waste ground, on disturbed soil, along roadsides and paths and in lawns. The flat habit of the plant renders it resistant to damage from trampling, so it often becomes the dominant plant in heavily trodden areas where other, less tolerant species are unable to survive.
Ⓑ🟠

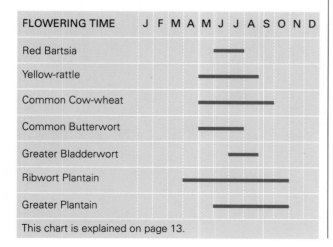

FLOWERING TIME	J	F	M	A	M	J	J	A	S	O	N	D
Red Bartsia						—	—					
Yellow-rattle					—	—	—					
Common Cow-wheat					—	—	—	—				
Common Butterwort					—	—						
Greater Bladderwort						—	—					
Ribwort Plantain				—	—	—	—	—				
Greater Plantain					—	—	—	—				

This chart is explained on page 13.

flower

Common Cow-wheat

Red Bartsia

flower
head

fruit

Ribwort Plantain

flower

fruit

Greater Bladderwort

bladder

flower
head

flower

fruit

seeds

leaf

flower

flower

fruit

Yellow-rattle

Common Butterwort

fruit

Greater Plantain

61

BROOMRAPE FAMILY

All 250 species of this family (Orobanchaceae) are parasites, relying almost entirely on the host for both food and water. Their roots develop into suckers and attach to the roots of the host. Broomrapes emerge from the soil close to the host. Some broomrapes are able to parasitize different types of hosts; others are specialized and restricted to a single host species.

Common Broomrape
Orobanche minor
Up to 50cm. This distinctive, yellowish parasite is often tinged reddish, brown or purple but it completely lacks any green chlorophyll. It forms a globular, scale-covered lump attached to its host's roots. On reaching maturity, an erect, scaly flowering spike rises above the soil surface; each flower has a curved tube and two lips. Widespread in Europe, except for the north and east, it is found in grassy places where it parasitizes clovers.
Ⓑ ⓜ

HONEYSUCKLE FAMILY

Most members of this family (Caprifoliaceae) are small trees or shrubs but some are herbaceous perennials or woody climbers. The petals are fused to form a tube with the five lobes either spreading or forming two lips. The flowers attract a wide range of pollinating insects including flies, wasps, bees and hawkmoths.

Honeysuckle
Lonicera periclymenum
Up to 6m. This climbing, deciduous shrub has oval leaves and long stems twining clockwise around other plants. Shorter shoots end in clusters of sweetly scented creamy-yellow, red-flushed flowers, each with a long tube ending in two curling lips. Poisonous red berries follow. Widespread in Europe, except the north, it grows in woodland, scrub, hedges and rocky places. Its sweet fragrance is strong at night, when it attracts moths.
Ⓑ ◐ ⓜ

SCABIOUS FAMILY

This small family (Dipsacaceae) is to be found centred on the Mediterranean region and the Near East. The flowers are packed into dense heads. The flowers around the rim of each head are often longer or larger than the rest, increasing their visual impact on pollinating insects. Each flower head has a ring of bracts beneath it.

Field Scabious
Knautia arvensis
25–100cm. This hairy perennial has a basal rosette of leaves that persist through the winter. These leaves vary from undivided to deeply lobed. The bristly stem has leaves divided into regular lobes. The flower heads have many small blue-lilac flowers crammed together in a flat 2–4cm diameter head. A common plant of dry grassland, banks and cornfields, it occurs widely throughout Europe.
Ⓑ ◐ ⓜ

The dainty Harebell is a common sight in summer, growing on the dry turf of chalk downs and on sandy heathlands.

Devil's-bit Scabious
Succisa pratensis
15–100cm. This hairy perennial has a rosette of elliptical basal leaves. The stem is usually branched, with a few narrower, sometimes toothed, leaves. The rounded flower heads, 15–25mm across, are made up of many small, dark bluish-purple flowers. It is found in damp grassy areas and damp woodlands throughout Europe.
Ⓑ ◐ ⓜ

BELL-FLOWER FAMILY

True to their name, many of the flowers in this distinctive family (Campanulaceae) are bell-shaped, the five petals being either partially or completely fused together. The predominant flower colour in the family is blue which is especially attractive to bees, although other insects also pollinate the flowers. Many species of bell-flower are easy to grow and make popular ornamental plants.

Harebell
Campanula rotundifolia
15–50cm. This slender, nearly hairless perennial has rounded basal leaves, and very thin stem leaves. The flowers are single or loosely clustered on long curving stalks. They are up to 15mm long, pale blue, and of the typical bell-shape that gives the family its name. A plant of dry grassland and heaths throughout Europe, it often grows in very poor soil. In Scotland, the Harebell is called the Bluebell.
Ⓑ ◑ ⓜ

Clustered Bellflower
Campanula glomerata
5–60cm. This upright downy perennial varies in size from tiny to large, depending upon the habitat. Its lower leaves are oval, on long stalks, with the stem-leaves narrower and stalkless. The flowers are borne in a tightly clustered head, with occasional single flowers below. Each flower is 15–20mm long, bell-shaped and purple, or deep violet. Found throughout Europe, it is a plant of grassland, particularly on soil over chalk or limestone, and is also well known in gardens.
Ⓑ ⓜ

FLOWERING TIME	J	F	M	A	M	J	J	A	S	O	N	D
Common Broomrape						▬	▬	▬				
Honeysuckle						▬	▬	▬				
Field Scabious					▬	▬	▬	▬				
Devil's-bit Scabious						▬	▬	▬	▬			
Harebell						▬	▬	▬				
Clustered Bellflower					▬	▬	▬	▬				
This chart is explained on page 13.												

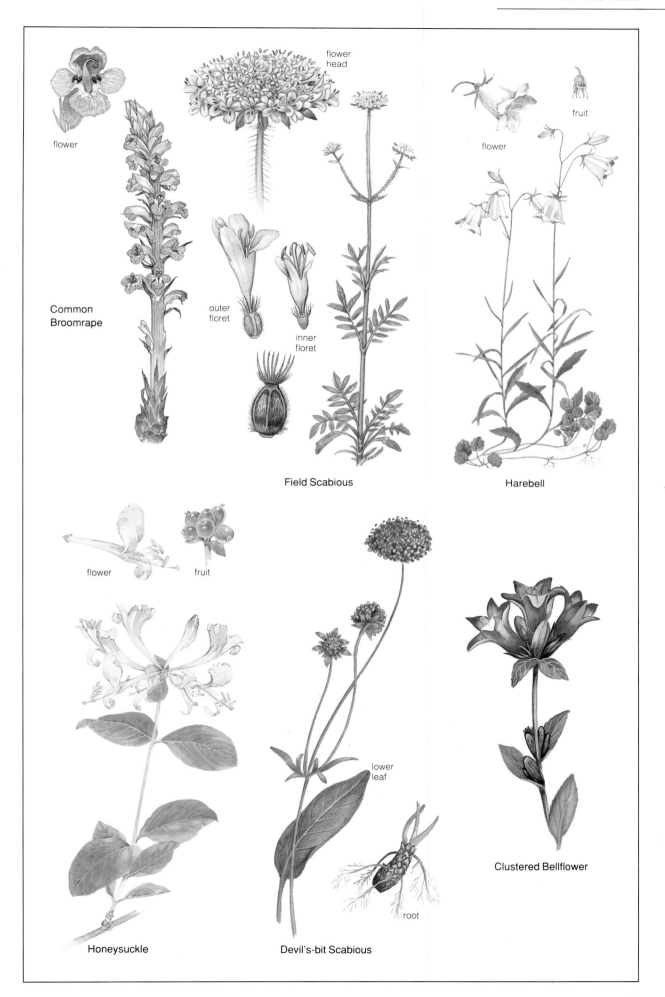

flower

Common
Broomrape

flower
head

outer
floret

inner
floret

Field Scabious

fruit

flower

Harebell

flower

fruit

Honeysuckle

lower
leaf

root

Devil's-bit Scabious

Clustered Bellflower

DAISY FAMILY

With over 21,000 species, this is the largest flowering plant family (Compositae). As well as common weeds, it contains numerous well-known garden flowers and vegetables. Many species have a milky sap containing latex. The characteristic flowers (florets) are small, somewhat simplified and packed into tight heads called capitula. The florets are of two kinds: a simple tube (disc floret) or a tube with a strap-shaped extension on one side (ray floret). The heads may be composed of ray florets only (as in dandelions), disc florets only (thistles) or a mixture with the ray florets surrounding the disc florets (daisies).

Sea Aster
Aster tripolium
15–100cm. This fleshy, short-lived perennial was commonly grown in gardens before the introduction of the modern Michaelmas Daisy. It is upright and hairless, with stout stems which have blunt-oval, three-veined basal leaves and narrow stem-leaves. The flower heads are in loose clusters, each head up to 20cm in diameter, with yellow disc florets and lilac-purple ray florets. The seeds have a parachute of white hairs. This species is common in salt-marshes and on sea cliffs, along European coasts.
Ⓑ☻

Hemp-agrimony
Eupatorium cannabinum
30–120cm. This downy, often branched perennial has reddish stems and leaves opposite, divided into three to five toothed segments. Its flower heads are small, rayless and few-flowered, held in dense clusters at the ends of stems. Each floret is whitish, or reddish-mauve. The seed has a parachute of white hairs. A plant of damp woods, marshes, streamsides, and waste places, it is found throughout most of Europe. Used by early herbalists as a crude purge and an emetic.
Ⓑ◑♣♨

Edelweiss
Leontopodium alpinum
Up to 10 cm. This is a typical alpine plant: short, tufted and covered with dense grey or white-woolly hairs. Its leaves are oblong, entire and broadest above the middle. The flower heads are borne in dense clusters, at the ends of stems and surrounded by large, white, woolly bracts. Each head is made up entirely of creamy-yellow disc florets. It grows in high meadows and on rocky slopes at altitudes of 1700–3400m and is now strictly protected.
♣⊗

Nodding Bur-marigold
Bidens cernua
7–60cm. This untidy looking, undistinguished, branched annual with sparse hair sports slightly fleshy stems. Its leaves are opposite, lance-shaped and unstalked. The flower heads are at the ends of short branches, arising

The Sea Mayweed, growing here on the Icelandic cliffs, is distinguished from several similar species by its fleshy leaves.

from leaf axils. They are about 15mm across, drooping, with yellow disc florets, and a ring of short ray florets. The mature fruits have small barbed bristles, which catch on to the coats of passing animals and are thus dispersed. It is common by watersides in much of Europe except the extreme north.
Ⓑ♣♨

Pineappleweed
Matricaria matricarioides
5–30cm. A great plant traveller, this upright, bluish-green annual was introduced into Britain from North America, although it is a native of north-eastern Asia. Its leaves are finely cut into narrow lobes, and the whole plant has a very strong pineapple scent when bruised. The flower heads are domed and composed solely of yellow-green disc florets, surrounded by a row of green bracts with white margins. Ray florets are never produced. It is now well established on waste ground throughout Europe.
Ⓑ♨

Sea Mayweed
Tripleurospermum maritimum
15–60cm. This weedy annual usually has straggling or prostrate stems and long leaves which are deeply divided into narrow and rather fleshy lobes. The flower heads are borne singly, at the ends of branches. They are 15–40mm across and composed of yellow disc florets and white ray florets. It grows along the coasts of western and northern Europe and also as a weed of waste places and disturbed ground. Mayweed, a contraction of 'maiden weed', was once a remedy for female ailments.
Ⓑ♨☻

Yarrow
Achillea millefolium
8–50cm. This creeping, downy perennial has foliage which is aromatic when bruised. Its leaves are divided into many narrow segments, hence the Latin name *millefolium*, meaning 'thousand-leaved'. The flower heads form flat-topped clusters. Each head is about 6mm across, with cream disc florets, and about five white or pink ray florets. It is a common weed of turf in most of Europe but is rare in the Mediterranean. Ornamental varieties are also grown.
Ⓑ♨🝔

Oxeye Daisy
Leucanthemum vulgare
20–70cm. This attractive perennial bears dark-green leaves. The flower heads are to 50mm in diameter, with yellow disc florets and white ray florets. It grows in grassy places throughout Europe and is often common enough to turn grassland into a mass of white and yellow. It is also known as Marguerite, Moon-daisy or Dog-daisy.
Ⓑ♨◗

Colt's-foot
Tussilago farfara
15–30cm. One of the most distinctive blooms of early spring, this perennial flowers before the leaves appear. The flowering stems have scale-leaves, tinged with purple. The single 15–35mm flower head is composed of yellow disc and ray florets. The seeds have a white parachute. The leaves are shaped like a colt's foot – hence the common name. They are pointed at the tip, and can be 30cm long when mature. A plant of waste places, it is found throughout Europe.
Ⓑ♨

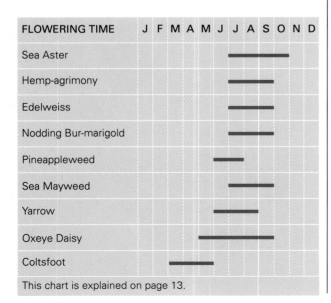

FLOWERING TIME	J	F	M	A	M	J	J	A	S	O	N	D
Sea Aster							▬	▬	▬	▬		
Hemp-agrimony							▬	▬	▬			
Edelweiss							▬	▬	▬			
Nodding Bur-marigold							▬	▬	▬			
Pineappleweed						▬	▬					
Sea Mayweed							▬	▬	▬			
Yarrow						▬	▬	▬	▬			
Oxeye Daisy					▬	▬	▬	▬				
Coltsfoot			▬	▬								

This chart is explained on page 13.

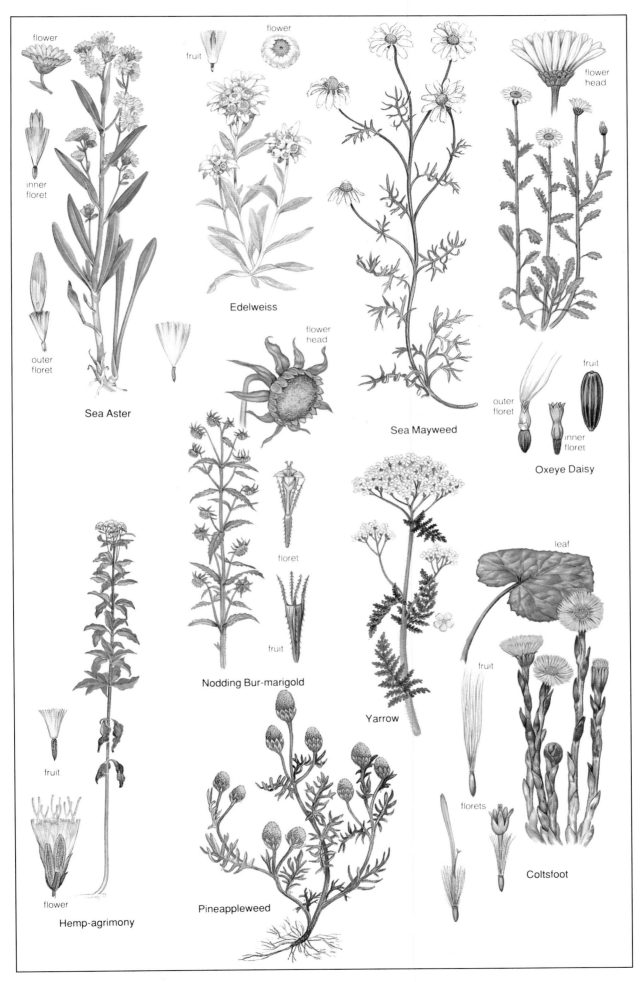

flower
fruit
flower
inner floret
outer floret
Sea Aster

Edelweiss

flower head

Sea Mayweed

flower head

fruit
outer floret
inner floret
Oxeye Daisy

floret
fruit
Nodding Bur-marigold

Yarrow

leaf
fruit
florets
Coltsfoot

fruit
flower
Hemp-agrimony

Pineappleweed

65

Butterbur
Petasites hybridus
15–30cm. This is another early plant, which flowers before its leaves appear. There are many flower heads, borne on a thick stem in the axils of scale leaves. Male and female plants are separate. Leaves develop after the flowers, and may be up to 90cm wide. This is a plant of wet meadows, hedgebanks and the sides of streams. Male and female plants have dissimilar ranges, female plants being rare or absent in parts of northern Europe, including much of Britain.
Ⓑ🌑⬭

Lesser Burdock
Arctium minus
60–150cm. This variable biennial has stems which are upright, furrowed and bear long-stalked lower leaves, with a heart-shaped base. The flower heads are in clusters and each head is 15–30mm, oval, with purple florets. The curved spines on the seed head attach to fur and clothing and are carried away, spreading the seeds to new areas. It is common along wood edges, and in waste places in Europe.
ⒷⓄⒺ

Common Ragwort
Senecio jacobaea
30–120cm. This biennial or perennial has much divided and dark green leaves. Flower heads are borne in clusters on the end of branched stems. They are 20–25mm across, with yellow disc and ray florets. The seeds have a white parachute of hairs. A plant of grassland and waste areas, the whole growth is poisonous. Only caterpillars of the Cinnabar Moth are able to make a good meal of it.
ⒷⒺ⬭

Groundsel
Senecio vulgaris
5–30cm. This very successful annual weed is fairly well-branched, with weak stems and bright green, irregularly toothed leaves. Its flower heads are in clusters at the ends of stems. Each head is about 4mm wide and composed of disc florets only. The seed has a white parachute of hairs. This plant is very common on waste and disturbed ground throughout Europe.
ⒷⒺ

Creeping Thistle
Cirsium arvense
30–150cm. Not as spiny as the Spear Thistle, this thistle has creeping roots that are almost impossible to eradicate from gardens or pasture. Its leaves are much cut and spiny, but the stems are smooth. The flowers are tubular and fragrant and the heads are oval, 15–25mm long and spiny. The male and female heads are usually on different plants. Each seed has a parachute of long, brownish hairs. It is common everywhere in grassy and waste places, and on cultivated ground. The nectar-full flowers attract many butterflies.
ⒷⒺ⬭

The chunky flower heads of Butterbur open early in the spring, and are over before the large leaves (left) begin to unfurl.

Spear Thistle
Cirsium vulgare
30–150cm. This downy biennial is very well defended, with a winged, spiny stem and deeply cut leaves. These have very sharp spines on each lobe. The oval heads reach 45mm across and are usually solitary, but sometimes clustered. The bracts around the head also have sharp-tipped spines. The narrow florets are tubular and lilac or red-purple. Each seed has a parachute of hairs. It is common in grassland and waste places everywhere.
ⒷⒺ⬭

Stemless Thistle
Cirsium acaule
Rarely to 30cm. Normally stemless, this thistle has a rosette of deeply cut leaves, which are well armed with sharp spines. Its flower heads are usually single, oval, 20–25mm across and spiny with tubular purple florets. Each seed has a parachute of hairs. It is a plant of short grassland on limestone or chalk and occurs from northern England and the Baltic southwards, but is absent from Mediterranean islands.
Ⓑ⬭

Carline Thistle
Carlina vulgaris
10–60cm. This distinctive, upright, spiny biennial bears leaves which are stalkless, lobed and divided, each lobe bearing several weak spines. Its flower heads are borne in clusters at the end of the stems. Each is composed only of disc florets, but straw-coloured bracts surround the head and double its size. The seeds have a parachute of rust-coloured hairs. It is found in grasslands and dunes throughout most of Europe.
Ⓑ⬭

Greater Knapweed
Centaurea scabiosa
30–90cm. This hairy perennial bears divided leaves with toothed segments. Its flower heads are 30–50mm in diameter. The florets are tubular and reddish-purple, the larger ones being those on the outer rows. The bracts on the head have a horseshoe-shaped, dark brown outer border. This is a plant of dry grassland, especially on chalky soil. It is found in most of Europe but is particularly common in the south.
Ⓑ⬭

Common Knapweed
Centaurea nigra
30–60cm. This very variable perennial has tough stems and basal leaves with shallow lobes. The stem leaves are untoothed. Its flower heads are knob-like, from which the common name of 'knob' or 'knap' weed comes. They are usually less than 20mm across, with reddish-purple florets, all of the same size. The tips of the bracts are triangular. It is a plant of grassy places in western and central Europe.
ⒷⒺ⬭

FLOWERING TIME	J	F	M	A	M	J	J	A	S	O	N	D
Butterbur			▬	▬	▬							
Lesser Burdock							▬	▬	▬			
Common Ragwort						▬	▬	▬	▬			
Groundsel	▬	▬	▬	▬	▬	▬	▬	▬	▬	▬		
Creeping Thistle						▬	▬	▬	▬			
Spear Thistle						▬	▬	▬	▬			
Stemless Thistle						▬	▬	▬				
Carline Thistle						▬	▬	▬	▬			
Greater Knapweed						▬	▬	▬	▬			
Common Knapweed						▬	▬	▬	▬			

This chart is explained on page 13.

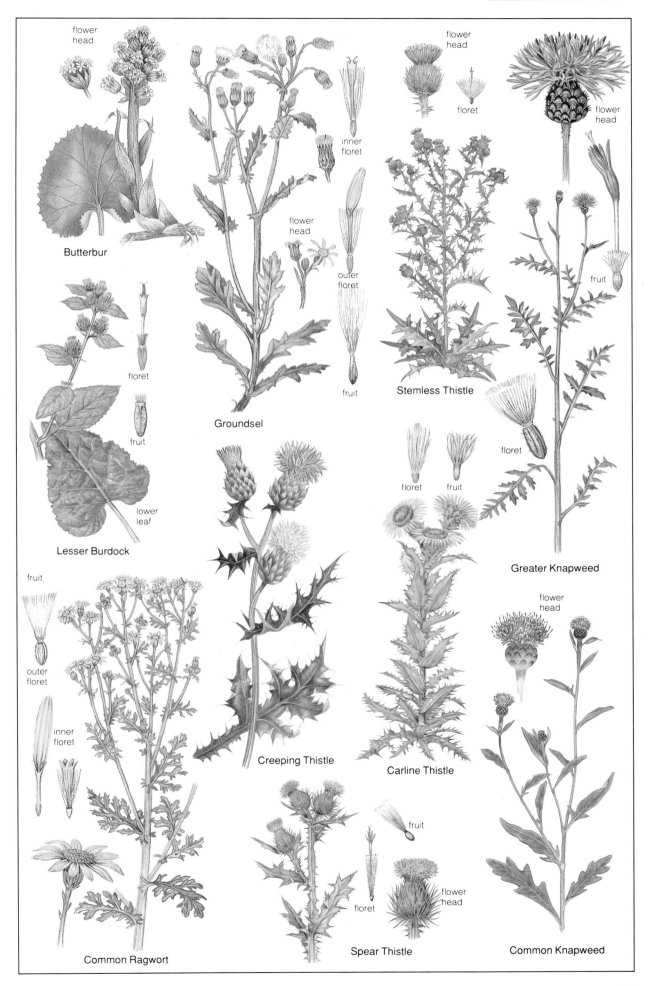

flower head

Butterbur

floret

fruit

Lesser Burdock

lower leaf

fruit

outer floret

inner floret

Common Ragwort

flower head

Groundsel

inner floret

outer floret

fruit

Creeping Thistle

Spear Thistle

fruit

floret

flower head

flower head

floret

Stemless Thistle

floret

fruit

Carline Thistle

flower head

floret

fruit

Greater Knapweed

flower head

Common Knapweed

Dandelions grow well and often flower twice in a year in upland hay meadows, especially those which are regularly fertilized.

Chicory
Cichorium intybus
30–150cm. This perennial has stiff, often widely-branched stems. Its lower leaves are stalked, toothed or lobed, and its stalkless upper leaves clasp the stem. The flower heads are 25–40mm across and made of bright blue ray florets, which open in the morning and usually close by noon. This plant grows in grassland and along roads in most of Europe though it is probably not native to many northern regions.
Ⓑ✪⊕

Goat's-beard
Tragopogon pratense
30–70cm. This distinctive, often single-stemmed, perennial has grey-green leaves, with the bases surrounding the stem. Its large yellow flower heads are composed of ray florets only and it has long wide-spreading bracts. The flowers open early in the morning and close by midday, giving the plant its alternative name 'Jack-go-to-bed-at-noon'. It is found in grassland and waste places in most of Europe.
Ⓑ✪⊕

Prickly Sow-thistle
Sonchus asper
20–150cm. This plant is an upright annual, branched sparingly with spiny leaves. The leaves clasp the stem with large, ear-like basal lobes. The yellow flower heads are 20–25mm across, in clusters at the top of stems and consist of ray florets only. Each seed has a hairy parachute. It is common on waste and disturbed ground throughout Europe.
Ⓑ✪

Smooth Sow-thistle
Sonchus oleraceus
20–150cm. This untidy, upright annual has lobed lower leaves and triangular upper ones, all softly spiny. All clasp the stem at the base, but the basal lobes are triangular and pointed, not rounded like those of a Prickly Sow-thistle. The yellow flower heads are in clusters at the top of stems; they are 20–25mm across and composed of ray florets only. Each seed has a parachute of hairs. It is widespread on waste and cultivated land. Supposedly the last meal of Theseus, before he accounted for the Minotaur, it is used as an animal food, and the young leaves can be eaten boiled.
Ⓑ✪

Cat's-ear
Hypochoeris radicata
20–60cm. As the Latin name suggests, the leaves of this plant all arise radically – that is, from the base. They are hairy, deeply-lobed and triangular or oblong toothed. The single flower heads are up to 40mm across and composed only of ray florets. The seeds have a parachute of hairs. A plant of grassland, and waste places throughout most of Europe, it is often a weed of lawns.
Ⓑ✪⊕

Common Dandelion
Taraxacum officinale
5–30cm. This plant is almost too familiar from folklore, and from its nuisance value as a weed. The toothed leaves resemble lions' teeth, hence its common name from the French *dent-de-lion*, whilst the supposed capacity of the plant to induce bed-wetting is well known. The large yellow flower heads, of ray-florets only, give way to dandelion 'clocks' of winged seeds by which generations of children have told the time. It is a common plant of grassland, roadsides, lawns and waste areas everywhere.
Ⓑ✪⊕

Autumn Hawkbit
Leontodon autumnalis
5–60cm. This usually hairless perennial has a rosette of deeply lobed shiny green leaves. The single flower heads are 12–35mm across. Each head is composed of golden-yellow ray florets, with the outer florets reddish streaked on the underside. A common plant of grassland and disturbed ground, it is found in most of Europe.
Ⓑ✪⊕

Wall Lettuce
Mycelis muralis
25–100cm. This handsome perennial has the lower leaves deeply lobed and stalked, and the upper ones stalkless and clasping the stem. Each flower-head is 7–10mm across and composed of five yellow ray florets. It is a characteristic plant of walls and rocks and also of woodlands, especially on chalky soils.
ⒷⓄ✪

Nipplewort
Lapsana communis
20–90cm. This untidy annual has lower leaves with a large lobe at the tip, and several smaller lobes, all of which are toothed. The stem leaves are entire. Its flower heads are 15–20mm in diameter and are borne in a loose-branched cluster. They are composed of yellow ray florets. The seeds lack a parachute of hairs. It is common on waste ground, hedge and wood-margins across Europe.
ⒷⓄ✪

FLOWERING TIME	J	F	M	A	M	J	J	A	S	O	N	D
Chicory							▬	▬	▬			
Goat's-beard						▬	▬					
Prickly Sow-thistle						▬	▬					
Smooth Sow-thistle						▬	▬	▬				
Cat's-ear						▬	▬	▬	▬			
Common Dandelion			▬	▬	▬	▬	▬	▬	▬			
Autumn Hawkbit						▬	▬	▬				
Wall Lettuce					▬	▬	▬	▬				
Nipplewort						▬	▬	▬				

This chart is explained on page 13.

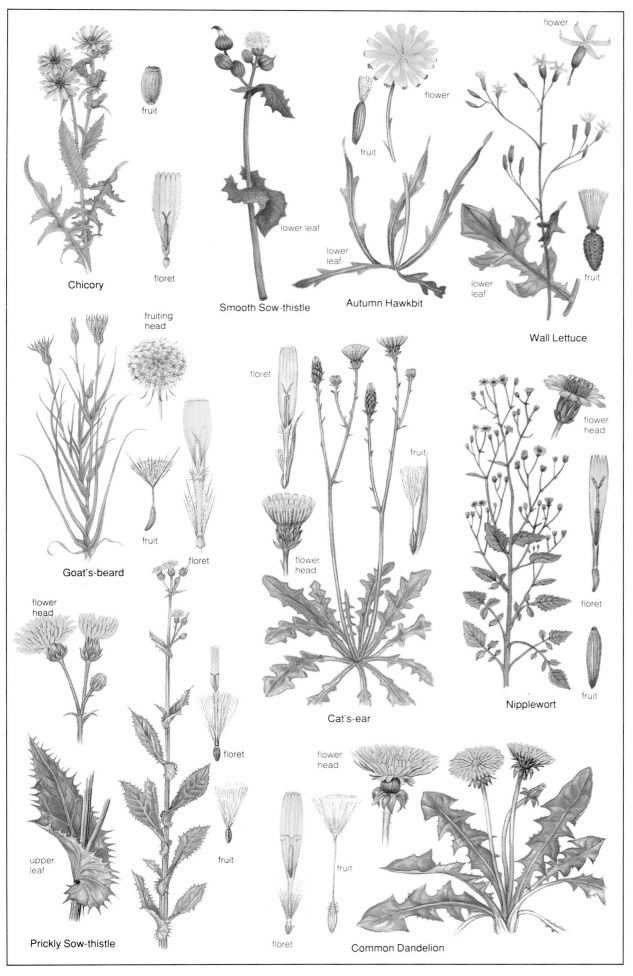

Chicory

fruit

floret

Smooth Sow-thistle

lower leaf

Autumn Hawkbit

flower

fruit

lower leaf

lower leaf

flower

fruit

lower leaf

Wall Lettuce

fruiting head

floret

fruit

floret

Goat's-beard

fruit

flower head

Cat's-ear

flower head

floret

fruit

Nipplewort

flower head

floret

fruit

Prickly Sow-thistle

upper leaf

floret

fruit

flower head

floret

fruit

Common Dandelion

Monocotyledons

PONDWEED FAMILY

This aquatic family (Potamogetonaceae) contains 90 species found in still or slow-moving fresh and brackish water everywhere. They are mostly perennials which, although they have slender rhizomes to anchor them to the bottom, often over winter as specialized buds called turions. These lie buried in mud until spring when they burst into growth. All species have slender, delicate and translucent submerged leaves; some species also have floating leaves which are broad, thick and opaque. The spikes of inconspicuous flowers either project above the surface of the water and are pollinated by the wind, or lie below the surface and are water-pollinated.

Broad-leaved Pondweed
Potamogeton natans
The stems of this perennial can reach 5m long, although 100cm is more normal. The long, ribbon-like lower leaves remain submerged, while those borne higher up the stems are stalked, with elliptical, floating blades. These blades are coloured green or reddish and often form large patches mottling the water's surface. Small, greenish flowers are carried on cylindrical, emergent spikes. This pondweed is found almost throughout Europe, growing in still or slow-moving fresh water such as ponds, lakes and canals.
Ⓑ🅔

WATER-PLANTAIN FAMILY

This small family (Alismataceae) contains about 100 species of herbs. They grow standing in water or on marshy ground. The flowers have three white or pinkish petals and three sepals. The petals last only about a day.

Water-plantain
Alisma plantago-aquatica
Up to 100cm. This perennial forms clumps of long-stalked, basal leaves with oval blades ribbed along their length, and which appear rather like those of the Greater Plantain. There is no relationship between the two plants, however. Its upright stems rise above the foliage and bear whorled branches carrying clusters of small flowers, each with three pinkish petals. Found almost throughout Europe, except in the Arctic, it grows in wet, muddy places and at the edges of ponds, streams and other bodies of fresh water.
Ⓑ🅔

FLOWERING-RUSH FAMILY

Closely related to water-plantains and frogbits, this family (Butomaceae) contains a single species.

Flowering-rush
Butomus umbellatus
Up to 150cm. This perennial with a creeping rhizome produces three-angled, strap-like leaves all arising from its base to the same height as the erect flowering stems. Each stem bears a single, terminal cluster of showy, three-petalled, pink flowers carried

The tiny female flowers of Canadian Waterweed float at the surface on the ends of long, slender stalks.

on slender stalks of varying length. It is found almost throughout Europe, except for the Arctic and parts of the Mediterranean region, and grows in mud in the shallows of still or slow-moving, fresh water. The rhizomes are said to be edible.
Ⓑ🅔

FROGBIT FAMILY

The 100 or so species in this entirely aquatic and mostly tropical family (Hydrocharitaceae) include plants found in both salt and fresh water. Some species are free-floating on the surface of the water and may develop 'sails' from modified organs.

Canadian Waterweed
Elodea canadensis
This submerged, aquatic perennial has branching stems which may reach 90cm long and are densely covered with small, oblong, dark green leaves borne in whorls of three. Thread-like stalks rise upwards, terminating in tiny, greenish-purple flowers which float on the surface. Introduced from North America in the 19th century, this plant became a pest, blocking waterways. It is now less of a problem, but remains widely naturalized in Europe, in still or slow-moving fresh water. Almost all European plants are female.
Ⓑ🅔

Frogbit
Hydrocharis morsus-ranae
This free-floating, aquatic perennial has slender stems bearing groups of long-stalked, circular to kidney-

shaped leaves up to 30mm across and which are green above and often reddish beneath. Its three-petalled, white flowers rise just above the water's surface. To overwinter in northern climates, it produces special buds which sink to the mud below water. These surface as small plantlets in spring. It is found throughout most of Europe in still or slow-moving, fresh water.
Ⓑ🅔

DUCKWEED FAMILY

The 30 plants of this family (Lemnaceae) always grow in still or stagnant water, either floating on the surface or completely submerged. They lack separate leaves and stems. Flowers are borne in pouches and are water-pollinated.

Common Duckweed
Lemna minor
Up to 4mm in diameter. This is one of the smallest flowering plants, with no stems or leaves, but a floating thallus which is a modification of either or possibly both. The thallus is rounded, nearly flat on both sides and floats on the water surface. Each plant has one root. The flowers are minute and held in a pocket-like pouch. The male flower consists of just two stamens, and the female of a one-celled ovary. A common plant of still water, it often covers the surface completely, when it can restrict the growth of water plants that do not have any surface leaves. It is found throughout Europe.
Ⓑ🅔

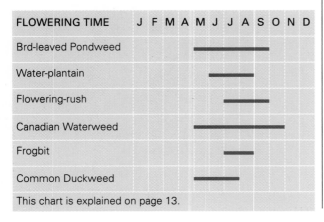

FLOWERING TIME	J	F	M	A	M	J	J	A	S	O	N	D
Brd-leaved Pondweed					▬	▬	▬	▬				
Water-plantain						▬	▬	▬				
Flowering-rush							▬	▬				
Canadian Waterweed					▬	▬	▬	▬				
Frogbit							▬					
Common Duckweed					▬	▬						

This chart is explained on page 13.

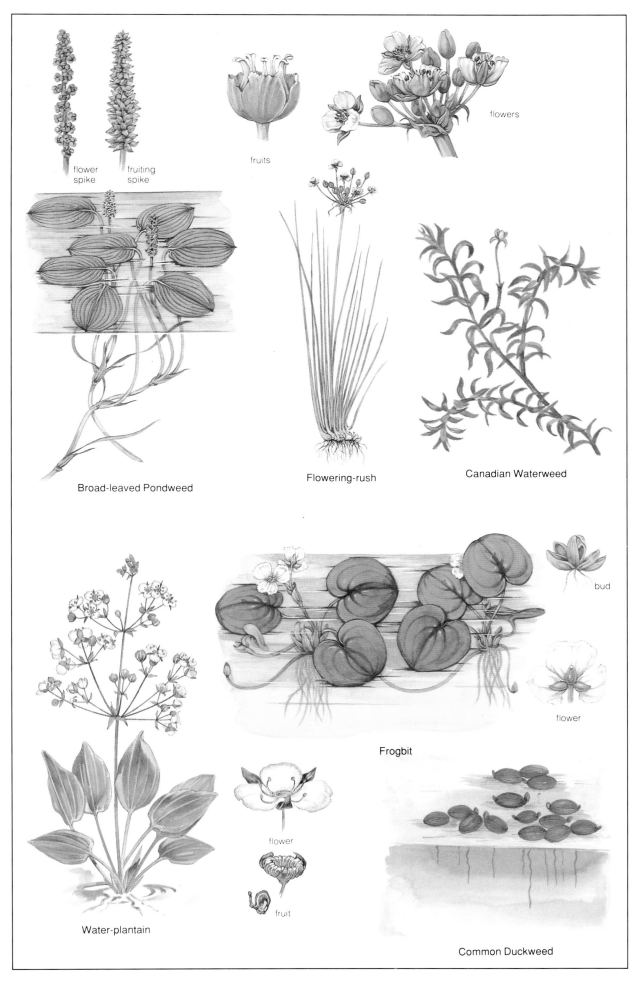

flower
spike

fruiting
spike

fruits

flowers

Broad-leaved Pondweed

Flowering-rush

Canadian Waterweed

bud

flower

Frogbit

Water-plantain

flower

fruit

Common Duckweed

LILY FAMILY

One of the largest flowering plant families with around 4000 species, the Lily Family (Liliaceae) contains many highly prized ornamentals. Well-known garden plants include tulips, lilies and hyacinths, as well as vegetables such as onions and garlic. Most species produce some sort of underground storage organs – either bulbs, corms, rhizomes or fleshy roots. The flowers are regular, with six petal-like segments – the equivalent of three sepals and three petals – all similar and arranged in two whorls, at times joined together into a tube. There are six stamens.

Asphodel

Asphodelus aestivus
Up to 200cm. This tuberous-rooted perennial has large tufts of long, narrow leaves and erect, branching stems bearing numerous star-shaped, white flowers, each petal with a pinkish mid-stripe. All its growth above ground begins to wither away once seed is set and, by summer, only the dry, dead stems remain. This dormant period ends with the onset of the autumn rains. This plant is widespread in the Mediterranean region, growing in dry grassland, rocky ground, on beaches and in waste and cultivated areas. Apparently the tubers were eaten by Greeks in times of hardship.
☻✿✿☻㎜

Bluebell

Hyacinthoides non-scriptus
Up to 50cm. This bulbous perennial spreads by seeds and often forms vast colonies. Its clumps of narrow, strap-shaped, shiny leaves appear in spring and are followed by erect stems bearing clusters of nodding, tubular to bell-shaped, blue flowers which all hang to one side. White or pink forms are sometimes seen as single plants among colonies of blue. Widespread in Atlantic countries of Europe northwards to Scotland, it grows in woodland, hedges, grassland and on sea-cliffs. Bluebells prefer light, acidic soils. Spring Squill (*Scilla verna*) is shorter and has a single bract under each flower.
Ⓑ✿㎜

Meadow Saffron

Colchicum autumnale
This curious plant produces crocus-like flowers up to 20cm high, straight from an underground corm in autumn. Each one has a long, white tube, which resembles a stalk, and six oblong, pink segments. The six stamens readily distinguish this flower from the autumn-flowering crocuses, which have only three stamens. The robust, shiny, strap-like leaves develop in late winter and reach 35cm long. They persist until early summer. Widespread in central and southern Europe, it grows in damp woodlands, preferring alluvial and clay soils. It is also often grown in gardens, although it is highly poisonous, containing colchicine, and is potentially lethal.
Ⓑ✿㎜

Ramsons, also known as Wild Garlic, gives a strong smell of garlic to many shady hedgerows and coppiced woodlands.

Fritillary

Fritillaria meleagris
Up to 40cm. This slender, bulbous perennial produces an erect stem bearing long, narrow, grey-green leaves. The head is bent over, carrying a normally solitary, pendulous flower, with broad segments chequered pink and dull purple. Widespread in central Europe, it grows in open woodland, grassy places and alpine pastures. It can form huge colonies in meadows subject to flooding in winter, but in many areas this habitat is being destroyed and the plant is becoming increasingly uncommon. It is also sometimes grown for ornament in gardens.
Ⓑ✿✿㎜⊗

Ramsons

Allium ursinum
Up to 50cm. This bulbous perennial forms large drifts of long-stalked, broadly spear-shaped, shiny green leaves which give off a rank smell of garlic. Its slender, upright stems end in clusters of star-like, white flowers. Widespread through most of Europe, it grows in woodland and hedges, preferring rich, limey soils. The presence of this plant is a good indication of ancient woodland. Its chopped leaves were put to culinary use in the past, being similar in taste to the cultivated garlic.
Ⓑ✿

Herb-Paris

Paris quadrifolia
Up to 40cm. This perennial has upright shoots, each bearing a single whorl of usually four spreading, oval leaves. Its solitary, green flower has four sepals and four petals forming an eight-pointed star. One black berry follows. Widespread through most of Europe, but rare in the south, it grows in damp woodland and other shady places. The name comes from the Latin *par*, meaning equal, and refers to the regularity of the leaves and flower parts.
Ⓑ✿✿

Solomon's-seal

Polygonatum multiflorum
Up to 80cm. This perennial with gracefully arching stems bears alternate, elliptical leaves spreading in opposite directions. Its tubular, greenish-white flowers hang in clusters on short, slender stalks below the arch of the stem, followed by berries which ripen blue-black. Widespread in Europe, it grows in dry woodland and scrub on limey or sandy soils. A hybrid with the related Angular Solomon's-seal is commonly grown for ornament in gardens.
Ⓑ✿

Butcher's-broom

Ruscus aculeatus
Up to 100cm. This evergreen, shrubby perennial has leathery, spine-tipped, leaf-like structures which are actually flattened shoots termed *cladodes*. These bear small, whitish flowers in the centre on the upper surface. Male and female flowers are usually on separate plants, the female flower being followed by globular berries ripening bright red from October to May. Widespread in western and southern Europe, it grows in scrub, woodland and on sea-cliffs and is cultivated in gardens.
Ⓑ✿✿

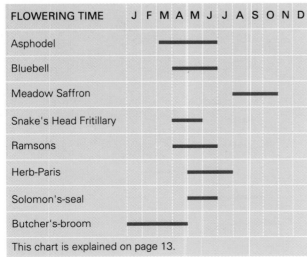

FLOWERING TIME	J	F	M	A	M	J	J	A	S	O	N	D
Asphodel					▬	▬						
Bluebell					▬	▬						
Meadow Saffron								▬	▬	▬		
Snake's Head Fritillary				▬	▬							
Ramsons				▬	▬	▬						
Herb-Paris					▬	▬	▬					
Solomon's-seal					▬	▬						
Butcher's-broom		▬	▬	▬	▬							

This chart is explained on page 13.

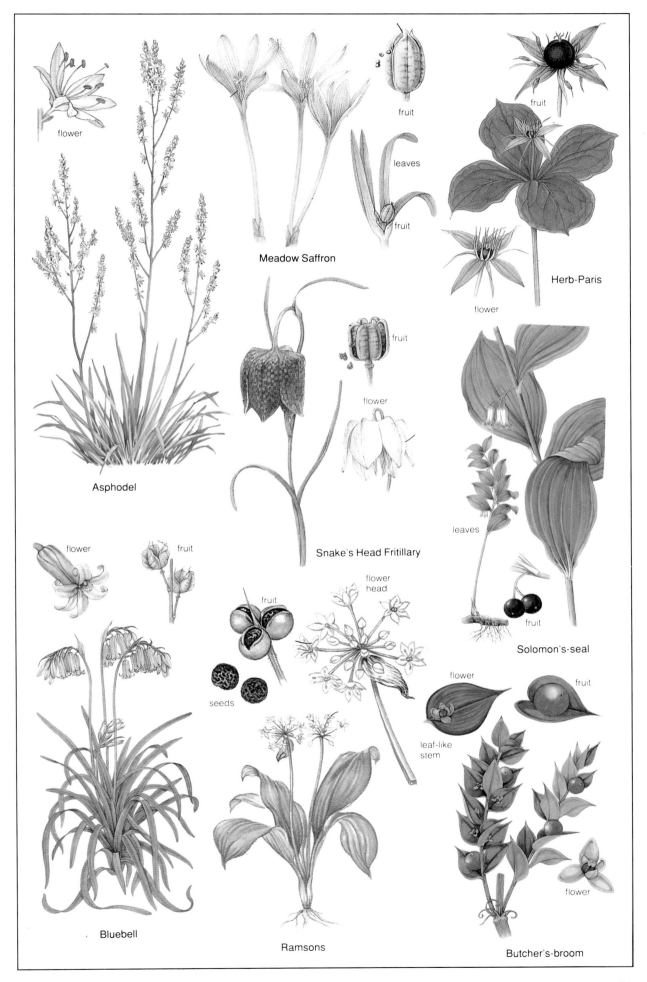

flower

fruit

leaves

fruit

fruit

Meadow Saffron

Herb-Paris

flower

Asphodel

fruit

flower

Snake's Head Fritillary

leaves

fruit

Solomon's-seal

flower

fruit

fruit

flower

seeds

flower head

flower

fruit

Bluebell

Ramsons

leaf-like stem

Butcher's-broom

flower

73

DAFFODIL FAMILY

This is a family (Amaryllidaceae) which, like the similar Lily Family, contains many popular ornamental plants such as daffodils and snowdrops. Most are early-flowering bulbous perennials. The showy flowers have three petals and three petal-like sepals. In some, such as the daffodils, there is also a central cup or trumpet called the corona. The inferior ovary (outside the petals) separates this family from the Liliaceae.

Snowdrop
Galanthus nivalis
Up to 25cm. This bulbous perennial has greyish-green, strap-shaped leaves and drooping white flowers. Each flower has three spreading, outer segments and three much shorter, inner ones which form a cup with green markings. Widespread in central and southern Europe, it grows in damp places and is naturalized in many areas north of its native range.
Ⓑ❍✿

Wild Daffodil
Narcissus pseudonarcissus
Up to 50cm. A bulbous perennial with strap-shaped, greyish-green leaves. It has solitary, usually drooping, flowers. The six spreading, outer segments are pale yellow and usually twisted, forming a whorl behind the deep yellow trumpet, or corona, which is flared at the rim. This plant is widely distributed in southern and central Europe, growing in woods, meadows and on rocky ground.
Ⓑ❍▦

IRIS FAMILY

This widespread family (Iridaceae) of about 1800 species contains many garden ornamentals, principally irises, gladioli and crocuses. All possess some form of overwintering storage organ, either corms (as in gladioli and crocuses), fleshy rhizomes (irises) or bulbs (some irises). The leaves are narrow or strap-like and often held in a flat fan. A few species are evergreen. In the complex flowers of irises the styles are also petal-like and lie over the downturned petals.

Yellow Iris
Iris pseudacorus
Up to 150cm. This perennial has a stout rhizome producing shoots with a fan of sword-shaped leaves. These shoots later elongate into tall, leafy stems terminating in clusters of large, bright yellow flowers with three of the segments broad, drooping and very conspicuous. Widespread across Europe, it grows in wet woods, swamps, fens and marshes.
Ⓑ❍▰

YAM FAMILY

Only about six species of the 630 in the Yam Family (Dioscoriaceae) occur in Europe. They are mostly tropical. Almost all species in the family are herbaceous twining perennials or woody climbers with large tubers. Unusually among monocotyledons, the leaves are net-veined. The fruit is a capsule or a berry.

Lords-and-Ladies can tolerate deep shade and often grows in the bottoms of thick hedgerows. It can be a troublesome garden weed.

Black Bryony
Tamus communis
This perennial herb develops slender stems up to 4m long which twine clockwise. Its leaves are either heart-shaped or three-lobed. Sprays of small, greenish-yellow to white flowers arise from the axils between the leaves and stems. Male and female flowers are on separate plants, the female being followed by berries which ripen a bright, shiny red. Widespread in western and southern Europe, it grows in woodland, scrub and hedges, preferring lime-rich soils. Although poisonous, it has been used medicinally.
Ⓑ❍▦

ARUM FAMILY

This mostly tropical family (Araceae) of nearly 3000 species also contains a few European species. The whole family has characteristic inflorescences. These consist of tiny flowers packed around a dense column called the spadix and around which is wrapped a large, leaf-like sheath, the spathe.

Lords-and-Ladies
Arum maculatum
Up to 50cm. This tuberous perennial has large leaves shaped like arrow-heads, often with dark blotches. Its pale green spathes are sometimes reddish-flushed and partially surround the deep reddish spadix, which attracts pollinating insects with its unpleasant odour. Spikes of orange-red berries follow in July and August. Widespread in Europe, except in the north-east, it grows in woodland and hedges, preferring rich, limey soils.
Ⓑ❍▦

Dragon Arum
Dracunculus vulgaris
Up to 100cm. This tuberous perennial has large, fan-shaped leaves divided into several segments. Its flat spathes are often large, deep brownish-purple on inner surface. The long, blackish-purple spadix emerging from the inflated base stinks of carrion. It is found in the Mediterranean region from Corsica eastwards and is naturalized further west, growing in scrub and rocky places, especially on rich, limey soils.
▰

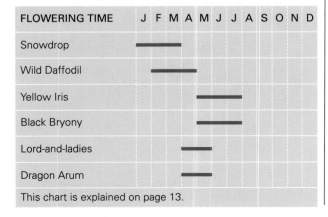

FLOWERING TIME	J	F	M	A	M	J	J	A	S	O	N	D
Snowdrop		▬	▬									
Wild Daffodil			▬	▬								
Yellow Iris						▬	▬					
Black Bryony						▬	▬					
Lord-and-ladies					▬							
Dragon Arum					▬							
This chart is explained on page 13.												

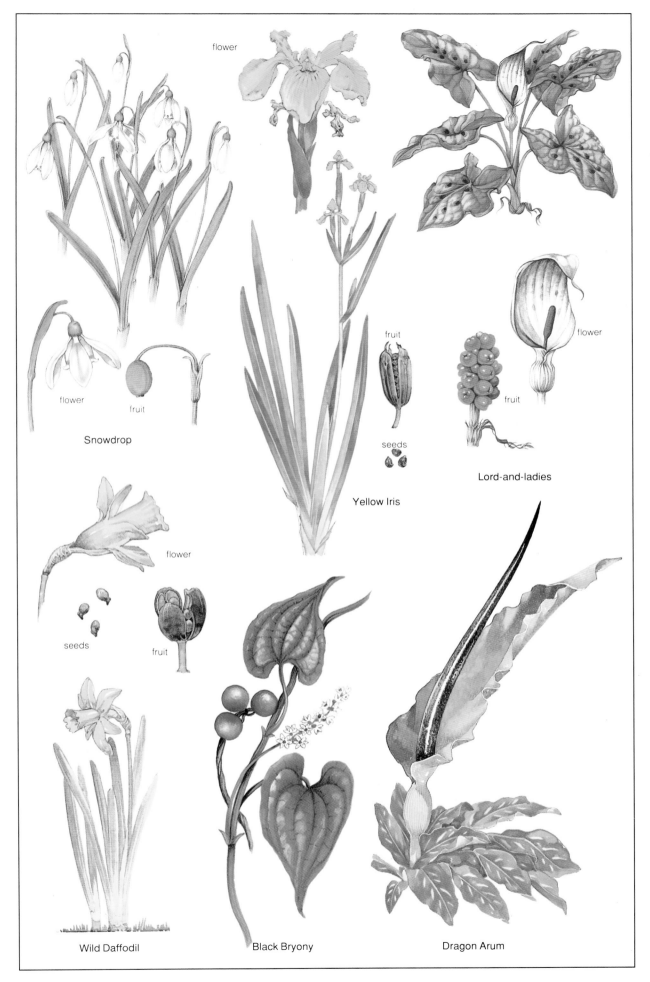

flower

flower

flower   fruit

Snowdrop

fruit

seeds

Yellow Iris

flower

fruit

Lord-and-ladies

flower

seeds   fruit

Wild Daffodil

Black Bryony

Dragon Arum

ORCHID FAMILY

Altogether there are about 18,000 species in the Orchid Family (Orchidaceae), many of them rare and little known. About half of them grow perched on trees, and are known as epiphytes. A few are saprophytes – plants devoid of chlorophyll which obtain food from decaying plant matter. Many hybrids and cultivars have been artificially produced for horticulture and floristry. Orchids have beautiful, complex and very varied flowers. There are three sepals and three petals. The sepals and two of the petals are similar but the third petal, called the labellum or lip is always different. The colour, scent, nectar and form of the flowers attract insect pollinators, often specific species. The tiny seeds need to associate with mycorrhizal fungi if they are to germinate.

FLOWERING TIME	J	F	M	A	M	J	J	A	S	O	N	D
Heart-flowered Serapias			▬	▬	▬							
Red Helleborine						▬						
Brd-leaved Helleborine							▬	▬				
Autumn Lady's-tresses								▬	▬			
Common Twayblade						▬						
Bird's-nest Orchid						▬						
Fragrant Orchid						▬	▬					
Greater Butterfly Orchid					▬	▬						

This chart is explained on page 13.

Heart-flowered Serapias
Serapias cordigera
15–45cm. This orchid has five to eight lance-shaped leaves, which sheath the stem. Each sheath has deep red speckles. The flower has the two upper sepals fused, and, together with the inner petals, forms a pointed helmet. The lip is heart-shaped, purple-maroon, with fine blackish streaks. It is a plant of heaths, grassland, woods and maquis in the Mediterranean region.
😊 🐝

Red Helleborine
Cephalanthera rubra
20–50cm. This plant flowers only where conditions of light and shade are exactly right. The stem is often red or purple-tinged, and the leaves are long, narrow and pointed. A well-grown plant may have as many as 10 flowers; each one with three wide-open outer sepals, hairy on the back, and three inner petals. The lower one is larger and yellowish-white, with a violet edge. A plant of beech woodland, on chalky soils, it is very rare in Britain, but more common elsewhere.
Ⓑ 〇 ⊗

Broad-leaved Helleborine
Epipactis helleborine
25–75cm. A well-grown stem of this orchid may carry 100 flowers. The shiny leaves are broad at the base. The flowers hang to one side of the stem. Each has three outer sepals and three inner petals, with the lower petal forming a heart-shaped lip. The petals and sepals are greenish, or purple. It is a plant of woodlands, especially on chalky soil.
Ⓑ 〇

Autumn Lady's-tresses
Spiranthes spiralis
7–15cm. This flower may be distinguished from other late orchids by the spiral arrangement of its flowers up the stem. The rosette of oval grey-green leaves at the stem base dies before the flowers open. The flowers are small, white and fragrant at night. Each has blunt sepals and a yellowish lip with a fringed edge. It is a plant of short turf and other dry, grassy places, especially on chalk, and occurs from Britain and Denmark southwards. Its numbers vary greatly from year to year.
Ⓑ 🐝

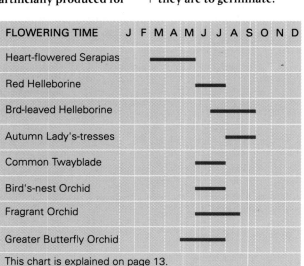

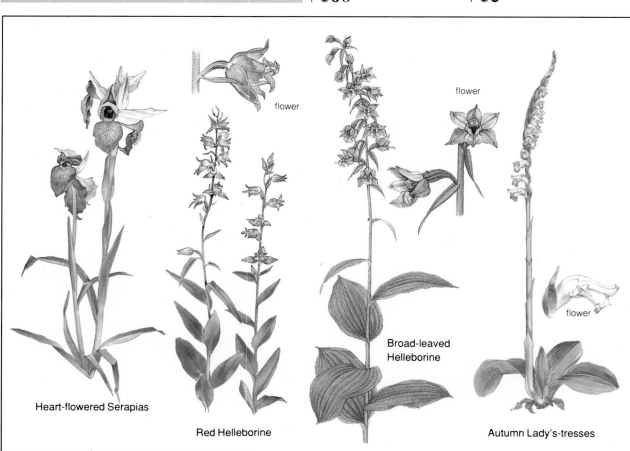

Heart-flowered Serapias

Red Helleborine

Broad-leaved Helleborine

flower

Autumn Lady's-tresses

flower

The Heart-flowered Serapias is one of a group of orchids known as tongue orchids because of the flower's broad, tongue-like lower lip.

Common Twayblade
Listera ovata

20–60cm. This rather inconspicuous plant is named for the two, or 'tway', large, broadly oval leaves, which are paired at the base of the flowering-spike. The yellowish-green flowers, sometimes up to 100 in a spike, have oval outer sepals, and narrow inner petals, with a long, narrow, two-lobed lip. This has a groove in the centre, which is full of nectar, to attract pollinators. Widely distributed in Europe, it is more common in the north, usually growing in woodland where it forms clumps. Lesser Twayblade, (*L. cordata*) is similar but has small leaves and reddish-green flowers.
Ⓑ Ⓞ

Bird's-nest Orchid
Neottia nidus-avis

20–45cm. Named for its untidy, bird's nest-like roots, this plant does not produce its own food but is a saprophyte. With the aid of a fungus on its roots, it is able to live on the products of decaying leaves. It has no chlorophyll, or leaves, and can grow happily in dark woodland where no ordinary green plants can survive. Its flowers have short, oval petals, and a long, two-lobed lip, with a papery bract beneath. Usually found in deep shade, often under beech, it occurs occasionally in more open situations and grows throughout most of Europe except parts of the far north.
Ⓑ Ⓞ

Fragrant Orchid
Gymnadenia conopsea

15–40cm. This orchid has long narrow-keeled leaves, the lowest with a distinctly blunt tip. Its flowers are very fragrant, rosy-pink and borne in a spike. The outer sepals are spreading, with the margins rolled up. The top two petals form a hood over the reproductive parts, and the lip has a long curved spur protruding backwards from the base. This is filled with nectar to attract pollinators – usually long-tongued moths or butterflies. It is a plant of grassland in much of Europe, except for some of the Mediterranean islands, and is usually found on chalky soil, often varying greatly in numbers from year to year.
Ⓑ Ⓜ

Greater Butterfly Orchid
Platanthera chlorantha

20–60cm. With a little imagination the greenish-white flowers of this orchid may be seen to resemble a thin-winged butterfly. The leaves are oval at the base and lance-shaped on the flowering spike, which can be long and many-flowered. Each flower is scented, with a very long thin lip which has a long downwardly-curving spur arising from the base. The pollen masses are further apart at the bottom than the top. It is a plant that occurs in woods and grassland in much of Europe, especially on chalky soil. The Lesser Butterfly Orchid (*P. bifolia*) is very similar, but is smaller and its pollen masses lie parallel in the flowers.
Ⓑ Ⓞ Ⓜ

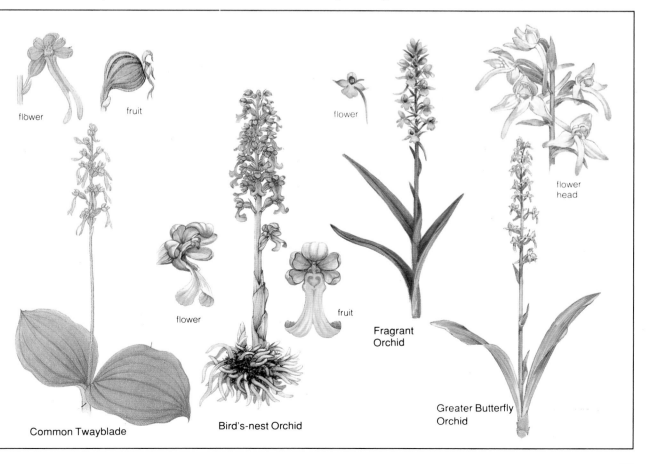

flower
fruit
flower
flower
flower head
flower
fruit

Common Twayblade
Bird's-nest Orchid
Fragrant Orchid
Greater Butterfly Orchid

Bee Orchid
Ophrys apifera
15–60cm. This plant mimic has a distinctive flower, the lip of which resembles and even smells like a female bumble-bee. This attracts the duped male bees, who attempt to mate with it and effect cross-pollination. This orchid has three pink or white sepals and the two upper petals are greenish or pink. It is found in grassland, especially chalk, over much of Europe and northward to Britain and Ireland. Numbers vary from year to year.
Ⓑ

Fly Orchid
Ophrys insectifera
15–60cm. This orchid uses the same tactics as the Bee Orchid to effect pollination, but instead of bumble-bees it attracts two small wasp species to its flowers. Each flower has three green sepals, two very narrow brown petals, which resemble an insect's antennae, and a narrow brown, furry and forked lip. There is also a band of blue towards the top of the lip. A local plant of woods and grassland, on chalky soils, it is rare or even absent in the south of Europe and much of the north.
Ⓑ ✿ ⊞

Mirror Orchid
Ophrys speculum
10–30cm. This orchid is similar in form to the Fly Orchid. Each flower has three green sepals, striped with red-brown. Petals are brown, with the lip a rich brown on the edges, and a centre which is large, blue and shiny. A plant of grassy places, open woodland and maquis, it occurs throughout the Mediterranean area.
☺

Early Spider-orchid
Ophrys sphegodes
10–45cm. Another deceiver, this orchid has a flower resembling a female bumble-bee rather than a spider, despite its name. The three sepals are large and green. Two of the petals are green, occasionally red-tinged, and the third forms the large, furry, dark red-brown lip which has a bluish 'H' or 'X' mark in the centre. A plant of grassland, woodland clearings and maquis, it prefers chalky soils and occurs from the Mediterranean area, north to southern England and Germany.
Ⓑ ✿ ⊞

Lizard Orchid
Himantoglossum hircinum
30–75cm. The species name *hircinum* does not refer to lizards but to goats and the goat-like smell of the flowers of this orchid. Each plant has up to eight leaves, decreasing in size up the stem. The flower-spike is many-flowered. Each flower has sepals and petals which form a greyish-green hood. The long, narrow three-lobed lip is the only separate petal and fancifully resembles a lizard. The plant usually dies after flowering. It grows in woods, sand-dunes and grassland, and is found mainly in southern and central Europe.
Ⓑ ✿ ⊞

Bee Orchids are commonly self-pollinated. These flowers clearly show the yellow pollinia dangling in front of the stigmas.

Early-purple Orchid
Orchis mascula
15–60cm. This is another plant with several local names, and as many legends attached to it. The purple-brown spots on the leaves are said to be Christ's blood, dropping from the cross and it was also an ingredient of love potions. A handsome plant, the purple flowers each have a hood composed of the sepals and two of the petals. The third petal forms a three-lobed lip, with a spur from its base. It is a fairly common plant of woods and grassland almost throughout Europe.
Ⓑ ✿ ⊞

Green-winged Orchid
Orchis morio
10–30cm. This is a fairly short-lived orchid. Its leaves are unspotted and shiny green. Its flower spike is loose and bears five to 12 flowers. The three sepals and the top two petals form a hood, and the third forms a broad three-lobed lip, which has a stout upwardly curving spur from its base. Flower colour is variable, from dark-purple, through pink, to white. The white forms show up the green veining on the wing-like side sepals. It is found in grassland, woods and scrub as far north as Norway.
Ⓑ ✿ ⊞

Common Spotted Orchid
Dactylorhiza fuchsii
20–60cm. This plant has heavily brown-spotted leaves, held almost horizontally. The flower-spike is many flowered. Each flower is pink, mauve or whitish, with purple dots. It has three spreading sepals, with two petals forming a hood over the top of the flower. The lip is formed from the third petal and is divided into three lobes. A fairly common plant of wood margins, scrubland and grassland in northern and central Europe.
Ⓑ ✿ ⊞

Pyramidal Orchid
Anacamptis pyramidalis
20–45cm. This is one of the latest flowering of the grassland orchids. It is slim, with green unspotted leaves, and a flower-head that starts out distinctly pyramidal. Each pink flower has the sepals spreading outwards, and the two upper petals form a hood over the reproductive parts. The third petal forms a lip with a long, thin spur at its base, and is divided into three deep lobes. The plant gives off a smell of fox. It grows on dry grassland, usually on chalky soil, throughout most of Europe.
Ⓑ ⊞

FLOWERING TIME	J	F	M	A	M	J	J	A	S	O	N	D
Bee Orchid						▬	▬					
Fly Orchid					▬	▬						
Mirror Orchid				▬								
Early Spider-orchid				▬	▬							
Lizard Orchid						▬	▬					
Early-purple Orchid				▬	▬							
Green-winged Orchid					▬	▬						
Cmn Spotted Orchid						▬	▬					
Pyramidal Orchid						▬	▬					
This chart is explained on page 13.												

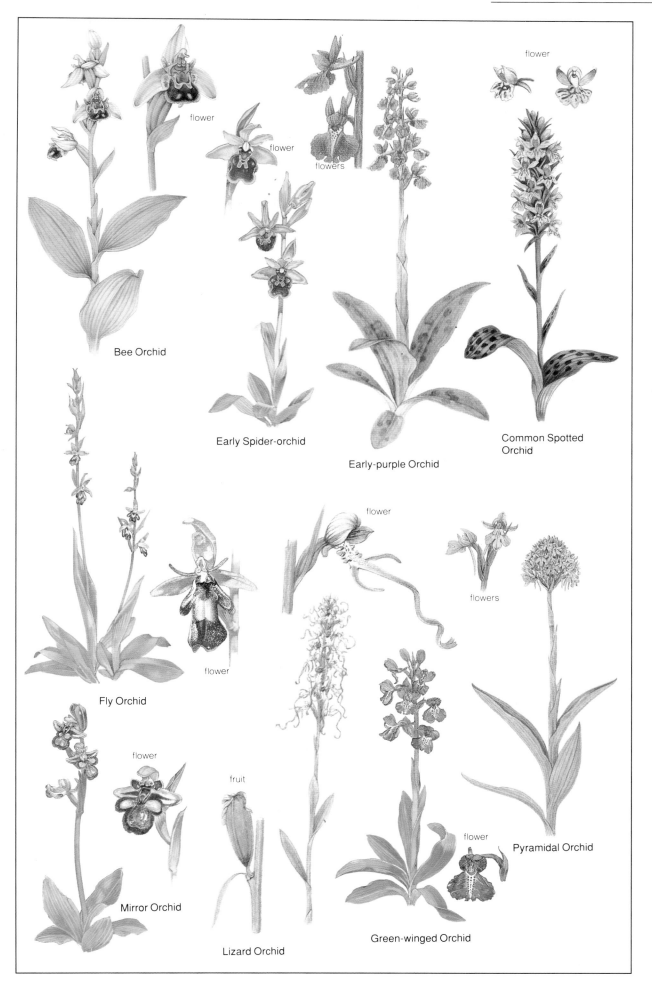

flower

Bee Orchid

flower

flowers

Early Spider-orchid

Early-purple Orchid

flower

Common Spotted
Orchid

Fly Orchid

flower

flower

flowers

Mirror Orchid

flower

fruit

flower

Pyramidal Orchid

flower

Lizard Orchid

Green-winged Orchid

BUR-REED FAMILY

This small family (Sparganiaceae) of aquatic plants is found mainly in the temperate regions. Most of the 20 or so species stand erect at the water's edge. The tiny wind-pollinated flowers are gathered into spherical heads, with male and female flowers in separate clusters.

Branched Bur-reed
Sparganium erectum
50–150cm. This stout, hairless perennial grows at the edge of still and slow-moving water. The male flower heads are always carried above the female clusters, which produce spiky fruits.
Ⓑ ☻

BULRUSH FAMILY

This family (Typhaceae) of tall plants grows in marshes and shallow water. The tiny wind-pollinated flowers are densely packed into cylinders at the tops of the stems. There are only about ten species. They were formerly called reedmaces and are also known as cat-tails.

Bulrush
Typha latifolia
150–250cm. This perennial grows in ponds and slow-moving streams. The female flowers form a thick, sausage-like spike, with the male flowers in a more slender spike above them. The female spikes break up to release their fluffy seeds in February.
Ⓑ ☻

RUSH FAMILY

The rushes (Juncaceae) are mostly slender perennials, commonly confused with grasses although their flowers are different. Each tiny flower has six papery perianth segments – three sepals and three petals – which are all alike and usually greenish white or brown. There are six stamens and three feathery stigmas and the flowers are pollinated by the wind. The fruit is a brownish capsule. True rushes (*Juncus* species) are hairless and their leaves are usually cylindrical, although in many species the leaves are minute scales at the bases of the cylindrical stems. Most of the 300 or so true rushes grow in damp places, especially in cool climates. Woodrushes (*Luzula* species) have flat, hairy leaves and are easily mistaken for grasses.

Jointed Rush
Juncus articulatus
Up to 80cm. This rather weak-stemmed rush is named for the transverse partitions in its leaves, which can be felt by pulling a leaf between the fingers. The smooth, dark green stems each bear two to seven leaves. No leaves spring directly from the ground. Dark brown flowers grow in loose clusters at the tops of the stems. Each flower usually has three pointed and three blunt segments. It is abundant in wet grassland.
Ⓑ ☻ 🌰 ✿

The fluffy fruiting heads of Common Cottongrass turn large areas of wet heath and peat bog snow-white in the summer.

Soft Rush
Juncus effusus
Up to 150cm. This rush forms dense tufts on damp ground almost everywhere but is most common on poorly-drained grassland. The glossy stems are up to 3mm in diameter and very smooth. Its leaves are reduced to reddish-brown scales at the stem base. The flower clusters are usually loose, but there is a variety with compact clusters.
Ⓑ ☻ 🌰 ✿

Field Woodrush
Luzula campestris
Up to 15cm. This grass-like plant has bright green leaf blades clothed with long hairs. Its star-like flowers are carried in loose clusters. It is abundant in dry grassy places almost everywhere.
Ⓑ 🌰

SEDGE FAMILY

The members of this large family (Cyperaceae) are mostly grass-like perennial herbs, but they have solid, unjointed stems. These are commonly triangular in cross-section, and the slender leaves are also arranged in triangular fashion: a useful mnemonic is 'sedges have edges'. The flowers are small and lack true petals. Those of true sedges (*Carex* species) are unisexual, with male and female flowers often forming separate spikes. Sedges are wind-pollinated. The fruits are mostly globular or three cornered grains. Most of the 4000 or so species grow in wet places.

Common Cottongrass
Eriophorum angustifolium
Up to 60cm. This wiry plant is abundant on wet heaths and bogs. The plants are most noticeable when the cottony white fruiting heads develop in summer. The deeply channelled leaves become golden-brown by mid-summer and soon die down, but they are later replaced by fresh green leaves. The related Harestail Cottongrass (*E. vaginatum*), common on moorland, carries its flowers and fruits in a single, erect spike.
Ⓑ ☻

Common Club-rush
Scirpus lacustris
Up to 3m. The smooth, rounded stems of this sedge form dense stands in still and slow-moving water. Its strap-like leaves are under the water. The flower head is a branching cluster of reddish-brown, egg-shaped spikelets, although many stems have no flowers. The plant was once known as the bulrush, but the *Typha* species have now taken over this name.
Ⓑ ☻

Great Fen Sedge
Cladium mariscus
Up to 3m. This sedge has smooth stems and wide, saw-edged leaves which can cut fingers very easily. The leaves often bend sharply downwards and the tightly packed flower heads stand far above them. It grows in fens and swamps, usually in alkaline water. It is used in thatching, especially for the decorative capping at the ridge. It is often known simply as sedge, especially in East Anglia.
Ⓑ ☻

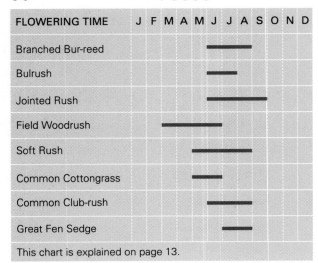

FLOWERING TIME	J	F	M	A	M	J	J	A	S	O	N	D
Branched Bur-reed						▬	▬					
Bulrush						▬						
Jointed Rush						▬	▬	▬				
Field Woodrush			▬	▬	▬							
Soft Rush						▬	▬					
Common Cottongrass					▬	▬						
Common Club-rush						▬	▬	▬				
Great Fen Sedge							▬					

This chart is explained on page 13.

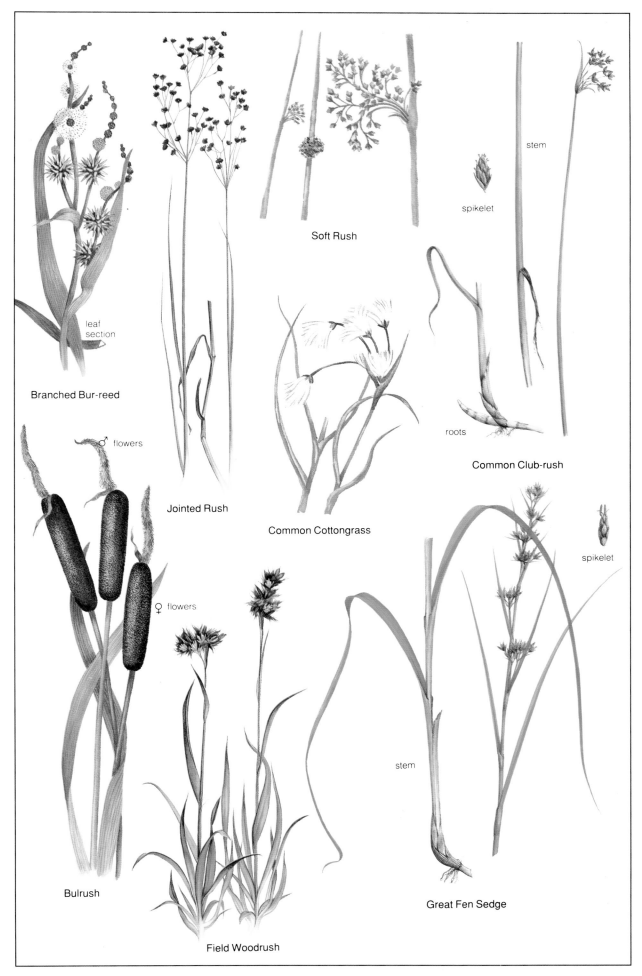

leaf section

Branched Bur-reed

♂ flowers

Jointed Rush

Bulrush

♀ flowers

Field Woodrush

Soft Rush

spikelet

Common Cottongrass

stem

roots

Common Club-rush

stem

spikelet

Great Fen Sedge

Greater Pond Sedge
Carex riparia

Up to 150cm. This typical waterside sedge grows in dense clumps around still and slow-moving water. Its sturdy stems are stiff, hairless and clearly three-cornered, with sharply keeled, bluish-green leaves. The flowers are typical of *Carex* species, with male and female flowers forming separate cylindrical spikes. Up to seven slender male spikes are clustered at the top of the stem and become golden-yellow as their stamens open to release their pollen. The female spikes develop lower down and have a greenish tinge when their stigmas are exposed.

Pendulous Sedge
Carex pendula

Up to 2m. This graceful sedge has leaves with rough edges and which are bright green above and bluish below. One or two male spikes develop above four or five slender female spikes, which may each be up to 16cm long. The spikes always droop. It grows on heavy soils, mainly in woods and by shady streams.

Glaucous Sedge
Carex flacca

Up to 50cm. This tufted sedge is sometimes called Carnation Grass because the undersides of its pale green leaves are a bluish colour. There are one to three male spikes and one to five relatively plump female spikes below them, all basically purplish brown. It is abundant on both dry and damp calcareous grassland.

GRASS FAMILY

With some 10,000 species, this family (Poaceae) is one of the largest plant families. Until recently the family was known as the Gramineae. Grasses grow in all parts of the world and in all kinds of habitats, both on land and in fresh water. Most are small herbaceous plants with narrow leaves and hollow, jointed stems, although the woody bamboos, some of which are 30m high, are also grasses. The lower parts of the leaf surrounds the stem and a small membranous collar called a ligule stands at the junction The shape of this ligule, seen by pulling back the leaf blade, is important in identifying grasses. The structure of the grass flower is described on p. 12. Unless otherwise stated, the grasses described below are all perennials.

Sheep's Fescue
Festuca ovina

Up to 50cm. This rather variable grass always has very slender, bristle-like leaves, which are often bluish-green. Its ligule is extremely short. It always grows in dense tufts, although these often link up to form turf. Flowers appear in fairly narrow panicles. Each spikelet is usually violet-tinged and contains three to five flowers. Abundant on dry grassland, especially on poor soils, it forms much of the springy turf on chalk downs.

Swayed by the slightest breeze, the male spikes of the Pendulous Sedge scatter their pollen over the more slender female spikes.

Giant Reed
Arundo donax

Up to 5m. This bamboo-like grass has tough stems that are up to 4cm in diameter. Its young shoots are often mistaken for Maize, because of their broad leaves. Large silvery flower heads, rather like those of the Common Reed, are produced during the summer. The plant grows in ditches and damp hollows in southern Europe and is widely planted to form wind-breaks for horticultural crops. The mature stems of this grass are also cut and used for this purpose, especially in the Rhône Valley in France.

Reed Sweet-grass
Glyceria maxima

Up to 2m. This stout waterside grass is easily distinguished from other tall species by its shiny, bright green leaves. Its ligule is of more or less even height all round and bears a sharp spike at the back. There is a brown band where the leaf joins the stem. This grass has a spreading panicle of many-flowered spikelets. It is often found growing in fairly deep water.

Common Reed
Phragmites australis

Up to 3m. This grass forms dense stands in fens and marshes and around the margins of lakes and rivers. Its fast-growing rhizomes make it a very invasive plant. The leaves are greyish-green, 60cm or more long and tapering to a fine point. Its ligule is a fringe of tiny hairs. The spikelets, containing two to ten flowers, are up to 15mm long and very hairy. They are clustered into dense brown or purplish panicles. The tough stems are in great demand for thatching.

Purple Moor Grass
Molinia caerulea

Up to about 100cm, although usually much less. This is a tough, tussock-forming grass of poorly drained ground and is especially common on heaths and moors. Its leaves are greyish-green and, although the grass is a perennial, they die down in winter. The ligule is a ring of hairs. Its slender flower spike is sometimes green but usually purple. The spikelets have two to four flowers, with violet-brown anthers.

FLOWERING TIME	J	F	M	A	M	J	J	A	S	O	N	D
Greater Pond Sedge					▬							
Pendulous Sedge						▬						
Glaucous Sedge				▬								
Sheep's Fescue					▬▬							
Giant Reed						▬▬▬						
Reed Sweet-grass						▬▬						
Common Reed						▬▬▬▬						
Purple Moor Grass						▬▬						

This chart is explained on page 13.

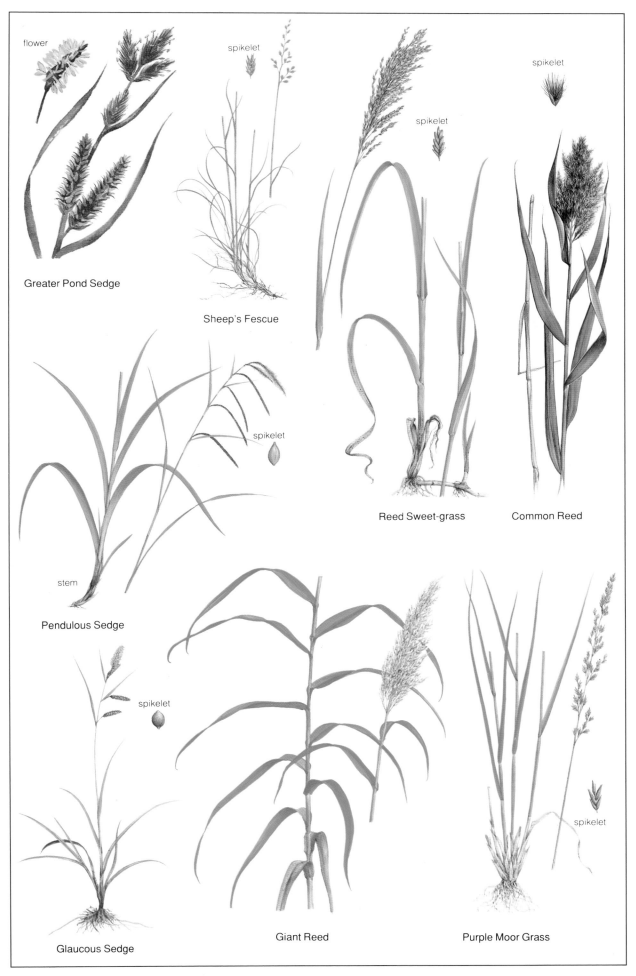

flower

Greater Pond Sedge

spikelet

Sheep's Fescue

spikelet

spikelet

Reed Sweet-grass

spikelet

Common Reed

spikelet

stem

Pendulous Sedge

spikelet

Glaucous Sedge

Giant Reed

spikelet

Purple Moor Grass

The GRASSLAND SCENE

Because we are surrounded by them, we often take grasslands for granted and assume that the countryside has always been dominated by them. But only the dry steppes in the very eastern end of Europe, and a few patches of montane, coastal, and riverine grassland are truly natural. The rest of our grasslands have been created by humans and their grazing animals and are only semi-natural.

Much of today's grassland is enclosed to form permanent pasture or hay and silage meadows. These fields and meadows once glittered with wild flowers, but ploughing and re-seeding with 'improved' grass mixtures have destroyed the flowers and most of the fields are now boringly green. There are, however, some exceptions. The sub-alpine hay meadows of various parts of Europe have never been ploughed and have been fertilized only with animal dung, and they carry a dazzling array of wild flowers – including many orchids, their accompanying butterflies and other insects. A few lowland meadows in Britain have also escaped the plough and are protected for the sake of the Fritillary and Meadow Saffron and other rare flowers. These lowland meadows also contain Cock's-foot, Meadow Foxtail, and other lush grasses.

The Rough Grazings

Most upland grassland is classed as unimproved hill pasture or rough grazing. Although dominated by grasses, the exact nature of the vegetation varies with the soil and the altitude. Basic grasslands, developing on alkaline soils, are typified by England's chalk downlands. These well-drained hillsides support a rich variety of herbs and are by far the best of the rough grazings. The short, springy turf, produced by countless generations of sheep and maintained more recently by rabbits, consists largely of Sheep's Fescue and Red Fescue. Other common grasses include Common Quaking Grass and Sweet Vernal Grass. Tor Grass and Upright Brome dominate areas with reduced grazing. Familiar flowers include Bulbous Buttercup, Stemless Thistle, Common Rockrose, Horseshoe Vetch, Marjoram and Bee Orchid. Grasshoppers and butterflies, notably the Chalkhill Blue and the Marbled White, abound on these grasslands. The turf supports many snails, and the snail-feeding Glow-worm is common in many areas.

Acidic grassland, developing over sandstones and other acidic rocks, is more widespread than basic grassland. The drier areas are dominated by a mixture of Common Bent Grass and Sheep's Fescue, while Mat Grass and Purple Moor Grass dominate damper areas, especially at higher altitudes where the grassland merges with the heather-clad moorland. With far fewer flowers than basic grassland, the acidic grasslands support fewer insect species.

Hedgerows

Hedgerows are major features of grasslands in many areas of Europe, although thousands of miles of them have been ripped out in recent decades to make way for wider roads and larger fields. Many hedges are clearly artificial – dead straight and consisting mainly of Common Hawthorn. Ancient hedges usually pursue wavy courses and contain a

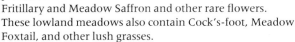
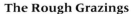

ABOVE: *The Meadow Grasshopper exists in many different colour forms, but it is always short-winged and unable to fly.*

FAR LEFT: *The mushroom* Hygrocybe coccinea *is commonly found in all kinds of grassland habitats. It is bright red at first but becomes orange and finally pink as it matures and dries.*

LEFT: *Never ploughed, and dressed only with farmyard manure, this alpine meadow supports an amazing variety of wild flowers, including Oxeye Daisies and Wood Cranesbill.*

wide range of shrubs. Some of these hedges are remnants of woodland left as boundaries when the woods were cleared. Others have grown up spontaneously on roadsides and on the no-man's land between villages. It is possible to date some of these old hedges quite accurately using a rule developed by the British naturalist Max Hooper. From a study of old maps and records, he traced the age of many British hedgerows and showed that the number of tree and shrub species in a 30-metre stretch of hedge agrees closely with the age of the hedge in centuries. In other words, a hedge with seven species in a 30-yard metre is likely to be about 700 years old.

Verges

Hedges and verges often go together, and it is not always easy to see where one stops and the other begins. Some roadside verges are the remnants of ancient grassland through which the roads were cut and, like hedgerows, they form important reservoirs and corridors for wildlife. They often carry a wealth of wild flowers. Most verges are relatively new, however, resulting from the widening of many of our roads. False Oat Grass often dominates new verges but, as long as they are not treated with herbicides and not cut too often, these verges will gradually acquire a rich flora, which will in turn attract a rich fauna.

LEFT: *A Sky Lark makes towards its nest with a beakful of food. It is unusual for a Sky Lark to alight on anything other than the ground.*

Perennial Rye-grass
Lolium perenne
Up to about 50cm, but sometimes taller. This very nutritious, but tough grass is widely sown for pasture and lawns and there are many cultivated varieties. The ligule is no more than 2mm high. The spikelets are flat, each with only one glume and up to 14 tiny flowers. The spikelets have their narrow edges facing the stem.
Ⓑ ◉ ✪

Annual Meadow Grass
Poa annua
Up to 35cm, but usually shorter. This sprawling species is found mainly on waste land and as a weed. It is normally an annual, although in mild areas it can survive for two or three years. The green, hairless leaves are often wrinkled and the ligule is up to 5mm. The flower head is pyramidal and the spikelets each contain up to ten flowers.
Ⓑ ◉ ✪

Alpine Meadow Grass
Poa alpina
Up to 40cm. This species resembles Annual Meadow Grass, but in most regions its flowers are usually replaced by small plantlets, whose thread-like leaves give the panicle a feathery appearance. As they get bigger, they weigh the stems down, and they take root when they touch the ground. This is a plant of cold, exposed grasslands.
Ⓑ ◔ ◍

Rough Meadow Grass
Poa trivialis
Up to 100cm. This loosely tufted grass can be distinguished from several similar species by its rough stems. Its leaves are deep green, often with a purplish tinge, and abruptly pointed. The ligule is 4–10mm long, with parallel sides and a triangular tip. As in most *Poa* species, the panicle is distinctly pyramidal. Its dull green or purplish spikelets contain two to four flowers. This grass is abundant in meadows and pastures, especially on moist soils, and also grows on waste land and as a weed of cultivation.
Ⓑ ◉ ✪

Cock's-foot Grass
Dactylis glomerata
Up to 150cm. This grass is named for the resemblance of the mature panicle to a chicken's foot. The ligule is more or less triangular and up to 12mm long. Spikelets, up to 9mm long, contain two to five flowers. Forming clumps in all kinds of grassland, this nutritious grass is regularly sown in hay meadows.
Ⓑ ◉ ✪

Quaking Grass
Briza media
Up to 75cm. This delicate grass is named for its drooping and freely swaying spikelets. It grows in loose tufts in all kinds of grassland and is common on many roadside verges. The leaves are bright green and hairless and the ligule is short and

The papery scales forming the spikelets of the Quaking Grass are clearly seen in this flower head bursting from its sheath.

blunt. The purplish spikelets are flat and shiny, oval or triangular in outline, and up to 7mm long. Each holds up to 12 flowers.
Ⓑ ◉ ✪

Wood Melick
Melica uniflora
Up to 60cm. This dainty woodland grass can be easily identified when in flower by its sparse brown spikelets. Up to 7mm long, each spikelet contains just one fertile flower. The leaf blade carries scattered long hairs and its sheath is usually downy, with a short bristle at the top. It carpets many woodlands, especially beechwoods, and shady banks.
Ⓑ ◐

Blue Moor Grass
Sesleria albicans
Up to 45cm. This grass has bluish green leaves which end in an abruptly pointed hood, rather like the prow of a boat. Its membranous ligule is almost non-existent. The spikelets, up to 7mm long and containing two to three flowers, are tightly bunched into greyish-green heads. A grass of dry, calcareous grassland, in the British Isles

it is confined to the older limestones of the uplands and is especially common in the Pennines.
Ⓑ ◐ ◉

Upright Brome
Bromus erectus
Up to 100cm. This is usually the most common tall grass on calcareous grasslands, often forming extensive stands on the chalk downs. The ligule is up to 3mm long and usually rather frilly. The spikelets are up to 3.5cm long, reddish or purplish-brown, and contain up to 14 flowers. It is absent from most of northern Europe.
Ⓑ ◉

Tor Grass
Brachypodium pinnatum
Up to 60cm. This stiff, hairless grass has yellowish-green leaves. Its ligule is short and blunt. The slender spikelets each contain up to 20 flowers. An unpalatable grass forming extensive patches on chalk and limestone hills, it has spread considerably since the rabbit population was reduced by myxomatosis. It is absent from most of northern Europe.
Ⓑ ◉

FLOWERING TIME	J	F	M	A	M	J	J	A	S	O	N	D
Perennial Rye-grass						▬▬▬▬▬						
Annual Meadow Grass	▬▬▬▬▬▬▬▬▬▬▬▬											
Alpine Meadow Grass						▬▬▬						
Rough Meadow Grass						▬▬▬▬						
Cock's-foot Grass						▬▬▬▬						
Quaking Grass						▬▬▬▬▬						
Wood Melick					▬▬▬							
Blue Moor Grass				▬▬▬								
Upright Brome						▬▬▬						
Tor Grass						▬▬▬						

This chart is explained on page 13.

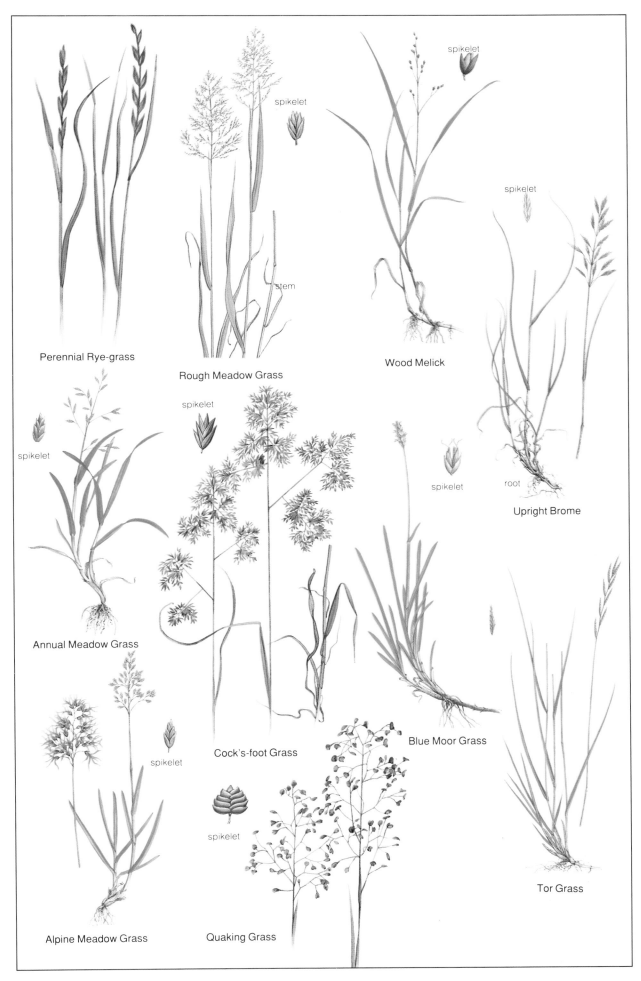

Perennial Rye-grass

Rough Meadow Grass

spikelet

stem

Wood Melick

spikelet

spikelet

Upright Brome

root

spikelet

Annual Meadow Grass

spikelet

spikelet

Cock's-foot Grass

Blue Moor Grass

spikelet

Alpine Meadow Grass

spikelet

Quaking Grass

Tor Grass

Common Couch Grass
Elymus repens
Up to 120cm. This familiar grass has rough, dull green or bluish-green leaves, which are normally slightly hairy on the upper suface. The ligule is under 1mm. Its spikelets are up to 20mm long, and each may contain up to six flowers. They are arranged with their broader faces pressed against the stem axis. It is abundant on roadsides and in wasteland places and is also a weed of cultivation. Its fast-growing, wiry, sharply pointed rhizomes often grow right through bulbs and potatoes.
Ⓑ ✪

False Oat Grass
Arrhenatherum elatius
Up to 150cm. This attractive, loosely tufted grass has shiny flower heads and bright green leaves which are rough to the touch, although at the most only lightly hairy. The ligule is up to 3mm long and smoothly rounded at the tip. Its stem bases are usually swollen like little bulbs. The spikelets are up to 11mm long and shiny green at first, becoming brown or purplish later. Each normally contains two flowers and has one or occasionally two long, bent awns. The panicle is slender at first but the branches, which are in small clusters, spread out when the flowers open. Abundant on roadsides and other rough grassland, it is often the first grass to colonize disturbed areas, and is sometimes a weed.
Ⓑ 🐛 ✪

Wavy Hair-grass
Deschampsia flexuosa
Up to 100cm. This delicate grass forms dense cushions of hair-like leaves which are bright green when young, but become reddish in late summer. Its shiny, brown or purple spikelets are up to 6mm long and two-flowered. Each is carried on a wavy, hair-like stalk in a graceful, open panicle. It grows on heaths and moors and in open woodland.
Ⓑ 🍂 ◐ ⬢

Yorkshire Fog
Holcus lanatus
Up to 100cm. This grass has greyish-green leaves clothed with soft hair. The ligule is up to 4mm long and flat-topped. Its spikelets are up to 6mm long white, green, pink, or purple. Each contains two flowers. They are borne in dense, hairy panicles which are lanceolate at first but become pyramidal as the flowers open. It is abundant on roadsides, waste ground and run-down pasture.
Ⓑ 🐛 ✪

Wall Barley
Hordeum murinum
Up to 60cm. This annual forms loose tufts. Its leaves are bright green and, where they join the sheaths, there are two long, overlapping flaps called auricles. The ligule is very short and ring-like. Its spikelets have very long awns and are borne in threes on the flattened spike. It grows on waste ground.
Ⓑ ✪

The tightly-rolled leaves of Marram Grass cut down water loss and help the plant to survive in sand dunes and other dry environments.

Common Bent Grass
Agrostis capillaris
Up to about 70cm. The bright green leaves of this grass are hairless, although slightly rough, and the ligule is short and ring-like. Its spikelets are 2–4mm long, one-flowered and borne on fine branches. It is common on grasslands of all kinds, but especially on poor, acidic soils. It forms a fine turf and is commonly used for lawns.
Ⓑ 🍂 🐛 ✪

Timothy Grass
Phleum pratense
Up to 150cm. This loosely tufted grass has pale green or greyish-green hairless leaves. The ligule is oval and up to 6mm long. Its spikelets are 3–4mm long, flat, and each has two short bristles which give the flower spike a rough texture – in contrast to the superficially similar Meadow Foxtail. The spikelets are one-flowered with greyish-purple anthers. Common on roadsides and in low-lying grasslands, this species is grown for hay and pasture.
Ⓑ 🐛 ✪

Feather Grass
Stipa pennata
Up to 100cm. This beautiful grass is unmistakable in fruit because of its feather-like awns. The leaf is bluish-green and rolled inwards, especially in dry weather. The spikelets,
up to 2cm long, are one-flowered and carried in small clusters. The awn carries the fruit away and twisting movements, in response to humidity changes, drive the grain into the ground. It grows on dry, stony slopes in the Alps.
🐛

Meadow Foxtail
Alopecurus pratensis
Up to 120cm. Superficially similar to Timothy Grass, this grass can be distinguished by its more or less square ligule and the very soft flower spike. The anthers are orange or purple. The rather flat, 4–6mm long spikelets are one-flowered and carry a single, soft awn. Abundant in grassland on heavy soils, it is absent from the Mediterranean region.
Ⓑ 🐛 ✪

Marram Grass
Ammophila arenaria
Up to 120cm. This sturdy maritime grass has stiff, greyish-green leaves with sharp points. The pointed ligule is stiff and up to 3cm long. Its spikelets are up to 16mm long, one-flowered and packed into dense pale spikes. Abundant on coastal sand dunes, it is also extensively planted to stabilize young dunes with its fast-growing rhizomes.
Ⓑ ⚇

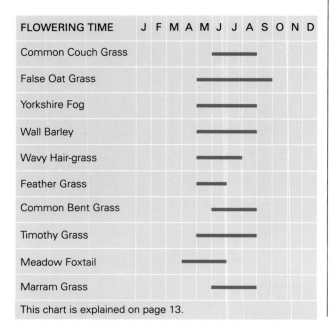

FLOWERING TIME	J	F	M	A	M	J	J	A	S	O	N	D
Common Couch Grass							—	—				
False Oat Grass						—	—	—	—			
Yorkshire Fog						—	—	—				
Wall Barley						—	—	—				
Wavy Hair-grass						—	—	—				
Feather Grass					—	—						
Common Bent Grass						—	—	—				
Timothy Grass					—	—	—	—				
Meadow Foxtail				—	—	—						
Marram Grass						—	—	—				

This chart is explained on page 13.

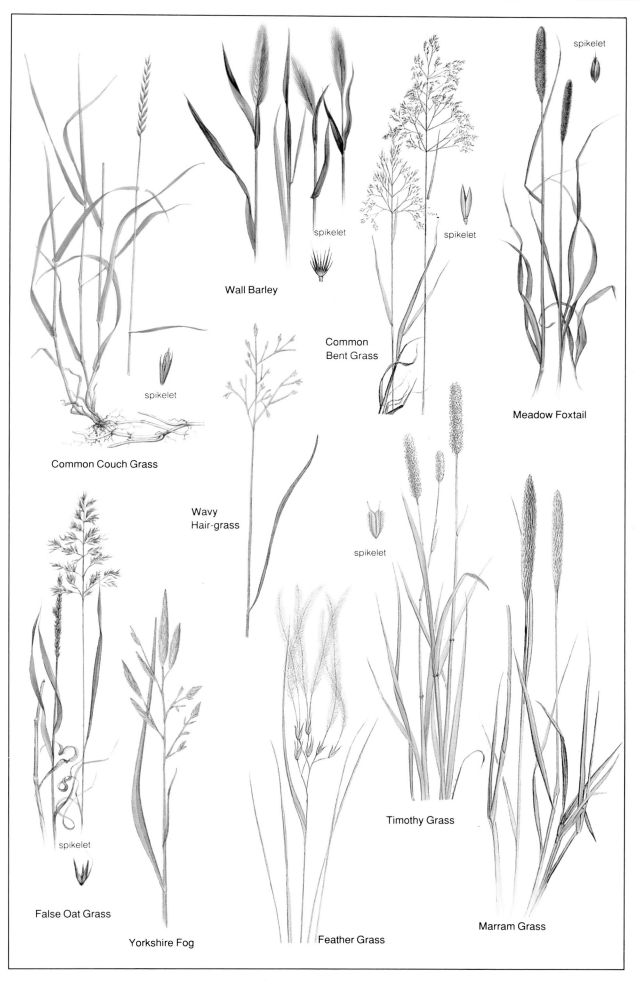

spikelet

Wall Barley

Common
Bent Grass

spikelet

spikelet

Meadow Foxtail

spikelet

Common Couch Grass

Wavy
Hair-grass

spikelet

Timothy Grass

spikelet

False Oat Grass

Yorkshire Fog

Feather Grass

Marram Grass

89

TREES AND SHRUBS

Unlike herbaceous plants, which produce little or no woody tissues, trees and shrubs possess a woody main stem and branches. Trees are defined as reaching 2m or more in height, with a single stem – the trunk – that only begins to branch well above ground level. Shrubs are defined as having several stems or trunks, with the first branches at or very close to ground level. They range from a few centimetres high to 5m or more, but are always bushy. This separation into trees and shrubs is somewhat arbitrary, with some shrubby species capable of forming trees and vice versa, so trees and large shrubs (at least 1m high) are dealt with together in this section. Dwarf and creeping shrubs are included in the Wild Flowers chapter.

Tree Groups

Trees and shrubs do not form a single, natural group of plants but occur in a wide range of unrelated families of seed-bearing plants. The only feature common to all trees and shrubs is the presence of woody support tissues. However, one major distinction is between the Classes Gymnospermae (the gymnosperms) and Angiospermae (the angiosperms). The gymnosperms, which include all conifers, have naked seeds unprotected by an ovary. All members of this class are trees or shrubs. The angiosperms or flowering plants have seeds protected within an ovary and angiosperm trees and shrubs have the same basic flower structure as herbaceous plants. The trees in this group are sometimes described as broad-leaved because their leaves are quite broad compared to the needle-like leaves of most gymnosperms.

A second difference within trees and shrubs is between evergreen and deciduous species. Evergreens retain their leaves for several years, the old leaves being gradually shed and replaced by new leaves, so that the tree is always in full leaf. Deciduous trees shed all their leaves each year, usually in autumn, and produce a complete new set of leaves each spring.

Habitats

Trees and shrubs grow wherever conditions are suitable. Growth conditions become progressively more difficult with increasing altitude and latitude until a point is reached where trees are unable to grow. This limit is known as the tree line.

There are three major forest belts in Europe (see p. 7). The northern belt, or taiga, is dominated by evergreen conifers. The southern belt is also evergreen forest but it mainly consists of broad-leaved trees, with conifers in the drier areas. Between these two lies a broad belt of predominantly deciduous forest.

Not all trees occur in forests. Some are most frequent as isolated individuals in hedgerows or open land. Shrubs occur as an understorey in woods, and on heaths, in scrub and in hedges.

The area over which a tree or shrub occurs naturally is its native range. Introduced species that become established in the wild are referred to as naturalized. There are over 400 native and naturalized trees in Europe, and numerous shrubs. Many foreign trees and shrubs are planted for timber or ornament.

LEFT: *The majestic, smooth-barked Beech dominates large areas of the deciduous forest belt in western Europe, especially on the well-drained soils over-lying chalk and sandstone rocks.*

BELOW: *Hazel is a typical shrub, with a number of woody stems springing from ground level.*

BELOW: *Ground vegetation in deciduous forests is most obvious in spring, before the tree leaves open fully and shade the ground.*

peeling bark
(Paper-bark
Birch)

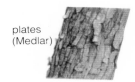

plates
(Medlar)

spiral ridges
(Sweet
Chestnut)

ABOVE: *Many trees have distinctive bark, which is useful for identification.*

BELOW: *Horse-chestnut twigs have sticky buds and horseshoe-shaped leaf scars.*

sticky bud

leaf scar

BELOW: *A variety of tree leaf shapes. Compound leaves are all divided into a number of separate leaflets.*

Trunk and Crown

Trees and shrubs have one to several trunks containing thickened support tissues – the wood. Unlike non-woody plants, trees and shrubs increase their girth each year. This can be seen in the annual rings exposed when a tree is felled. The trunk is protected by bark, a layer of often corky tissue that may be cracked or fissured into distinctive patterns. It is constantly renewed to accommodate the increase in girth.

In most trees and shrubs the trunk branches repeatedly to form the crown. An exception is the Palm Family in which there are no branches, the crown consisting only of large leaves crowded at the top of the trunk. The crown shape varies between different species. It can also vary within a species depending on the age or situation of the plant.

Some trees produce suckers – additional stems growing from root buds. These can form thickets around the parent trunk and may eventually become established as separate trees, especially if the parent dies.

Twigs and buds

Twigs are the slenderest branches and usually bear the leaves, flowers and fruits. They provide several characteristics for identification, especially of deciduous species, which are otherwise bereft of clues in winter.

Young twigs are often distinctively coloured, and may also be hairy. Bare older twigs often have leaf-scars, which can be quite prominent and have a particular shape or distribution. They indicate the arrangement of the absent leaves. Breathing pores, or lenticels, are often best seen on twigs. They appear as pale or dark warts. Sometimes the twigs have spines or thorns.

Buds are borne at the tip of the twig and in the angle formed with the leaves or leaf-scars (the axil). Flower buds are large, while the smaller buds contain the undeveloped leafy shoots; both kinds are protected by scales. The size, shape, colour and hairiness or stickiness of the buds are distinctive. The buds also provide a clue to the arrangement of the leaves on the twig.

Leaves

Leaves are the food factories of plants. They are green due to the pigment chlorophyll which is involved in photosynthesis. This is the process by which plants use sunlight to convert carbon dioxide and water to sugars.

Leaves vary greatly in their arrangement, shape and texture, all of which are important in identification. Leaves are usually alternate along the stem or borne in opposite pairs; whorled leaves are rare. Leaves are either simple or compound. Compound leaves are divided into leaflets. In pinnate leaves the leaflets are arranged in two rows, often paired and usually with a single leaflet at the tip. Palmate leaves have leaflets spreading from the tip of the leaf-stalk. Simple leaves have a single blade which may be pinnately or palmately lobed but is never completely divided into separate leaflets. The margins of the leaves or leaflets can be unbroken or toothed or even spiny.

The young leaves may be pale or brightly coloured. Some species have bluish leaves; others have bronze, reddish or variegated leaves. The often spectacular colours of autumn leaves are due in part to a build up of waste products. Leaves may be wrinkled or smooth and range from thin as in many deciduous trees to tough as in evergreens. They also vary in hairiness.

Stipules are small, leaf-like structures at the base of the leaf-stalk. They often fall very early.

LEAF SHAPES

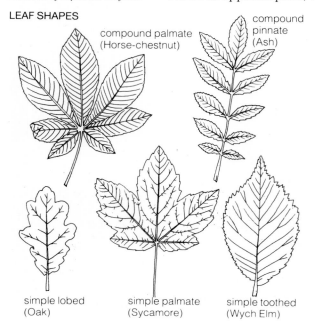

compound palmate
(Horse-chestnut)

compound pinnate
(Ash)

simple lobed
(Oak)

simple palmate
(Sycamore)

simple toothed
(Wych Elm)

Flowers

Angiosperm trees and shrubs have flowers that are identical in basic structure to those of herbaceous plants but many are wind-pollinated and have catkins – long clusters of tiny flowers often lacking petals and sepals. They produce pollen which is borne by the wind to the flowers of other individuals. Gymnosperm trees are mainly coniferous – they have cones instead of flowers and fruits – and are wind-pollinated. Male cones consist of scales bearing pollen sacs. Female cones are made up of whorls of seed-bearing scales which become woody. An exception is the genus *Juniperus* where the scales coalesce to form a berry-like structure.

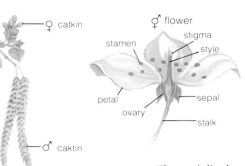

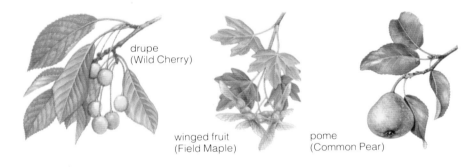

ABOVE: *The specialized structures of a typical catkin (left) designed for wind-pollination, and a flower (right) designed to attract pollinating insects.*

Fruits

Fruits may be dry or fleshy. The nut is a common dry fruit with a woody coat and a single seed. Berries are juicy fruits with several seeds. The skin is often thin but may be quite thick as in oranges. Drupes, or stone fruits, have a woody inner layer (the stone) surrounding a single seed. Cherries, plums and peaches are examples. The Walnut is also a drupe, but its outer regions are leathery. Apples and pears are known as pomes. The fleshy, edible part is the swollen top of the flower-stalk in which the seeds are embedded. A few species, such as alder, have cone-like fruits that are similar in overall appearance to those of conifers. The latter have true cones which take one to three years to ripen, when the woody scales usually spread apart to release the seeds. Afterwards the old cones may persist on the tree for years. In some species the cone breaks up on the tree, leaving only a bare central spike; in others it may fall entire to break up slowly on the ground.

The form of the fruit is often closely related to the method of seed dispersal. Fleshy fruits such as berries and pomes are eaten by animals and birds which scatter the seeds in their droppings. Dry fruits are often wind-dispersed. Those of maples are winged and act as propellers while those of willows have a parachute of hairs. A few fruits, such as those of Box, are explosive, the seeds being violently shot some distance from the capsule.

ABOVE: *The tension in this Broom seed's drying walls will eventually make it burst open and fling out its seeds.*

LEFT: *Examples of a pome, a winged seed and a drupe.*

Uses

The major economic uses of trees are for timber, paper and fuel, and vast areas are managed as plantations for these purposes and experimental plantings of new species are constantly made. Conifers are especially important as they are fast-growing and thrive in areas considered unsuitable for many broad-leaved species. Less widespread but still important are fruit trees and species used for shelter and soil-stabilization, tanning, medicines and ornament. Shrubs have a similar variety of uses but are especially important as ornamentals and, in a few cases, for providing stock-proof boundaries to fields. The uses of each tree are shown in the charts accompanying the text. The key to these charts is shown opposite.

KEY TO CHART	
⚙	Used for making timber
🏠	Ornamental or street tree
🌱	Soil stabilizer or sand binder
🍴	Edible, medicinal, or used as flavouring
🪑	Used for making furniture
🌲	Planted for hedging or as a windbreak

Cone-bearing Trees

PINE FAMILY

This is a major family (Pinaceae) of 200 mostly evergreen trees from the northern hemisphere. They are major forest trees in the north but also occur in southern mountains. The needle-shaped leaves may be borne singly (firs and spruces), in bundles of 2–5 (pines), or in rosettes (cedars and larches). The cones consist of spirally arranged scales. Male and female cones are separate. The female cones become woody as they ripen.

Common Silver-fir
Abies alba
Up to 50m. An evergreen, conical tree, this species has grey, square-plated bark. The needles are whitish beneath and spread each side of the shoots. Cylindrical female cones stand erect. Widespread in central Europe, it forms forests, usually in mountains, up to 2100m. Sometimes planted for timber, it is prone to damage from aphids. It flowers from April to May.
⊕

Douglas-fir
Pseudotsuga menziesii
Up to 55m. This tall, narrowly conical evergreen tree eventually becomes flat-topped. Its bark is reddish-brown. The needles spread to each side of the shoot and are dark green with two white bands beneath. They leave raised elliptical scars after they have fallen. The oblong female cones are hanging and ripen in the first year. Distinctive three-toothed bracts project from beneath each cone scale. A native of Pacific North America, it is widely planted in Europe in plantations and parks. It flowers from May to July.
⊕ ✿

Norway Spruce
Picea abies
Up to 60m. This evergreen, conical tree has dark green, four-sided needles. They spread alongside and above the shoots, leaving short peg-like projections when fallen. Cylindrical female cones hang down and ripen in their first year. It is a common forest tree in northern and central Europe. This species is extensively planted for timber, shelter, ornament and for use as Christmas trees. It flowers from April to June.
Ⓑ ⊕ ✿

Sitka Spruce
Picea sitchensis
Up to 55m. This evergreen, narrowly conical tree has its lowest branches arching downwards. Its flattened and pointed needles are bright green with two purplish-white bands beneath. They spread each side of the shoots. The cylindrical female cones hang down. Native to North America, it is grown for timber and ornament in central and northern Europe. It flowers in May.
Ⓑ ⊕ ✿

Being a deciduous tree, the European Larch allows far more vegetation to grow beneath it than other conifers.

Atlas Cedar
Cedrus atlantica
Up to 40m. An evergreen tree, it spreads when mature with large, level tiers of foliage. The needles are clustered in rosettes on woody spurs on mature shoots. Barrel-shaped female cones stand upright, ripening in their second year to break up and shed winged seeds. Native to North Africa, it is now naturalized in some parts of Europe where it has been widely planted for ornament. It flowers in September.
✿

European Larch
Larix decidua
Up to 35m. This conical tree is deciduous. The light green needles cluster in rosettes on woody spurs, and turn yellow before falling in autumn. Short, egg-shaped female cones with broad, rounded scales ripen in the first year but persist for several years. Native to central Europe, it grows on mountain slopes up to 2500m. It flowers from March to June.
Ⓑ 🍂 ⊕ ✿

Scots Pine
Pinus sylvestris
Up to 40m. This evergreen tree is initially conical-shaped but later forms a domed crown with flattened top. Its long, bare trunk is reddish.

The paired, bluish-green needles are 3–7cm long. Pointed female cones ripen in their second year, and are persistent. Widespread in Europe, although restricted to mountains in the south, it prefers drier soils. It flowers from May to June.
Ⓑ 🍂 ⊕ ✿

Dwarf Mountain Pine
Pinus mugo
Up to 3.5m. This is a dark, evergreen shrub with ascending branches. The shoots bear paired, deep green needles and pointed female cones which ripen in their second year, and are held upright or hang down slightly. It is found in the mountains of central Europe and the Pyrenees, growing on rocky ground, in lime-rich soils. This shrub flowers from May to June.
✿

Austrian Pine
Pinus nigra subsp. *nigra*
Up to 50m. This evergreen tree, with a conical crown, bears paired, deep green needles up to 19cm long. Pointed female cones ripen in their second year and hang down. It is native to mountain forests in central Europe, but is often seen outside its native range. It flowers from May to June.
⊕ ✿

USES OF TREES	🪚	🏠	🎆	🍴	🪑	🌲
Common Silver-fir	●	●				
Douglas-fir		●	●			●
Norway Spruce		●	●			●
Sitka Spruce		●	●			
Atlas Cedar		●	●			
European Larch		●	●			●
Scots Pine		●				●
Dwarf Mountain Pine		●				
Austrian Pine		●	●			●

The key to this chart is on page 93.

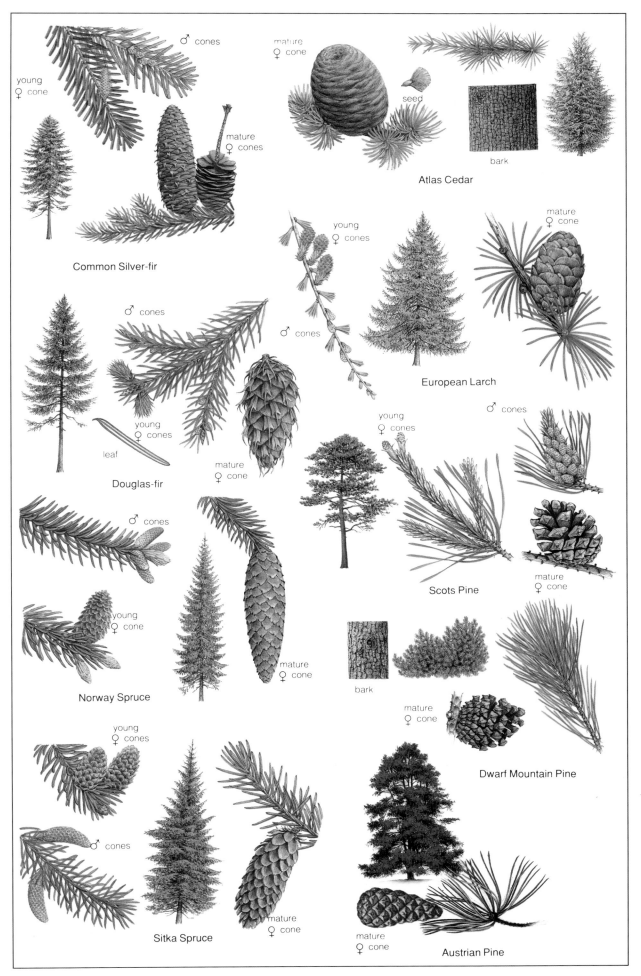

♂ cones

young
♀ cone

mature
♀ cones

Common Silver-fir

mature
♀ cone

seed

bark

Atlas Cedar

♂ cones

young
♀ cones

leaf

mature
♀ cone

Douglas-fir

young
♀ cones

♂ cones

European Larch

mature
♀ cone

young
♀ cones

♂ cones

mature
♀ cone

Scots Pine

♂ cones

young
♀ cone

mature
♀ cone

Norway Spruce

bark

mature
♀ cone

Dwarf Mountain Pine

young
♀ cones

♂ cones

mature
♀ cone

Sitka Spruce

mature
♀ cone

Austrian Pine

Corsican Pine
Pinus nigra subsp. laricio
Up to 50m. This evergreen conical or columnar tree has greyish-green needles which are softer and more flexible than those of the closely related Austrian Pine. The female cones are hanging and yellowish or grey-brown when ripe in their second year. A forest tree native to the central Mediterranean region, it has been widely introduced and is grown on a large scale in many parts of Europe. It is planted for shelter and as a sand-binder, as well as a timber tree. It flowers in June.

Maritime Pine
Pinus pinaster
Up to 40m. This evergreen, grey-barked tree has level branches which are retained even when dead. The paired, stout needles reach 25cm in length. Pointed, hanging female cones, up to 22cm long, ripen in their second year and persist on the tree. Widespread on coasts of south-western Europe, it is planted for timber, shelter and to stabilize dunes. Resin is obtained from the trunk. This pine flowers in June.

Aleppo Pine
Pinus halepensis
Up to 25m. An evergreen tree with a domed crown, it has twisting branches and pale grey bark reddening and fissuring with age. The paired, very slender needles are 6–15cm long. Pointed, hanging female cones,

5–12cm long, ripen in their second year. Widespread in the Mediterranean region, it often forms woodlands. It is resistant to summer drought and is planted for timber, shelter and in parks and streets. Resin is collected from cuts in the trunk. This species flowers in June.

Stone Pine
Pinus pinea
Up to 30m. An evergreen, this tree is umbrella-shaped with a broad crown. The bark is reddish-brown, fissured into vertical plates. Paired needles are often twisted, and 10–20cm long. Large, globose female cones, 8–15cm long, ripen over three years and hang downwards. Widespread in the Mediterranean region, usually near the coast, it forms woodlands on deeper and moister soils than the Maritime Pine. Frequently grown for its edible seeds, it is also planted for ornament and shade. It flowers in June.

Arolla Pine
Pinus cembra
Up to 25m. This evergreen, conical tree has spreading branches and reddish-grey bark. The twigs bear bluish-green needles in bundles of five. The upright female cones have swollen, pointed scales concealing edible, nut-like seeds. Native to the mountains of central Europe, it forms woodland on poor, acidic soils. It is planted for timber and ornament. It flowers from May to June.

Growing on an exposed slope and shaped by the wind, this Yew tree displays its reddish brown bark. The timber is similarly coloured.

YEW FAMILY

This small family (Taxaceae) of evergreen trees or shrubs occurs mostly in the northern hemisphere. The narrow leaves are arranged spirally, but are often spread so as to appear in two rows. Female cones resemble berries, with a fleshy layer around a single hard seed.

Yew
Taxus baccata
Up to 25m. This evergreen tree or shrub has reddish-brown, flaky bark. The leaves are dark green above, paler beneath. Female flowers are followed by fruits with the tip of the seed exposed in the centre of a fleshy, scarlet cup – the aril. The foliage, in particular, is poisonous. Widespread in Europe, the species is found in woodland, among scrub and on rocky slopes, preferring lime-rich soils. It is commonly planted for ornament and hedging in parks, churchyards and gardens and is estimated to have a lifespan of up to 2000 years. It flowers from February to April.

CYPRESS FAMILY

A family (Cupressaceae) of 100 or more species of evergreen trees which grow in the cooler regions of the world. They often have two kinds of leaves: needle-like juvenile leaves, and scale-like adult leaves. Female cones have scales meeting edge-to-edge, and are woody, or fleshy and berry-like.

Italian Cypress
Cupressus sempervirens
Up to 30m. The wild form of this evergreen tree grows broad, low and irregularly conical. The more commonly seen cultivated form is narrowly columnar and spire-like. Its paired, scale-like leaves, less than 1mm long, form four ranks pressed along the shoot. The female cones are woody. A native of south-eastern Europe, it is widely planted and naturalized throughout southern Europe.

Common Juniper
Juniperus communis
Up to 6m. This is a dense, columnar, evergreen shrub or small tree with sharp needles arranged in whorls of three. They are greyish, with a single white stripe above. Female flowers are followed by berry-like cones which are blue when ripe, then turn black over two or three years. Widespread in Europe, it grows on lime-rich soils or heathlands, moors and in pinewoods. Prostrate forms occur in montane regions. Oils taken from the 'berries' are used for flavouring gin. It flowers from May to July.

Prickly Juniper
Juniperus oxycedrus
Up to 14m. An evergreen shrub or small tree, it has a conical or spreading crown. Needles are arranged in whorls of three, each needle has two white stripes above. Fleshy cones ripen through yellowish-brown to reddish in their second year. Various forms exist in the south, including the Mediterranean region. It flowers from November to February.

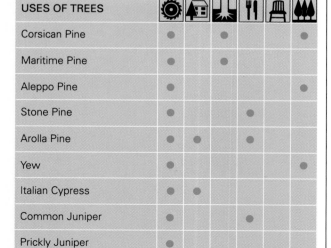

USES OF TREES					
Corsican Pine	●		●		●
Maritime Pine	●		●		
Aleppo Pine	●				●
Stone Pine	●			●	
Arolla Pine	●	●		●	
Yew	●				●
Italian Cypress	●	●			
Common Juniper	●			●	
Prickly Juniper	●				

The key to this chart is on page 93.

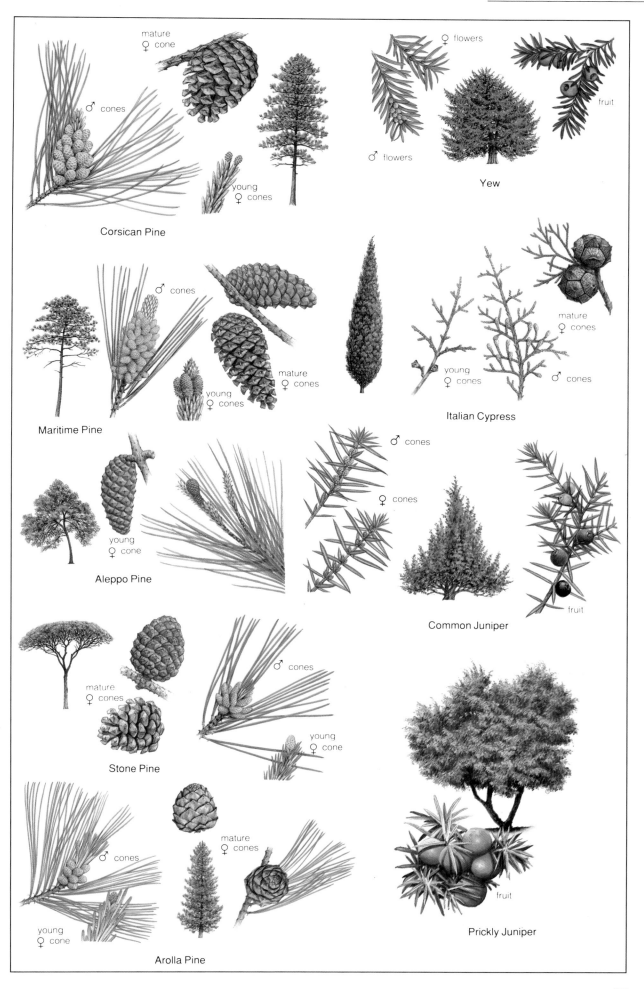

mature
♀ cone

♂ cones

young
♀ cones

Corsican Pine

♀ flowers

♂ flowers

Yew

fruit

Maritime Pine

♂ cones

young
♀ cones

mature
♀ cones

Italian Cypress

mature
♀ cones

young
♀ cones

♂ cones

Aleppo Pine

young
♀ cone

♂ cones

♀ cones

Common Juniper

fruit

Stone Pine

mature
♀ cones

♂ cones

young
♀ cone

Arolla Pine

♂ cones

mature
♀ cones

young
♀ cone

Prickly Juniper

fruit

The CONIFEROUS FORESTS

Natural coniferous forests, dominated by various cone-bearing trees, develop in areas where the climate is too cold for broad-leaved forests (see p. 126). The conifers are almost all evergreens and their tough, needle-like leaves are well adapted to shed heavy winter snows and to survive the cold winds. The most extensive of these forests are found in a broad belt across northern Europe and on mountains in southern and central regions. Smaller areas exist in lowlands of eastern Europe. Coniferous timber is in great demand for building and paper manufacture and, apart from those on the highest mountain slopes, few forests are now without some mark of human activity.

The Northern Forest

The cold northern forest, known as the boreal forest or the taiga, is dominated by Norway Spruce and Scots Pine. The Spruce is by far the more common of the two and in many areas of the taiga it is the only tree to be seen. Scots Pine dominates regions with drier, sandy soils. It also forms the Scottish outliers of this great forest, although only scattered fragments of the Caledonian Forest have survived forest clearance. Norway Spruce is not native to the British Isles, but it is planted for timber and many trees have 'escaped' to the wild.

    The taiga is as dense as a plantation in some areas, but there are numerous clearings, especially where poor drainage has led to the development of bogs and lakes – commonly known as mires. Rowans and birches often grow in the clearings and are joined by alders and willows in the damper areas. Elk browse on these trees and wallow in the mires.

ABOVE: *Larch forests clothe many mountain sides. A deciduous conifer, the Larch turns a rich gold colour in the autumn.*
LEFT: *The Pixie-cup Lichen* Cladonia fimbriata *is abundant on dead tree stumps in the coniferous forests.*

Elk are among the few animals that benefit from forestry operations in the taiga, as the trees on which they feed spring up rapidly in cleared areas and flourish until the next generation of conifers overtakes them.

    The shrub layer is represented by low-growing species such as the Bilberry. This plant can survive in dense shade but, like most other taiga plants, it is more abundant in the forest clearings. Other species growing in the clearings include Stone Bramble, Cloudberry, Twinflower and various wintergreens. Raspberries commonly grow where

ABOVE: *The European Lynx is a rare nocturnal predator from the taiga, also found in the montane forests of Iberia and the Balkans.*
BELOW RIGHT: *The potentially deadly Panther has a striated margin and pure white scales on its reddish brown or coffee-coloured cap.*

trees have been felled. Few plants can survive under the denser stands of conifers, partly because of the shade and partly because the thick layer of fallen needles decay so slowly in the cold climate that the soil becomes impoverished. Bilberries can grow there as, like the conifers, their roots contain mycorrhizal fungi (see p. 141). Ferns, mosses, and lichens are common on the forest floor, and huge numbers of fungi spring up in the autumn.

Montane Forests

Coniferous forests clothe the slopes of most European mountains, where the ubiquitous Norway Spruce and Scots Pine are joined by Silver Fir, Black Pine (sometimes called Austrian Pine), Mountain Pine, and – in the south – Arolla Pine. The European Larch is also common and is often the first tree to colonize bare slopes after rock-falls. Differing from most conifers in being deciduous, it assumes a magnificent golden coat in the autumn.

The montane forests are usually very dense and have an even poorer flora than the taiga. Juniper – itself a conifer – forms a shrub layer in some places. Hard Fern is common, while the field layer flowers include Wood Sorrel, Hepatica and the Violet Bird's Nest Orchid, which lives off dead organic matter on the forest floor.

Animals of the Coniferous Forests

Animal life is less varied than in the deciduous forests, partly because of the cold, and also because conifer needles are unpalatable to many creatures. There are, however, plenty of leaf-eating caterpillars in the trees and they provide food for insectivorous birds, such as the Crested Tit. Wood ants also eat these insects. Many insect larvae bore into the conifers and these attract several kinds of woodpeckers. Abundant seed awaits the crossbills and other birds that can deal with the cones. Chewed cones reveal a good deal about the animal population, because mice, squirrels and crossbills each have their own way of opening the cones. The birds and small mammals fall prey to the Pine Marten and other carnivores, including the Wolverine, the Wild Cat, and the very rare Lynx.

Wildlife of the Northern Forest
1 Northern Three-toed Woodpecker
2 Red Squirrel
3 Pine Marten
4 Scots Pine
5 Rowan
6 Russula paludosa
7 Twinflower
8 Capercaillie
9 Bilberry
10 Common Crossbill
11 Norway Spruce
12 Elk

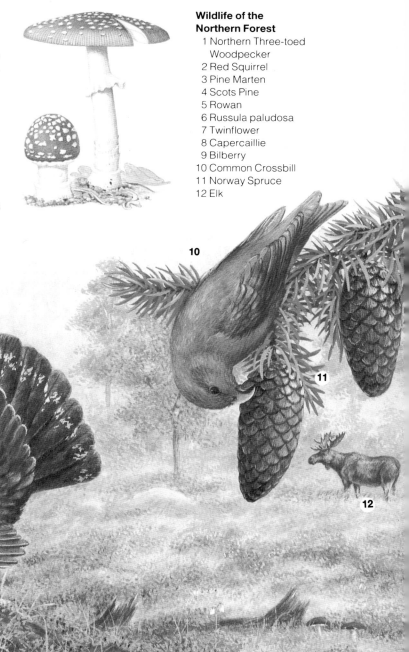

Flowering Trees

WILLOW FAMILY

The 350 or so species of willows and poplars (Salicaceae) are mostly found in the cooler northern regions of the world. Willows are small trees or shrubs, although some dwarf arctic and alpine willows may be only a few centimetres in height. Poplars are generally tall trees. Willows and poplars are commonly found in wet places. The leaves often have large, leafy stipules at the base of the leaf-stalk. The seeds are tufted with long hairs in order to catch the breeze.

White Poplar
Populus alba
Up to 30m. This deciduous, suckering tree with pale bark becomes blackish and rugged with age. The leaves vary from being almost round to three or five-lobed. They are a white-woolly texture when young but later lose the hairs from the upper surface. The catkins droop, and appear before the leaves unfurl. Native to central and south-eastern Europe, this species grows in damp woodlands and is planted for shelter and ornament on roadsides and in parks and gardens. It flowers in March.
Ⓑ❂✿

Aspen
Populus tremula
Up to 20m. This deciduous, suckering tree has twisting branches, a broad, open crown and smooth, greyish-brown bark which is darker and ridged on older trees. Its leaves are round or oval, irregularly and bluntly toothed at their margins. They emerge orange-brown from slightly sticky buds, later turning greyish-green. They flutter and tremble in the slightest breeze – hence the scientific name. Widespread in Europe, although restricted to mountains in the south, this species grows in damp forests, fens, on heaths and moors, and in mountainous areas. It flowers from February to May.
Ⓑ◕❂♠

Black Poplar
Populus nigra
Up to 30m. This deciduous, rarely suckering tree has a short trunk and a few massive branches supporting a large, domed crown. The bark is brown and deeply fissured. Its leaves are oval-triangular in shape, emerging reddish from sticky buds and becoming shiny bright green. Its catkins are drooping, appearing before the leaves develop. Widespread in Europe, it grows in moist places and is frequently planted for shelter and ornament. The Lombardy Poplar is a common cultivar with a columnar crown which grows up to 35m. It flowers from March to April.
Ⓑ❂✿♠✿

White Willow
Salix alba
Up to 25m. This deciduous tree has a tall, domed crown, upright main branches and dark grey, thickly ridged bark. Its narrowly elliptic leaves are initially covered with pale, silky hairs, which give the tree a greyish appearance. The catkins are ascending, and produced at the same time as the unfurling leaves. Widespread in Europe, it grows by fresh water. Cultivars are planted for ornament, or for strong, light timber. This tree flowers from April to May.
Ⓑ❀

Golden Weeping-willow
Salix x sepulchralis nv. *chrysocoma*
Up to 22m. This broadly domed, deciduous tree has upwardly angled branches with slender, weeping, yellowish twigs that reach nearly to the ground. Its bark is pale grey-brown and its narrow, spear-shaped, finely toothed leaves are bright yellowish-green above and paler beneath. Catkins appear with the leaves in spring. Most are male as female catkins are rarely produced. A hybrid of the White Willow and the Chinese Weeping-willow, it is so common in Europe that it often appears to be a native tree.
Ⓑ✿

Crack Willow
Salix fragilis
Up to 25m. This deciduous tree has long, ascending branches and a broadly conical crown, becoming domed with heavy, twisting branches in old specimens. The bark is rugged, dark grey and netted with ridges. Its narrowly elliptical leaves are hairless, pale underneath and borne on twigs easily snapped off at the base – hence the scientific name. Ascending catkins are produced as the leaves unfurl. Widespread in Europe, it grows by fresh water and often hybridizes with the White Willow. It flowers from April to May.
Ⓑ❀

Goat Willow
Salix caprea
Up to 15m. This deciduous shrub or tree has an open crown, with ascending branches. The greyish bark is at first smooth, then becomes widely fissured. The leaves are oval with pointed tips, smooth or finely indented and are grey-hairy below. Bare twigs produce short, stout catkins in winter and early spring. The male catkins are golden yellow and the female, borne on separate trees, are silvery green – both are attractive to bees. It is widespread in Europe in woodlands, hedges and among scrub, often on damp ground. It flowers from March to April. Grey Willow (*S. cinerea* subsp. *cinerea*) has more oblong leaves.
Ⓑ❂❀

Crack Willow, named for its fragile twigs which break with a loud crack when they are bent, is a very common riverside tree.

USES OF TREES	⚙	🏠	🎆	🍴	🪑	🌲
White Poplar		●				●
Aspen		●				
Black Poplar		●				●
White Willow	●	●				
Golden Weeping-willow		●				
Crack Willow			●			
Goat Willow				●		

The key to this chart is on page 93.

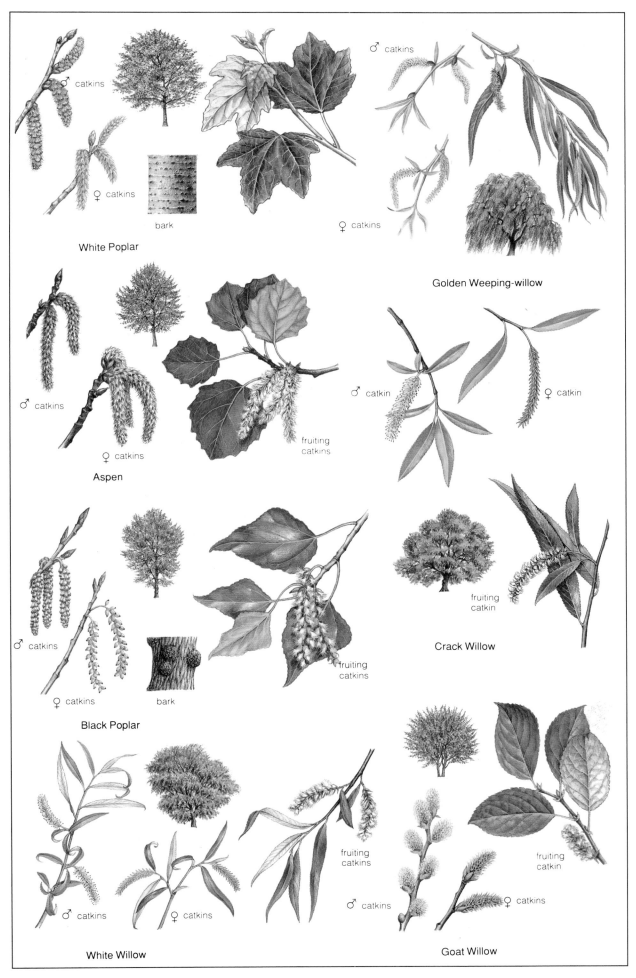

catkins

♂ catkins

♀ catkins

bark

White Poplar

♂ catkins

♀ catkins

Golden Weeping-willow

♂ catkins

♀ catkins

fruiting catkins

Aspen

♂ catkin

♀ catkin

♂ catkins

♀ catkins

bark

fruiting catkins

Black Poplar

fruiting catkin

Crack Willow

♂ catkins

♀ catkins

fruiting catkins

White Willow

♂ catkins

♀ catkins

fruiting catkin

Goat Willow

WALNUT FAMILY

This small family (Juglandaceae) contains just 59 deciduous trees. All leak a sticky latex when cut. Their alternate leaves have aromatic, pinnate leaflets. Wind-pollinated flowers are borne in male and female catkins on the same tree. Their fruit is a drupe, with a spongy husk and a woody 'stone' surrounding the seed.

Walnut
Juglans regia
Up to 30m. A deciduous, broad-domed tree, this species has heavy, twisted branches. The scented leaves are composed of 3–4 pairs of oval leaflets with a single terminal leaflet. Male flowers are borne in catkins while female flowers occur in small clusters. The fruit has a thick husk and a hard stone – the familar walnut. It is native to south-eastern Europe but widely planted and naturalized in many areas.
Ⓑ ◯

BIRCH FAMILY

There are about 130 species in this family (Betulaceae). All are deciduous trees or shrubs. The flowers are wind-pollinated, with both sexes borne on the same tree – the males in drooping catkins. The fruit is either a tiny, winged nutlet (birches, alders) or a large woody nut wrapped in a leafy sheath or cup, known as the involucre.

Alder
Alnus glutinosa
Up to 20m. This deciduous tree has a conical crown and dark, greyish-brown bark fissured into small plates. Hairless twigs bear round leaves with toothed margins and 5–8 pairs of veins. Male catkins expand to shed pollen before the leaves unfurl and the egg-shaped, woody female catkins, persist at least until the spring. Widespread in Europe, this species grows on wet soils. It flowers from February to March.
Ⓑ ◯ ●

Grey Alder
Alnus incana
Up to 25m. This deciduous, suckering tree has smooth, grey bark that becomes fissured with age. The leaves are oval with pointed tips, serrated margins and 7–12 pairs of veins. Its twigs and leaves are grey-hairy when young. Widespread in north-eastern and central Europe, it is often planted on unstable soils because of its rapid growth and low nutrient requirements. It flowers from February to March.
Ⓑ ◯ ● ✿

Silver Birch
Betula pendula
Up to 30m. A deciduous tree with a high-domed crown, it has drooping younger stems and white, papery, peeling bark, fissured black at the base. Hairless young twigs bear kite-shaped leaves which have double-toothed margins. Male catkins shed pollen when the leaves unfurl and then soon fall; the female catkins persist through summer and autumn, bearing seeds. Widespread in Europe,

These Hornbeams show clear signs of pollarding – cutting 2–3 metres above the ground to produce successive timber crops.

it grows in open forests, among scrub and on heaths, preferring light soils. It is often planted in streets and gardens, where ornamental cultivars exist. It flowers from March to May.
Ⓑ ● ◯ ✿

Downy Birch
Betula pubescens
Up to 25m. Unlike the Silver Birch, the young stems of this deciduous shrub or tree do not droop. The bark is pale grey with no black fissures. The twigs and leaf-stalks are hairy when young and leaves are oval with pointed tips and simply toothed margins. Widespread in northern and central Europe, it grows in open forests, on wet heaths and moorland, preferring damp, acidic soils. It flowers from March to May.
Ⓑ ● ◯

Hazel
Corylus avellana
Up to 6m. This deciduous shrub has reddish-brown bark and round, sparsely hairy leaves with pointed tips and serrated margins. Male catkins hang like tails before the leaves develop, while the female flowers are small and bud-like, and recognized only by their feathery, red stigmas. They are followed by rounded, edible nuts ripening in September and October and enclosed by an involucre. Widespread in Europe, it grows in woods and hedges. This shrub is frequently cut back to near ground-level (coppiced) to produce long,

straight poles, and is also planted for its nuts in gardens. It flowers from January to March.
Ⓑ ◯ ✿

Hop-hornbeam
Ostrya carpinifolia
Up to 18m. This small, conical, deciduous tree has reddish brown, hairy twigs which bear oval, pointed leaves with double-toothed margins. The leaves are hairy at first, becoming shiny dark green above, paler below, and have 12–15 pairs of veins. The slender male catkins appear with the leaves. The female catkins become hop-like in fruit, the nuts enclosed in elliptical white or pale brown papery bracts. It is native to central and eastern areas of southern Europe but is also planted elsewhere.
◯ ✿

Hornbeam
Carpinus betulus
Up to 25m. This deciduous tree has a broad crown and grey, fissured bark. Its leaves are oval with drawn-out tips and sharply serrated margins. Male catkins expand as the leaves unfurl and female catkins are followed by nutlets, which form long, hanging clusters. Widespread in central and southern Europe, it sometimes forms pure stands and favours clay soils. It is frequently planted for its tough and durable timber, ornament and hedging. This tree flowers from April to May.
Ⓑ ◯ ✿

USES OF TREES	⚙	🗄	💥	🍴	🪑	🌲
Walnut		●		●		
Alder		●	●			
Grey Alder			●			
Silver Birch		●				
Downy Birch		●	●		●	●
Hornbeam		●	●			●
Hazel		●	●	●		●
Hop-hornbeam		●	●			

The key to this chart is on page 93.

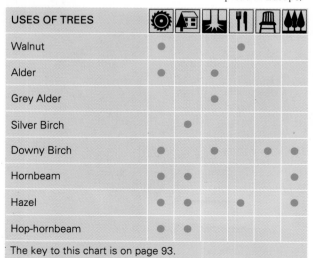

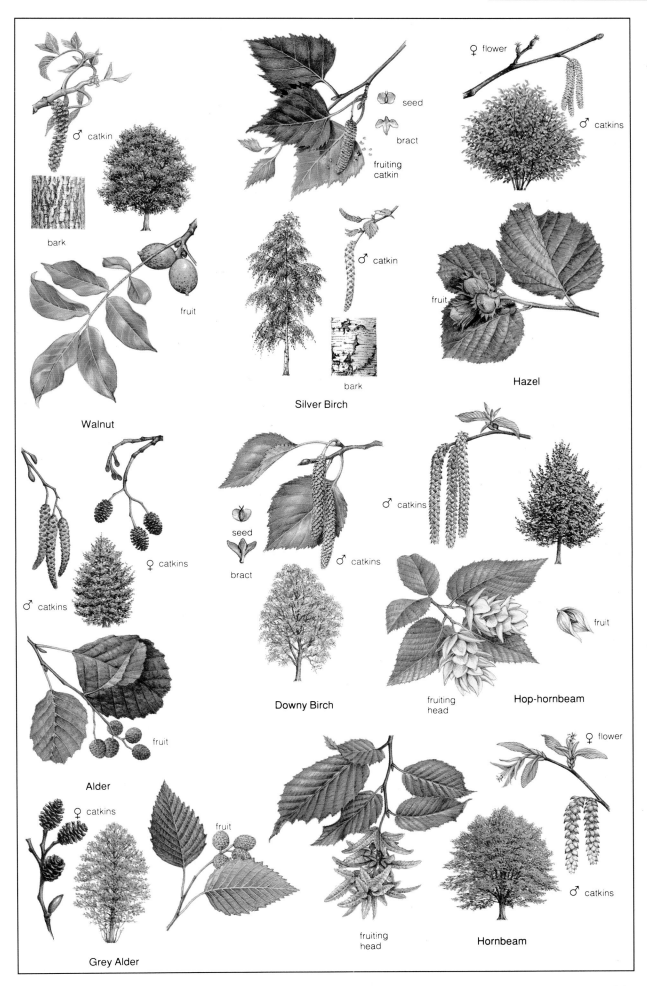

♂ catkin

bark

fruit

Walnut

seed

bract

fruiting catkin

♂ catkin

bark

Silver Birch

♀ flower

♂ catkins

fruit

Hazel

♂ catkins

♀ catkins

seed

bract

♂ catkins

Alder

♂ catkins

fruit

Downy Birch

♂ catkins

fruiting head

Hop-hornbeam

fruit

♀ catkins

fruit

Grey Alder

fruiting head

♀ flower

♂ catkins

Hornbeam

103

BEECH FAMILY

The 1000 or so species in this important family (Fagaceae) include oaks, beeches and chestnuts. They often dominate deciduous forests and woodlands in temperate regions north of the equator. All species are economically important as major sources of hardwood timber. Most species are deciduous, a few are evergreen.

Beech
Fagus sylvatica

Up to 30m or more. This deciduous tree has a domed crown, smooth, silvery-grey bark and oval leaves, shiny dark green above. Male flowers are borne in hanging tassels as the leaves unfurl. The female flowers are followed by prickly fruits which open to reveal small, shiny, brown nuts called mast. Widespread in central Europe, it grows in forests often as pure stands. It is widely planted for timber and in parks and gardens, where the ornamental dark-leaved Copper Beech is a cultivar. It flowers from April to May.
Ⓑ〇✿

Evergreen Oak
Quercus ilex

Up to 25m. An evergreen tree with ascending branches, this species has a broadly domed crown and dark, greyish, fissured bark. The leaves are oval to spear-shaped, and smooth or spiny at the margin. They are dark and have dense, pale hairs beneath. The acorn cups have short, felty scales pressed flat. Common in the Mediterranean region, it is planted for ornament further north and sometimes naturalized. It flowers from April to June.
Ⓑ◓✿〇

Kermes Oak
Quercus coccifera

Up to 15m. An evergreen tree or shrub, its dense foliage forms a rounded crown or irregular mound when heavily grazed. The leaves are small and holly-like with prickly margins, unfurling reddish and becoming dull green. They are similar to low leaves of the Evergreen Oak but are hairless beneath when mature. The acorns are usually long and cylindrical, held in cups covered with sharp, prickly scales. This species is widespread in the Mediterranean region. It flowers from April to May.
◓〇

Cork Oak
Quercus suber

Up to 20m. This evergreen tree has low, twisting branches and a spreading crown. Its deeply ridged, fissured bark is stripped as a source of cork every 12 years, exposing a reddish trunk. The leaves are white-hairy beneath with toothed margins. The deep acorn cups have scales that are longer towards the rim. Native to south-western Europe, it often grows in pure, semi-natural stands managed for cork production. It flowers from May to June.
◓〇

Sessile Oak is the dominant oak of upland areas in north-western Europe, where it grows on well-drained slopes.

Turkey Oak
Quercus cerris

Up to 35m. This deciduous tree has a broadly domed crown and grey, fissured bark. Hairy twigs bear long-stalked leaves with deep, jagged lobes. The almost stalkless acorn cups have long curling, green scales. Native to south-eastern Europe, it forms forests with other trees. It flowers from May to June.
Ⓑ〇

Pedunculate Oak
Quercus robur

Up to 45m. This deciduous has a domed crown and it has twisting branches. Its short-stalked, oblong leaves are indented into rounded lobes, with two small flaps at the base of each blade. The long-stalked acorn cups are finely scaled. Widespread in Europe, it often forms pure stands. It is also known as the English Oak. This species flowers from April to May.
Ⓑ〇✿

Sessile Oak
Quercus petraea

Up to 40m. This deciduous tree has rather straight, spreading branches. Its leaves have rounded lobes but no flaps at the base of the blade. The acorn cups are hairless and almost stalkless. Widespread in Europe, it often forms forests with the Pedunculate Oak, or replaces it with pure stands on drier, more acidic soils. It flowers from April to May.
Ⓑ〇

Downy Oak
Quercus pubescens

Up to 25m. A deciduous tree with a wide crown and densely hairy twigs, its leaves with rounded lobes are initially hairy beneath. The acorn cups are almost stalkless, hairy and covered with small scales which are pressed flat. Widespread in central and southern Europe, it flowers in May.
〇

Sweet Chestnut
Castanea sativa

Up to 30m. This deciduous tree has spirally ridged bark. Its erect catkins have yellow male flowers above and green female flowers below. Prickly, globular fruits contain large, reddish-brown, edible nuts. It is native to southern Europe but planted and widely naturalized further north. It flowers in July.
Ⓑ〇✿

USES OF TREES	🪚	🏠	⚒	🍴	🪑	🌲
Beech	●	●		●		●
Evergreen or Holm Oak	●	●				
Kermes Oak	●					
Cork Oak	●	●				
Turkey Oak		●				
Pedunculate Oak	●	●				
Sessile Oak	●					
Downy Oak	●					
Sweet Chestnut	●	●		●		

The key to this chart is on page 93.

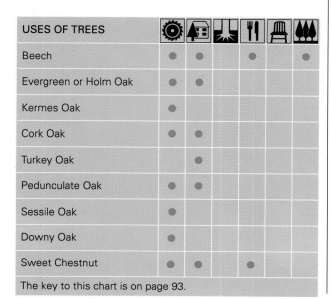

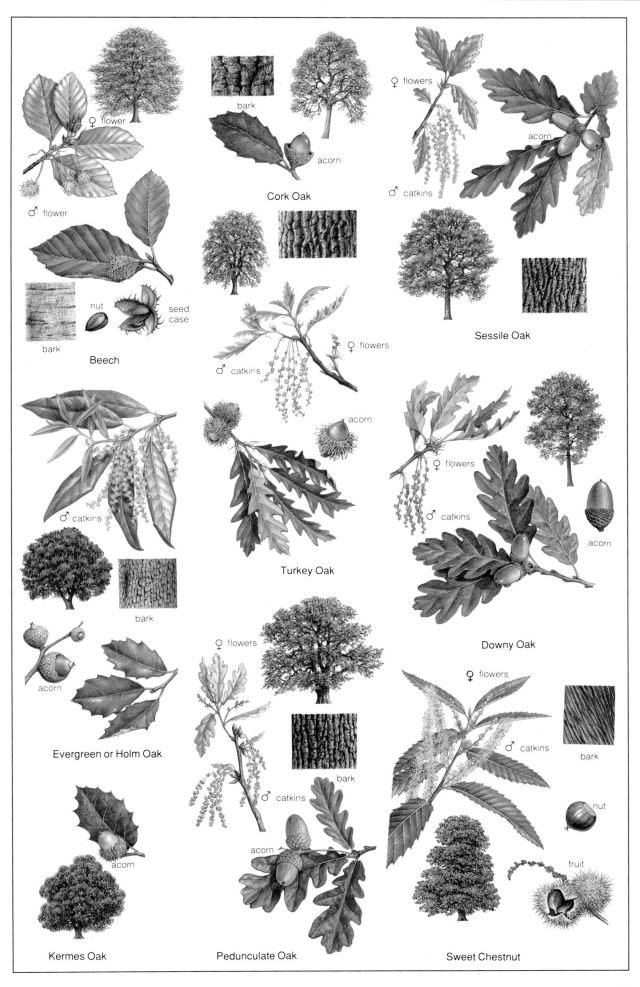

♀ flower

♂ flower

bark

nut

seed case

bark

Beech

bark

Cork Oak

acorn

♂ catkins ♀ flowers

acorn

♀ flowers

acorn

♂ catkins

♀ flowers

♂ catkins

Turkey Oak

♀ flowers

♂ catkins

Sessile Oak

acorn

♀ flowers

♂ catkins

acorn

Downy Oak

acorn

bark

Evergreen or Holm Oak

♀ flowers

♂ catkins

acorn

bark

♀ flowers

♂ catkins

bark

nut

fruit

acorn

Kermes Oak

Pedunculate Oak

Sweet Chestnut

BOG-MYRTLE FAMILY

Bog-myrtles are much the largest group within this small family (Myricaceae). They grow in bogs, heaths and fens throughout the New World, northern Europe, and parts of Africa and Asia. All are trees or shrubs with aromatic, gland-dotted foliage. The small, rough fruits often have a thick, waxy covering.

Bog Myrtle
Myrica gale
Up to 2.5m. A deciduous, suckering, willow-like shrub, this has upright, reddish twigs bearing narrowly oval, bluish-green leaves, toothed towards the tip and downy beneath. The flowers are borne in upright catkins before the leaves appear. The whole plant is covered with yellow glands exuding a sweetly fragrant resinous substance. Widespread in north-western Europe, it forms scrub on wet heaths and in bogs and fens on peaty and acidic soils. It flowers from April to May.
ⓑ◓

ELM FAMILY

A family (Ulmaceae) of some 2000 trees and shrubs including elms, nettle-trees and hackberries. While elms grow in the cooler northern regions, nettle-trees and hackberries are found predominantly in warmer climes. The leaves of this family often have asymmetric bases. The flowers are unisexual or bisexual, inconspicuous and pollinated by the wind. They have sepals but not petals. Fruits are either fleshy with hard stones, or nut-like and usually with papery wings. The grained wood of elms is resistant to rot when waterlogged. Several other species belonging to this family produce useful fibres.

Wych Elm
Ulmus glabra
Up to 40m. This deciduous tree has a broadly domed crown, arching lower branches and smooth, grey bark becoming darker and ridged with age. Initially hairy twigs bear broadly elliptic, pointed leaves, which are asymmetric at their base and have serrated margins. Flowers appear as reddish tufts, followed by clusters of papery, disc-shaped, pale green fruits, each with a notched tip and centrally placed seed. These are conspicuous on the leafless trees in May. Widespread in Europe, it grows in woodland and along hedgerows. Ornamental cultivars of this species can also be obtained. It flowers from February to April.
ⓑ◓

English Elm
Ulmus procera
Up to 30m. A deciduous tree, narrow in its lower part but broadening out above, this species has dark brown bark, deeply fissured into small square plates. Its twigs are persistently hairy, with rounder leaves than those of the Wych Elm. English Elm produces fruits with their seeds located near the terminal notch but these are rarely produced in the north. Found primarily in western and southern Europe, it grows in woodland and along hedgerows. It is usually seen as a bushy growth of suckers, since most trees of this species have succumbed to Dutch Elm Disease. It flowers from February to March.
ⓑ◓✪

Smooth-leaved Elm
Ulmus carpinifolia
Up to 30m. This deciduous, suckering tree has ascending branches that droop at the tips. Its greyish-brown bark has long, deep, vertical fissures and thick ridges. The initially hairy twigs produce smooth leaves, with a shiny green upper surface. Disc-like fruits have their seed located near the terminal notch. Widespread in Europe, it grows in woodland and along hedgerows. Local forms and hybrids are common, making exact identification difficult. This elm flowers from February to March.
ⓑ◓

Southern Nettle-tree
Celtis australis
Up to 25m. This deciduous tree has a graceful, slender habit and smooth, greyish bark. The common name refers to the leaves. They are oval to spear-shaped, toothed and with drawn-out and often twisted tips, and appear nettle-like. Green flowers are followed by solitary, long-stalked, globular fruits. These ripen blackish in August and have sweet-tasting flesh and edible, nut-like seeds. Widespread in southern Europe, this species grows in woodland and scrub, and is planted as a roadside tree. It flowers in May.
◓✪

Fig trees are common in southern Europe, springing up on all kinds of waste land where birds – and people – have dropped the seeds.

MULBERRY FAMILY

Vital sources of fruit and rubber, the 3000 species of mulberries and figs (Moraceae) occur in the warmer and tropical regions of the world. All are trees or shrubs, many of them evergreen. Their milky sap contains latex which is used to produce rubber. Wind-pollinated, unisexual flowers are borne in catkins or small heads and it is the whole head which forms the fleshy and edible fruit. The flowers of figs are enclosed in fleshy receptacles. Figs have a complex system of pollination, involving gall wasps.

Fig
Ficus carica
Up to 10m. This deciduous, rounded shrub or small tree has open habit, thick twigs and smooth, grey bark. Its bristly leaves are large, broad, and cut into three, five or seven rounded lobes which leave a prominent scar when they fall. The tiny flowers are packed on the inside wall of a small, green, pear-shaped structure which swells after pollination to become the familiar, edible fruit. This ripens to blackish-purple from July to October the following year. Possibly native to the Aegean region, it is widely cultivated in Europe and naturalized in rocky places in the south. It flowers from September to November.
◓✪

USES OF TREES	⚙	🏠	🎇	🍴	🪑	🌲
Bog Myrtle				●		
Wych Elm	●	●				
English Elm	●					
Smooth-leaved Elm	●	●				
Southern Nettle-tree		●		●		

The key to this chart is on page 93.

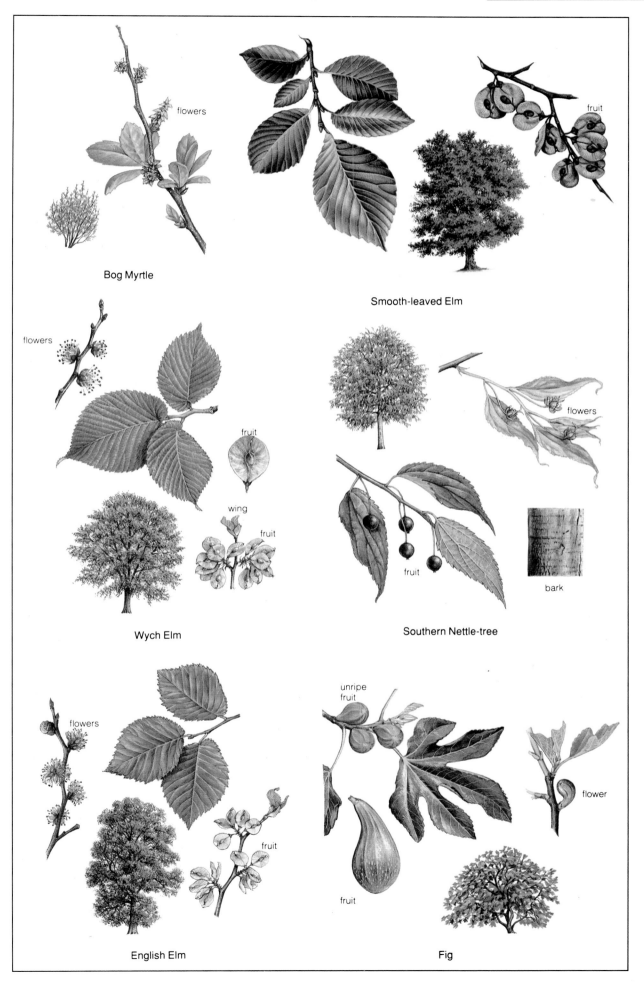

flowers

Bog Myrtle

fruit

Smooth-leaved Elm

flowers

fruit

wing

fruit

Wych Elm

flowers

fruit

flowers

fruit

bark

Southern Nettle-tree

English Elm

unripe fruit

flower

fruit

Fig

LAUREL FAMILY

This very large family (Lauraceae) consists of about 2200 evergreen trees and shrubs. It is mostly found in tropical and subtropical regions and its species include laurels and avocados. Laurels possess alternate leaves which are densely dotted with aromatic oil glands. Their fruit is berry-like and sometimes fleshy.

Sweet Bay
Laurus nobilis
Up to 20m, but often smaller. The foliage of this small evergreen tree or shrub has a distinctively spicy scent. It has a short, grey-barked trunk with a broadly conical crown of upwardly-arching branches. The leathery leaves have wavy edges and are dark green above, paler below and dotted with numerous tiny oil glands. Dull whitish-yellow male flowers and greenish-white female flowers are borne in separate clusters on the same tree. The fruit is a blackish berry. Native to the Mediterranean region, it is cultivated in many areas of Europe as far north as Britain. The leaves are used for flavouring food.

PLANE FAMILY

A family (Platanaceae) of large, deciduous trees containing just 10 species, only two of which are found outside North America. They have thin bark which is shed in large flakes. The palmately-lobed leaves have spreading, pointed lobes and bear star-shaped hairs. The tiny flowers are wind-pollinated and grouped in chains of spherical, unisexual heads. The seeds have a parachute of hairs and are dispersed by the wind.

London Plane
Platanus x hybrida
Up to 45m. A tall deciduous tree with twisted branches, it is believed to be a hybrid between the Oriental Plane and American Plane (*P. occidentalis*). The bark is a grey-brown colour, and scales away in large flakes, leaving the trunk with a mottled pale yellow appearance. The leaves are glossy and palmately five-lobed. Tiny flowers are borne in globular heads, males and females on the same tree. The males form chains of two to six heads. The females, each 2.5cm across, are usually in

The hardy Rowan, also known as the Mountain Ash, thrives in exposed places and produces a brilliant display of fruits in autumn.

chains of two. Valued as an ornamental tree in towns because of its high tolerance to atmospheric pollution, it is one of the commonest street trees in Europe. It flowers from April to June.

Oriental Plane
Platanus orientalis
Up to 30m. This tall tree has a broad, irregular, domed crown and huge branches, the lower ones often drooping. Similar to the London Plane, it also has scaling bark, but is recognized by its more deeply lobed leaves which are narrower at the base. Male and female flowers are produced in separate ball-like heads on long, hanging stalks. Fruiting heads up to 3cm across contain numerous individual fruits, each surrounded at the base by bristly hairs. It is native to south-eastern Europe and commonly planted in parks and gardens. This species flowers from April to June.

♂ flowers

♀ flowers

fruit

Sweet Bay

♂ flowers

♀ flowers

bark

London Plane

flower heads

flower

fruiting heads

Oriental Plane

ROSE FAMILY

This large family (Rosaceae) contains not only herbaceous plants, but also many trees and shrubs, including some of the most widespread orchard trees such as apples, cherries and peaches. Deciduous or evergreen, some species have thorny or spiny twigs. The flowers have five petals and five sepals which often persist in a withered state at the tip of the fruit. The fruits are varied, but in the tree species they are usually juicy and berry-like, or firm and fleshy, with one to several stony seeds or leathery pips. Apples and pears bear false fruits known as pomes.

Quince
Cydonia oblonga
Up to 7.5m. This spiny, deciduous, small tree or shrub is often broadly spreading. Its blunt oval leaves are green and smooth above, but greyish and woolly beneath. The large solitary flowers are bowl-shaped with densely hairy sepals and pink or occasionally white, slightly notched petals. The flesh of its pear-shaped fruit is hard and woody, but becomes yellow and very fragrant when ripe. This species is native to Asia but was introduced in ancient times to Europe. It is grown as a fruit tree in southern Europe but mainly as an ornamental in the north and west. This species flowers from April to May.
Ⓞ Ⓧ ⓦ

Wild Pear
Pyrus pyraster
5–15m. A large deciduous, often thorny, shrub or tree with rough, fissured bark. This species has almost orbicular leaves, which are usually only toothed towards the apex, and are hairless when mature. The flowers appear at the same time as the leaves and have pure white petals, followed by hard, globular or pear-shaped fruits, which become yellow-brown or black when ripe. Found wild in most of Europe except in the north, it is usually seen as an isolated tree in hedgerows, thickets, and open woods. It flowers from April to May. It is thought possibly one of the parents of the similar Garden Pear (*P. communis*), which is less bushy and spiny and has larger, sweeter fruit. The Garden Pear is widely naturalized.
Ⓑ Ⓞ Ⓧ ⓦ

Crab-apple
Malus sylvestris
Up to 11m. This large deciduous shrub or small tree has a dense, rounded crown, and is distinguished from the cultivated apple by its thorny branches. The oval leaves have finely toothed margins and are hairy only when young. The flowers have oval, white petals tinged with pink. Its fleshy but hard, round fruits are sour, yellowish-green, and sometimes tinged with red when ripe. A tree of woodland and hedgerows, it is native to most of Europe and south-west Asia. It is one of the parents of the hybrid orchard apple. It flowers from April to June.
Ⓑ Ⓞ Ⓧ

Rowan
Sorbus aucuparia
Up to 15–20m. A slender, deciduous tree with ascending branches and smooth greyish bark. The pinnate leaves are divided into oblong, finely toothed leaflets. Creamy-white flowers are borne in dense, flat-topped clusters, and are five-petalled, with three to four styles. The globular, fleshy fruits turn scarlet when ripe. A woodland tree widespread in Europe, it is also found in scrub and on rocky slopes, at higher altitudes in the Alps than any other deciduous tree. Often cultivated, and frequently found by roads, it flowers from May to June.
Ⓑ Ⓞ Ⓞ Ⓧ

USES OF TREES	⚙	🏠	🔥	🍴	🪑	🌲
Sweet Bay				●		
London Plane	●	●				
Oriental Plane		●				●
Quince		●				
Wild Pear				●		
Crab-apple				●		
Rowan	●			●		
The key to this chart is on page 93.						

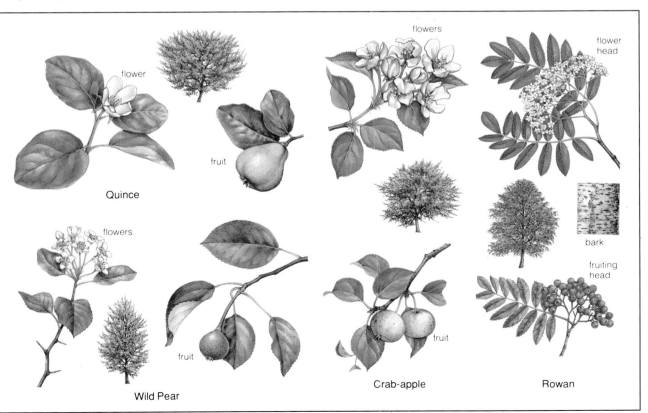

Quince

Wild Pear — flowers, fruit

Crab-apple — flowers, fruit

Rowan — flower head, bark, fruiting head

Service-tree
Sorbus domestica
Up to 20m. Broadly similar in its foliage to the more widespread Rowan, this is a larger tree with spreading branches. Its orange-brown bark is rough and fissured, and the young twigs are green with silky hairs. The white or pink flowers are larger than those of the Rowan and have five styles. The distinctive green or brownish fruits are apple or pear-shaped and bitter-tasting, but are sometimes used to make an alcoholic beverage. Native to southern Europe, North Africa, and western Asia, it is planted throughout Europe for ornament and fruit. This species flowers in May.
Ⓑ ⬤ ✪

Wild Service-tree
Sorbus torminalis
Up to 25m. This deciduous tree with a broad crown is easily recognized by its distinctive maple-like leaves with triangular, long-pointed, toothed lobes which, unlike those of many species of *Sorbus*, are green on both sides. The flowers have five white, rounded petals. Its berry-like fruits are brown and speckled with numerous, conspicuous lenticels. They are edible when ripe, and are sometimes used to make jam. A woodland tree scattered throughout much of Europe except the far north, it grows mainly on clay soils, and is occasionally planted in gardens. This tree flowers from April to June.
Ⓑ ⬤

Common Whitebeam
Sorbus aria
Up to 15–25m. The leaves of this deciduous, smooth-barked tree are among its most distinctive features. They are variable in size and shape but often oval, dull yellow-green above, and silvery white beneath, with a dense covering of hairs. Scented flowers in branched clusters are followed in September by fleshy, berry-like fruits, which ripen to scarlet. A common invader of ungrazed chalk and limestone grassland, it is often confused with similar species in the south. Several cultivars are planted as street trees. It flowers from May to June.
Ⓑ ◐ ✪ ⬤

Swedish Whitebeam
Sorbus intermedia
Up to 15m. This deciduous tree has a short trunk and a dense, broadly domed crown. Its toothed leaves are elliptical in outline, but shallowly lobed one third of the way to the mid-rib, though lobes near the leaf base are often deeper. The upper surface is smooth and green while the lower is clothed with dense yellowish-grey wool. Its white flowers form large branched clusters. The berry-like fruits are much longer than they are broad, and ripen to red with a few small scattered lenticels. An upland species, native around the Baltic, it flowers more intensively than many Whitebeams and is commonly planted elsewhere. In some places it has become naturalized. It flowers in May.
Ⓑ ◐ ⬤ ✪

Quivering in the breeze, this Common Whitebeam shows the pale undersides of the leaves from which the tree gets its name.

Loquat
Eriobotrya japonica
Up to 10m. This small evergreen tree sports twigs, leaves and flowers which are all densely covered with rusty brown hairs. Its leathery, toothed leaves are dark glossy green above and velvety below. Its sweet-tasting fruits resemble apricots but are elliptical to pear-shaped, and each contains several large seeds. Native to China, it has been widely planted in the Mediterranean region as a fruit tree and sometimes further north for ornament. It flowers from April to June.
✪

Snowy Mespil
Amelanchier ovalis
Up to 3m. This deciduous shrub has blackish bark and downy, young twigs. Its leaves are small and oval, finely toothed and initially white-downy beneath, later becoming hairless. The flowers have distinctive, narrow, widely spaced white petals which have woolly hair beneath. The bluish-black fruit is fleshy and sweet. It is a plant found on rocky slopes and crevices, mountains and open woods, usually on limestone, up to 2400m in southern and central Europe. It flowers from April to June.
⬤ ⬤

Medlar
Mespilus germanica
Up to 6m. This small deciduous tree or shrub has a dense, spreading and tangled crown. The crinkled leaves are minutely toothed near the tip. The underside is covered with dense white hairs. Large, solitary flowers have narrow sepals which are longer than the white petals. The fruit is brown when ripe and roughly

globular, with a sunken centre surrounded by persistent sepals. The fruit is hard until frosted, when it becomes edible. Native to woods and hedges in south-eastern Europe, it is also cultivated and has become naturalized in many areas. It flowers from May to June.
Ⓑ ⬤ ✪

Common Hawthorn
Crataegus monogyna
Up to 5m, but occasionally as high as 18m. A spiny shrub or small tree, it has many branches, often starting near the base. The bark is silvery-grey and rough and the oval leaves are deeply cut into 3–7 lobes. The flowers, in flat-topped clusters, usually have white petals and sweet scents. Scarlet berry-like fruits, called haws, contain a single stony seed, and ripen in autumn. Common throughout Europe in woods and hedgerows, it is also widely planted to make hedges. This species flowers from May to June.
Ⓑ ⬤ ✪

Midland Hawthorn
Crataegus laevigata
Up to 10m. This deciduous, thorny, many branched shrub or tree is widespread in central Europe. Similar to the more frequent Common Hawthorn, it is distinguished by flowers which have two or even three styles, and two, or occasionally three, stony seeds in each fruit. Its leaves are also less deeply lobed. Growing in woods, hedges and scrub in the wild, it is planted for hedging. Pink and double-flowered cultivars are grown for ornament. It often forms hybrids with the Common Hawthorn. It flowers from April to May.
Ⓑ ◐ ✪

USES OF TREES	⚙	🏠	🔥	🍴	🪑	🌲
Service-tree		⬤	⬤		⬤	
Wild Service-tree					⬤	
Common Whitebeam			⬤		⬤	
Swedish Whitebeam			⬤			
Loquat			⬤		⬤	
Snowy Mespil			⬤			
Medlar					⬤	
Common Hawthorn						⬤
Midland Hawthorn			⬤		⬤	⬤

The key to this chart is on page 93.

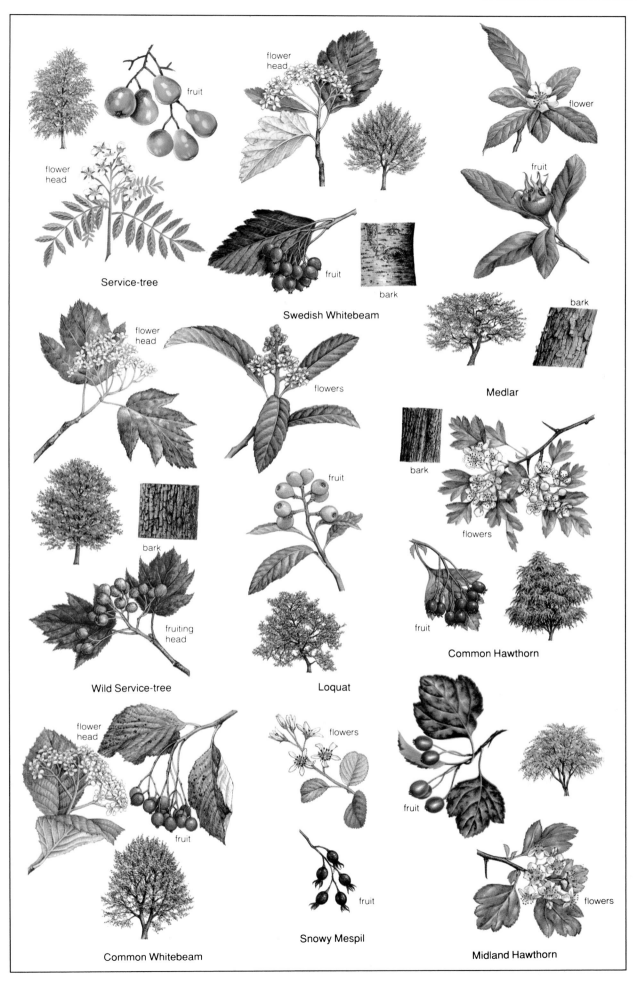

fruit

flower
head

Service-tree

flower
head

fruit

Swedish Whitebeam

bark

flower

fruit

bark

Medlar

flower
head

flowers

bark

bark

flowers

fruit

fruiting
head

Wild Service-tree

fruit

Loquat

Common Hawthorn

flower
head

flowers

fruit

fruit

fruit

Snowy Mespil

flowers

Common Whitebeam

Midland Hawthorn

111

Azarole
Crataegus azarolus
Up to 8m. A deciduous shrub or small tree, it has, at most, very few spines. It is easily recognizable by white downy hairs on young twigs and leaves. Edible fruits are round and turn yellow or orange-red when ripe. This species is native to Crete, and is widely cultivated in southern Europe as a fruit tree. It flowers from March to April.
☻◐♂

Cherry Plum
Prunus cerasifera
Up to 8m. This deciduous shrub or small glossy green tree is similar to a plum but distinguished by its hairless twigs and rather glossy leaves. The flowers are typically white but a variety with pink petals, as well as dark reddish leaves, is widely grown for ornament. Round fruits ripen yellow or red, but are not produced every year. Mainly found in south-eastern Europe in woods and hedges, it is often planted elsewhere. It flowers in March.
Ⓑ◐♂

Wild Cherry
Prunus avium
Up to 25m. This deciduous tree has smooth, shiny, reddish-brown bark, which peels off horizontally in thin, papery strips. Its dull, pale green, oval leaves droop, and unfurl only after the conspicuous, white-petalled flowers have already opened. Its globular fruits ripen to glossy dark red. Found in woods and hedges in most of Europe, it is widely grown for

its sweet or bitter fruit. Double-flowered cultivars are grown for ornament. It flowers from April to May.
Ⓑ◐♂

Blackthorn
Prunus spinosa
Up to 4m. This very thorny, much-branched, deciduous shrub, or occasionally a small tree, has black twigs and often forms dense thickets. Its pure white flowers bloom in early spring before the leaves have emerged. The rounded fruits, known as sloes, are bluish-black with a whitish bloom. Extremely astringent, they are used to make jam and wine, and to flavour gin. It is common in hedges, woods and banks on most soils, but it avoids heavy shade. This species flowers from April to May.
Ⓑ◐♂

Bird Cherry
Prunus padus
Up to 15m. This deciduous tree or shrub has strong-smelling bark, which often peels in bands. The heavily-scented flowers are borne in drooping clusters. Common in woods and beside streams, this species prefers limestone soils. Several of its cultivars are planted as ornamentals. This tree flowers in May.
Ⓑ◐♂

Cherry Laurel
Prunus laurocerasus
Up to 6m. This evergreen shrub or small tree often has several stems. The oblong leaves are large, thick and leathery, smelling of bitter almonds when crushed.

Wild Cherry or Gean is basically a woodland tree, but birds carry its seeds all over the place and it springs up in many habitats.

Creamy-white flowers are borne in long upright spikes. A poisonous plant, it is native to the woodlands and thickets of the eastern Balkan Peninsula. Tolerant of shade and widely grown in other parts of Europe, it often becomes established and naturalized. It flowers from April to May.
Ⓑ◐♂

PEA FAMILY

This very large family (Leguminosae) contains numerous trees and shrubs, many of which are popular ornamentals. There are deciduous and evergreen species. The leaves are pinnate, composed of three or more leaflets. In most of the species the flowers are pea-like and grouped in loose clusters. The fruit is a pod.

Carob
Ceratonia siliqua
Up to 10m. This is a drought resistant, evergreen tree. Its leathery leaves consist of 2–5 pairs of oval to almost circular leaflets which are notched at the tips. Greenish flowers are borne in short spikes, with males and females on different trees. They have no

petals, and the sepals soon fall. The pods contain seeds buried in sugary pulp. Native to the Mediterranean region, it is naturalized in some areas. This tree flowers from August to October.
☻

Silver Wattle
Acacia dealbata
Up to 30m. This silvery evergreen has delicate, feathery foliage. The leaves are divided into 8–20 pairs of segments, each segment with 30–50 pairs of leaflets. Tiny, yellow tubular flowers are crowded into globular heads. Native to south-eastern Australia, this species has been planted for timber and soil stabilization in southern Europe and is widely naturalized there.
◐♂☙

Golden Wreath
Acacia cyanophylla
Up to 10m. This evergreen tree or shrub has leathery, bluish foliage. The drooping, narrow leaves are often curved. Globular flower heads are up to 1–2cm across and the pods are constricted between each seed. Native to western Australia, it has been widely planted in dry coastal parts of the Mediterranean. It flowers from March to May.
♂☙

USES OF TREES	⚙	🏠	🪓	🍴	🪑	🌲
Azarole				●		
Cherry Plum		●		●		●
Wild Cherry	●	●		●		
Blackthorn				●		
Bird Cherry		●		●		
Cherry Laurel		●				●
Carob			●			
Silver Wattle	●	●	●			
Golden Wreath		●	●			

The key to this chart is on page 93.

flowers

flowers

flowers

fruit

Azarole

Blackthorn

fruit

Carob

fruit

flower head

flowers

flowers

pink variety

fruit

Cherry Plum

flower head

fruit

Bird Cherry

fruit

bark

Silver Wattle

flowers

flower head

flowers

bark

fruit

Wild Cherry

fruit

Cherry Laurel

fruit

Golden Wreath

113

Judas-tree
Cercis siliquastrum
Up to 10m. A very striking deciduous tree, it has upwardly angled, spreading branches and one or more slim trunks, with grey-black bark. Its leaves are rounded, heart-shaped and bluish when young. Flowers appear before the leaves and often grow directly from the trunk. Seed-pods are up to 10cm long, and brown when ripe. Found in rocky areas all over the Mediterranean, it is often planted elsewhere. It flowers from April to May.
☻

Scotch Laburnum
Laburnum alpinus
Up to 10m. A deciduous shrub or small tree, its twigs are green and hairless, except when young. The long flower-spike has 15–40 flowers. The pods stay on the tree after the seeds are shed. Found in mountain areas in southern and central Europe, it is often planted elsewhere for ornament. All parts of the tree are poisonous, especially the seeds. It flowers from May to June.
Ⓑ✪☻

Common Laburnum
Laburnum anagyroides
Up to 7m. A tree with arching branches, it bears numerous pendulous flower spikes. It is similar to the Scotch Laburnum, but its green twigs retain their early covering of silky hairs and the roughly elliptical leaflets are dull greyish-green. The pods are 4–6cm, and dark brown when ripe with black seeds. Like the Scotch Laburnum, the tree is highly poisonous.

Native to the mountains of southern and central Europe, it is now widely grown for ornament and often becomes naturalized. It flowers from May to June.
Ⓑ❍❂

False Acacia
Robinia pseudacacia
Up to 25m. This medium-sized tree occasionally suckers to form fairly dense thickets. Individual trees have a broad crown. The pinnate leaves have spiny stipules and up to 20 elliptical leaflets. Up to 25 white flowers are borne in clusters in leaf axils and the brown pods are 10cm long. This native of North America has been widely planted in Europe and has become naturalized in southern and western regions. It flowers from June to July.
Ⓑ❍❂

Broom
Cytisus scoparius
Up to 2m. This branched deciduous shrub is more or less hairless, with ridged stems. The leaves vary from single stalkless leaflets on young twigs to stalked, trifoliate leaves on older wood. Its yellow flowers are 20mm, on 10mm stalks, and are followed by 2.5–4cm black pods. It is found on heathland and in open woodland. It flowers from June to September.
Ⓑ🌰❍✿☺

Spanish Broom
Spartium junceum
Up to 3m. This is an upright shrub with greyish-green, smooth, round stems. Its small, elliptical leaves soon fall, the work of

photosynthesis being carried out by the green stems. The scented flowers are a rich golden-yellow colour, 20–25mm, and form a loose spike. The pods turn black when ripe. Found in rocky areas and on scrub, it is also grown in gardens, and often becomes naturalized in southern Europe. It flowers from May to July.
Ⓑ🌰❂☺

Gorse
Ulex europaeus
Up to 2.5m. This evergreen, much-branched shrub is often as broad as it is tall. It has upright, sparsely hairy, main branches. The leaves are recognizable only on young plants; on older plants they become changed into very sharp, deeply furrowed spines that measure up to 2.5cm long. The flowers measure 15mm, and are borne in leaf axils on short, hairy stalks and smell strongly of coconut. Its small black pods split explosively with a sharp snap on warm summer days. Also known as furze, it is common in grassy places and on heaths. It flowers all year, but chiefly from March to June.
Ⓑ🌰❂☺

Gorse is a tough shrub, but it is killed by severe frost and is absent from the higher and more exposed hillsides.

MAHOGANY FAMILY

This is an economically important family (Meliaceae). Most species, including the mahoganies, are found in the tropics, and only one occurs in Europe. All members of the family have twice-pinnate leaves and flowers that are borne in large, branched clusters.

Persian Lilac
Melia azedarach
Up to 15m. A slender, often short-lived, deciduous tree or shrub, it is native to eastern Asia. It is recognizable by glossy green, twice-pinnate leaves with small, oval, toothed leaflets. Its flowers are also distinctive; they are fragrant, with spreading lilac petals and 10 stamens fused to form a violet tube. Long-stalked, globular fruits turn yellow when ripe, and remain on the tree long after the leaves have fallen. Often grown in southern Europe for ornament in parks, or as a street tree, it has become naturalized in places. It flowers in June.
❂

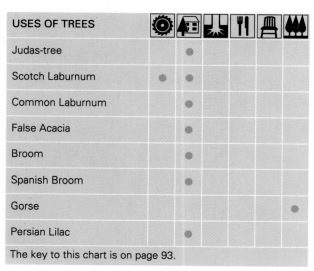

USES OF TREES	⚙	🏠	🔥	🍴	🪑	🌲
Judas-tree		●				
Scotch Laburnum	●	●				
Common Laburnum		●				
False Acacia		●				
Broom		●				
Spanish Broom		●				
Gorse						●
Persian Lilac		●				

The key to this chart is on page 93.

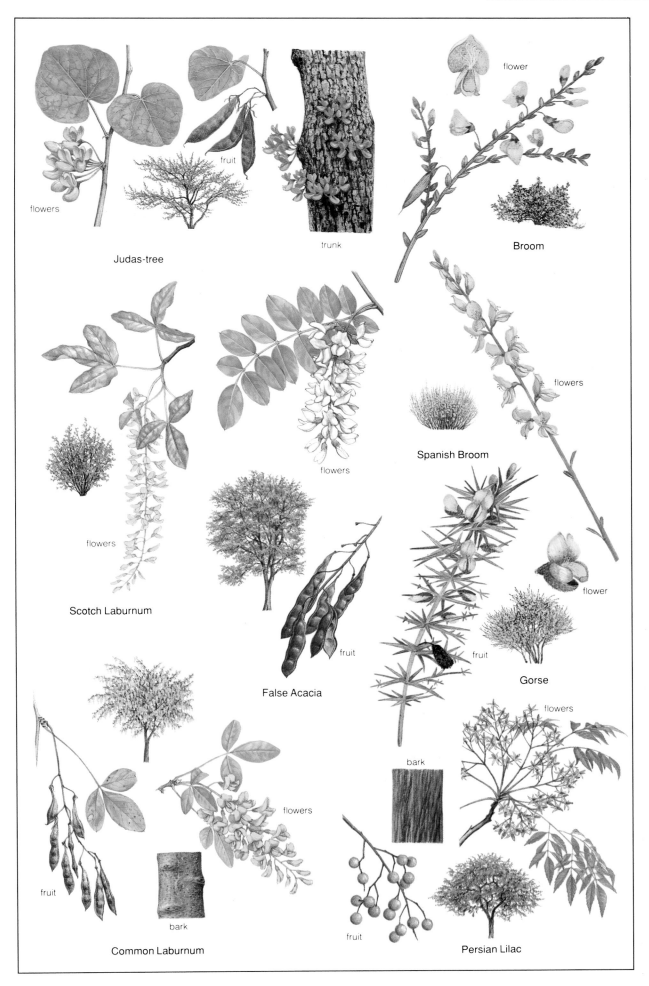

flower

flowers

fruit

trunk

Broom

Judas-tree

flowers

Spanish Broom

flowers

flowers

Scotch Laburnum

fruit

False Acacia

flower

fruit

Gorse

flowers

bark

fruit

fruit

bark

Common Laburnum

Persian Lilac

115

CASHEW FAMILY

Spread throughout the warmer regions of the world, this family (Anacardiaceae) includes the Cashew, Mango and Poison ivy. Altogether it contains about 600 species of trees and shrubs, most of which produce toxic resins that may be exuded or even leak out during rain, sometimes causing severe skin rashes. The European species, which include Sumach and Pistacio, mainly occur in dry scrubland. The leaves are usually pinnate, with or without a single leaflet at the tip. The small flowers of this family generally have parts in fives, although the petals are sometimes absent. The fruits are fleshy or stony; many are commercially important.

Smoke-tree
Cotinus coggygria
Up to 3m, occasionally 5m. This dense shrub has widely spreading branches and frequently forms a dome that is considerably wider than it is high. Its few small, yellowish, fertile flowers are in loose, branched, pyramidal clusters, and interspersed with numerous sterile flowers. After flowering, the flower-stalks elongate and become feathery as silky, and spreading hairs develop, giving the plant a pinkish-grey appearance. An aromatic shrub found on hills, rocky slopes, banks and in open woodland, it is a native of central and southern Europe, where it thrives on poor soil. Its cultivated varieties with purple foliage are popular in gardens. This shrub flowers from May to July.
☻❂

Mastic-tree
Pistacia lentiscus
Up to 3m, occasionally 8m. An aromatic shrub, or occasionally a small tree, this species can be distinguished from the closely related Turpentine-tree by its evergreen, pinnate leaves with narrow leaflets and spine-like tips. The leaf stalk is narrowly winged. Its yellowish or purplish flowers occur in dense, spike-like clusters – male and female flowers are found on separate plants. The globular fruits turn black when ripe. It grows in similar habitats to the Turpentine-tree and hybridizes with it. Mastic gum, obtained from the sap, is used in medicine, varnishes and chewing gum. It flowers from April to June.
☻

Like many trees, the Horse Chestnut displays its beauty to the full when unhindered by neighbouring trees.

Turpentine-tree
Pistacia terebinthus
Up to 10m. A shrub or tree with resiniferous twigs. Its deciduous pinnate leaves have oval leaflets with a single leaflet at the tip. Greenish-brown flowers occur in spreading clusters. The edible, egg-shaped fruits ripen to a bluish bloom. Native to open woods and rocky slopes in the Mediterranean region, it commonly occurs on dry limestone soils. It flowers from March to July.
☻

HORSE-CHESTNUT FAMILY

This very small family (Hippocastanaceae) contains only 15 trees, nearly all of them horse-chestnuts; in America they are called buckeyes. Typically tall, spreading, deciduous trees, they have palmate leaves and flowers that are grouped in large, conical clusters. The fruit consists of a large, brown seed – the familiar conker – which is enclosed in a thick,

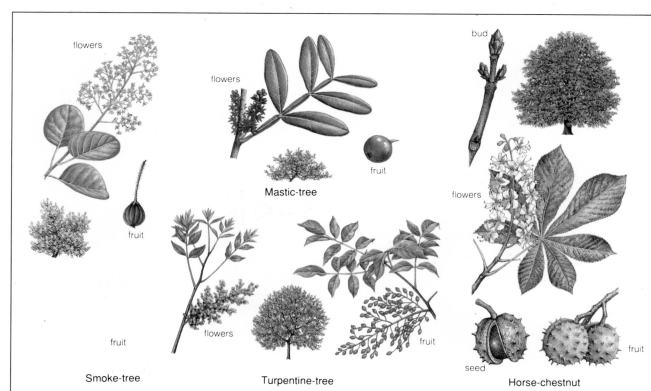

Smoke-tree

Mastic-tree

Turpentine-tree

Horse-chestnut

sometimes spiny husk. In contrast to the unrelated Sweet Chestnut, the fruit is not edible. A feature characteristic of all horse-chestnuts is the large and very sticky winter buds.

Horse-chestnut
Aesculus hippocastanum
Up to 25m. This deciduous, broad-crowned tree is well known for its sticky winter buds. The large palmate leaves have 5–7 leaflets, and 'candles' of flowers up to 30cm long appear with the leaves. Each flower is 2cm across, white with pink spots. Prickly fruits contain one or more shining brown conkers. Native to mountain woods in the Balkans, it is widely planted elsewhere and often naturalized. It flowers from May to June.
Ⓑ Ⓞ ✪

MAPLE FAMILY

A family (Aceraceae) of just over 100 trees, most of them maples. They are renowned for their spectacular autumn colour. A few species are evergreen. Their leaves have palmate-spreading lobes or occasionally are pinnate and divided into two rows of leaflets.

Field Maple
Acer campestre
Up to 26m. A deciduous tree, it is often seen only as a hedgerow shrub. The leaves are palmate with 3–5 lobes, measuring about 10cm across. They are tinged pink when young and turn yellow or amber in autumn. The small, upright clusters of flowers which appear with the leaves, finally form fruits with horizontally spreading wings, in clusters of four pairs. Common in hedges and woods, mainly on chalky soil, it is a prized source of fine timber. This maple flowers from May to June.
Ⓑ Ⓞ ✪

Montpelier Maple
Acer monspessulanum
Up to 12m. This deciduous tree or small shrub has three-lobed leaves – the bottom two lobes are at 90 degrees to the middle one. Mature leaves are thick, shiny, dark green above and slightly blue tinged beneath. In autumn, they become flame orange, especially in the south. The flowers are in long-stalked, green-yellow heads. Red-flushed fruits have parallel wings. This species is scattered through a wide area, and occasionally planted, but is generally found in southern Europe. It flowers in June.
Ⓞ ✪

Norway Maple
Acer platanoides
Up to 30m. This is a tall deciduous tree, with comparatively few main branches. The stout, shiny, reddish twigs bear palmate, five-lobed leaves, tinged pink when open, and bright, shiny green when mature. In autumn, they turn yellow, and finally orange-brown, before falling. The flowers occur in upright clusters, opening before the leaves. The fruits have wings. A forest tree, found in much of Europe, it is often planted as a decorative tree, and occasionally for timber. It flowers from March to April.
Ⓑ Ⓞ ✪

Sycamore
Acer pseudoplatanus
Up to 35m. A very large deciduous tree with massive branches, it is often as wide as it is high. The large, dark-green, palmate leaves, up to 15cm long, often have a reddish tint when they open, and turn yellow in fine autumns. The yellow flowers appear before the leaves, in long dangling spikes of up to 50 flowers. The fruits have wings diverging more or less at a right angle. A native of central and southern Europe, but widely planted, it has naturalized in many places, often competing with native species. It flowers in April.
Ⓑ Ⓞ ✪

USES OF TREES	🪚	🏠	🎆	🍴	🪑	🌲
Smoke-tree			●			
Mastic-tree					●	
Turpentine-tree			●			
Horse-chestnut			●			
Field Maple	●		●			
Montpelier Maple			●			
Norway Maple	●		●			●
Sycamore	●		●			

The key to this chart is on page 93.

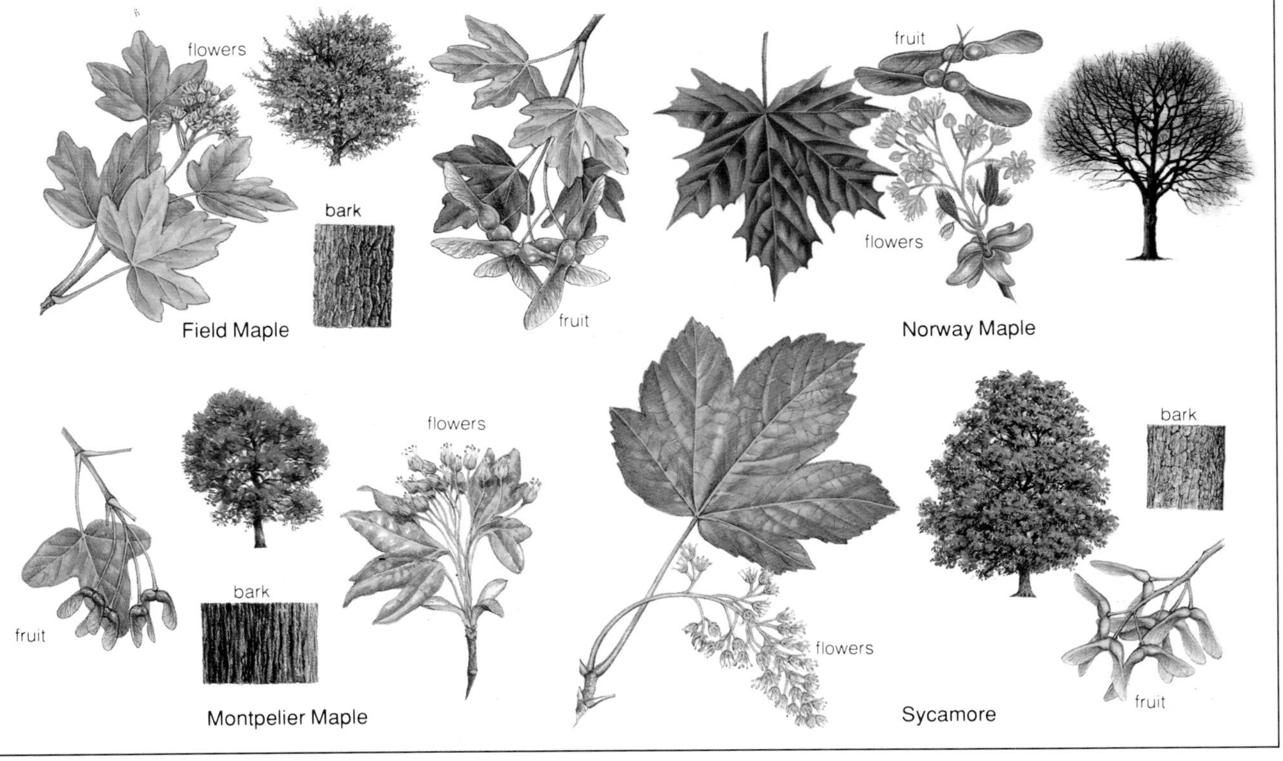

Field Maple

flowers

bark

fruit

Norway Maple

fruit

flowers

Montpelier Maple

flowers

bark

fruit

Sycamore

bark

flowers

fruit

HOLLY FAMILY

All but three of the 400 or so species in this family (Aquifoliaceae) are hollies. Small trees or shrubs, they are usually evergreen with glossy and usually prickly or spiny leaves. Old trees often produce unarmed leaves, and some species and cultivars never have prickles. Some garden forms have variegated leaves. The four-petalled flowers are either bisexual or unisexual with males and females on separate trees. The fruit is a berry. Hollies generally grow in scrubland or thickets but can also tolerate the deep shade of woods.

Holly
Ilex aquifolium
Up to 10m. This evergreen shrub is most often found in Beech or Oak woods, where it grows well despite the deep summer shade, but rarely flowers. Likes growing in open sites it may form a tree and reach double its usual height. The typical wavy, spiny leaves are dark glossy green on top, lighter underneath. Older branches have leaves which often only possess one pair of spines. Each plant is either male or female; both have white, waxy, sweet-smelling flowers. Only female plants develop red berries during autumn. Holly is commonly found in woodland and as a single tree in hedges. Native to southern and western parts of Europe, it is widely planted elsewhere. It has a long association with pre-Christian beliefs as, for example, the hiding place of wood spirits in winter. It flowers from May to June.
Ⓑ ◐ ✪

SPINDLE FAMILY

This widespread family (Celastraceae) contains about 1300 species of shrubs, trees and woody vines, but only the spindles occur in Europe. They are shrubs or small, twiggy trees with very striking fruits. These are four-lobed capsules, often brightly coloured, which open to reveal seeds covered with an equally bright or contrasting fleshy layer which attracts birds. The small, greenish flowers have the same number of sepals, petals and stamens, usually 4–5, which are attached to a fleshy, green disc.

Spindle-tree
Euonymus europaeus
Up to 5m. A small, straggly, deciduous shrub, its twigs are green when young, becoming distinctly four-angled later, with corky wings on older branches. The leaves are oval or lance-shaped, with a toothed margin. They are mid-green, but turn a spectacular yellow and crimson in autumn. The small, greenish-white flowers are borne in clusters in leaf axils, and have four widely separated petals. The flowers are usually hermaphrodite, but some plants may have only male or female flowers. The four-lobed fruits are coral pink, and split to expose bright orange seed coats. This shrub is predominantly a hedge and edge-of-woodland plant, growing on chalk soils. Its wood is very hard, and was formerly used for making spindles. Absent from the far north or south, it flowers from May to June.
Ⓑ ◐

Despite their prickly leaves, these Holly trees are regularly browsed by cattle grazing in the field. Trees growing in good light bear white flowers and female trees also grow bright red berries.

BOX FAMILY

This is a small family (Buxaceae) of about 100 evergreen shrubs and small trees of which the boxes are best known and the only members found in Europe. They have leathery leaves and unisexual flowers which lack petals. The fruits are woody capsules which split explosively to release the seeds. Boxes are popular ornamentals.

Box
Buxus sempervirens
Up to 5m. This evergreen shrub, or occasionally a small tree, often forms large thickets. Its leaves are opposite, oval or elliptical, glossy green above, paler underneath, and are carried on a short stalk. The flowers are tiny, each cluster containing one female flower surrounded by several males. The three-horned, woody capsules split explosively to shoot out black, shiny seeds. A rare plant of woodland on chalky soils, it grows well under Beech. Box is much used in formal gardens and for topiary and its wood is heavy enough to sink in water when freshly cut. The very stable wood is used for wood-carving and for making chess pieces. It flowers in April. The only other European member of the family is the rare Balearic Box (*B. balearica*), a pinkish-barked tree from Spain, the Balearic Islands and Sardinia.
Ⓑ ◐ ✪

OLEASTER FAMILY

All parts of these deciduous and often thorny shrubs or small trees are covered with minute silvery or golden scales. The tubular flowers have a calyx of either two or four-fused sepals but lack petals. The fleshy fruits are taken by birds. Most of the 50 species in this family (Elaeagnaceae) are found on dry or sandy coasts and steppes in the northern hemisphere. They are popular ornamentals.

Sea Buckthorn
Hippophae rhamnoides
Up to 10m. This spiny deciduous shrub often forms large sprawling bushes at lower height in windswept areas. The whole plant is covered with a silvery scurf. Its leaves are long and narrow, with rolled under margins. The small yellow flowers appear before the leaves, in clusters towards the ends of new branches. Male and female flowers occur on separate plants. Orange berries are formed in the autumn, and remain on the shrub all winter. Found on sand dunes, sea cliffs or gravel river banks in uplands, it is planted as an ornamental and a stabilizer. It flowers from March to April. The Oleaster (*Elaeagnus angustifolia*) is similar but has larger flowers and red berries. It is grown for ornament.
Ⓑ ◐ ◑ ✿

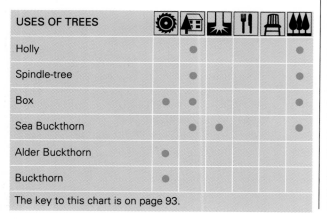

USES OF TREES	⚙	🏠	💥	🍴	🪑	🌲
Holly		●				●
Spindle-tree		●				●
Box	●	●				●
Sea Buckthorn		●	●			●
Alder Buckthorn	●					
Buckthorn	●					

The key to this chart is on page 93.

BUCKTHORN FAMILY

This world-wide family (Rhamnaceae) contains about 900 species of trees and shrubs including the edible Jujube. They are rather variable, being evergreen or deciduous, with opposite or alternate leaves. The flowers are small with parts in whorls of four or five and the fruits are berry-like or nut-like. Many species are spiny or thorny.

Alder Buckthorn
Frangula alnus
Up to 4.5m. This deciduous shrub has upright branches and oval leaves, which are bright green when young, turning red and yellow in autumn. Its small flowers appear in leaf axils, singly or in clusters, on new growth. The fruit is a berry, yellow at first, that turns to black when ripe. A plant of wet and marshy woods throughout most of Europe, its wood has been used for charcoal and also for butchers' skewers. A laxative drug can be prepared from the bark, and both the bark and the berries have been used in the preparation of dyes. This species flowers from May to June.
Ⓑ ⃝

Buckthorn
Rhamnus catharticus
Up to 10m. This deciduous shrub or small tree has spiny twigs. The leaves are more or less opposite, up to 7cm long, oval with toothed edges, and with three to four prominent lateral veins. They are bright green, and in autumn have a yellow tint. The small, sweetly scented flowers, with males and females on separate plants, are on short shoots. They are yellow-green and four-petalled. The ripe berries are black. Found in hedgerows and wooded areas on chalky soils, this species is sometimes one of the dominant shrubs of chalk downland. Extracts of the bark and the berries were used as a purgative and the wood was once used for charcoal. It flowers from May to June. The similar Mediterranean Buckthorn (*R. alaternus*) is an evergreen shrub that lacks spines.
Ⓑ ⃝ ⓦ

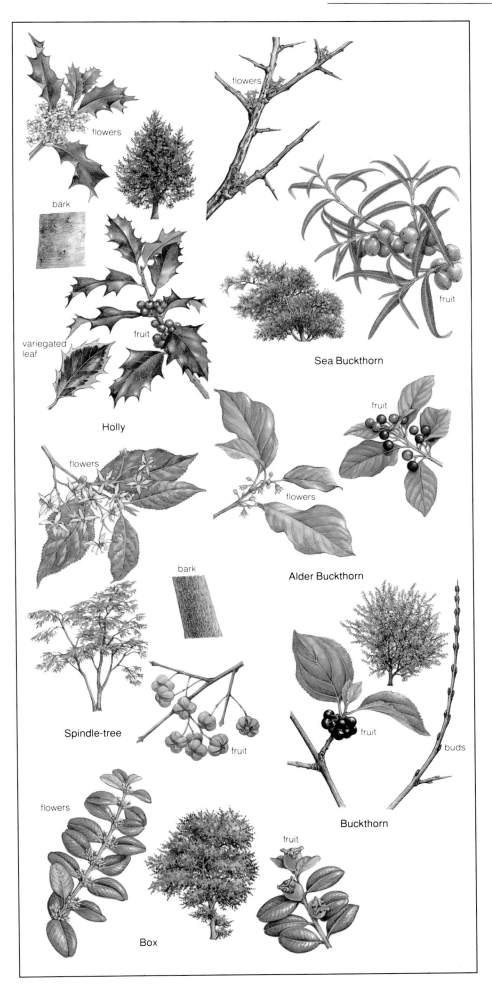

flowers

flowers

bark

variegated leaf

fruit

Holly

fruit

Sea Buckthorn

flowers

fruit

flowers

bark

Alder Buckthorn

Spindle-tree

fruit

fruit

buds

Buckthorn

flowers

fruit

Box

ROCKROSE FAMILY

Most of the 160 or so species in this essentially Mediterranean family (Cistaceae) are shrubs, some of them very low and creeping. Most grow in dry, rocky areas. Their leaves are opposite, frequently very hairy and covered with oil glands. The flowers are showy and they are made up of five sepals, two of which are often very small, and five often crumpled petals.

Narrow-leaved Cistus
Cistus monspeliensis
Up to 1m. This erect branched shrub has lance-shaped stalkless leaves. Each is dark green and shiny above, with grey hairs below; leaf margins are enrolled beneath, while glands on the surface make it feel sticky to the touch. The white-petalled flowers in one-sided clusters are relatively small. A strongly aromatic plant, it grows on dry, stony slopes and in pine woods in the Mediterranean region. It flowers from April to June.

Large Pink Cistus
Cistus incanus
Up to 1.5m. This densely branched shrub has oval to elliptical leaves, which are greyish green and hairy with undulate margins. The large, crumpled-looking flowers have five pink petals, which usually fall after just one day. Its fruit is a densely hairy capsule. This species thrives in warm, sunny places in the Mediterranean region, and is sometimes grown in gardens. It flowers from April to June.

Sage-leaved Cistus
Cistus salvifolius
Up to 1m. This small branched shrub has erect or spreading branches. Its broader, stalked leaves – which resemble those of the True Sage – distinguish it from the Narrow-leaved Cistus. They are dull green above and white-haired below and their surfaces have a wrinkled appearance. Long-stalked flowers occur in small, loose clusters of 1–3; the petals are white, often with a basal orange blotch. Also cultivated as an ornamental, it is one of the most common species in the wild, growing across the Mediterranean region in pine woods and dry, stony places. It flowers from April to June.

TAMARISK FAMILY

Most of the 87 members of this unusual family (Tamaricaceae) are tamarisks – salt-tolerant, evergreen shrubs and small trees, all of which have a wispy, feathery appearance. They are found in dry, sandy and coastal habitats. Used in the Middle East for its medicinal properties, one desert species of tamarisk is thought to have been the source of the biblical manna. The leaves, adapted to reduce water loss, are tiny and scale-like. They are spirally arranged on the stems. The flowers are also tiny, white or pink, and crowded into dense cylindrical spikes. The seeds are tufted with hairs to aid dispersal.

Lime trees, coppiced in the traditional way, send up several poles from each stool. Wood Anemones carpet the floor beneath them.

Tamarisk
Tamarix gallica
Up to 8m. This species can be a small tree, but is more often seen as a straggly shrub. Its tiny, clasping leaves are about 2mm long and lie flat to the stem, giving each branch a very distinctive appearance. The flowers are small and pink. This tree is common in south-western Europe, especially by the sea, because it tolerates salt winds. It is planted as a windbreak and stabilizer, along shingle river banks, and is also grown as an ornamental. It flowers from July to September.

LIME FAMILY

This is a mainly tropical family (Tiliaceae) of deciduous trees and shrubs. Only the limes extend into cooler north temperate regions. They have heart-shaped, alternate leaves. Their green, yellow or white flowers are very attractive to bees. The flowers are grouped in stalked clusters which arise from oblong, wing-like bracts. The small fruits are hard and nut-like. They are not related to the citrus fruits known as limes.

Small-leaved Lime
Tilia cordata
Up to 30m. This deciduous tree is dense and unevenly domed, with the branches arching downwards. The leaves are 3–8cm long and heart-shaped with short points, finely-toothed and shiny green on top. Up to 15 flowers rise in an upright cluster from the centre of a green bract. This becomes a 'wing' for wind dispersal when the fruits ripen. A tree that thrives on chalky soils throughout Europe, it is also planted for timber, and as an ornamental. This tree flowers in July.

Large-leaved Lime
Tilia platyphyllos
Up to 40m. This tree is similar in shape to the Small-leaved Lime, but with a narrow crown, and upwardly angled branches. The leaves are 6–15cm long, heart-shaped, with a short point and toothed margins. They often bear galls – reddish spikes, induced by mites in the leaf tissue. Sweet-scented flowers, 2–5 together, hang down from a yellow-green bract – the 'wing' of the eventual fruit. Found on chalky soils throughout Europe, it is often planted in parks, or as a street tree. It flowers in June.

Common Lime
Tilia x vulgaris
Up to 45m. A hybrid between the Large and Small-leaved Limes, this tree is tall and unevenly domed. The leaves are 5–10cm long, with a short point and rounded teeth, and are only just heart-shaped at the base. They also often bear galls, just like the Large-leaved Lime. The flowers hang in clusters of 5–10. Found naturally wherever both parents occur, this tree is also common in streets, despite its tendency to attract aphids, which feed on the sap and drip sticky honeydew as a consequence. It flowers in July.

USES OF TREES	⚙	🏚	🎆	🍴	🪑	🌲
Narrow-leaved Cistus		●				
Large Pink Cistus		●				
Sage-leaved Cistus		●				
Tamarisk		●	●			●
Small-leaved Lime	●	●				
Large-leaved Lime	●	●				
Common Lime	●	●				

The key to this chart is on page 93.

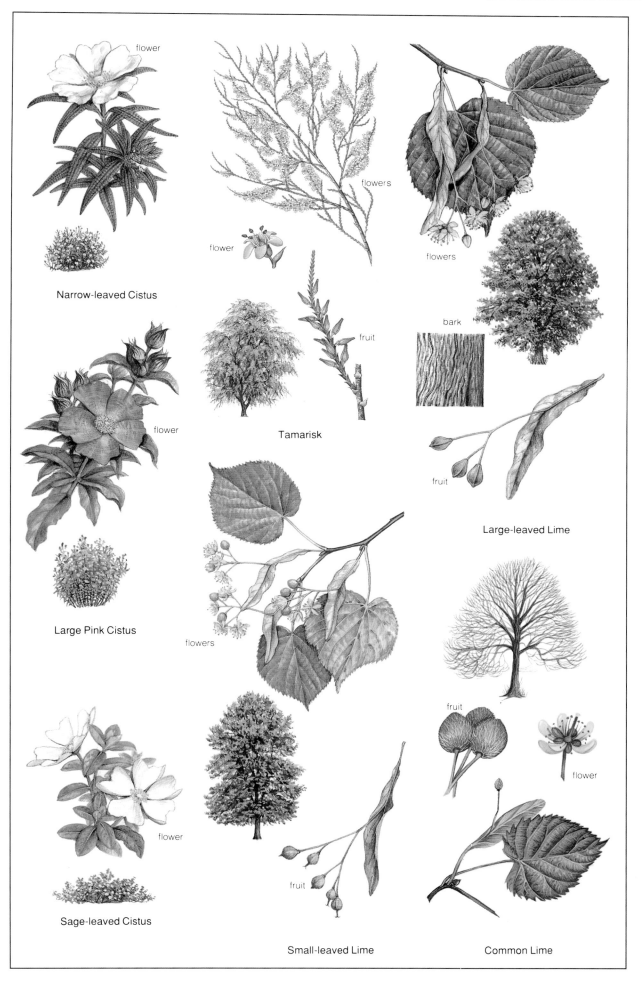

flower

Narrow-leaved Cistus

flowers

flower

fruit

Tamarisk

flowers

flower

Large Pink Cistus

flower

Sage-leaved Cistus

flowers

Small-leaved Lime

bark

fruit

Large-leaved Lime

fruit

flower

Common Lime

121

DOGWOOD FAMILY

The Dogwoods make up the largest group within this family (Cornaceae) of 90 or so small trees and shrubs. The flowers are typically crowded into clusters, which are often surrounded by large, petal-like bracts. The fruit is berry-like. A number of species are also grown for their brightly coloured stems which are especially attractive in winter.

Dogwood
Cornus sanguinea
Up to 5m. This shrub forms dense thickets. Its leaves are opposite, oval, pointed, and display prominent veins. The flowers are four-petalled, greenish-yellow, and have an unpleasant smell that attracts pollinating flies. Black, waxy berries follow. In winter, the new wood shows blood-red. It is a common shrub on chalky soil. The wood has been used for skewers, burnt for charcoal and the oil from its berries was once used as lamp-oil. It flowers in June.

Cornelian Cherry
Cornus mas
Up to 8m. This small tree has a short trunk and spreading or downswept branches. Its clusters of yellow, four-petalled flowers are borne on bare twigs in early spring. Pairs of oval, long-pointed leaves with curved veins appear later. The red fruits are cylindrical, with edible flesh surrounding a single stony seed. Native to central and south-eastern Europe, it has become naturalized elsewhere. It flowers from February to March.

MYRTLE FAMILY

A major source of spices and oils, this family (Myrtaceae) contains myrtles, cloves and the gums or eucalyptuses of Australia. All have aromatic, evergreen foliage. Myrtles have opposite leaves, while gums produce paired juvenile and alternate adult leaves.

Tasmanian Blue Gum
Eucalyptus globulus
Up to 40m. A fast-growing tree, it has smooth grey-blue bark that peels every year. The resinous foliage smells of eucalyptus oil. Bluish juvenile leaves are opposite and lack stalks, while dark-green adult leaves are stalked and measure up to 30cm long and 4cm wide. Covered by a pale waxy cap in bud, each flower has many stamens. The fruit is woody and ribbed. Grown in Mediterranean areas for shade, timber or wood pulp, this species is now very common. It flowers from September to December.

Myrtle
Myrtus communis
Up to 3m. This evergreen, aromatic shrub has stalkless, dark, glossy green leaves, oval to elliptical in shape with a short point. Stalked flowers are borne in the axils of the leaves. They are about 2cm across, with five rounded white petals. The numerous stamens are arranged in several rings. After pollination, the single ovary develops as an edible berry. Myrtle is native to southern Europe, but is often planted in northern areas. It flowers from June to August.

Pomegranates can often be seen growing on waste ground and roadsides in the Mediterranean region.

POMEGRANATE FAMILY

This family (Punicaceae) consists of two species of small, deciduous trees, one of which is confined to the island of Socotra off the Horn of Africa. The other species is the Pomegranate, long cultivated in Europe and Asia for its edible fruit and beautiful flowers.

Pomegranate
Punica granatum
Up to 8m. This small deciduous tree or shrub has a short trunk and a bushy crown of upwardly angled branches. The twigs are usually four-angled, and may bear spines. The leaves are 2–8cm long, oblong or oval, opposite, shiny and almost stalkless. The showy flowers are up to 4cm across. They have 5–7 crumpled, scarlet or white petals and numerous stamens. The fruit, up to 8cm in diameter, is globular. It ripens a reddish brown and contains numerous seeds in a yellow or purple pulp. A native of Asia Minor, it has been cultivated in Europe for many centuries and is often a naturalized species in the Mediterranean region. It flowers from June to September.

STORAX FAMILY

This small family (Styracaceae) contains trees and shrubs with resinous bark. Most are from the warmer regions of the world and many are grown as ornamentals.

Storax
Styrax officinalis
Up to 7m. All parts of this small tree are covered with white, star-shaped hairs. The oval, blunt leaves are especially hairy beneath. Fragrant, white, bell-shaped flowers, each with five to seven white petals, form hanging clusters at the tips of the twigs. The grey, egg-shaped fruits are tipped with the slender style and cupped by the persistent sepals. Native to woods and thickets from Italy eastwards, it is sometimes naturalized elsewhere. It flowers from April to May.

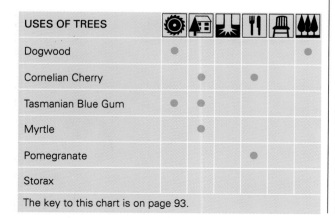

USES OF TREES					
Dogwood	●				●
Cornelian Cherry		●		●	
Tasmanian Blue Gum	●	●			
Myrtle		●			
Pomegranate				●	
Storax					
The key to this chart is on page 93.					

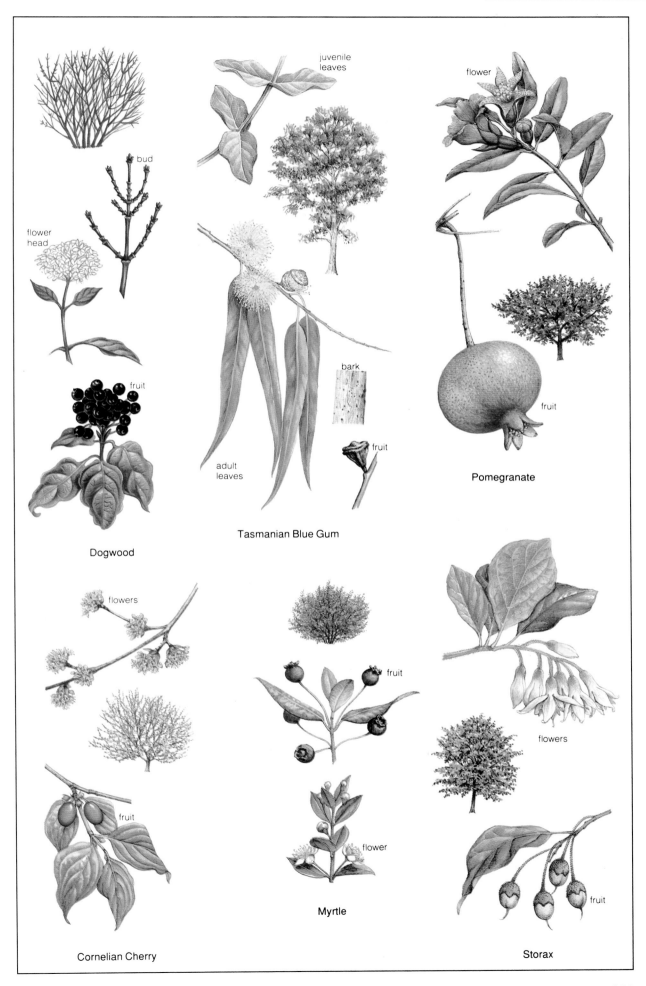

juvenile
leaves

flower

bud

flower
head

fruit

bark

fruit

adult
leaves

fruit

Pomegranate

Dogwood

Tasmanian Blue Gum

flowers

fruit

flowers

fruit

flower

fruit

Cornelian Cherry

Myrtle

Storax

Olives have been cultivated for thousands of years, and many of the trees in olive groves like this are hundreds of years old.

OLIVE FAMILY

These evergreen or deciduous trees and shrubs (Family Oleaceae) are found throughout Europe in a variety of habitats. Some species, such as the Ash, are northern forest trees while the Olive is typical of Mediterranean regions. Many are ornamentals, others are of economic importance. The leaves, in opposite pairs, are either simple or divided into two rows of leaflets. The four petals often form a tube, but in some species both petals and sepals are absent. The fruit is either fleshy or dry and is sometimes winged.

Ash
Fraxinus excelsior
Up to 40m. A high-domed, deciduous tree with bark that is smooth or cracked, and pale grey. Its winter buds are black. The opposite leaves are pinnate, with 9–13 leaflets, appearing after the flowers. The small flowers have no sepals or petals and some are hermaphrodite, but most are either male or female. The two sexes occur in separate clusters and some trees are single-sexed. The fruits, called keys, are winged to aid dispersal. Widespread in hedgerows and mixed woods, this plant is commonly found on chalky soils, but less so on acid soils. It sometimes forms pure ashwoods, and is also planted for its tough, white timber. Several varieties are grown as ornamentals, such as the cultivar 'Pendula', which is grafted to the trunk of the common form. Ash flowers from April to May.
Ⓑ Ⓞ

Manna Ash
Fraxinus ornus
Up to 24m. This tree is similar to the more common Ash, but is identified in winter by its brown (not black) buds. Its pinnate leaves have 5–9 leaflets. The creamy white fragrant flowers are in large pyramidal heads. Each flower is hermaphrodite, with four narrow petals. A woodland species, it grows wild in central Europe and in the Mediterranean region. Edible gum, known as manna, is obtained from cuts made in the bark. It flowers in May.
Ⓞ Ⓧ

Privet
Ligustrum vulgare
Up to 5m. This many-stemmed, large, straggly shrub is totally deciduous during very hard winters, but largely evergreen during mild ones. The leaves are lance-shaped, up to 6cm long, and glossy green on a short stalk. Strongly scented white flowers occur in dense clusters at the ends of twigs. The fruit is a shiny black berry. It is commonly found in hedges and scrubland, especially on chalky soils. It flowers from June to July.
Ⓑ Ⓞ Ⓧ Ⓜ

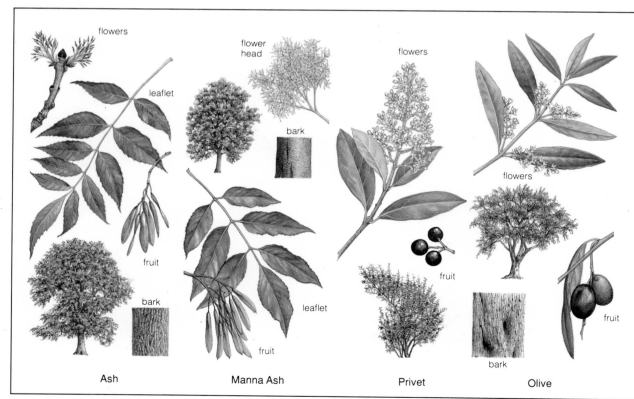

Ash — flowers — leaflet — fruit — bark

Manna Ash — flower head — bark — leaflet — fruit

Privet — flowers — fruit — bark

Olive — flowers — fruit

Olive
Olea europaea
Up to 15m. A very gnarled evergreen tree, often with a short trunk that is deeply pitted with holes on old trees. The bark is silvery-grey. Silvery twigs bear opposite, lance-shaped leaves, that are grey-green on top and paler beneath. The white flowers form long spikes from the leaf axils. The oily fruit is green at first, but ripens to almost black in the second year. This is a a a tree of open woods and rocky scrub all over the Mediterranean region. Wild trees are spiny and smaller than cultivated trees, whose fruits yield olive oil. It flowers from July to August.
☻✿

HEATH FAMILY

Most members of this family (Ericaceae) are large or small shrubs, together with a few small trees. Their leaves are either small and needle-like or much larger, broad, glossy and leathery. Four or five petals are usually fused for most of their length to form an urn-shaped flower, but in rhododendrons they are fused only at the base, producing a bell-shaped flower. The fruit is a berry or a capsule.

Alpenrose
Rhododendron ferrugineum
Up to 1m. An evergreen, well-branched shrub, this species is usually bushy. The leaves measure up to 2.5cm long, and are elliptical, deep shiny green with rolled-under margins. Their undersides are covered in a rusty-red down. The flowers form in clusters, at the ends of the branches. Each flower is about 2cm across, bell-shaped, and varies in colour from pale pink to deep rose. This is a plant of mountain slopes up to 3200m, scrubland, or open woods. It often forms dense thickets. It flowers from May to August.
☻

Rhododendron
Rhododendron ponticum
Up to 10m. A large invasive evergreen shrub, with glossy green leaves, up to 12cm long, which are oval or elliptical, and dark green in colour above, paler underneath. The flowers occur in clusters of up to 15, at the ends of branches and measure about 5cm across. Native to Asia Minor, it has become naturalized in many places, often forming huge thickets. This shrub flowers from May to June.
Ⓑ☻◐④

Strawberry-tree
Arbutus unedo
Up to 9m. This shrub or small, dense evergreen tree has red bark, which peels in strips. Bell-shaped flowers are borne in hanging clusters, followed by warty berries, 2cm in diameter, which are at first yellow, then turn red. They ripen slowly so that flowers can appear alongside last year's ripe fruits. It is found in evergreen woods and dry, scrubby places mostly in the Mediterranean region and along mild western coasts. This species is frequently planted as an ornamental. It flowers from October to November.
Ⓑ☻④

Tree Heath
Erica arborea
Up to 8m. This is usually a large, straggling, evergreen shrub, with several stems, but it sometimes forms a small tree. Its leaves are small, in whorls, with the margins tightly rolled over. The flowers are borne on short branches off the main stem on shoots about 10cm long. These give the appearance of a dense mass of flowers. The flowers themselves are ash-white, urn-shaped and fragrant. This is a typical species of the Mediterranean scrub. It is also cultivated as an ornamental. It flowers from March to April.
☻

USES OF TREES	⊙	🏠	⚒	🍴	🪑	🌲
Ash	●	●				
Manna Ash				●		
Privet		●				
Olive				●		
Alpenrose		●				
Rhododendron		●				●
Strawberry-tree		●		●		
Tree Heath		●				
The key to this chart is on page 93.						

flowers

fruit

flower head

flowers

flowers

bark

fruit

Alpenrose

Rhododendron

Strawberry-tree

Tree Heath

The DECIDUOUS FORESTS

Deciduous forests, dominated by beech, oak, and other trees which drop their leaves for the winter, once covered much of Europe (see p. 6), but most of this natural forest cover had disappeared by Roman times and only fragments now remain. Most of today's deciduous woodland is secondary woodland, which has grown up during the last few centuries on land that was once used for agriculture. This secondary woodland has a good mixture of trees, and in Britain it includes a fair amount of the introduced sycamore. Some deciduous woodlands have also been planted – notably the Sweet Chestnut forests of France, which are grown for timber as well as for their nuts.

The ancient woodlands, or wildwood, have existed for over 8000 years – ever since the land warmed up after the last glaciation. They are usually dominated by just one or two species – such as beech, oak, lime, ash, and hornbeam – and the dominant species depends largely on the soil. Beech, for example, dominates on the lighter soils, whereas the heavier soils of the lowlands are dominated by oaks. Climate also helps determine the nature of the forest. Birches are pioneer trees, usually paving the way for larger trees and then dying out, but in the far north, where the climate prevents other trees from growing, birches form permanent woods in their own right. Sweet Chestnut dominates some of the drier woodlands in south-eastern Europe.

ABOVE: *This beechwood, seen in its autumn colours, shows the lack of ground vegetation resulting from the dense summer shade.*
LEFT: *The Hazel Dormouse usually nests in dense shrubs in the summer and thrives best in coppiced woodland.*

Woodland Management

The ancient woodlands are not entirely natural. In fact, many have survived only because they produced valuable timber and they show numerous signs of human activity. The present-day tree trunks often spring from huge stools, showing that the woods have been coppiced on many occasions. But coppicing does not destroy the woodland because the trees are cut down on a strict rotation, and are allowed to grow again. So the continuity of the community has been maintained, resulting in the rich flora and fauna of the woods. Thick carpets of Bluebells and Wood Anemones, together with certain lichens and insects, are sure indications of wildwood. Coppicing has almost disappeared from Britain, although it is still carried out in many continental woods, and is used on many nature reserves. A rotational coppice regime with tree growth in various areas ranging from one to 20 years is marvellous for wildlife.

The Bonnet Mycena plays a major role in the decay of tree stumps and branches on the woodland floor.

being able to manufacture food in the winter if it is not too cold. The shrub layer is very rich in birds and insects and also shelters various small mammals such as dormice. Below the shrubs is the field layer, consisting of ferns and all the familiar woodland flowers, such as Bluebells, Primroses and Wild Daffodils. Most of these flowers appear in the spring, before the tree leaves expand and cut off the light. The richest flora develops in oak and ash woods, where the tree leaves open relatively late in the year and cast less shade.

The lowest forest layer – the ground layer – consists of mosses and lichens and the all-important fungi, although the latter are generally concealed in the leaf litter and are evident only at certain times of the year. This is the forest's recycling department, where the fungi, assisted by bacteria and various beetles and other small animals, break down the fallen leaves and twigs and even the stumps of dead trees. They return carbon dioxide to the atmosphere, and minerals are returned to the soil where the plant roots can take them up again ready to form another year's crop of leaves and flowers.

Forest Layers

The forest community consists of several distinct layers, each with its characteristic assemblage of animal life. The uppermost layer, formed by the crowns of the trees, is the canopy. This is where the sun's energy enters the forest food chains, converting carbon dioxide from the air into food in the tree leaves. Many insects live in the canopy, feeding on the leaves, flowers and fruits of the trees, and being eaten in their turn by the numerous woodland birds, especially the tits and the summer-visiting warblers. Most of the trees are wind-pollinated and they flower early in the year, before their leaves open fully and obstruct the drifting pollen.

Some way below the canopy there is usually a shrub layer, which is often dominated by Hazel and Common Hawthorn. The shrub layer is poorly developed in beechwoods because the beeches cast such a dense shade, although there may be a few evergreen species, such as Holly and Yew. These evergreens survive by virtue of

The Lesser Horseshoe Bat emerges soon after sunset, engaging in low, erratic flight.

Wildlife of an Oakwood

 1 Great Spotted Woodpecker
 2 Meripulus giganteus
 3 Wood Sorrel
 4 Honey Fungus
 5 Primrose
 6 Bluebells
 7 Hazel
 8 Stag Beetle
 9 Silver-washed Fritillary
10 Bramble
11 Polecat
12 Wood Warbler
13 Wood Pigeon
14 Holly
15 Male Fern
16 Ivy

BUDDLEIA FAMILY

A small, mainly tropical, family (Buddlejaceae). buddleias are deciduous shrubs or small trees. Their fragrant flowers have a bell-shaped calyx and a tubular corolla.

Buddleia
Buddleja davidii
Up to 5m. This deciduous, shrub has long, slender twigs bearing spear-shaped leaves, green above and white-woolly beneath. Terminal flower heads are long and pointed. Each flower is pale lilac to deep violet with an orange ring at its mouth. Native to China, this species is naturalized in western and central Europe on wasteland. Widely grown in gardens, its fragrant, nectar-rich flowers attract many butterflies. It flowers from July to October.
Ⓑ ✿

HONEYSUCKLE FAMILY

As well as trees and shrubs, this family (Caprifoliaceae) includes a few herbaceous plants and woody climbers such as the honeysuckles. They are evergreen or deciduous with opposite leaves. Five-petalled flowers are arranged in pairs or in large circular heads. The berries are bright red or purplish-black when they ripen.

Elder
Sambucus nigra
Up to 10m. This deciduous shrub or small tree has greyish-brown, corky bark. Its pinnate leaves have two or three pairs of serrated leaflets with one at the tip. They release a sickly smell when crushed. Small, creamy-white, fragrant flowers are crowded into broad, much branched, flat-topped clusters. The black, berry-like fruits are edible. Widespread in Europe, it grows in woods, hedges and on waste areas. It flowers from June to July.
Ⓑ ○ ✿ ⏏

Red-berried Elder
Sambucus racemosa
Up to 4m. This deciduous shrub has greyish bark, and is similar in habit to its relative. It has greenish-white flowers in egg-shaped or conical clusters. The bright red fruits are inedible. Native to mountainous areas of central Europe, it grows in deciduous or coniferous woodland and shady, rocky places. It is also planted for ornament in gardens, where cultivars exist, and it has become naturalized in the north. It flowers from April to June.
Ⓑ ○ ④ ✿

Guelder Rose
Viburnum opulus
Up to 4m. This deciduous shrub has grey, hairless twigs bearing palmate, three- or five-lobed leaves, deeply toothed at their margins. White flowers are carried in much branched, flat-topped clusters with small, fertile flowers towards the centre and a ring of conspicuous large, sterile flowers at the rim. Globular, berry-like, poisonous fruits are glossy bright red. Widespread in Europe, it grows in woods, hedges and among scrub, preferring damp ground. It flowers from June to July.
Ⓑ ○

The leaves of the European Fan-palm are up to a metre across. Male and female flowers develop on separate plants.

Wayfaring-tree
Viburnum lantana
Up to 6m. This deciduous shrub has oval, pointed and serrated leaves with a wrinkled surface, green above and densely grey-hairy beneath. The small, creamy-white, fragrant flowers are carried in flat-topped clusters. Flattened, poisonous fruits ripen first red, then black. Widespread in central and southern Europe, it grows in woods, hedges, among scrub and on rocky ground, and prefers lime-rich soils. It is sometimes planted for ornament. This tree flowers from April to June.
Ⓑ ○ ⏏

PALM FAMILY

Most of the 2600 or so palms (Palmae) are tropical or subtropical trees; few grow in cooler regions and only two species are native to Europe. Palms are economically very important in many areas of the world, providing a variety of useful materials. The very large evergreen leaves are either fan or feather-shaped, with numerous leaflets, and form a tuft at the top of the trunk.

European Fan-palm
Chamaerops humilis
Up to 3m or more. This usually almost stemless, suckering palm forms dense clumps or, when cultivated, develops a trunk covered with matted fibres. Its large, round, fan-shaped leaves are held on stout, spiny stalks and are deeply cut into many stiff, pointed strips. The only common native European palm, it is found in sandy or rocky coastal ground from Malta westwards. It is widely planted for ornament in Mediterranean parks, gardens and streets. This palm flowers from March to June.
✿ ✿ ✿

Canary Island Date-palm
Phoenix canariensis
Up to 20m. This stout palm has a thick trunk patterned with old leaf bases and scars, below a spreading crown of up to 200 feather-shaped leaves. The leaves are very large, up to 5–6m, with 150 to 200 pairs of longitudinally folded leaflets and a spiny leaf stalk. The orange fruit is inedible. Native to the Canary Islands, it is the most widely planted ornamental palm in the Mediterranean region. This species flowers from March to May.
✿ ✿

USES OF TREES	⚙	🏠	🔥	🍴	🪑	🌲
Buddleia		●				
Elder		●		●		
Red-berried Elder		●				
Guelder Rose		●				
Wayfaring-tree		●				
European Fan-palm		●				
Canary Island Date-palm		●				

The key to this chart is on page 93.

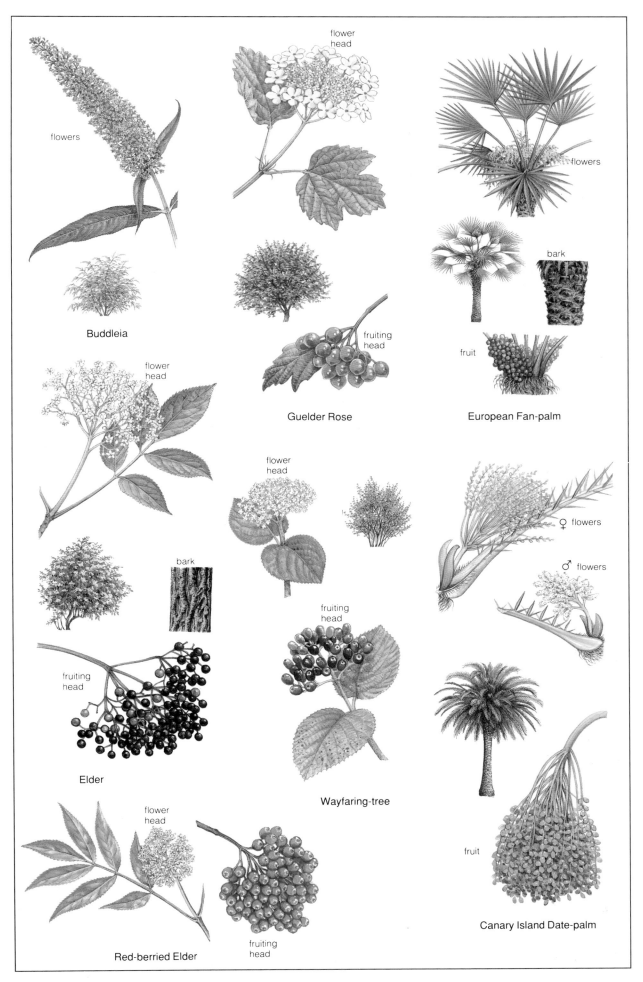

flowers

Buddleia

flower head

fruiting head

Guelder Rose

flowers

bark

fruit

European Fan-palm

flower head

fruiting head

Elder

bark

flower head

fruiting head

Wayfaring-tree

♀ flowers

♂ flowers

fruit

Canary Island Date-palm

flower head

fruiting head

Red-berried Elder

FERNS AND MOSSES

Ferns, horsetails and clubmosses are flowerless plants which reproduce by scattering spores. All have roots and a system of tubes for carrying water. The three groups were once all put in the Phylum Pteridophyta, but are now placed in separate phyla. True mosses and liverworts are also flowerless, spore-bearing plants, but they lack true roots and water tubes.

LEFT: Much of the dew sparkling on this Common Hair Moss will soak into the spongy cushion and help to keep the delicate leaves moist in dry weather.

Ferns

There are 10,000 fern species (Phylum Filicinophyta). European ferns are herbaceous plants with short stems. The leaves, or fronds, are tightly coiled when young. Each frond is usually divided into leaflets. The spores form in capsules, which are borne in clusters called sori.

Spores are scattered in the summer. Given moist conditions, each grows into a heart-shaped plate, or prothallus. The sex organs are borne on this and, in damp conditions, male cells swim to the female cells, which stay in the plate. After fertilization the female cell forms a new plant.

Horsetails

Horsetails (Phylum Sphenophyta) are structurally very different from the ferns, but they have similar life cycles. The leaves consist of rings of scales on the stems. Spores are borne in cones at the stem tips. The prothalli are circular with upright lobes. There are about 25 species.

Clubmosses

These plants (Phylum Lycopodophyta) resemble true mosses but are much stiffer. The spores are in capsules at the bases of certain leaves, which are often grouped into club-shaped cones. The prothalli grow underground in association with fungi. There are about 1000 species.

The Hart's-tongue Fern, in common with many other ferns, flourishes around waterfalls, where the spray provides ideal conditions for their reproductive stages.

Mosses and Liverworts

These plants (Phylum Bryopha) number about 20,000 species. Mosses (Class Musci) all have stems clothed with small leaves. Most liverworts (Class Hepaticae) have a similar structure. The main difference lies in the spore capsule. Most moss capsules are urn-shaped, with a detachable lid and teeth that allow the spores to escape only in dry weather. Liverwort capsules are spheres that split open at maturity and look like little four-rayed stars.

Male and female sex organs are borne on the moss or liverwort plant. Fertilization takes place in damp conditions, and the fertilized female cell develops into the stalked spore capsule.

LIFE CYCLE OF THE FERN   LIFE CYCLE OF THE MOSS

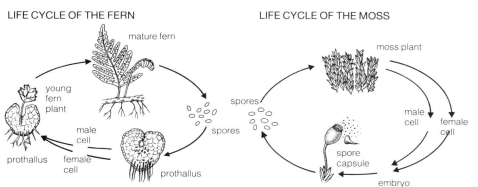

mature fern

young fern plant

male cell

prothallus   female cell

spores

prothallus

spores

moss plant

male cell   female cell

spore capsule

embryo

The life cycles of a fern (left) and a moss (right) both involve fertilization of a female cell by a male cell.

Ferns

The European ferns are almost all terrestrial herbaceous plants with leaves springing from stems at or below ground level. They are nearly all perennials, but the leaves or fronds usually die down in the winter and are replaced by new ones in the spring. Most species have a short, stocky stem with a crown of fronds at the top, but some have creeping rhizomes which spread through the soil and send up fronds at intervals. The shape of the fronds and the arrangement of their leaflets is important in the classification and identification of the species, as is the arrangement of the sori – the clusters of spore capsules. Although ferns grow most abundantly in habitats that are moist, individual plants often survive in remarkably dry places. Several small species are common on dry stone walls – but they can complete their life cycles and produce a new generation only during periods of damp weather.

Water Fern
Azolla filiculoides
Family Azollaceae
This unusual floating fern is a native of North America, but has become widely established on still and slow-moving waters in southern and central Europe. Its branching stems are covered with small hairy leaves which often turn red in autumn. Spores are borne on the undersides of the plants, but vegetative reproduction is more important. The plants break up very easily and each fragment can grow into a complete new plant, enabling this fern to carpet large areas of water in a very short time.
Ⓑ⊜

Royal Fern
Osmunda regalis
Family Osmundaceae
This large fern of fens, damp woods and other wet places has fronds up to 3m high and 1m wide, with numerous oblong leaflets up to 6cm

long. The spores are carried only on the upper parts of the inner fronds, where the slender leaflets are brown and consist of little more than the tightly packed spore capsules. Although widely distributed in western Europe, this fern is rare in most regions.
Ⓑ⊜Ⓞ④Ⓐ⊜

Bracken Fern
Pteridium aquilinum
Family Hypolepidaceae
This is the most common of all ferns, growing in suitable habitats all over the world. Its fronds are distinctly triangular in outline and grow singly from creeping rhizomes. They can reach heights of 4m, but are usually much shorter. The sori are born around the edges of the leaflets. This fern spreads rapidly by means of its rhizomes and it is a troublesome weed in many hill pastures. Less confined to damp places than most other ferns, it is absent from the wettest soils. It is also rare on lime-rich soils and, because young fronds are damaged by frost and cold winds, it seldom grows on the more exposed hillsides.
Ⓑ⊜Ⓞ④Ⓐ⊞

Hard Fern
Blechnum spicant
Family Blechnaceae
Named for its tough fronds, this plant is also called Ladder Fern because it carries its spore capsules on erect, ladder-like fronds. The normal fronds grow up to 50cm long, are vaguely comb-like and persist for two years or more. The fertile fronds die after shedding their spores. Generally widespread in woodlands and upland regions, this fern is absent from limestone areas.
Ⓑ⊜Ⓞ④

Maidenhair Fern
Adiantum capillus-veneris
Family Adiantaceae
This delicate fern has black stalks and fan-shaped leaflets. Its sori are borne on the undersides of the leaflets. The fronds are up to 30cm long, and spring from creeping rhizomes on damp cliffs and rocks, usually near the sea, and also on the undersides of bridges. A rare fern, it is found mainly in southern Europe and along the western seaboard.
Ⓑ⊜⊜

The Hard Fern is extremely common on banks in woodland, but only where the soil is on the acidic side.

Wall Rue
Asplenium ruta-muraria
Family Aspleniaceae
This common species grows on rocks and walls, often with Maidenhair Spleenwort. Both plants prefer lime-rich rocks and so are quite happy putting down their roots in the mortar of old walls. Its evergreen fronds may be up to 15cm long and bear a number of round, triangular or diamond-shaped leaflets. They are often mistaken for the leaves of flowering plants until the rows of sori are seen under each leaflet. The sori merge into a single mass when they are mature.
Ⓑ⊜Ⓞ

Hart's-tongue Fern
Phyllitis scolopendrium
This is one of the few fern species with undivided fronds. Its fronds are up to 60cm long and very shiny and they persist well into their second year. The spore capsules are borne in rows on the undersides of the fronds. The rows are covered by two flaps at first, but the flaps are pushed aside as the capsules mature. This fern commonly grows on rocks and walls, as well as on damp ground, but it is rare in northern Europe.
Ⓑ⊜Ⓞ④⊜⊜

Rusty-back Fern
Ceterach officinarum
Named for the dense brown scales on the undersides of the fronds, this fern grows in crevices in rocks and walls and can survive drought better than most species. Its leaves curl up when they become dry and the scales then prevent them from losing too much water. The fronds may grow up to 20cm long and bear spore capsules in slender rows on their undersides, although the scales hide the capsules. It is found mainly on Europe's western seaboard and in the Mediterranean region.
Ⓑ⊙

Maidenhair Spleenwort
Asplenium trichomanes
This common fern of damp rocks and walls can be easily identified by its wiry black leaf stalks and oblong or oval leaflets. The latter survive for more than a year and then fall to leave the naked stalks which fall later. Its sori are initially covered by pale flaps and borne on the undersides of the leaflets. The fronds may grow up to 40cm long. Green Spleenwort (*A. viride*) has green leaf stalks and does not lose its leaflets.
Ⓑ⊜Ⓞ

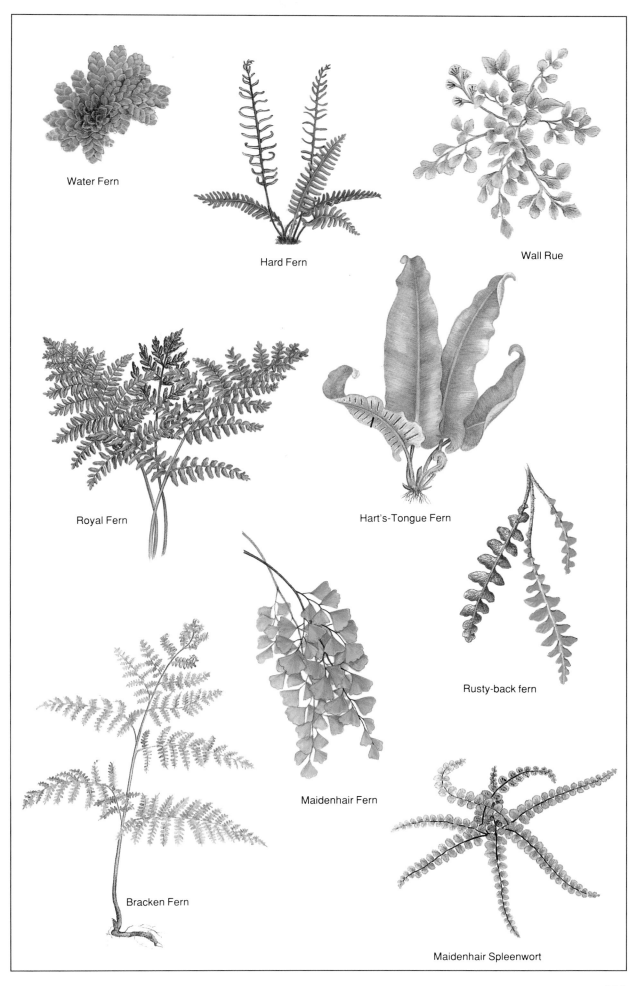

Water Fern

Hard Fern

Wall Rue

Royal Fern

Hart's-Tongue Fern

Rusty-back fern

Maidenhair Fern

Bracken Fern

Maidenhair Spleenwort

This Common Polypody fern is growing among rocks clothed with map lichens.

Male Fern
Dryopteris filix-mas
Family Dryopteridaceae
This very common woodland fern looks rather like a large green shuttlecock. Its fronds may grow up to 150cm long, with pale brown scales on their stalks. Each one is divided into 20–35 tapering lobes called pinnae. The longest pinnae are near the centre of the frond. Each pinna is divided into a number of smaller toothed lobes called pinnules, although these are not all completely separated. The underside of each pinnule carries up to a dozen sori, each of which is covered by a heart-shaped flap which shrivels as the spores ripen.
Ⓑ◐○④

Hard Shield Fern
Polystichum aculeatum
This woodland fern is very like the Male Fern in general appearance but its fronds are tougher and bristly, and rarely over a metre long. The lowest pinnule on each pinna is much larger than the rest. Its sori are also covered by a round flap rather than a heart-shaped one as in *Dryopteris* species.
Ⓑ○④

Broad Buckler Fern
Dryopteris dilatata
This species resembles the Male Fern, but its evergreen fronds are more triangular and its pinnules are more deeply divided. They are strongly toothed and sometimes have short stalks. Plants on mountain slopes are often much paler than woodland forms. The Hay-scented Buckler Fern (*D. aemula*) is similar, but its sweetly scented fronds rarely exceed 60cm long. It grows in wooded valleys and other sheltered spots.
Ⓑ◐◑○④

Common Polypody
Polypodium vulgare
Family Polypodiaceae
This common fern of damp woodland often grows epiphytically on trees. It also grows on damp rocks and walls. The creeping, scaly rhizome is often freely exposed on the surface and the fronds, which grow up to 45cm long, arise singly from it. These are long-lived and the upper leaflets (pinnae) are often incompletely separated. The sori are normally rounded and form two rows under each pinna, although some geographical races have oval sori.
Ⓑ○④◑◒

Adder's Tongue Fern
Ophioglossum vulgatum
Family Ophioglossaceae
This small fern is easily overlooked in damp grassland and woodland. Each plant produces just one undivided oval frond, which can easily be mistaken for a plantain leaf, although it lacks the prominent veins. Its spore capsules are carried on a slender tongue-like spike arising from the base of the frond in mature plants. The closely related moonworts (*Botrychium* species) have divided fronds and branched, fertile spikes. They grow in grassland, often in quite dry habitats.
Ⓑ○◍

Horsetails

This group of fern allies, or pteridophytes, contains only about 25 species, all belonging to the Family Equisetaceae. All are perennials with underground rhizomes and slender, green stems. The stems of some species carry whorls of slender branches, but other species are unbranched. The scale-like leaves form little collars on the stems. These are usually covered with crystals of silica, which make them rough to the touch and led to their use as pot scourers in the past. They are still known as scouring rushes in some places. The spore-bearing cones are carried at the tips of normal stems or on short-lived fertile stems. The latter lack chlorophyll and are white or pale brown. The sterile green stems usually die down in the winter, but the stems of some species can survive for several years. About ten species live in Europe, most of them in damp places.

Water Horsetail
Equisetum fluviatile
Growing in or close to water, the sparsely branched stems of this horsetail may grow up to 150cm high. They are smooth to the touch and bear narrow collars of black-tipped scale leaves. Some stems may be completely unbranched. Small, blunt-topped, brown cones develop at the tips of otherwise normal stems and scatter their spores in June and July. The Marsh Horsetail (*E. palustre*) grows in similar places and on damp ground in general, but is normally only 50cm high. Its stems are rough and generally branched. It also has more pointed cones.
Ⓑ◙

Field Horsetail
Equisetum arvense
The sterile stems of this horsetail grow up to about 80cm high and are green with numerous whorled branches. Its fertile stems are up to 25cm high and each leaf sheath has 6–12 teeth. These stems appear before the green sterile stems in the spring and die after scattering their spores during April and May. This plant prefers drier habitats than the Great Horsetail and is abundant on waste land. It is also a serious weed on cultivated land, for its fast-growing rhizomes, often extending a metre or more below the surface, are extremely difficult to eradicate.
Ⓑ○◍

Great Horsetail
Equisetum telmateia
This handsome species is the largest of the European horsetails. Its sterile stems are white with black-tipped scale leaves and dense whorls of bright green branches, and grow up to 2m high. The fertile stems are up to 40cm high and 2cm in diameter, and appear before the sterile stems in the spring. Each leaf sheath has 20–30 dark teeth. The spores are scattered from the cones during April and May and the fertile shoots then die. This plant grows in damp, shady places, especially on clay soils, and is commonly found on many roadsides and river banks. It is often so dense that it smothers all other plants.
Ⓑ○◐◒✿◍

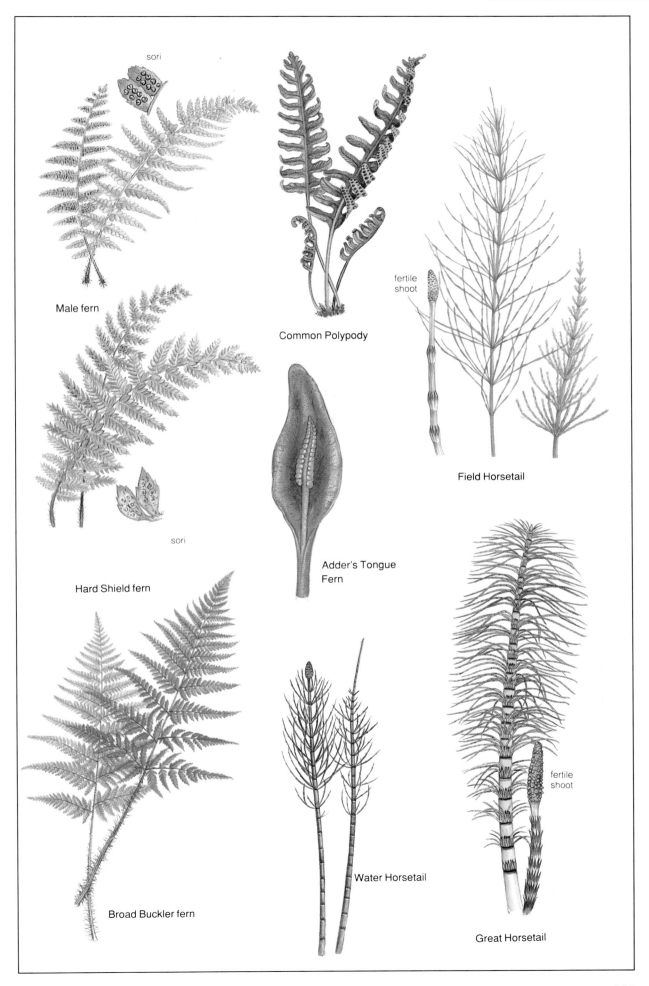

sori

Male fern

Common Polypody

fertile
shoot

Field Horsetail

Hard Shield fern

sori

Adder's Tongue
Fern

Broad Buckler fern

Water Horsetail

fertile
shoot

Great Horsetail

Racomitrium heath, dominated by Racomitrium lanuginosum, *here forms a thick blanket over volcanic lava in Iceland.*

Clubmosses

These pteridophytes get their common name for the club-shaped or cigar-shaped cones in which they carry their spores. Although they often form mats or cushions like the true mosses, they are generally larger and their leaves are a good deal stiffer and tougher. There are approximately a dozen European species, growing mainly on heathland and in some upland areas.

Stag's-horn Clubmoss

Lycopodium clavatum
Family Lycopodiaceae
This clubmoss has much-branched, wiry stems which creep over the ground, rooting at intervals and producing extensive carpets. Its fertile branches turn upwards and bear pairs of slender yellowish cones. The spores ripen from June to September. The plant is most common in upland areas, especially on moorland and in open woodland, usually on acid soils.
Ⓑ◑◓◐◔

Fir Clubmoss

Huperzia selago
This plant of upland moors and rocky slopes has forking, upright stems which are clothed with stiff, sharply pointed leaves. Pale spore capsules grow in the axils of many of the leaves, but there is no cone-production. The spores ripen from June to August.
Ⓑ◔◓

Mosses

These low-growing plants, belonging to the Class Musci, have no proper roots and are most abundant in damp, shady places, although many species can survive long periods of drought. Their tightly packed leaves are well suited for conserving water. Mosses are particularly common in woodlands. Most species form dense cushions or mats on the ground, although several grow on tree trunks and on rocks and walls. Male and female organs develop on separate shoots or even on separate plants and, after fertilization, the female organs produce spore capsules. Many species are also able to reproduce by scattering tiny flakes or tissue, called gemmae, which grow directly into new plants. Although family names are given for each species described below, bryologists usually prefer to use the order names, which are given after the family names.

Sphagnum papillosum

Family Sphagnaceae
Order Sphagnales
This species is one of the most common of those known as bog mosses. Forming dense, round hummocks on the surface of upland and low-land bogs, it is an important peat-forming moss. The hummocks consist of long stems carrying whorls of stout branches that form conspicuous rosettes at the surface. The rosettes are usually yellowish-brown, but may be green or reddish. The branches are clothed with small triangular leaves which, as in all bog mosses, give the plant its spongy nature and allow it to carry its own water supply. As the lower parts die, they are gradually converted into peat. Male and female organs develop on separate plants and when spore capsules develop, which is rare, they are like tiny matches sticking up from the rosettes. The capsules explode when they are ripe and fire out the spores.
Ⓑ◔

Leucobryum glaucum

Family Leucobryaceae
Order Dicranales
The large cushions which this moss forms in woodlands and also on wet moors are easily identified by their greyish-green colour which is quite unlike that of any other moss. In dry weather the cushions become almost white. They often become detached from the ground, but will continue to grow as long as the conditions remain fairly moist. The spore capsules are small and curved, but rarely produced. Popular with flower-arrangers, this moss has become scarce in many woodlands.
Ⓑ◔◓◔

Common Hair Moss

Polytrichum commune
Family Polytrichaceae
Order Polytrichales
This is one of our largest mosses, forming dark green carpets up to 20cm thick on many areas of moorland. The leaves have toothed edges and turn back to lie almost perpendicular to the stems. Male and female organs are carried on separate plants and the tips of the male shoots look as if they are carrying little red or orange flowers when the male organs are ripe. The ripe spore capsule looks like a four-sided box on a long stalk, but in the early stages it is covered by a golden hood. *P. formosum* is a very similar species which grows in woodland, but its leaves do not bend back so far from the stem and its box-like spore capsule usually has five or six sides.
Ⓑ◔◔

Racomitrium lanuginosum

Family Grimmiaceae
Order Grimmiales
This robust moss clothes huge tracts of tundra and mountain-top and forms a community known as Racomitrium heath. Each leaf ends in a long white point, giving the branched shoots a greyish-green and rather woolly appearance. Its spore capsules are egg-shaped but rarely produced.
Ⓑ◔◔◔

Swan-necked Thread Moss

Mnium hornum
Family Mniaceae
Order Bryales
This very common woodland moss is named for the elegantly curved stalk of the spore capsule. Its stems are up to 4cm high and densely matted, with male and female parts ocurring on separate plants. The fresh light green leaves of spring contrast with the dark older leaves. It is often found on rotten wood, peat and rock ledges, as well as on the ground.
Ⓑ◔

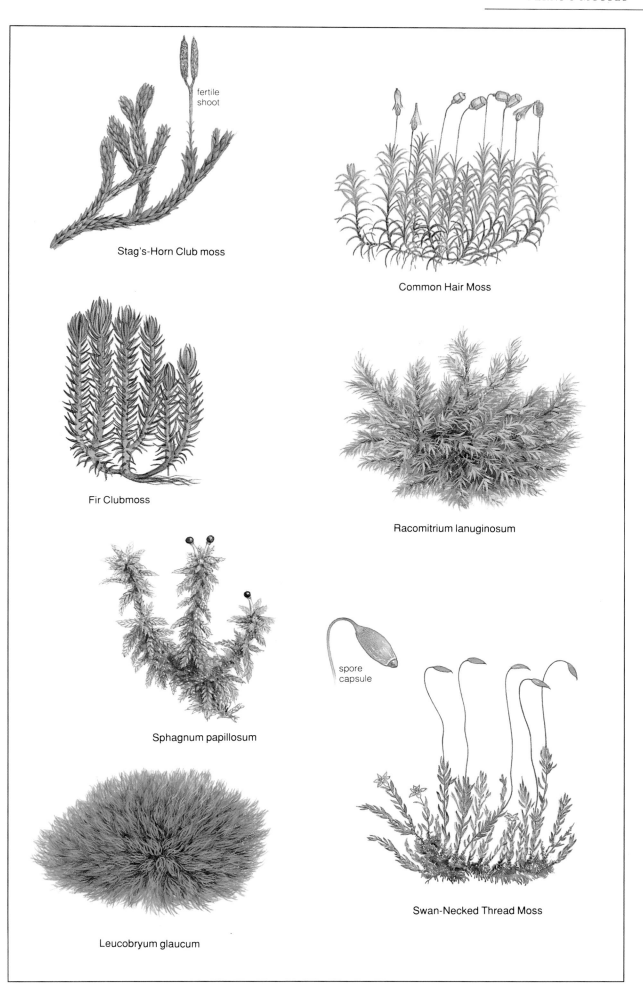

fertile
shoot

Stag's-Horn Club moss

Common Hair Moss

Fir Clubmoss

Racomitrium lanuginosum

Sphagnum papillosum

spore
capsule

Leucobryum glaucum

Swan-Necked Thread Moss

The liverwort Marchantia *produces its spore capsules on the undersides of these delicate, parasol-like structures.*

Thuidium tamariscinum
Family Thuidiaceae
Order Thuidiales
This beautiful woodland moss is easily recognized by its regular branching, which gives it the appearance of a miniature Christmas tree. Its stems are black, but the upper parts are densely clothed with heart-shaped or triangular bright green leaves. It likes shady places on heavy, wet soils but in the cooler and wetter climate of the north and west it also grows in open grassland. The sausage-shaped spore capsules are borne horizontally on red stalks, but they are rarely produced.
Ⓑ Ⓞ ④

Bryum capillare
Family Bryaceae
Order Bryales
This is one of the most common European mosses. It grows in almost every habitat but is most noticeable when it forms neat little cushions on rocks and old walls. Each oblong leaf ends in a hair-like tip which becomes twisted when dry. The drooping spore capsules are bright green at first, ripening to reddish-brown. *B. argenteum* is a silvery grey species which commonly grows on roadsides and in pavement cracks, even in towns, where few other plants manage to get a foothold.
Ⓑ ⊕ ☂

Silky Wall Feather Moss
Homalothecium sericeum
Family Brachytheciaceae
Order Hypnobryales
Easily recognized by the shiny yellow tips of its main shoots, this moss forms extensive mats on walls, boulders, and tree stumps. The secondary shoots are greener and grow vertically, forming a deep 'pile' in the centre of the mat. The triangular leaves taper to a fine point. The spore capsules are erect yellowish-green cylinders, borne on orange or red stalks. The pale yellowish-green *H. lutescens* is a closely related species that prefers to grow in turf on calcareous soils.
Ⓑ Ⓞ ✪

Eurhynchium praelongum
Abundant in shady places on heavy soils, this weak-stemmed, trailing moss also covers stones and piles of rubble and often grows on coastal rocks. Its main stems are clothed with heart-shaped leaves, but the leaves on the side branches are much narrower. The spore capsule is egg-shaped, with a long beak when young. Green at first, it becomes reddish brown when ripe, but it is only rarely developed.
Ⓑ Ⓞ ④ ⊕ ☂

Hylocomium splendens
Family Hypnaceae
This robust, red-stemmed moss has branches more or less perpendicular to the main stem. Its leaves are yellowish green and very shiny. The spore capsules are rarely developed. This moss grows in a wide range of habitats, but is especially common in upland woods.
Ⓑ ⊜ Ⓞ ④ ☂

Liverworts

By far the best known of the liverworts (Class Hepaticae) are the thalloid liverworts, which are not divided into leaves and stems. They grow flat on the ground or on rocks and look rather like green seaweeds. They can survive only in habitats that are very damp. Several of the species bear their gemmae (see p. 136) in prominent cups, from which they are scattered by rain drops. Most of the liverworts actually look very much like mosses, having small leaves that are clustered around slender, upright or creeping stems. They can be distinguished from the mosses, however, because the leaves of liverworts are lobed and lack obvious mid-ribs. The leaves of mosses are unlobed and usually do have mid-ribs. But the main difference between the two classes lies in the spore capsules (see p. 132). The moss-like liverworts, which are generally known as leafy liverworts, usually grow in turf or in association with mosses in other habitats. The leafy liverworts all belong to the order called Jungermanniales.

Crescent-cup Liverwort
Lunularia cruciata
Family Lunulariaceae
Order Marchantiales
Named for the crescent-shaped gemma cups on the bright green thallus, this very common species grows on river banks and also occurs frequently on damp paths, walls and particularly in greenhouses, where it is often a weed on flower-pots. There are separate male and female plants and spore capsules are rarely produced.
Ⓑ ⊜ ⊕

Marchantia polymorpha
Family Marchantiaceae
Order Marchantiales
This common liverwort of wet paths, river banks, greenhouses, and other damp places, is easily identified by its goblet-shaped gemma cups and by the hexagonal pattern on the surface. There are separate male and female plants which bear their sex organs on raised, parasol-like structures. Simple spore capsules develop under the female parasols pictured above. The male parasols are flatter and generally unlobed. The parasols appear mainly in the spring.
Ⓑ Ⓞ ⊜ ⊕

Pellia epiphylla
Family Pelliaceae
Order Metzgeriales
This large thalloid liverwort carpets large areas of stream banks and other moist, shady places, especially on acid soils. Its irregularly branched, shiny thallus, up to a centimetre wide and several centimetres long, bears no gemma cups. Male and female organs develop on the same plant and greenish black spore capsules rise on pale stalks in the spring.
Ⓑ ⊜ Ⓞ ⊜

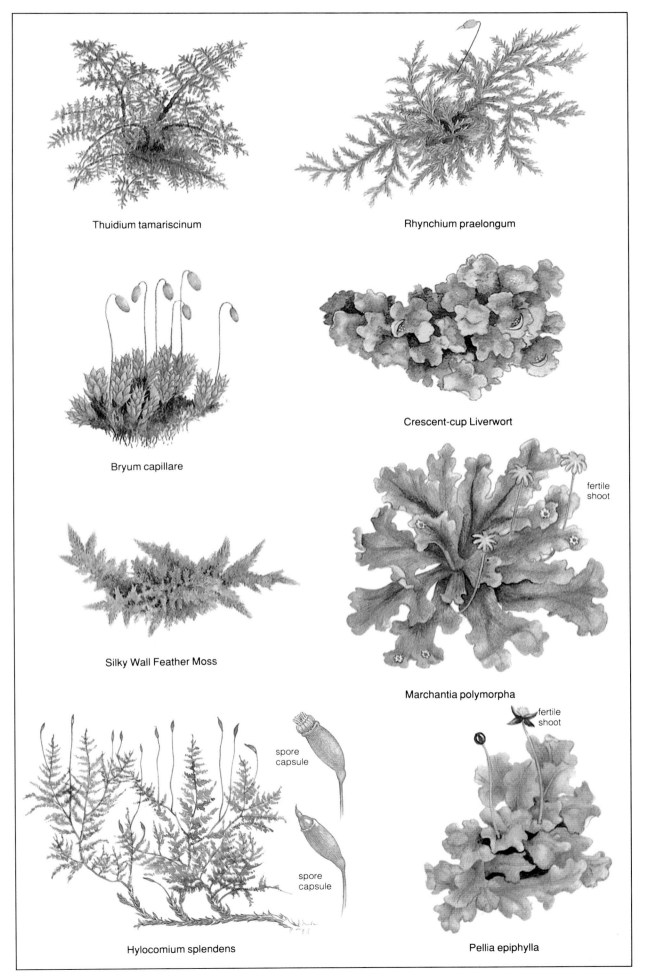

Thuidium tamariscinum

Rhynchium praelongum

Bryum capillare

Crescent-cup Liverwort

Silky Wall Feather Moss

fertile
shoot

Marchantia polymorpha

spore
capsule

spore
capsule

fertile
shoot

Hylocomium splendens

Pellia epiphylla

139

FUNGI

The Fungi Kingdom is one of the largest groups of organisms, currently estimated to contain around 800,000 species, grouped into over 400 families. The overwhelming majority have yet to be described, especially the tropical species, and even in Europe our knowledge of fungi is far from complete. Fungi are an ancient group, with some fossil evidence dating back to Cambrian-Ordovician time, about 500 million years ago.

LEFT: *Slimy Beech Caps, also known as the Poached Egg Fungus because of its slimy white caps, grows only on beech trees and usually appears in the autumn.*

What is a Mushroom?

A mushroom is only the reproductive part, or fruitbody, of a fungus within the Class Basidiomycetes, and exists solely to produce and disperse the microscopic spores. Fungi are composed entirely of minute, microscopic threads called hyphae (singular: hypha). The main body of a fungus consists of a dense network of these hyphae, called a mycelium, which lies buried in the ground or tree trunk or whatever substrate the fungus grows in. Unlike plants, fungi do not contain chlorophyll and so cannot photosynthesize their food. Instead the mycelium secretes enzymes, which break down material in the substrate to obtain nutrients.

Fungi Groups

Fungi are usually divided into three major groups or classes. Zygomycetes are microscopic and include many common moulds, such as bread moulds. Ascomycetes are the largest class, and include the powdery mildews, the cup fungi and the flask fungi. The spores are produced within a cell called an ascus and are shot out through the tip. Basidiomycetes are the most familiar group, containing the mushrooms and toadstools, the bracket fungi and the boletes. The spores are formed on a club-shaped cell called the basidium and are usually dispersed by the wind. This book is concerned mainly with the Basidiomycetes, although a number of the Ascomycetes are also included.

Ripe Earthstars pump out millions of spores at the slightest disturbance: even a leaf falling on the fungus can induce a puff of spores.

Reproduction

Fungi produce millions of spores. These are dispersed from the fruitbody, and when they land on a suitable substrate they germinate and form a mycelium. If the mycelium comes into contact with a mycelium of the same species they fuse. Then, if levels of food material, temperature, light and moisture are suitable, a fruitbody forms.

Habitats

Fungi occur almost anywhere, growing in the soil, amongst grass and dead leaves, and on living and dead trees. They can be found amongst moss, on dung, on burnt ground, and even in rivers.

Certain fungi and trees find it mutually beneficial to grow together in a mycorrhizal relationship. The fungus surrounds the roots and channels nutrients into them from the soil. In return it absorbs nutrients from the tree. In contrast to the mycorrhizal fungi are the parasitic species, which cause a white rot that kills the tree. Such relationships offer useful clues to identity, as different types of woodland and even individual tree species have their characteristic fungi.

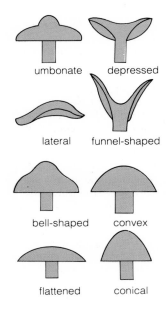

umbonate   depressed

lateral   funnel-shaped

bell-shaped   convex

flattened   conical

Mushroom fruitbodies vary a lot in shape and the shape of the cap is important in identification. Some common forms are illustrated here.

The development of the Death Cap, showing how the specialized structures of the fruitbody are formed.

The Parts of a Mushroom

A mushroom fruitbody is essentially an umbrella, protecting the spore-producing area on the underside and supported by a central stem. All the specialized structures are developed in the early stage or button. When conditions are suitable, the fruitbody takes in water very rapidly and expands to appear above the substrate. The expansion continues until the fruitbody reaches maturity, so mushrooms may change shape as they grow.

Cap The cap of a mushroom may be convex, flattened, bell-shaped, conical, funnel-shaped, or depressed; or it may be laterally attached to the substrate. The surface is often distinctively coloured, and it may break up into scales.

Gills Gills are radiating plates on the underside of the cap, which produce the spores. The thickness and spacing of the gills, as well as the way they are attached to the stem, provide important clues to identity.

Stem The stem is usually central and vertical, and elongates until maturity. Sometimes it is laterally attached or even absent. Typically it is cylindrical, but may be club-shaped with a swollen base, and is either solid or hollow.

Veils Some mushrooms have additional protective layers called veils. A universal veil completely envelops the button stage then, on expansion of the fruitbody, ruptures and may leave scales on the cap and a cup-like volva at the stem base. There may also be a partial veil, which covers the gills in the button stage and eventually breaks down to leave a ring on the stem.

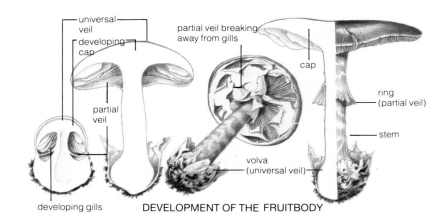

universal veil — developing cap — partial veil breaking away from gills — cap — ring (partial veil) — stem — partial veil — volva (universal veil) — developing gills — DEVELOPMENT OF THE FRUITBODY

Flesh The flesh may be distinctively coloured and may change colour when bruised or exposed to the air. The smell of the flesh is often distinctive.

Spores The spores are of great help in identification. Many are pigmented and textured, but detailed examination of the spores requires a microscope. The spore colour can be ascertained by taking a spore print – place a fresh cap on a piece of paper and in a few hours the spores will be deposited.

Eating Wild Fungi

There are many edible species found in the wild. There are also a number of poisonous fungi, ranging from those that cause mild stomach upsets to the deadly poisonous species such as the Death Cap. Some species can be eaten only after cooking and some cause unpleasant effects only in certain individuals or when eaten with alcohol. The edibility of the species in this book is shown in the charts, the key to which is given left. It is essential to be certain of the identity of a species before eating it. If you know nothing about wild fungi, enlist the aid of an expert when attempting an identification.

Lichens

Lichens (pp. 158–161) are composite plants consisting of a fungus – usually an Ascomycete – and an alga living in symbiosis. Each derives benefit from the partnership but the fungus cannot survive alone and lichens are often regarded just as special fungi which require the help of an alga to survive.

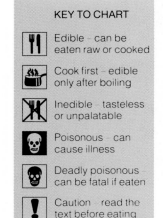

KEY TO CHART

Edible – can be eaten raw or cooked

Cook first – edible only after boiling

Inedible – tasteless or unpalatable

Poisonous – can cause illness

Deadly poisonous – can be fatal if eaten

Caution – read the text before eating

BASIDIOMYCETES

The Class Basidiomycetes comprises 130 families distributed through 32 orders, and containing about 25,000 species. Most of the familiar, large, fleshy fungi belong here, including the mushrooms and toadstools, club and coral fungi, tooth fungi, bracket fungi and the jelly fungi. Most species in this class are saprophytes, growing on dead wood or other plant remains; some are coprophilous, developing on dung; and a number are parasitic on trees. The spores are produced on a cell called a basidium.

EDIBILITY TABLE	🍴	🔥	🚫🍴	☠	💀	❗
Chanterelle	●					
Horn of Plenty	●					
The key to this chart is on page 142.						

Chanterelles

The chanterelles (Order Cantharellales) comprise about 12 species in Europe. Much valued for their flavour, they are always found on the ground, often in clusters, usually in beech or oak woods. The funnel-shaped fruitbodies have soft flesh but lack the thin, narrow gills on the underside of the cap of true mushrooms and toadstools. Instead they develop either thick, radiating narrow ridges or the surface remains smooth. All produce a white spore deposit.

Chanterelle
Cantharellus cibarius
Family Cantharellaceae
Cap up to 15cm across. The fruitbodies of this fungus are bright yellow to orange and form small groups in mixed woods. Thick and fleshy, the cap bears widely spaced, thick ridges on the underside of the tapering stem, which is not clearly separated from the cap. The yellow flesh smells of apricots. This species occurs from June to November, especially after heavy rains. Edible and delicious, it is often sold in markets. The unrelated False Chanterelle (*Hygrophoropsis aurantiaca*) is very similar, but it has crowded, true gills rather than ridges.
Ⓑ🍲Ⓞ④⊗

Horn of Plenty
Craterellus cornucopioides
Cap up to 8cm across. Also known as the Black Trumpet, this fungus has a hollow, tapering fruitbody with no clear division between cap and stem. The fibrous-scaly cap has thin flesh and a wavy edge, while the under surface is pale grey, waxy and powdery, and lacks any ridges. Large clusters are often hidden beneath fallen leaves in deciduous woods from August to November.
Ⓑ Ⓞ ④

Chanterelle

Horn of Plenty

Mushrooms and Toadstools

The names mushrooms and toadstools are given to the most well known order of larger fungi, the Agaricales. Their typical features are an umbrella-shaped fruitbody with a central, vertical stem supporting a circular cap. Below are suspended radiating gills that produce the reproductive spores. World-wide, there are 250 genera containing more than 4000 species, ranging from membranous and minute forms to large and fleshy species, growing on soil, wood, leaf-litter, dung and even other fungi. Characters used in identification include the colour of the spore deposit, the mode of gill attachment, the presence of veil layers, and microscopic structures, particularly the spores.

Conical Slimy Cap

Hygrocybe conica
Family Hygrophoraceae
Cap up to 5cm across. The thin-fleshed and conical cap of this mushroom has a point at the centre. Both cap and stem are bright orange and shiny at first but become streaky and black. The gills are at first white but also blacken. It occurs from June to November in grassland. This species can cause stomach upsets if eaten. *H. conicoides*, which has a cherry-red cap, is found in sand-dunes.
Ⓑ ☕ ⊗

St George's Mushroom

Calocybe gambosa
Family Tricholomataceae
Cap up to 12cm across. This is the largest and most conspicuous edible mushroom growing in spring (April to June). Its convex cap is fleshy, with a wavy, enrolled margin. It is white to pale buff-brown, borne on a solid, stocky stem. The gills are whitish and densely crowded. It grows in grassland and scrubland, preferring chalky soil.
Ⓑ ☕

Honey Fungus

Armillaria mellea
Cap up to 12cm across. This fungus forms clumps on stumps and at the base of trees and shrubs, and is regarded as a pest. It occurs from June to November. The convex cap has small, dark brown, fibrillose scales. The gills are off-white to pale pink, often with rusty spots and the stem is cylindrical. Young, fresh caps are edible but can cause stomach upsets.
Ⓑ ◐ ④ ✿

Wood Woolly Foot

Collybia peronata
Cap up to 4cm across. This species has a convex cap which soon becomes flattened. Its thin flesh is reddish-brown but drying paler with a similarly coloured stem, which has yellowish hairs at the base. Its gills are yellowish, narrow and well spaced. It is found amongst dead leaves, especially in beech woods, from August to November.
Ⓑ ○

Honey Fungus is an insidious killer, destroying huge numbers of forest trees every year with its all-pervading hyphae.

Amethyst Deceiver

Laccaria amethystea
Cap up to 4cm across. Bright violet to purplish lilac when moist and fresh, this species can become almost whitish in dry settings. Together with the similar Deceiver (*L. laccata*), this is one of the commonest toadstools in Europe, growing on the ground in woodlands from August to November. The cap is rather scurfy-scaly, with a striated margin. The stem is long, fibrous and twisted. The gills are widely spaced with a white, powdery surface. Although harmless to eat, it is insipid and tough.
Ⓑ ◐ ○ ④

Fairy Ring Mushroom

Marasmius oreades
Cap up to 5cm across. This is a very common grassland species, frequently found on lawns in autumn. It usually forms fairy-rings, especially in a wet season, but it can also survive drought. The cap is convex with a raised centre, smooth and pale brown. The gills are white and widely spaced, and the stem is slender, cylindrical and a similar colour to the cap. This is a good edible species, especially collected for stews and casseroles.
Ⓑ ◐ ✿ ☕

Wood Blewit

Lepista nuda
Cap up to 12cm across. This species is often found in large numbers, growing among the leaf litter in both deciduous and coniferous woods. It is easily recognized by its lilac to violaceous colouring. The cap is thick and fleshy, but soon becomes depressed, and it is dry and smooth, with a wavy margin. The gills are initially bright lilac and densely crowded. The stem is also bright violet, thick, stocky and fibrous. The pale flesh has a strong aromatic smell, which often attracts insect larvae. It is found from September through the winter. This is one of the best-known edible species, with a strong flavour, but it must be cooked and never eaten raw.
Ⓑ ○

Bonnet Mycena

Mycena galericulata
Cap up to 3cm across. This species has a conical cap with a wrinkled centre and thin, greyish-brown flesh with a grooved edge. The gills are pale pink and widely spaced but often with interveining. The stem is greyish-brown, smooth and shiny; several stems are often fused at their base. It is commonly found on old rotting stumps and roots of deciduous trees from May to November.
Ⓑ ○

Tawny Grisette

Amanita fulva
Family Amanitaceae
Cap up to 8cm across. This is a tall, slender mushroom with a tawny-orange, thin-fleshed cap which is first bell-shaped but soon becomes flattened with a finely grooved margin. The gills are white and crowded and the stem is fragile and hollow. It is common from June to November in all kinds of woodland, preferring sandy soils. This species is edible but it does contain poisons so it must always be boiled and the water discarded.
Ⓑ ◐ ○ ④

EDIBILITY TABLE	🍴	🔥	🍴	☠️	💀	❗
Conical Slimy Cap				●		
St George's Mushroom	●					●
Honey Fungus		●				●
Wood Woolly Foot			●			
Amethyst Deceiver	●					
Fairy Ring Mushroom	●					●
Wood Blewit		●				
Bonnet Mycena	●					
Tawny Grisette		●				

The key to this chart is on page 142.

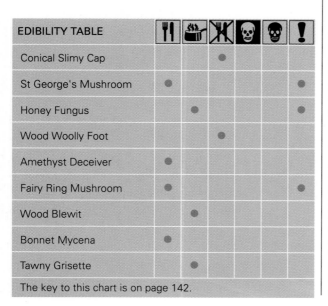

Conical Slimy Cap

Wood Woolly Foot

Wood Blewit

St George's Mushroom

Amethyst Deceiver

Bonnet Mycena

Honey Fungus

Fairy Ring Mushroom

Tawny Grisette

Fly Agaric
Amanita muscaria
Cap up to 25cm across. This familiar mushroom forms very large fruitbodies, with its scarlet-red, flattened cap covered with concentric rings of small white scales. The gills are whitish and crowded, and the stem is also white with a swollen base. Near the top of the stem is a hanging ring. It is found from August to November, under birch or conifers. Although not deadly, it contains dangerous sweat-inducing poisons and mild hallucinogens.
Ⓑ◐◯④❀

False Death Cap
Amanita citrina
Cap up to 8cm across. This species is easily confused with the Death Cap, which is much less common. Its smooth cap is convex and lemon-yellow but often much paler with white veil patches. The gills are white, thin and very crowded and the white stem has a swollen base on which the volva forms a rim; a yellowish, hanging ring is attached near the top of the stem. It is found in all types of woodland, from July to November, but it should not be collected for eating.
Ⓑ④

Death Cap
Amanita phalloides
Cap up to 10cm or more across. This is the most deadly of all fungi and responsible for 90 per cent of all deaths from mushroom poisoning in Europe. Hands should be washed immediately after touching it. The smooth, shiny cap is convex, often yellowish-green with darker streaks. The gills are white and crowded. The stem emerges from a sack-like volva, which has a white ring and a zig-zag pattern. Usually rare, it occurs from July to October, mostly under oak.
Ⓑ◯❀

Blusher
Amanita rubescens
Cap up to 15cm across. This species has a thick and fleshy cap which is convex then flattened, pink to reddish-brown and covered with small, greyish scales. Its gills are white, sometimes with pinkish spots. The stem is reddish-brown and stocky but lacks a volva, retaining a prominent grooved, hanging ring. The white flesh turns pinkish when broken open. Probably the most common *Amanita* species, it is found in all kinds of woodlands, even in mountainous regions, from June to October. It is edible but contains toxins so must be boiled first and the water discarded.
Ⓑ◐◯④

Horse Mushroom
Agaricus arvensis
Family Agaricaceae
Cap up to 15cm across. This large, white edible mushroom is found in open grassland throughout the autumn. Its cap is convex and white, but discolours or bruises to pale yellow, often with the remains of the veil hanging from the edge. The crowded gills are pale grey, becoming blackish-brown. The stem has a membranous hanging ring, with a cog-wheel pattern.
Ⓑ◑◍

Field Mushroom
Agaricus campestris
Cap up to 8cm across. This fungus is often confused with the Cultivated Mushroom, which has a large fleshy ring. Its cap is convex becoming flattened, whitish, dry and sometimes slightly scaly. The gills are at first bright pink, becoming dark chocolate-brown. The stem is white and short. The white flesh discolours pinkish when broken open. It is commonly found in grassland from July to October. A good edible species.
Ⓑ◑◍

Parasol Mushroom
Macrolepiota procera
Cap up to 20cm across. This is one of the largest mushrooms and is prized as an edible species. Young fruitbodies resemble drumsticks. The greyish-brown cap is soon flattened but with a raised darker centre covered with shaggy-woolly scales. The gills are white, broad and very crowded. The stem has a snake-skin pattern, it bears a thick, double-edged ring. Found during autumn in open woodland and near hedgerows.
Ⓑ◯◍

The Fly Agaric gets its name because in parts of northern Europe the caps are crumbled in milk and used to attract and kill flies.

Shaggy Ink-cap
Coprinus comatus
Family Coprinaceae
Cap up to 14cm high. The mature cap of this species is cylindrical. Brown and smooth at the apex, it breaks up below into shaggy scales. The gills are crowded and white. The stem is tall, white and hollow. It grows from April to November in grass or on bare ground. It is best eaten when young.
Ⓑ❀◍

Trooping Crumble Cap
Coprinus disseminatus
Cap up to 1cm across. This common, tiny species grows in huge numbers on rotting wood. The bell-shaped cap is yellowish-brown becoming greyish. The gills are at first white but turn dark grey. The stem is slender, white and brittle. It is found from April to November and is probably edible.
Ⓑ◯

Sulphur Tuft
Hypholoma fasciculare
Family Strophariaceae
Cap up to 4cm across. This species has a sulphur-yellow colour and a tufted habit on old tree stumps. Its cap is bell-shaped to convex, smooth and dry. The crowded gills are greenish, darkening to a purplish-brown. It is found throughout the year.
Ⓑ◯④❀

EDIBILITY TABLE	🍴	🍳	🚫	☠	☠☠	!
Fly Agaric				●		
False Death Cap						●
Death Cap					●	
The Blusher		●		●		
Horse Mushroom						●
Field Mushroom						●
Parasol Mushroom	●					
Shaggy Ink Cap						●
Trooping Crumble Caps	●					
Sulphur Tuft			●			
The key to this chart is on page 142.						

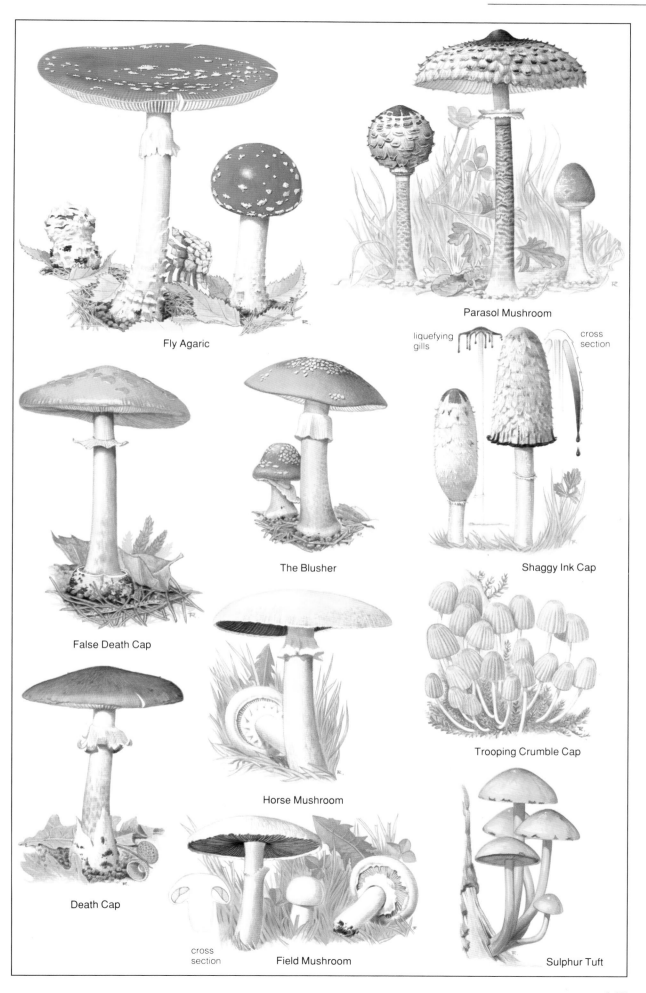

Fly Agaric

Parasol Mushroom

liquefying gills

cross section

The Blusher

Shaggy Ink Cap

False Death Cap

Trooping Crumble Cap

Horse Mushroom

Death Cap

cross section

Field Mushroom

Sulphur Tuft

MAN-MADE HABITATS

People have had a tremendous effect on the landscape in the last 5000 years or so and, apart from the northern tundra and a few mountain tops, very little of Europe's countryside is truly natural. Our grasslands owe their existence to the activity of humans and their domestic animals (see p.84), and the remaining patches of deciduous forest in Europe have all been modified to some extent by human activity (see p.126). But the biggest changes wrought by humans have been the creation of huge tracts of arable land and, more recently, the spread of industrial and urban development.

ABOVE: *Black-headed Gulls thrive on farmland in the autumn and winter, feeding on worms and insects exposed by the plough.*
LEFT: *House Martins return to the same houses year after year to rear their families in the same mud nests.*

Wildlife on the Farm

Arable land covers millions of hectares, but it supports little animal life because modern farming causes so much disturbance. The plough or the combine can create a totally new environment in just a few hours. Skylarks and hares breed among the crops in the spring, and harvest mice build their nests among the cereal stalks; gulls follow the plough, and lapwings scour the fields after harvest, but few other vertebrates are attracted to arable land.

Modern herbicides have greatly reduced the number and variety of weeds in arable fields. Only rarely do we see the fields scarlet with poppies these days – usually where some disturbance has brought ancient seeds to the surface – but plenty of weeds still exist. Most of them are annuals that scatter their seeds before harvest and thus survive to spring up again the following year. They include Scarlet Pimpernel, Corn Marigold and Scentless Mayweed. Many of these annuals originated on unstable cliffs and river banks where fresh soil is continually being uncovered, and they are ideally suited for growth in ploughed fields.

Hedgerows, which are treated in this book as part of the grassland habitat (see p.85), are characteristic of many arable areas, and are important corridors for a wide range of plant and animal life.

Wildlife in the Home

Many plant and animal species are being lost as their homes fall to the bulldozers, but not all wildlife suffers from human activity. Gardens are superb habitats. Walls, hedges, lawns, flower beds, and vegetable patches support an amazing range of wildlife, from weeds and their associated insects to foxes. Old walls are good for insects and spiders, and provide nesting sites for Wrens, while new house walls are used by the House Martin. Plenty of insects live inside houses, making use of our food, furniture and woodwork. Most of these animals live naturally in the countryside, but some species, such as the House Sparrow, are rarely found away from humans.

away. Oxford Ragwort is a well known invader. A native of Sicily, it escaped from the Oxford Botanic Garden late in the 18th century and spread rapidly along Britain's railway lines, where the cinder tracks are not unlike the volcanic soils of its native home.

Even towns and cities support plenty of wildlife, although a city worker might not see any more than the pigeons and sparrows that flourish on the food crumbs dropped on the streets. Kestrels have moved into the city centres to feed on the sparrows and the house mice. Parks and cemeteries are full of trees and shrubs which attract birds and other animals normally inhabiting woodland margins. Street trees attract birds for roosting if not for nesting. Foxes and Badgers live in many towns – probably arriving by way of railway lines and canal banks. They make their homes on waste land, and also in cemeteries and the larger gardens, and find plenty of food in the form of mice and other small animals. They also dine well on restaurant refuse and the contents of domestic dustbins.

FAR LEFT: *The Evening Primrose, from North America, is established on waste ground throughout Europe.*
LEFT: *The Garden Tiger moth commonly inhabits gardens and waste ground.*

Wildlife on the Move

Reservoirs, canals, railway lines and motorway verges all teem with life. Motorway verges are important new areas of relatively undisturbed grassland which might make up for the loss of some of our meadowland. The verges are full of voles and are great hunting grounds for kestrels. Ordinary roadside verges also provide homes for many wild flowers and insects, and a lot of other small animals. Several alien plants occur on roadsides, having been introduced initially as seed with some kind of imported produce and accidentally dropped from lorries. Roadside species are spread very rapidly by the traffic, for their seeds are often picked up on tyres and dropped many miles

Urban Wildlife

1 Nipplewort
2 Ivy-leaved Toadflax
3 Great Black Slug
4 Wall Germander
5 Hedgehog
6 Annual Meadow Grass
7 Dandelion
8 Garden Snail
9 Perennial Rye Grass
10 Red Fox
11 Bat
12 Tawny Owl
13 Bramble

Brown-gilled Mushrooms

This order (Cortinariales) contains the huge genus *Cortinarius*, which has more than 600 species in Europe alone. The warty spores enable them to be easily distinguished from other brown-gilled genera. They all form mycorrhizal associations with the roots of individual tree species, and their fruitbodies may form large clusters on the woodland floor. Individual species are generally very difficult to identify accurately. None is edible, and a few are deadly poisonous.

Red-banded Cortinarius
Cortinarius armillatus
Family Cortinariaceae
Cap up to 10cm across. This species has a smooth fleshy cap, reddish to yellowish-brown with radial streaks. The gills are cinnamon to rusty-brown at maturity and produce a rusty-brown spore deposit. The pale brown stem is tall and cylindrical with a swollen base, but bearing several distinct brick-red bands. It is found from August to October, usually near birch trees or conifers.
Ⓑ🌢🍃④

Yellow Slimecap
Cortinarius delibutus
Cap up to 9cm across. This species has a distinctive slimy cap and stem. It is common during autumn, under beech and birch. The shiny, smooth cap is deeply convex, and is yellow at first, becoming paler. The crowded gills are attached to the stem apex. At first deeply violaceous, the gills fade to yellowish and then cinnamon-brown as the spores mature. The stem, which is swollen towards the base, is white with yellow flecks and zones. It is inedible.
Ⓑ◐

Orange Pholiota
Gymnopilus junonius
Cap up to 12cm across. This tufted mushroom has a rusty brown spore deposit, tinted bright tawny to golden-brown. The cap is convex and fleshy and the gills are crowded and yellowish, becoming rusty-brown. The thick, fibrous stem has a brown ring. It is found from August to December, growing at the base of deciduous trees and old stumps. The flesh is bitter and poisonous.
Ⓑ◐✪

Soft Slipper Toadstool
Crepidotus mollis
Family Crepidotaceae
Cap up to 7cm across. The fruitbodies are gregarious, usually forming bracket-like tiers on trunks and branches of broad-leaved trees, particularly oak and ash. They can be readily separated from the Oyster Caps by the brown spores which discolour the gills as they mature. The cap is shell to kidney-shaped, yellowish-brown with a striated margin and soft and pliable. The scaly surface becomes slimy when moist. The crowded gills darken to cinnamon-brown. This fairly common species occurs from May onwards, and is inedible.
Ⓑ◐✪⊗

The Emetic Russula, often called the Sickener, is easily distinguished from the Fly Agaric by its smooth, ringless stalk.

Brittle Gills and Milk Caps

This group (Order Russulales) contains two genera, *Russula* (Brittle Gills) with 160 European species, and *Lactarius* (Milk Caps) with 80 European species. Although mushroom-like, these species differ from true mushrooms and toadstools in their crumbly flesh and pale coloured, ornamented spores. *Lactarius* species also release a milky latex when broken open. All grow with specific trees, which is useful for identification, as is the colour of the spore deposit, and the mild or peppery taste. Many species are edible but they are generally more popular with east European palates.

Emetic Russula
Russula emetica
Family Russulaceae
Cap up to 10cm across. This is one of a number of red-capped species found growing in coniferous woods in damp places from July to October. Its cap is scarlet to blood-red, convex and shiny, with a surface layer that can be peeled away. The gills are white and well spaced and the tall stem is pure white. The white, brittle flesh has a slightly fruity smell but a very hot and peppery taste which can cause vomiting if it is consumed raw.
Ⓑ◐④

Common Yellow Russula
Russula ochroleuca
Cap up to 10cm across. This species occurs in coniferous and deciduous woods from August to November. The cap is convex to depressed, dull ochre-yellow and weakly grooved. The crowded gills are pale cream and the brittle, white stem discolours pale grey. The spore deposit is pale cream. At first mild, the flesh becomes hot and peppery, and is not recommended.
Ⓑ◐④

Saffron Milk Cap
Lactarius deliciosus
Cap up to 20cm across. This edible but bitter-tasting species has a reddish-orange, depressed cap with faint concentric zoning. The very crowded gills are orange-yellow. The stem is short and smooth. When broken, the yellow flesh releases a carrot-red latex. A common species, it occurs under conifers from August to October.
Ⓑ🌢④

Ugly Milk Cap
Lactarius turpis
Cap up to 20cm across. This common species is found under birch trees, often in heathland, from July to October. Its smooth, sticky, depressed cap is greenish brown but darkens to almost black, and has an incurved margin. The crowded gills are creamy yellow with greyish-brown spots. A white latex is released from the flesh. This milk cap is said to be edible after parboiling but is not recommended.
Ⓑ🌢◐▥

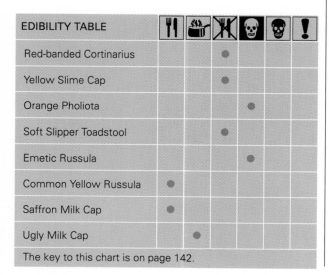

EDIBILITY TABLE	🍴	🍲	🍴✕	☠	☠	❗
Red-banded Cortinarius				●		
Yellow Slime Cap				●		
Orange Pholiota					●	
Soft Slipper Toadstool				●		
Emetic Russula					●	
Common Yellow Russula	●					
Saffron Milk Cap	●					
Ugly Milk Cap		●				

The key to this chart is on page 142.

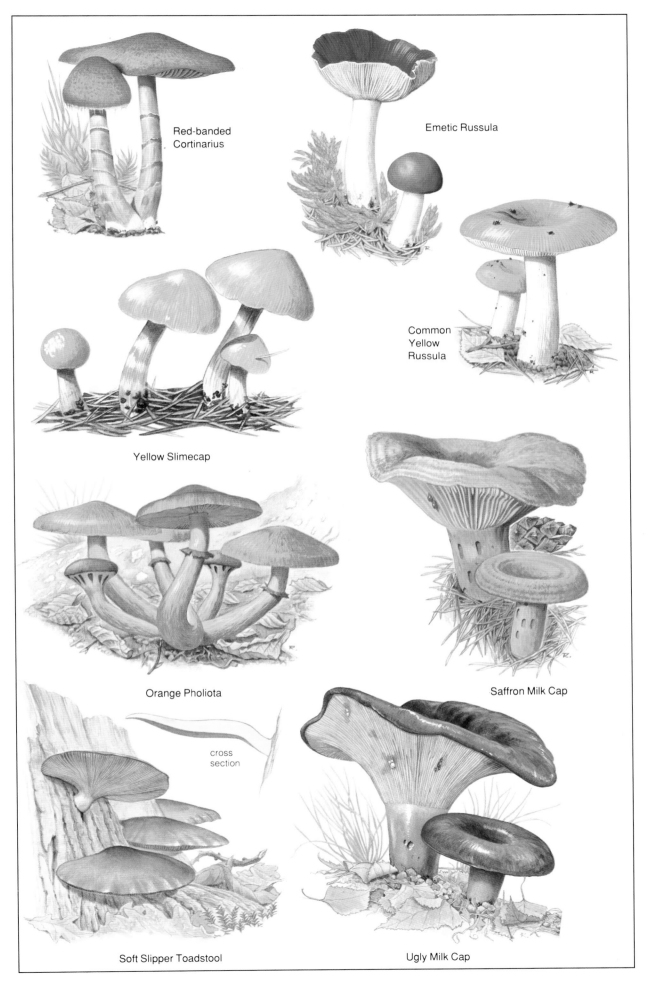

Red-banded
Cortinarius

Emetic Russula

Common
Yellow
Russula

Yellow Slimecap

Orange Pholiota

Saffron Milk Cap

cross
section

Soft Slipper Toadstool

Ugly Milk Cap

Boletes

There are about 100 species of boletes (Order Boletales) in Europe. Most are typified by the development of a 'spongy' tissue under the cap, where the spores are produced, comprising a layer of narrow, vertical tubes, each opening by a terminal pore. Unlike the bracket fungi, however, the flesh is soft and quickly rots. Many form mycorrhizal relationships with tree species and thus are abundant in temperate regions of the world. Some are sought-after for their fine flavour, and the Penny Bun Boletus is one of the most prized fungi. Others, such as the Devil's Boletus, are poisonous.

Penny Bun Boletus
Boletus edulis
Family Boletaceae
Cap up to 13cm across. This common species occurs from June to November, usually under beech and oak. The convex cap is coffee-brown to chestnut-brown, sometimes whitish to blackish-brown, and sticky only when moist. Its tubes are up to 2cm long with minute, white to olive-yellow pores. The pale brown stem is robust and swollen towards the base and its upper part is covered with a fine net-like pattern. The spore deposit is olive-brown. Also know as the Cep, this is one of the best edible species.
Ⓑ🍄Ⓞ④

Devil's Boletus
Boletus satanas
Cap up to 30cm across. This bolete has a white to grey cap with olive-brown tints, and is at first smooth but finally cracks. Its tubes are short and reddish but bruise bluish. The stem is yellow above, with a red, net-like pattern, and reddish below. The yellow flesh discolours blue, and has an unpleasant smell. The spore deposit is cinnamon-brown. It grows singly in beech woods but is only occasionally found, from July to October. The flesh causes severe stomach upsets.
ⒷⓄ

Brown Birch Boletus
Leccinum scabrum
Cap up to 10cm across. One of the most common boletes, this species grows in birch woods, often in large numbers, between June and October. The light greyish-brown cap is mottled and velvety. The tubes are long and whitish, ending in pale greyish to yellowish-brown pores. The stem is tall and white but covered with tiny black scales and the spore deposit is brown.
ⒷⓄ

Slippery Jack
Suillus luteus
Cap up to 10cm across. This common species is found under pines from July to October. Its convex cap is chocolate-brown and covered with a greyish slime or pellicle. The tubes are lemon-yellow, and the pores yellow to brownish. The stem is slender, cylindrical and cream coloured, with tiny granules, and bears a membranous, white ring which becomes darker with age. The spore deposit is snuff-brown. The fruitbodies are edible if the slimy pellicle is removed. The closely related *S. grevillei* is similar but has a yellowish-orange cap and always grows under larch trees.
Ⓑ🍄④

Bay Boletus
Xerocomus badius
Family Xerocomaceae
Cap up to 15cm across. This species has a bay-brown to chocolate-brown cap which is convex then flattened. It is sticky when wet, but velvety when dry. Its tubes and pores are lemon-yellow, bruising blue-green. The tall, solid stem is paler than the cap. The yellowish flesh discolours blue-green when broken. The spore deposit is cinnamon-brown. A common species, it grows in mixed woodland from August to November.
ⒷⓄ④

False Chanterelle
Hygrophoropsis aurantiaca
Family Paxillaceae
Cap up to 6cm across. This species was once placed in the Family Cantharellaceae due to its similarity to the Chanterelle, but it has forking, true gills rather than ridges. The yellow to orange cap has an inrolled margin and the stem becomes brown near the base. The spore deposit is white. Commonly found, it occurs from August to November, under conifers and on heathland. It is edible but is not recommended.
Ⓑ🍄🤢④

The cap of the Oyster Mushroom varies from yellowish-brown to bluish grey or violet. It becomes pale grey as its ages.

Bracket Fungi

Like the boletes, most bracket fungi (Order Poriales) have a layer of tubes, each opening by a pore, on the underside of the cap. However, they differ in having a firm, rigid texture. Most grow on living or dead tree-trunks, and some are parasitic and destructive. In Europe there are around 100 genera and 250 species, arranged in 10 families. These fungi are regarded as advanced in evolutionary terms, and the flesh is sometimes formed by a complex system of different types of hyphae. The fruitbodies are amongst the largest known, and many species are perennial.

Beefsteak Fungus
Fistulina hepatica
Family Fistulinaceae
Cap up to 20cm across. The cap of this species is bracket or cushion-shaped, with a pinkish to orange-red, finely warty, sticky surface. The tubes are very unusual in not being fused but separable from each other. At first pale yellowish, they discolour reddish-brown. The flesh is soft and succulent, up to 5cm thick and white but soon becoming reddish. The spore deposit is white. It is found on oak trees from July to October. The common name refers to the raw steak-like appearance of the flesh but, although it is edible, it does not live up to its name and old specimens contain unpleasant tannins.
ⒷⓄ

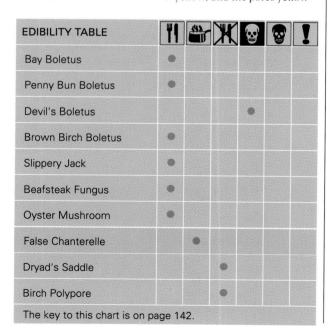

EDIBILITY TABLE	🍴	🍳	🚫🍴	☠️	💀	❗
Bay Boletus	●					
Penny Bun Boletus	●					
Devil's Boletus				●		
Brown Birch Boletus	●					
Slippery Jack	●					
Beafsteak Fungus	●					
Oyster Mushroom	●					
False Chanterelle			●			
Dryad's Saddle					●	
Birch Polypore					●	

The key to this chart is on page 142.

Oyster Mushroom
Pleurotus ostreatus
Family Lentinaceae
Cap up to 10cm across. The presence of gills in this species often leads to it being placed with the true mushrooms and toadstools (Order Agaricales), but the microscopic structure indicates a closer alignment with the polypores. The shell-shaped cap is attached by a short, lateral stem. The moderately crowded gills radiate from the cap and are white to pale yellowish. The spore deposit is pale lilac. Commonly found, it forms clusters on deciduous trees, especially beech and poplar, from October onwards, and sometimes survives through a mild winter. Edible and good, especially when young, it is now grown commercially throughout Europe.
Ⓑ ◐

Dryad's Saddle
Polyporus squamosus
Family Polyporaceae
Cap up to 50cm across. This very large bracket forms clusters on tree trunks, especially elm and beech, from May to August. The yellowish cap is kidney-shaped, and the surface bears concentric zones of blackish, triangular scales. The tubes are short but the white pores are 1–2mm wide, and often radially elongated. The stem is short and solid, with a black, wrinkled base. The spore deposit is white. Young specimens are regarded as edible, but are they not recommended.
Ⓑ ◐ ✤

Birch Polypore
Piptoporus betulinus
Family Coriolaceae
Cap up to 20cm across. This species is found only on dead or living birch trees, where it is common and abundant throughout the year. The smooth, greyish-brown cap is kidney or hoof-shaped, with a very short, stem-like lateral attachment, and a broadly rounded margin. The pore-surface is white and the pores are minute. The spore deposit is white. The flesh is white and up to 5cm thick but soon becomes tough and corky, rendering the species inedible. This fungus causes a reddish-brown rot, eventually killing the tree on which it grows.
Ⓑ ❀ ⬭ ④

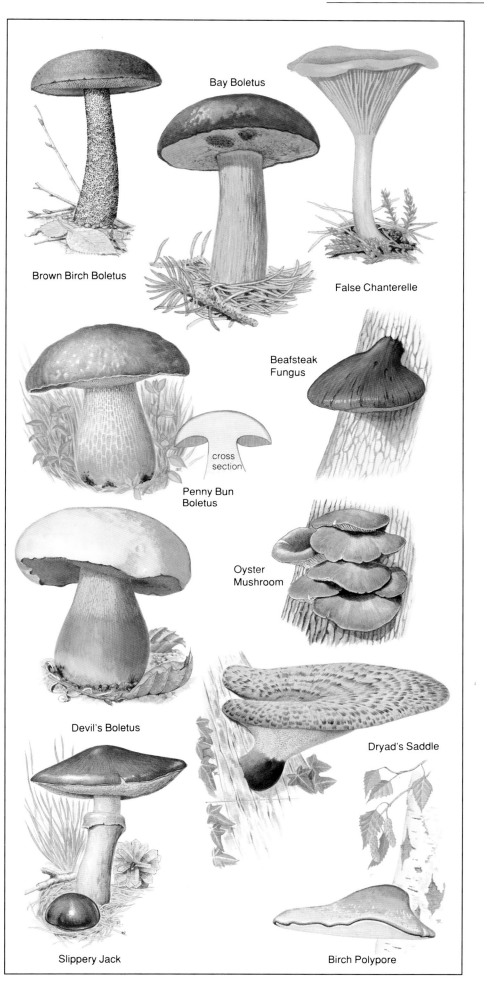

Bay Boletus

Brown Birch Boletus

False Chanterelle

Penny Bun Boletus

cross section

Beafsteak Fungus

Oyster Mushroom

Devil's Boletus

Dryad's Saddle

Slippery Jack

Birch Polypore

Earthstars, Puffballs and Stinkhorns

These species (Order Gasteromycetales), often called stomach fungi, form a large group of basidiomycetes, in which a spore-mass or gleba is produced inside the fruitbody. At maturity the spores become powdery and are usually dispersed by air-currents. The outer layer is called the peridium. This order contains about 230 European species.

Collared Earthstar
Geastrum triplex
Family Geastraceae
Fruitbody about 6cm across when fully open. This fairly common species occurs in groups under birch trees from July to October. The young, unopened fruitbody resembles a tulip bulb. The outer layer splits and peels back as six to eight fleshy, pinky-brown rays, which lift it above the leaf-litter. The upper surface of the rays then cracks, leaving a fleshy collar at the base. The membranous spore-sack contains a dark brown spore-mass.
Ⓑ Ⓞ

Giant Puffball
Langermannia gigantea
Family Lycoperdaceae
Fruitbody up to 60cm across, but may reach 160cm. This species produces the largest fruitbody of any fungus. It resembles a white football with a smooth, felty surface. At maturity the surface turns greenish-yellow and flakes away to release the spore mass. An average specimen produces about seven billion spores, making this the most productive organism on earth. It occurs from July to September, on rich soils in fields, woods and hedgerows. Only the young white flesh is edible and is delicious.
Ⓑ ⬮ Ⓞ ✪ ⬛

Lawn Puffball
Vascellum pratense
Fruitbody up to 4cm high. This small, creamy white puffball is commonly found in short grass, often on lawns, from late summer to early autumn. It grows singly but sometimes forms fairy rings. This species is pear-shaped with a short stalk and its surface is covered by tiny, scurfy granules which are easily rubbed off. The gleba is at first white with moist flesh, but becomes yellow and finally olive-brown and powdery. The spores are released from an apical pore.
Ⓑ ⬮ ⬮ ⬮ ✪ ✪ ⬛

Pestle-shaped Puffball
Calvatia excipuliformis
Fruitbody up to 15cm high and 7cm wide. This puffball has a pure white to pale buff fruitbody which slowly turns brown. It occurs from July to October. Its swollen head contains the spore mass on top of a long, spongy stem. The surface is initially covered with tiny spines and granules. At maturity, the gleba becomes olive-brown and powdery, and the spores escape from an irregular tear at the apex. The flesh is white and succulent when young.
Ⓑ ⬮ Ⓞ ⬛

The Collared Earthstar is quite common, but often very hard to see among the dead leaves, especially in dappled sunlight.

Stump Puffball
Lycoperdon pyriforme
Fruitbody up to 6cm high, but usually smaller. The only puffball that grows on wood, this common species occurs in large clusters on or around stumps in deciduous woods, from July to November. The fruitbody is often pear-shaped and has a white to pale yellowish surface, finely covered with minute scurfy scales. The gleba is at first white with succulent flesh, but turns olive-brown and powdery. The fruitbody develops an apical pore to release the spores. Young specimens are edible.
Ⓑ Ⓞ ✪

Bird's Nest Fungus
Cyathus striatus
Family Nidulariaceae
Fruitbody about 15mm high. This common species grows in large clusters on decaying plants, rotting twigs and conifer needles. The cup-like fruitbody is at first covered by a white membrane which eventually ruptures. The hairy outer surface is rusty-brown, while the inner surface has conspicuous vertical grooves in which develop 10–15, greyish spore-packets, resembling eggs. It occurs from July to October.
Ⓑ ④

Common Stinkhorn
Phallus impudicus
Family Phallaceae
Egg up to 4cm across. This common species may be found from June to September in all types of woodland. It starts as a globose, white egg which ruptures to release the fast-growing fruitbody. This comprises a white, spongy, hollow stem bearing the gleba, which is conical, ridged and covered with a dark olive-green slime. It is often located by its pungent, nauseating smell of rotting meat. This attracts insects, which eat the slime and disperse the spores.
Ⓑ Ⓞ ④

Common Earthball
Scleroderma citrinum
Family Sclerodermataceae
Fruitbody up to 10cm across. This species has a fruitbody resembling a slightly flattened ball, with a hard, ochre-yellow outer layer. Its coarse, scaly surface cracks open to reveal the inner gleba. This is whitish but soon turns purplish-black and finally dark brown and powdery. It is very common, especially on sandy heaths and woodland, from July to October. This species is believed to be poisonous.
Ⓑ ⬮ Ⓞ ④ ⬛

EDIBILITY TABLE	🍴	🍲	🍴✕	💀	💀	❗
Collared Earthstar			●			
Giant Puffball	●					
Pestle-shaped Puffball	●					
Lawn Puffball	●					
Stump Puffball	●					
Bird's Nest Fungus			●			
Common Stinkhorn	●					
Common Earthball					●	

The key to this chart is on page 142.

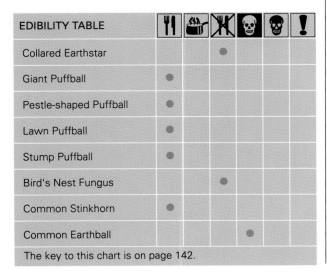

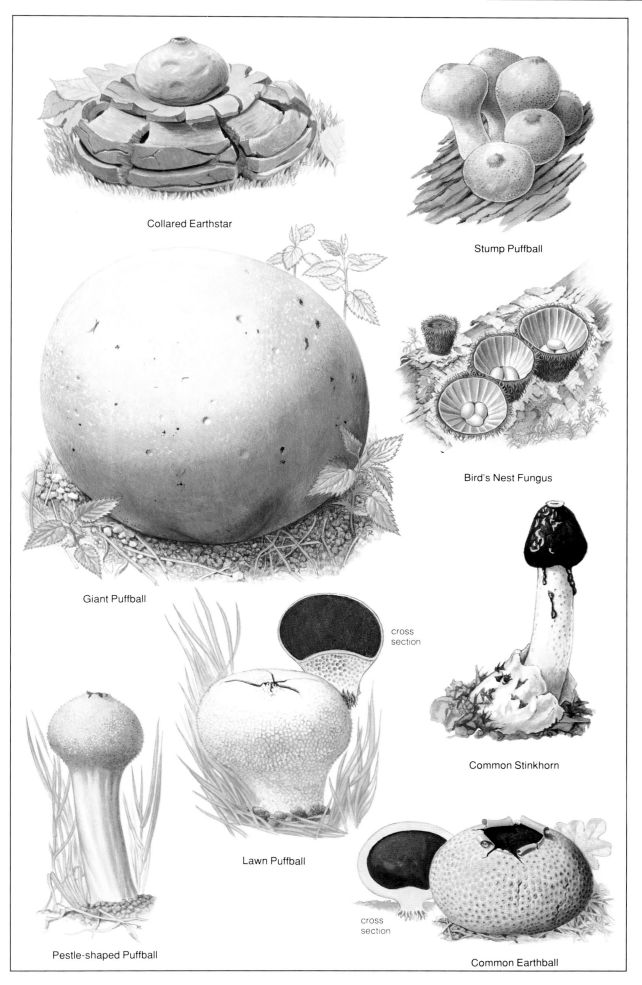

Collared Earthstar

Stump Puffball

Bird's Nest Fungus

Giant Puffball

cross
section

Common Stinkhorn

cross
section

Lawn Puffball

Pestle-shaped Puffball

Common Earthball

Jelly Fungi

The jelly fungi (Subclass Heterobasidiomycetes) virtually all grow on wood. There are about 150 European species, characterized by their texture, which ranges from soft and gelatinous to tough and rubbery. They vary from minute pustules to large clubs and projecting brackets.

Jelly Antler Fungus
Calocera viscosa
Family Dacrymycetaceae
Fruitbody up to 8cm high, but often smaller. The fruitbody of this species is club-like with many flattened, bright yellow branches. It has a shining, sticky surface and the flesh is yellow and gelatinous.

The spore deposit is white. It is commonly found growing in small tufts on stumps and fallen trunks of conifers, from September to October.
Ⓑ Ⓐ

Jew's Ear
Auricularia auricula-judae
Family Auriculariaceae
Fruitbody up to 10cm across. This edible but tasteless fungi forms clusters of brackets all year round on trunks or branches of elder and sometimes sycamore. Its ear-shaped fruitbody is reddish to date-brown, gelatinous, and finely velvety. Its lower surface is pale purplish-brown. The flesh is thin, elastic but tough, becoming hard when dry. The spore deposit is white.
Ⓑ Ⓞ Ⓧ

CUP-FUNGI AND FLASK-FUNGI

The Ascomycetes form the largest class of fungi, with 230 families containing more than 400,000 species world-wide. Many are microscopic. They occur in and on the soil, on leaves and wood, on dung, on animals and in the sea. The spores are produced within a cell called an ascus. The simplest forms are the yeasts, consisting of a single cell, but a fruitbody is formed in most species. Few are edible, although the morels and truffles are highly prized exceptions.

Common Morel
Morchella esculenta
Family Morchellaceae
Fruitbody up to 20cm high. This fungus is found from April and May throughout Europe. Its fruitbody is an irregular-shaped cap, borne on a thick stem and covered by angular pits and ridges, varying from pale yellowish-brown to black. The cream to light brown stem is short, hollow and swollen. The spore deposit is deep cream. It grows singly or in rings in

The rubbery Jelly Antler Fungus makes a bright splash of colour on the forest floor, where it springs from rotting conifer wood.

woods and hedgerows. It is edible but should not be eaten raw or confused with the deadly Turban Fungus (*Gyromitra esculenta*), which has a more brain-like cap.
Ⓑ Ⓞ Ⓧ

Common White Helvella
Helvella crispa
Family Helvellaceae
The pale yellowish brown cap of this common species is saddle-shaped and has two or three lobes and an undulating margin. The white surface of the stem is irregularly ribbed and fluted. Found in sandy soil in mixed woods from August to November, this species is edible after thorough boiling.
Ⓑ Ⓞ Ⓧ Ⓜ

Orange Peel Fungus
Aleuria aurantia
Family Pezizaceae
Cup up to 10cm across. This fungus looks like discarded orange peel. Its cup is bright reddish-orange on the inner surface with a paler, scurfy outer surface. Its flesh is white and brittle and the spore deposit is white. It occurs singly or in groups, often at the edge of woods, from September to January. It is edible when well cooked.
Ⓑ Ⓞ Ⓐ Ⓧ Ⓜ

Périgord Truffle
Tuber melanosporum
Family Tuberaceae
Fruitbody up to 10cm across. This is the most prized truffle and occurs only in southern Europe. It usually grows under oak trees in alkaline soil, 2–20cm deep, from November to May. The reddish-black to black fruitbody is covered with grooved, polygonal warts. The gleba is reddish to violet-

black, and marbled with white veins which discolour reddish. The spore mass is dark brown. The fruitbodies are hunted by their odour with the use of dogs and pigs.
Ⓔ Ⓞ

Coral Spot Fungus
Nectria cinnabarina
Family Hypocreaceae
Fruitbody up to 0.5mm across. This common fungus grows in dense clusters, often covering fallen twigs and branches of deciduous trees, throughout the year. The fruitbody is globose with a projecting pore and bright red to reddish-brown in colour but darkening. The spore deposit is white.
Ⓑ Ⓞ Ⓧ

King Alfred's Cakes
Daldinia concentrica
Family Xylariaceae
Fruitbody up to 6cm across. This species has a fruitbody which is hemispherical, hard, reddish-brown to black and covered with tiny pores through which the spores emerge. The inner structure shows concentric growth zones, alternating from black to silver-grey. A common species, it is usually found on the fallen wood of ash, and occasionally, alder and beech, from June to October.
Ⓑ Ⓔ Ⓞ

Candle Snuff Fungus
Xylaria hypoxylon
Fruitbody up to 6cm high. This common woodland fungus is found on dead wood throughout the year. The fruitbody produces several branches at the top, which are at first white but in late winter they become black with tiny, raised pores. The spore deposit is black.
Ⓑ Ⓞ Ⓐ

EDIBILITY TABLE	🍴	🥫	🚫🍴	☠️	💀	❗
Jelly Antler Fungus			●			
Jew's Ear	●					
Common Morel			●			●
Common White Helvella			●		●	
Orange Peel Fungus			●			
Périgord Truffle	●					
Coral Spot Fungus			●			
King Alfred's Cakes			●			
Candle Snuff Fungus			●			

The key to this chart is on page 142.

Jelly Antler Fungus

Périgord Truffle

Coral Spot Fungus

Jew's Ear

Commmon White Helvella

cross
section

King Alfred's Cakes

Common Morel

Orange Peel Fungus

Candle Snuff Fungus

LICHENS

Lichens are very hardy organisms that can survive in some of the hottest and coldest places on earth. Some of the larger species are commonly confused with mosses, but the lichen body, normally called a thallus, actually consists of fungal threads and minute algae in an intricate partnership. The fungus partner makes up the bulk of the organism, but it cannot survive without the aid of the symbiotic algae from which it obtains food, and its tough, dry nature is very different from that of other fungi. However, most biologists now consider lichens to be an aberrant group of fungi.

Lichen Groups

There are three main groups of lichens. Crustose lichens form crusty coatings on rocks and other hard surfaces. They may be broken into hexagonal plates, but have no obvious lobes. Foliose lichens consist of numerous scales or leaf-like lobes, often forming circular patches on rocks and tree trunks. Fruticose lichens are like miniature bushes. Many grow on the ground, but others grow as epiphytes on trees. Many species reproduce asexually by scattering powdery granules, called soredia, which grow directly into new lichens. Most species also reproduce sexually by producing spores on certain areas of the thallus known as apothecia. These fungal spores can grow into new lichens only if they are quickly joined by the right kind of alga. Growth is very slow in most lichens, but many species are very long-lived – some patches are known to be over 4000 years old.

Lichens grow in a wide variety of habitats, but are rarely found in industrial areas, as few species can tolerate air pollution. They favour the clean air of the Arctic and the moist woodlands along Europe's western coasts. Nearly 20,000 species are known in the world, and over 3000 occur in Europe.

The lichen Cladonia coccifera, *with the bright red, spore-producing apothecia developing around the edges of the cups.*

Usnea florida

Family Usneaceae
One of the 'beard lichens', this fruticose species forms erect or drooping, tangled clumps on the branches and trunks of trees and shrubs. The related *U. subfloridana* is similar but lacks the saucer-shaped apothecia. Its tangled branches bear numerous white patches of soredia. It is most abundant in the west, where the climate is damper.
Ⓑ Ⓞ ✦

Parmelia caperata

The crinkled yellowish-green lobes, covered with powdery soredia, distinguish this from almost all other lichens. A foliose species, it has chestnut-coloured apothecia growing near the centre of the thallus. It occurs mainly on old tree trunks, although it is sometimes found on rocks.
Ⓑ Ⓞ ✪

Map Lichen

Rhizocarpon geographicum
Family Rhizocarpaceae
This common and distinctive crustose lichen, grows on acid rocks, mainly in upland areas. The yellowish-green thallus is split into numerous angular sections and edged by a thin black line. When several plants grow together their margins form boundaries resembling those drawn on maps. The spore-producing apothecia are black and scattered all over the surface. There are several similar species.
Ⓑ Ⓢ Ⓦ Ⓦ

Hypogymnia physodes

Family Parmeliaceae
This foliose species is abundant on trees, rocks and walls. The thallus lobes are hollow and appear rather inflated. They are solidly fixed to the substrate, not attached by fine hairs as in many other lichens, and are very dark underneath. Soredia are borne on the upturned tips. Apothecia are rarely produced. This is one of the few large lichens to survive in polluted urban areas. A slightly greyer form is common on heather stems.
Ⓑ Ⓢ Ⓞ ✦ ✪

Reindeer Moss

Cladonia rangiferina
Family Cladoniaceae
This lichen's common name does not refer to its shape but to the fact that it forms the staple diet of reindeer in the far north. A much-branched, fruticose species, it forms thick carpets in montane and Arctic regions, where it is often one of the most abundant plants. It may grow up to about 8cm tall. The branches of each stem all bend in the same direction and bear apothecia on their drooping tips.
Ⓑ Ⓢ Ⓞ Ⓦ

Cladonia portentosa

The yellowish-grey shoots of this fruticose lichen branch in all directions and the smallest branches are arranged in threes, not in fours as in the related *C. rangiferina*. Like *C. arbuscula*, it sometimes has a yellowish tinge caused by the presence of usnic acid. This is the most abundant of the bushy *Cladonia* species in lowland regions, often forming extensive mats on bogs and wet heathland.
Ⓑ Ⓦ

Cladonia arbuscula

This fruticose species grows in thick, bushy tufts with a yellowish tint, caused by the presence of usnic acid, an antibiotic. The hollow stems are repeatedly branched with the tips on each branch bent in one direction. Small brown spores are produced on the tips. This lichen is commonly found on hills, mountains, heaths, moors, dunes and peat soils in many parts of Europe.
Ⓑ Ⓢ Ⓞ Ⓦ

Cladonia coccifera

This is one of a group of fruticose species known as pixie-cup lichens, and is widely distributed on moorland and other areas of acidic soils. The cups are borne on scaly, cone-shaped shoots, and bear bright red apothecia on their rims.
Ⓑ Ⓞ Ⓦ

Cladonia floerkeana

Although a fruticose species, this lichen is not at all bushy. It forms a carpet of greenish scales on the ground and sends up erect grey spikes, which are either simple or sparsely branched. They bear large, bright red apothecia at their tips. Rarely over 2cm high, this lichen is common on the peaty soils of heaths and moors, especially amongst heather.
Ⓑ Ⓦ

Cladonia fimbriata

This fruticose species species is abundant on rocks, walls and tree stumps as well as on the ground on banks and dunes. It forms mats of greenish scales from which spring cups with slender stalks. The cups are coated with fine grey-green soredia and the rims of the cups bear the spores. *C. pyxidata* is very similar but the cups have much shorter stalks. Both species belong to the group known as pixie-cup lichens.
Ⓑ Ⓢ Ⓦ Ⓞ ✦ ✪

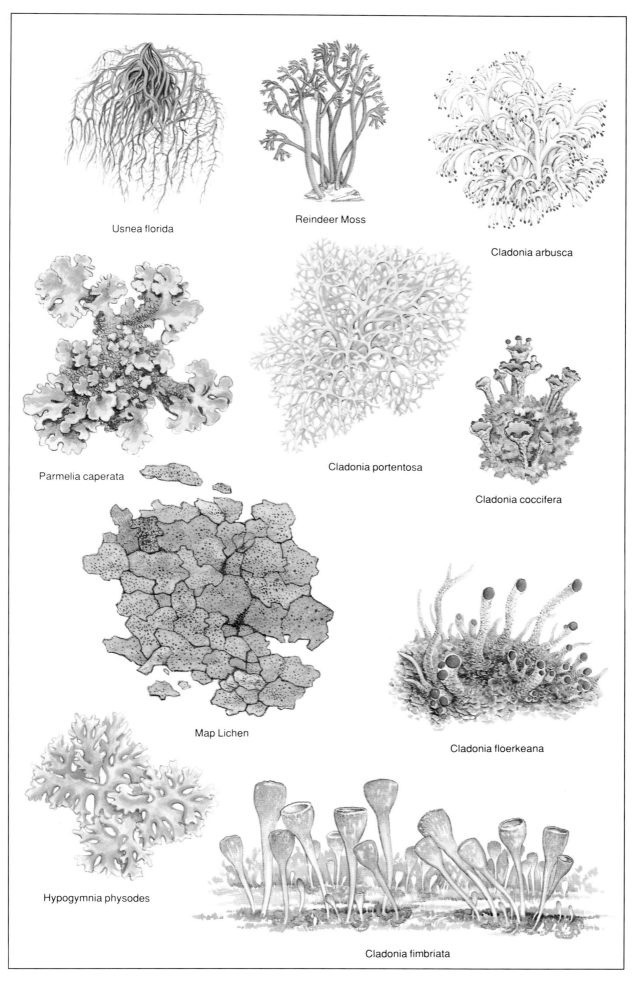

Usnea florida

Reindeer Moss

Cladonia arbusca

Parmelia caperata

Cladonia portentosa

Cladonia coccifera

Map Lichen

Cladonia floerkeana

Hypogymnia physodes

Cladonia fimbriata

Sea Ivory
Ramalina siliquosa
Family Ramalinaceae
Growing mainly on coastal rocks, the thallus of this fruitcose species is composed of strap-shaped branches. Uniformly greenish-grey they, bear disc-shaped apothecia at or near the tips.
Ⓑ 🌊

Dog Lichen
Peltigera canina
Family Peltigeraceae
This large, foliose, dull brown lichen is common on the ground in grassy places and on sand-dunes. The underside is white and felt-like, with a network of veins and numerous fine, root-like hairs. It becomes pale and brittle when dry. Chestnut-coloured apothecia develop at the tips of narrow lobes springing from near the margins of the primary lobes. There are a number of very similar species.
Ⓑ ◗ 🌊 🌾

Xanthoria parietina
Family Teloschistaceae
This is one of a number of orange foliose lichens found on rocks, old walls and tree trunks. It also grows on concrete and asbestos, and is especially common in coastal areas and around human habitations. It particularly favours surfaces that are rich in nitrogen from bird droppings. The thallus in this species varies a good deal in form – sometimes it is circular with slender, radiating branches; at other times it forms irregular patches of broad, flat lobes. The apothecia, which are usually slightly darker than the thallus, are generally numerous near the centre.
Ⓑ ◗ ✪ 🌊

Tree Lungwort
Lobaria pulmonaria
Family Stictaceae
This large foliose lichen is loosely attached to tree trunks and rocks. Under normal

Xanthoria parietina *is one of the brightest of the lichens. Spore-bearing apothecia can be seen all over the plant.*

conditions it is dark green with prominent sculpturing on the upper surface, but it becomes greyish-brown and papery when dry. Apothecia are reddish-brown, but rarely produced. This species is intolerant of any atmospheric pollution and is most commonly found in coastal woodlands, especially in western areas.
Ⓑ ○

Graphis elegans
Family Graphidaceae
This crustose species forms pale grey, wrinkled crusts on smooth-barked trees. The black lines are the apothecia. Each is surrounded by a deeply furrowed margin. *G. scripta* is similar but the apothecial margins are not furrowed. It is most common in woodland in western areas.
Ⓑ ○ ✪

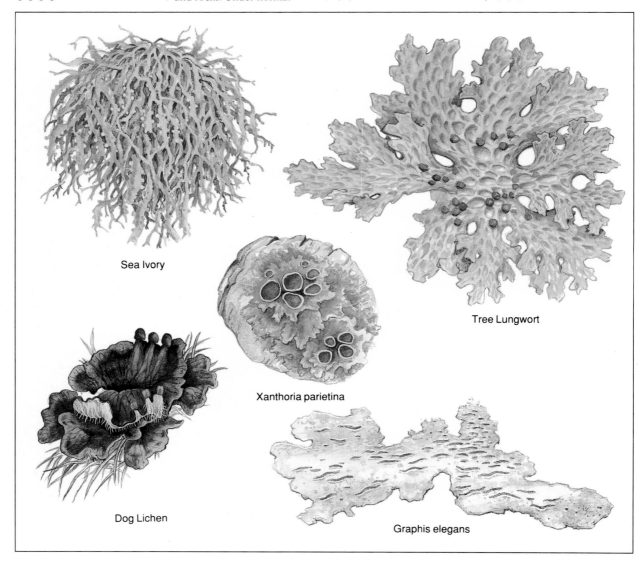

Sea Ivory

Tree Lungwort

Xanthoria parietina

Dog Lichen

Graphis elegans

SEAWEEDS

Seaweeds belong to the group of flowerless plants known as algae, most of which live in water. They have no roots and the body, known as a thallus, is never clearly divided into leaf and stem. Many algae consist of just a single cell. These algae turn pond water green in the summer. They also play a vital role in ocean ecology, for they form the phytoplankton – the living 'soup' on which marine animals depend for their food and energy.

The algae were once regarded as a single division of the Plant Kingdom, but they are a very diverse group of plants, and botanists now believe that they include several divisions which are not all closely related.

Seaweed Groups

Seaweeds belong to three groups: green, brown, and red algae. These were once regarded as classes, but botanists now regard them as phyla. Some species grow to several metres and they have a more complex structure than other algae. Many species attach themselves to rocks by suckers, or holdfasts, and there may be a stalk-like region between these and the flat blade.

Although many seaweeds are brown or red, they all contain green chlorophyll and they make their own food by photosynthesis. The brown and red pigments that mask the chlorophyll improve the absorption of light.

Non-sexual reproduction is common among the algae, the most frequent method being the release of flagellated cells, called zoospores, which swim about and eventually grow directly into new plants. Seaweeds and other algae also reproduce sexually, and some of their life cycles are very complex.

BELOW: Chlamydomonas, *a microscopic, freshwater alga, swims by waving its flagella. Its light-sensitive red spot guides it into the the optimum position for photosynthesis.*

BELOW: *The thick, fronds of Oarweed form dense forests just below low-tide level, and collapse when exposed by very low tides.*

SEAWEEDS

Green algae live in fresh and salt water and a few species live in damp situations on land. Many are single-celled organisms, while many more exist as fine hair-like threads. Green seaweeds live in the shallowest waters around the shore and also cover the mud of many estuaries. A coating of mucus ensures that they do not dry up too quickly when exposed to the air. Nearly all the brown algae live in the sea and they include the largest of all seaweed species. None is unicellular. The most abundant seaweeds of cool seas, they occupy all zones from the upper shore to below low-tide level and often form dense carpets on the rocks. The red algae are almost all marine plants and they are most common in the warmer seas. Some live in rock pools, but most inhabit deeper waters. Their colours range from pale pink to deep red and violet and they vary widely in form. There are a few unicellular species, some grow crust-like on the rocks, many are filamentous, and others have leaf-like thalli. Many are elaborately branched, often secreting thick coats of calcium carbonate around themselves, and are sometimes mistaken for corals.

Fresh strap-like fronds of Thongweed grow from the button-like bases each winter to replace the previous year's fronds.

Green Algae

Sea Lettuce
Ulva lactuca
Family Ulvaceae
This world-wide species has thalli, up to 45cm long, which resemble thin lettuce leaves. It grows on all shore zones, but is most frequently found on the upper shore and is common in estuaries and bays where fresh water runs over the shore.
Ⓑ☻

Enteromorpha intestinalis
This very common seaweed has a tubular thallus rather like a contorted sausage skin inflated with gas. Up to 60cm long, it grows on rocks and mud in estuaries and also where streams trickle over the upper shore.
Ⓑ☻

Spirogyra
Family Zygnemataceae
This genus of filamentous algae contains several common species of ponds and streams, either floating or fixed to stones. Green chloroplasts – the chlorophyll-containing bodies – form spirals in each cell. Division of the cells leads to an increase in the length of the filaments, and each broken fragment form a new strand. The threads often mat into dense sheets.
Ⓑ☻

Brown Algae

Peacock's Tail
Padina pavonia
Family Dictyotaceae
This seaweed has a curved, fan-shaped thallus up to 15cm high and grows in rock pools, or on rocks just below low-tide level. It is a short-lived species, common around coasts of southern Europe.
Ⓑ☻

Bladder Wrack
Fucus vesiculosus
Family Fucaceae
Up to 90cm long, the fronds of this very tough seaweed are recognized by the paired air-filled bladders which buoy them up in the water. However, the bladders are often absent where the fronds are pounded by strong waves. The plant occupies large areas the middle shore and also grows on groynes and piers. The tips of the fronds house the reproductive organs.
Ⓑ☻

Serrated Wrack
Fucus serratus
The flat fronds of this seaweed, 100cm or more in length, are easily recognized by their toothed margins. The swollen tips are also less obvious than in other wracks. The plant grows abundantly on the middle and lower shore but is absent from areas where wave action is strong.
Ⓑ☻

Channelled Wrack
Pelvetia canaliculata
Named for the deep channels running along its branches, this seaweed is abundant on the upper zones of rocky shores and also on estuarine mud-flats and salt-marshes. Its fronds grow up to 15cm long and the water trapped in their channels enables them to survive on the shore for several days.
Ⓑ☻

Thongweed
Himanthalia elongata
Family Himanthaliaceae
The strap-like fronds of this seaweed grow up to 3m long, on rocks on the middle and lower shore – usually just below the Serrated Wrack. Small pits scattered over its surface house the reproductive organs. Young plants resemble buttons until the thongs start to grow.
Ⓑ☻

Sugar Kelp
Laminaria saccharina
Family Laminariaceae
The single, tough frond of this seaweed may grow 9m long and 45cm wide. It grows from just below low-tide level down to depths of about 20m, attaching itself to small stones on muddy and sandy shores. Each frond lasts for just a few months; old ones are washed up. A white deposit of sugar develops on the dry fronds – hence the common name.
Ⓑ☻

Oarweed
Laminaria digitata
This plant forms dense beds from around the low-tide level down to about 30m. Its long-stalked, rubbery frond is up to 3 metres long and attached to stones and boulders. It is oar-shaped, although the blade is usually split into narrow strips. This species lies flat when uncovered by extreme low tides: the stalks of the very similar Cuvie (*L. hyperborea*) remain upright.
Ⓑ☻

Red Algae

Coralweed
Corallina officinalis
Family Corallinaceae
This stiff, bushy seaweed has lime-coated fronds which can reach lengths of about 15cm. Pink to purple while living, it soon turns white after death. It grows in pools and on stones from the middle shore down to fairly deep water.
Ⓑ☻

Red Laver
Porphyra umbilicalis
Family Bangiaceae
The thin, leaf-like lobes of this seaweed can be up to 25cm across, but are often split into ribbon-like strips. Usually green when young, it later ranges from purplish red to olive green. It grows on rocks on all parts of the shore. This plant is widely eaten.
Ⓑ☻

Irish Moss
Chondrus crispus
Family Gigartinaceae
This common seaweed grows in rock pools and on other rocks on the lower and middle shore. Its fronds can grow up to 15cm long and may be green in sunlit pools, but more often range from pink to a deep reddish brown. In wave-battered areas the frond divisions may be much narrower than shown here.
Ⓑ☻

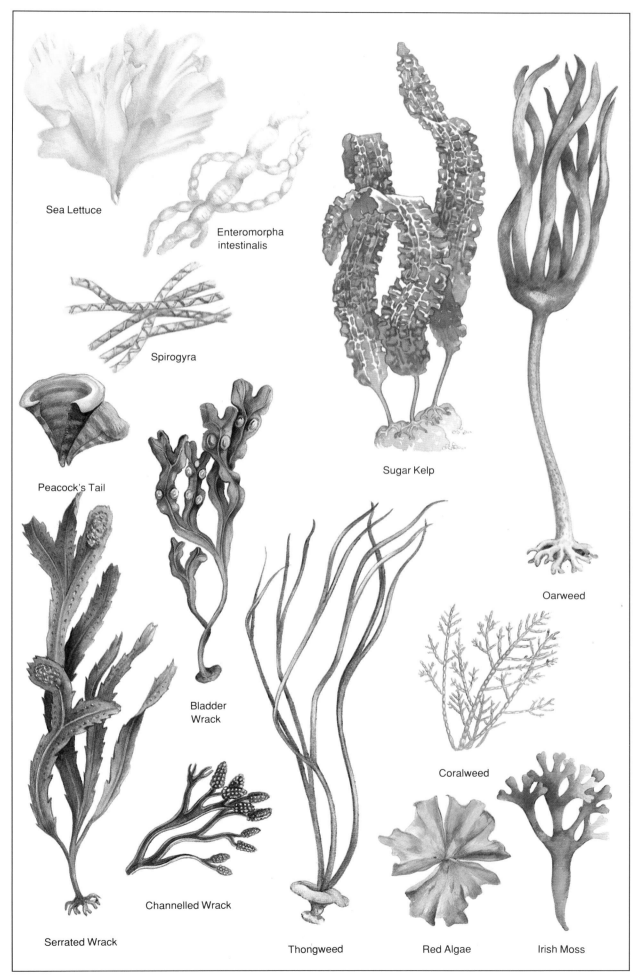

Sea Lettuce

Enteromorpha intestinalis

Spirogyra

Peacock's Tail

Sugar Kelp

Oarweed

Bladder Wrack

Coralweed

Serrated Wrack

Channelled Wrack

Thongweed

Red Algae

Irish Moss

MAMMALS

The members of the Class Mammalia all feed their young with milk secreted from the mammary glands of the mother, but they also share many other characteristics. Most species have a covering of fur or hair, and all are warm-blooded. All mammals have backbones and are quadrupeds, having four limbs, or at least vestiges of the limbs.

The first mammals evolved around 150 million years ago and were small, secretive creatures rather like tree shrews. It was not until around 70 million years ago that mammals began to dominate the world. Today's mammals have diversified enormously in form and shape from their ancestors – some have the limbs modified for flight, others for swimming, climbing, burrowing or running. While most have fur or hair, some are almost naked and others have hair modified into scales.

The basic tooth complement of a mammal is 44 peg-like teeth – 6 incisors, 2 canines, 8 premolars and 6 molars on each of the upper and lower jaws. However, there is great variation, and the moles and the Wild Boar are the only European species with a full complement. Baleen whales lack teeth but filter food with baleen plates. Most mammals can be identified from their jaws and teeth.

LEFT: The agile Pine Marten climbs rapidly through the trees in its hunt for birds and small mammals.

Mammal Groups

There are three main groups of mammals – the monotremes, the marsupials, and the placental mammals. The monotremes – the Duck-billed Platypus and the Echidna – are the most unusual mammals in that they lay eggs. The marsupials are pouched mammals, including the kangaroos. They bear young at an early stage of development and carry the babies in their pouches. The great majority of the world's 4400 mammals, including the 170 or so European species, are placental mammals. The young develop in the mother, where they are fed through a placenta, and are perfectly formed at birth.

The greatest diversity of mammals occurs in the tropics. There is, however, much diversity within the European mammals, ranging from the Pygmy White-toothed Shrew to the Blue Whale, and nine of the 21 orders are native to Europe. There are also a number of introduced species, as well as a few feral species – domesticated species that have escaped and become wild.

ABOVE: This Common Mole, surfacing from its tunnel, reveals the enormous shovel-like front feet which it uses for digging.

The world's largest and smallest mammals are both found in Europe – the Blue Whale, which is up to 31 metres long, and the Pygmy White-toothed Shrew, which has a body length of just 5 centimetres.

Blue Whale

Pygmy White-toothed Shrew

165

The Great Horseshoe Bat has suffered alarmingly from the disturbance and poisoning of its habitats and is now very rare in most parts of Europe.

Habitats

Whereas reptiles, amphibians, fishes and invertebrates are largely dependent on the temperature of their surroundings, mammals – like birds – are warm-blooded, which means they can maintain their body temperature, and thus be active even in extreme cold. This has enabled them to colonize almost all the habitats in the world, and in Europe mammals are found from the Arctic regions of Scandinavia to the semi-deserts of Spain and Greece. However, humans have modified virtually all the natural habitats of Europe and the mammals have had to adapt to these changes. Those that fail to adapt become extinct. Most of the larger mammals that once inhabited the fertile lowlands of Europe, where human impact on the natural habitats has been greatest, became extinct as the land was turned into farmlands. Drainage and pollution of wetlands is leading to further reduction of natural habitats, which has led to drastic reductions in species such as Otters and bats.

However, not all mammals suffer because of human activity. A number of species have proved to be remarkably adaptable, and flourish even in cities and towns. The most obvious of these are the rats and mice, which frequently become pests, damaging food and property and carrying diseases transmissible to humans. Bats have adapted to roosting in houses as well as tunnels and mines. However, the widespread and indiscriminate use of pesticides for timber treatment has led to major declines in house-dwelling bats. Foxes and Jackals frequently scavenge around cities and suburbs, despite efforts to eliminate them, and almost any piece of waste ground or parkland will support several species of rodents and insectivores.

New-born mammals have to stay with their mothers for some time because they need her milk. These young Hedgehogs will be weaned at about six weeks and will then gradually disperse.

Breeding

The breeding habits of mammals are extremely varied, as would be expected of a group containing species as diverse as whales and bats. Although all young mammals are suckled on their mothers' milk, the young of many species are active within hours of birth, or in the case of the whales and dolphins, within minutes of birth.

Some species build nests, and give birth to naked, blind and helpless young, which do not become independent until after lengthy parental care. In most species the male plays little or no part in the care of the young, but in some carnivores the male may take food to the young.

Habits

In common with their diversity of form and habitats, mammals exhibit a wide range of behavioural adaptations. Many species are nocturnal, and the bats use ultrasonic sounds to navigate in darkness. Other mammals, such as shrews, also use ultrasonics to communicate in the total darkness of their runs. After centuries of persecution by humans, many mammals that might be expected to be active by day have adopted nocturnal lifestyles.

Many mammals hibernate in order to save energy when food is in short supply over winter. Most mammals are relatively sedentary, but whales and dolphins undergo seasonal migrations, and are more likely to be seen in spring and autumn than at other times of year.

Some species have a complex social structure and live in colonies, such as those of the ground squirrels. Others, such as deer, form herds, whose structure varies from season to season. Outside the mating season or rut, males and females often live in separate groups.

Certain behavioural traits can be used for identification, such as the playful breaching of the Humpback Whale.

hazel nut gnawed
by Dormouse

hazel nut gnawed
by Squirrel

pine cone
stripped by
Squirrel

Tracks and Signs

Because of their shy, secretive nature it is often necessary to rely on the tracks and signs left by mammals to study them. A mammal-watcher will look for a whole range of signs, rarely actually seeing most species. Footprints are amongst the most obvious signs and those of many species are shown in this book. The remains of food can often be used to identify a species. Squirrels attack pine cones in a manner entirely different from mice, and dormice have a characteristic way of opening nuts. The droppings or scats of most mammals are quite easy to identify and will indicate what species live in an area. Many species deposit droppings in a prominent position as territory markers. Droppings can be identified by shape and size, and also by their contents – bat droppings have the hard remains of insects, whereas similar-sized mouse droppings are fibrous. The more distinctive droppings are illustrated. Other signs left by mammals include wallows and cast antlers of deer, nests of Harvest Mice, burrows of rabbits and badgers, runs and hills of moles, and the skulls and skeletons of many species.

ABOVE: *Left-overs often show which mammals have been feeding in an area.*

LEFT: *Each kind of mammal has its unique dentition and skulls can usually be identified quite easily.*

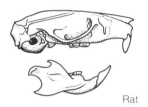

Rat

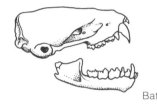

Bat

Shrew

Distribution

Most mammals are relatively sedentary, and knowledge of their normal distribution helps to identify a species encountered in the wild. Even though bats are nearly as mobile as birds, and some species migrate, they are rarely encountered outside their known range. Similarly, marine mammals, although often highly migratory, occur only sporadically outside their main range. Since both bats and marine mammals have undergone drastic declines in the past century, it is perhaps increasingly unlikely that they will occur outside their known range. Species that have restricted habitat requirements often have a highly fragmented distribution, occuring only in a few suitable areas within the total range.

The distribution maps show the main range of the species, within which it is likely to occur in any suitable habitat, in dark green. The species' secondary range, within which it is found only sporadically or its occurrence is poorly documented, is shown in a paler tint of green.

KEY TO MAPS

main range

secondary range

River disturbance and pollution has meant that Otters are now often seen on remote parts of the coast.

Insectivores

There are about 365 species in the Order Insectivora, divided into eight families world-wide, three of which are found in Europe. All display features generally considered to be representative of primitive mammals, such as the full complement of 44 simple, peg-like teeth, and five clawed digits on all limbs. Although insectivore means a feeder on insects, many species take a wide range of small animals.

HEDGEHOGS

The 17 species in this family (Erinaceidae) are confined to the Old World. Most have fur modified into hard spines.

Hedgehog
Erinaceus europaeus
Head and body 8.7–31cm, tail 2–4cm. This is a familiar, spiny, nocturnal animal that rolls up when attacked. It is well-adapted to suburban woodland and hedgerow habitats – although mainly insectivorous, it will feed on almost any small animal and also takes birds' eggs. It builds several nests of leaves and grasses, the most snug and secure one kept for its winter hibernation from October to April. Up to two litters are produced each year, between June and September, and the 4–5 young are born helpless with soft spines.

MOLES AND DESMANS

In Europe there are two sub-families of the Talpidae: the burrowing Talpinae and the aquatic Desmaninae. Several species of the former, occuring in Europe, have only recently been recognized.

Pyrenean Desman
Galemys pyrenaicus
Head and body 11–15.6cm, tail 12.6–15.6cm. This aquatic mole has several remarkable adaptations to living in fast-flowing mountain streams. Its long snout can be used like a snorkel, its powerful hind feet are webbed, and its tail is slightly flattened to act as a rudder. Mostly nocturnal, it consumes at least two-thirds of its body weight in food a day, feeding on aquatic invertebrates and small fish. It is found in the Pyrenees, north-western Spain and Portugal.

Common Mole
Talpa europaea
Head and body 11.3–15.9cm, tail 2.5–4cm. This burrowing mammal has short, velvety, blackish fur and enormous shovel-like forepaws. Mostly occurring in grassland and deciduous woodland, it spends almost its entire life underground, though it may surface in very dry weather. Feeding mainly on earthworms and insect larvae, it stores surplus food. It is widespread over Europe except for the extreme north and south, and Ireland.

The Water Shrew's fur traps air underwater, giving it a silvery look. When it comes to land, it squeezes through tunnels to dry itself.

SHREWS

The family of shrews (Soricidae) contains 272 species. Those found in Europe are the common shrews (*Sorex*) and water shrews (*Neomys*), both of which have red-tipped teeth, and the white-toothed shrews (*Suncus* and *Crocidura*).

Common Shrew
Sorex araneus
Head and body 5.5–8.5cm, tail 3.4–4.7cm. This small insectivore has red-tipped teeth, and short velvety fur, chocolate-brown above with paler flanks and pale undersides. The nest is made from undergrowth and grasses and is often hidden in hedgebottoms. Although seldom seen, its high-pitched squeaking can often be heard. It is widespread and abundant over much of northern and eastern Europe.

Pygmy Shrew
Sorex minutus
Head and body 3.9–6.4cm, tail 3.2–4.4cm. This very small shrew, the most widespread in Europe, has a proportionally long, thick tail. Brown above and pale below, it is the lightest in colour of the red-toothed shrews. The nest is made out of grasses. Rarely visible, this shrew's shrill squeaking can often be heard in hedgebottoms.

Alpine Shrew
Sorex alpinus
Head and body 5.9–8.3cm, tail 5.6–7.4cm. This is a distinctive, dark grey shrew, often almost black, with red-tipped teeth and a long tail. Found in coniferous forest, often near water, it occurs in the Alps, the Balkans, Harz and Carpathian mountains of Europe, at altitudes from 500m up to the tree line. The nest is built of grasses in burrows.

Water Shrew
Neomys fodiens
Head and body 7–9.6cm, tail 5.1–7.2cm. The largest European shrew, it is blackish above and sometimes black but usually white below. Normally found close to water, it swims and dives well, appearing silvery under water. It feeds on aquatic invertebrates and also on small fish and frogs. It is widespread throughout mainland Europe and Britain, except for most of Iberia and the Balkans.

Lesser White-toothed Shrew
Crocidura suaveolens
Head and body 4.9–7.8cm, tail 2.7–5cm. This is the smallest of the white-toothed shrews, with colouration that varies from grey to dark brown above, paler below. Found throughout much of Europe, it is absent from the

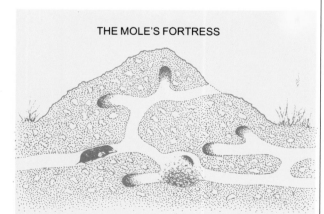

THE MOLE'S FORTRESS

The Mole excavates a complex fortress containing a nest chamber and tunnels radiating to its runs.

main British Isles, but is present on many smaller islands, including the Isles of Scilly, Jersey and Sark. It is found in many habitats, including the seashore, where it lives among seaweed.
Ⓑ ◐ ☀ ✿ ☻

Miller's Water Shrew
Neomys anomalus
Head and body 6.7–8.7cm, tail 4–5.2cm. Also known as the Mediterranean Water Shrew, it is often less aquatic than the Water Shrew and always has a whitish underside. The last third of its tail and its feet have characteristic fringing. It is found mainly in mountainous regions but, in eastern Europe, it also occurs in lowlands. It is widespread throughout southern and eastern Europe.
◐ ☻

Pygmy White-toothed Shrew
Suncus etruscus
Head and body 3.6–5.3cm, tail 2.1–3cm. Also known as Savi's or the Etruscan Shrew, this is one of the smallest mammals in the world, and likened to a furry beetle. It weighs less than 2g, and feeds on spiders and small insects. It is found by human habitations, in dry woodland, scrub and olive groves only in the Mediterranean region.
◐ ◑ ✿

Hedgehog

Miller's Water Shrew

Pyrenean Desman

Common Shrew

Common Mole

Alpine Shrew

Pygmy Shrew

Lesser White-toothed Shrew

Water Shrew

P W-t Shrew

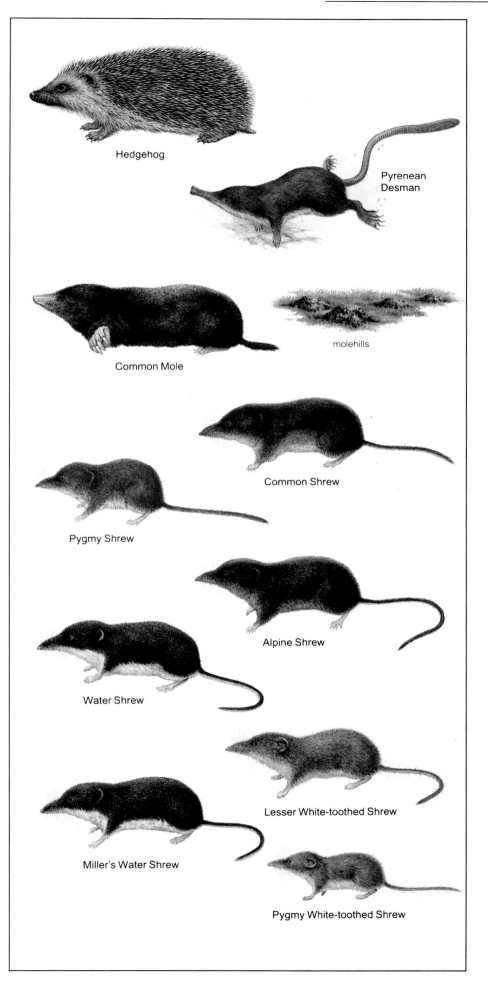

Hedgehog

Pyrenean Desman

Common Mole

molehills

Common Shrew

Pygmy Shrew

Alpine Shrew

Water Shrew

Lesser White-toothed Shrew

Miller's Water Shrew

Pygmy White-toothed Shrew

Bats

There are 1000 or so species of bat (Order Chiroptera) found throughout the world. The three European families – the horseshoe bats (Rhinolophidae), the free-tailed bats (Mollossidae) and the vespertilionid bats (Vespertilionidae) – are all insectivorous, and belong to the sub-order Microchiroptera. They hunt and navigate using echolocation. They have leathery wings, and usually a membrane between the legs and tail. The horseshoe bats possess a 'noseleaf', which they use to produce the ultrasonics. The vespertilionids all have a 'tragus' – a lobe of skin in the ear, which is often useful for identification. Apart from the two horseshoe bats, the species described below all belong to the family Vespertilionidae.

Greater Horseshoe Bat
Rhinolophus ferrumequinum
Head and body 5.7–7.1cm, tail 3.5–4.3cm, wingspan 33–40cm. This is the largest European horseshoe bat. Roosting singly or in large clusters, it hangs from the roof with its wings loosely wrapped around its body. It is found in caves, attics and tunnels in areas of open woodland, often near water. Populations of this species have undergone a massive decline due to changing agricultural practices, indiscriminate use of pesticides and disturbance. It is almost extinct in Britain.
Ⓑ🌣✿✿⊗

Lesser Horseshoe Bat
Rhinolophus hipposideros
Head and body 3.7–4.5cm, tail 2.3–3.3cm, wingspan 19.2–25.4cm. This is the smallest of the European horseshoe bats, and is found mostly in woodland habitats, particularly in limestone regions. In northern parts it usually roosts in attics in the summer, and hibernates in canal tunnels and cellars in the winter. In the south it is more often confined to caves and mines. Although the most widespread of the horseshoe bats, this species has undergone a serious decline throughout most of Europe.
Ⓑ🌣✿✿

Natterer's Bat
Myotis nattereri
Head and body 4.2–5.55cm, tail 3.8–4.7cm, wingspan 22–30cm. A medium-sized *Myotis*, it has fairly large ears, and whitish underparts. At close quarters its most distinctive feature is the fringe of stiff bristles along the edge of the tail membrane. Hibernation takes place in relatively low temperatures, usually in caves and mines. It occurs throughout most of Europe, except northern Scandinavia and the Balkans, but is endangered in many parts of its range.
Ⓑ🌣✿⊗

Greater Mouse-eared Bat
Myotis myotis
Head and body 6.7–7.9cm, tail 4.5–6cm, wingspan 35–45cm. This is one of the largest European bats, and has thick, greyish brown fur. It is found in a wide variety of habitats, including towns. In summer it frequents attics and lofts, and in winter it roosts in cellars, mines, caves and tree holes. Although this species was once widespread over most of Europe, its numbers have declined in recent years by 80 per cent. The British population became extinct in 1991.
🌣✿✿⊕⊗

Noctule Bat
Nyctalus noctula
Head and body 6–8cm, tail 4.1–6cm, wingspan 32–40cm. This large bat, with distinctively golden brown fur has narrow, pointed wings and often flies high and fast, with steep dives. Chiefly a woodland species, it often roosts in woodpecker holes. In areas where old trees have been felled and cleared, it is threatened if no alternatives are available. Widespread over most of Europe, including many islands, but increasingly rare.
Ⓑ🌣✿⊕⊗

Whiskered Bat
Myotis mystacinus
Head and body 3.5–4.8cm, tail 3–4.3cm, wingspan 19–22cm. This is the smallest of the European *Myotis* bats. Its colouration is variable, being dark to light brown above and greyish below. It often hunts over water and sometimes flies by day. In summer it roosts in bird and bat boxes, hollow trees and attics. In winter it likes damp, cold caves and tunnels. It is found in most of Europe.
Ⓑ🌣✿✿⊕

Serotine
Eptesicus serotinus
Head and body 6.2–8.2cm, tail 3.9–5.9cm, wingspan 24.5–30cm. This large, broad-winged bat has long, dark brown fur. It hunts in broad loops along hedges, woodland edges and around street lamps, often travelling several kilometres to its feeding area. It is widespread over most of Europe, occurring as far north as southern England, Denmark and southern Sweden, but is rarely found in large concentrations. Its summer roosts are usually in buildings so this species is extremely vulnerable to poisoning by chemical timber treatments.
Ⓑ🌣✿⊕⊗

Common Pipistrelle
Pipistrellus pipistrellus
Head and body 3.2–5.1cm, tail 2–3.6cm, wingspan 18–24cm. This is the smallest and most widespread European bat, with short, triangular ears. Frequently found roosting in houses, it has undergone a massive decline in many areas, largely due to poisoning by the chemicals used in treating roof timbers. Usually emerging soon after dusk, it often flies along a regular route with a characteristic twisting, fluttering flight. The single litter may contain two young although British bats produce only one.
Ⓑ🌣✿✿✿✿⊕

A Greater Horseshoe Bat about to capture a moth. Bats often use their wing and tail membranes to scoop up their prey.

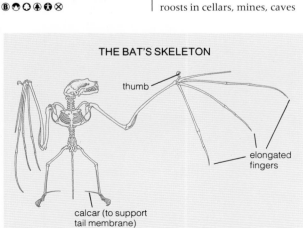

THE BAT'S SKELETON

thumb

elongated fingers

calcar (to support tail membrane)

Northern Bat
Eptesicus nilssoni
Head and body 4.5–6.4cm, tail 3.5–5cm, wingspan 24–28cm. This is a medium-sized bat, with dark brown fur above, and a paler underside. The fur is yellow-tipped, giving it a slightly glossy sheen. It flies fast, making sharp turns, often over water or at tree-top height. Found in open woodland, usually near houses, it roosts in cracks in walls and under roofs. This species is widespread in northern and central Europe, and is the only bat to occur north of the Arctic Circle.

Brown Long-eared Bat
Plecotus auritus
Head and body 4.2–5.5cm, tail 3.2–5.5cm, wingspan 24–28.5cm. A medium-sized bat with huge ears. Its under-fur is brownish when parted. A relatively common species, it is found throughout most of Europe, except the extreme north. Preferring woodland, gardens and parks, it feeds with a slow, fluttering and hovering flight. In summer it frequently roosts in houses, and in winter it hibernates in relatively cold places, such as close to the entrances of caves. The single litter contains one, occasionally two, young.

Greater
Horseshoe Bat

Whiskered Bat

Lesser
Horseshoe Bat

Common
Pipistrelle

Natterer's Bat

Serotine

Greater Mouse-
eared Bat

Northern Bat

Noctule Bat

B Long-eared Bat

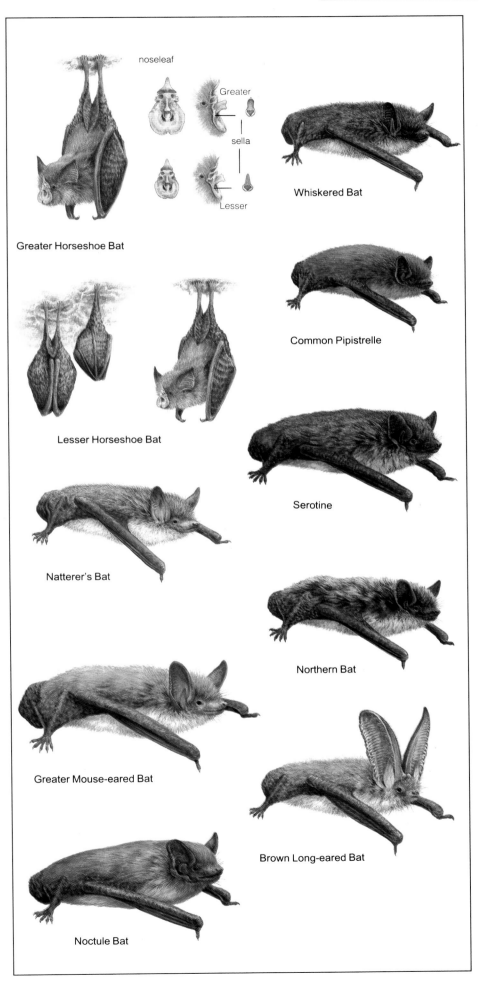

noseleaf

Greater

sella

Lesser

Greater Horseshoe Bat

Whiskered Bat

Lesser Horseshoe Bat

Common Pipistrelle

Natterer's Bat

Serotine

Greater Mouse-eared Bat

Northern Bat

Brown Long-eared Bat

Noctule Bat

Rabbits and Hares

World-wide, there are about 65 species of rabbits, hares and pikas, in the Order Lagomorpha. The European species all have long ears and relatively long hind legs, giving them a hopping gait. The European Rabbit digs burrows, which often form extensive warrens, but all other species generally live above ground. Lagomorphs can be distinguished from rodents by the presence of a second pair of small incisors, located behind the large ones, on the upper jaws. Rabbits and hares belong to the Family Leporidae.

Rabbit
Oryctolagus cuniculus
Head and body 38–55cm, tail 4.5–7cm. This is one of the best-known and most frequently observed wild animals in Europe. It usually excavates extensive burrows (warrens) in light soils, and grazes around the entrance. The small round droppings are characteristic, as is the hopping gait. The Rabbit can be a serious agricultural pest but in Britain, and some other parts of its range, the disease myxomatosis periodically reduces the population by up to 99 per cent. Formerly confined to the western Mediterranean region, it has been introduced elsewhere and is now widespread across Europe. Up to five litters are born a year, containing 3–8 blind young.
Ⓑ🐾➴◔🐾☂

Brown Hare
Lepus europaeus
Head and body 50–70cm, tail 7–11cm. Weighing up to 7kg, the hare is often conspicuous in open fields, steppes and woodland. The long, black-tipped ears, and tail which is black above and white below, are characteristic. It grazes and browses on grasses, leaves, shoots and twigs, and is both nocturnal and diurnal. Although normally silent, it produces a loud scream when in distress. It has an extensive distribution over most of Europe except northern Scandinavia and higher altitudes where it is often replaced by the Mountain Hare. It has been introduced into Ireland. Up to four litters are born a year, in a shallow depression (form). The 1–5 young are furred and have open eyes at birth.
Ⓑ➴◔🐾☂

Mountain Hare
Lepus timidus
Head and body 46–65cm, tail 4.3–8cm. Also known as the Varying or Arctic Hare, it is slightly smaller than the Brown Hare and has an all-white tail and shorter ears. Found mainly in tundra, heathland and montane grassland, it is greyish brown in summer, and, in most parts of its range (except Ireland), it turns white in winter. It makes its nest (form) in rock clefts, occasionally excavating a short tunnel. This species occurs in Scandinavia, the Baltic states, Alps, Pyrenees, Scotland and Ireland, and has been introduced into the British Isles. It bears two or three litters a year; the 2–5 young are furred and have open eyes at birth.
Ⓑ➴🐾➴◔☂

Brown Hares 'boxing'. It was once thought that these were males fighting, but it is often the female warding off an unwanted male.

Rodents

The majority of the world's mammal species are in the Order Rodentia, with over 1790 species known. Rodents are gnawing mammals with well-developed incisor teeth, a diastema (gap) and a row of grinding cheek teeth. One or more species of rodent is found in almost all habitats, except the sea, and the permanently frozen polar regions. There are aquatic, arboreal and burrowing species, which may be nocturnal or diurnal.

SQUIRRELS

Of the 250 species of squirrel (Family Sciuridae), only five are native to Europe. These are the Red Squirrel, the European Souslik, the Spotted Souslik, the Alpine Marmot and the Flying Squirrel. The last named is essentially a Siberian species, but it occurs in Finland and the Baltic states.

Red Squirrel
Sciurus vulgaris
Head and body 18–27cm, tail 14–20cm. Its colouring is variable from light red to bright chestnut and, rarely, almost jet black. In winter the ears have prominent tufts. It is found in a variety of wooded habitats. This is the only squirrel found throughout most of Europe and, although the species has declined in England, it is still abundant in Scotland and Ireland. In Britain, where it overlaps with the Grey Squirrel, the Red Squirrel is generally confined to coniferous woodlands. Contrary to popular belief, neither of these squirrels hibernates.
Ⓑ➴◔🐾

Grey Squirrel
Sciurus carolinensis
Head and body 23–30 cm, tail 14–24cm. Although occasionally tinged with russet, the fur is grey and the ears do not have tufts. It builds its nest (drey) in holes or forks in trees and in lofts of buildings. In autumn it makes caches of nuts and beech mast. Introduced into Britain from eastern North America at the end of the 19th century, it is more adaptable than the native Red Squirrel and has largely replaced it in England and Wales.
Ⓑ➴◔🐾

European Souslik
Spermophilus citellus
Head and body 17.5–24cm, tail 4–8cm. This ground squirrel lives in colonies which excavate deep and extensive burrows, by agricultural land, open steppe and pasture. It stands upright to watch for predators and, when alarmed, it emits a high-pitched whistle. Its range extends from southern Poland and eastern Germany, south to northern Greece. Its recent decline may be due to intensified agriculture.
🐾☂

RABBIT DEFENCE STRATEGIES

Rabbits are colonial, and when a predator such as a Stoat appears, they warn each other by thumping with the back legs, and flashing the white tail 'scut'.

Alpine Marmot
Marmota marmota
Head and body 40–60cm, tail
13–20cm. A large, heavily
built ground squirrel, it lives
in colonies throughout the
Alps and Carpathian
mountains, where since 1880
there have been several
successful translocations and
reintroductions. In the
mornings it emerges from its
burrow to sunbathe, typically
sitting on its haunches as it
keeps watch for predators. At
the sight of danger, it emits a
distinctive whistle. This
species hibernates for about
seven months in the winter.
During this time it will
occasionally awaken to feed.
❂

BEAVERS

**The species in this small
family (Castoridae) are
confined to the northern
hemisphere. Beavers are
among the few mammals
capable of large-scale
habitat modification.**

European Beaver
Castor fiber
Head and body 75–100cm,
tail 30–40cm. The largest
European rodent, it has a
broad, flattened tail and large,
orange incisor teeth. It builds
extensive 'lodges' and dams,
and tunnels into river banks
using its forefeet. Once found
in aquatic habitats across
Europe, it was reduced by
hunting. Now reintroduced, it
pairs for life and produces one
litter a year.
◐◉●

Rabbit	Grey Squirrel
Brown Hare	European Souslik
Mountain Hare	Alpine Marmot

Red Squirrel	European Beaver

Rabbit

gnawed
hazel nut

Grey Squirrel

Brown Hare

European Souslik

summer   winter

Alpine Marmot

tree stump left
by Beaver

Mountain Hare

stripped
pine cone

dark form

red form

European Beaver

Beaver's lodge

Red Squirrel

DORMICE

This is a small family (Gliridae) comprising about 16 species found in Europe, Asia and Africa. Most dormice look superficially similar to small squirrels or chipmunks, with well-furred tails. The European dormice are all fairly vocal, making a variety of squeaks and chirping noises. They mostly inhabit woodlands and forests, but also occur in orchards and gardens. Their diet consists of seeds, buds and insects. Dormice are arboreal and frequently nocturnal. The European species go into a long hibernation in the autumn, usually on or under the ground.

Forest Dormouse
Dryomys nitedula
Head and body 7.7–11cm, tail 6–9.5cm. In general appearance this species resembles the Garden Dormouse but is smaller, with less black colouring. Like other dormice, it has a furry tail and is an agile climber, though rarely seen because it is nocturnal and secretive. The summer nest is a ball of grasses, and the winter nest is underground. It eats insects and other animal life, but is generally more vegetarian.

Found mainly in dense forest, it hibernates only in the north; in the south, it may have two litters a year. Its range extends from central Europe as far north as Poland and Germany, and south to Yugoslavia and Greece.

Edible Dormouse
Glis glis
Head and body 12–20cm, tail 11–19cm. The largest of the European dormice, it is grey and has a particularly bushy tail, giving it the appearance of a miniature squirrel. It is generally found in well-wooded habitats with undergrowth, such as orchards and gardens, and may enter houses or sheds, particularly in autumn and winter, when it can be noisy. It is so-called because it was eaten by the Romans as a delicacy, and is also known as the Fat Dormouse as it becomes very plump before hibernating. Distributed throughout most of Europe and successfully introduced into a small area in England. Up to eight young are born in mid-summer.

Garden Dormouse
Eliomys quercinus
Head and body 10–18cm, tail 9–13cm. Also known as the Oak Dormouse, it is sandy or grey above and white below with a distinctive black mask, extending below the ears. The tail is long and furry, tipped black-and-white. Although it does occur in gardens, it is most abundant in forests and woodland. In winter it hibernates, often communally, making a nest in a tree hole, building or burrow. Largely omnivorous, it occasionally takes birds' eggs and young mammals as a supplement to the usual diet of buds, berries and seeds. The Garden Dormouse is found throughout most of Continental Europe. A related species is the little-known, greyish Mouse-tailed Dormouse (*Myomimus roachi*) found in Bulgaria and Greece. It is distinguished from all other dormice by having short hair on its tail.

Hazel Dormouse
Muscardinus avellenarius
Head and body 6–8.5cm, tail 5.5–8cm. This small, bright orange-brown animal with a furry tail is strictly nocturnal and is very rarely encountered. It prefers deciduous woodland, with dense vegetation, such as coppiced woods, where it is an agile climber. Its nest is usually close to ground level, and often incorporates shredded honeysuckle bark. It eats hazelnuts, leaving a smooth, round hole without teeth-marks. From autumn to spring it hibernates. Once popular as a pet, it remains widespread over most of western Europe. Up to two litters, each of 3–5 young, are born in the summer.

A Hazel Dormouse feeding on berries. Before winter hibernation dormice eat large amounts of fruit and seeds to accumulate fat reserves.

Forest Dormouse

gnawed nut

Edible Dormouse

Garden Dormouse

THE MOLE RAT'S TUNNELING METHOD

Mole Rats use their enlarged incisors to excavate extensive tunnels, pinching the skin across the mouth to avoid swallowing too much soil.

RATS, MICE, VOLES AND HAMSTERS

The Muridae is the largest family of mammals in the world with over 1160 species currently recognized. It includes the true mice and rats, the hamsters, lemmings and voles, and, outside Europe, the gerbils. Most are usually small, have several litters a year, and are relatively short-lived. Several species are considered pests, causing extensive damage to agriculture, stored food and other property. Some species also carry diseases which kill people, including plague and leptospirosis. Although many species are difficult (sometimes impossible) to identify in the field, the cheek teeth are characteristic and vary considerably between the main groups.

HAMSTERS

There are 25 species in this sub-family (Cricetinae), three of which occur in Europe. They are short-tailed, short-legged rodents that burrow extensively and store food underground. Wild hamsters have richer colours than domesticated ones. Hamsters thrive in the rainless steppes of eastern Europe.

Common Hamster
Cricetus cricetus
Head and body 22–34cm, tail 2.8–6cm. A large rodent with virtually no tail. Colouration is very variable, with black underparts and pale patches on its sides. It lives in colonies and stores food, such as grain or potatoes, in extensive burrows. Food is also carried in its cheek pouches which it inflates if cornered. When disturbed, it can jump up to a metre high. It hibernates throughout the winter. Populations can build up to plague proportions. Originally confined to the east European steppes, it spread westwards with the clearing of the forests, but has declined recently due to changes in agriculture.

MOLE RATS

Of the eight species in this sub-family (Spalacinae) two occur in Europe, the others in the southern USSR, Asia Minor and the eastern Mediterranean. They are very well adapted to a subterranean life, using their incisors to dig, and kicking the earth behind them with their hind feet. None displays any external signs of possessing sight or hearing.

Greater Mole Rat
Spalax microphthalmus
Head and body 15–27cm. A thick-set rodent, it has no tail and non-functional eyes concealed in fur. The head is flattened to bulldoze soil and the incisors are enlarged for digging. It excavates its own system of tunnels with extensive chambers used as nests, stores and latrines. Found in open steppes, grassland and farmland, it feeds on roots and tubers, sometimes causing damage to crops when abundant. Mainly nocturnal and subterranean, it only occasionally comes above ground, to bask in the sun. It has a fragmented range, occurring in Yugoslavia and Greece, and north up to the south-western Ukraine. One litter of 4–5 young is born in spring.

Forest Dormouse

Hazel Dormouse

Edible Dormouse

Common Hamster

Gdn Dormouse

Mole Rat

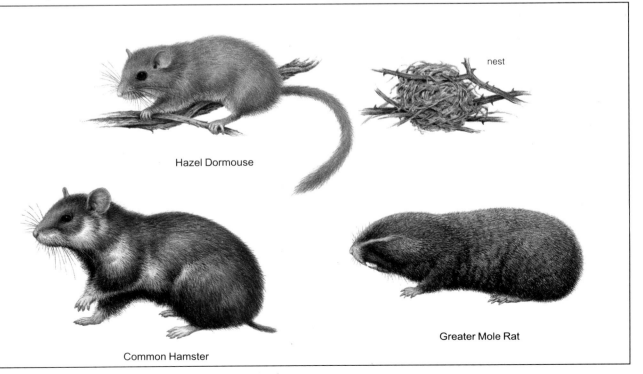

Hazel Dormouse

nest

Common Hamster

Greater Mole Rat

LEMMINGS AND VOLES

There are over 130 species of this sub-family (Microtinae) found throughout the world, and 25 or more have been recorded in Europe. The actual figure may be higher as several species (particularly pine voles) are extremely difficult to separate in the field. They are mostly brownish or greyish, with short legs, short ears, small eyes and blunt muzzles, living in runs and tunnels and feeding primarily on grasses and other vegetation. Some species, particularly in northern areas, can become extremely numerous and then suffer dramatic population crashes.

Muskrat
Ondatra zibethica
Head and body 25–40cm, tail 19–25cm. This is a large aquatic rodent with webbed hind feet and a long, hairless tail. Found in lakes and slow-flowing rivers with dense vegetation and twigs, it can swim underwater for long distances. Mainly vegetarian, it also eats fish, crustaceans and freshwater mussels. Muskrats usually live in pairs. Originally from North America, it was widely bred in captivity for its fur (musquash) and descendants of escaped animals have now spread over much of Europe. It once bred in Great Britain but has been exterminated.

Norway Lemming
Lemmus lemmus
Head and body 13–15cm, tail 1.5–2cm. A large, vole-like rodent with a distinctive pattern, it digs extensive tunnels and can live and breed beneath snow, feeding exclusively on plants. During favourable conditions it undergoes population explosions and, when numbers reach around 100–250 per hectare, emigration takes place. Many die on these emigrations, drowning as they attempt to cross water, but their range is temporarily extended. When the snows melt, the ball-shaped winter nests are exposed on the ground. It is normally confined to the sub-alpine zone of mountain tundra of Scandinavia and the northern USSR.

Wood Lemming
Myopus schisticolor
Head and body 5–12.5cm, tail 1–2cm. This rodent is easily confused with true voles, but has a very short tail. Found in coniferous forests, particularly where overgrown with *Sphagnum* moss, it is the only small mammal in Europe to live almost exclusively on mosses and liverworts. Once thought to occur in isolated populations only, it is now known to be fairly widespread from Norway to Finland and the USSR. It has two litters a year, of up to seven young each. Due to a mutation, some females apparently give birth only to females.

Water voles feed mostly on vegetation, such as this one eating willow leaves. However, they also eat substantial amounts of animal matter, including fish if they find them dead.

Bank Vole
Clethrionomys glareolus
Head and body 8–12cm, tail 3–6.5cm. This vole is reddish brown above, grey on its sides and paler below, with fairly prominent ears. It is found in a variety of habitats but particularly in hedgerows and woodland. Its nest is usually underground, often below a log. Although it feeds mainly on seeds, nuts, berries and shoots, it does occasionally eat invertebrates. Widespread in Europe, it is frequently one of the most abundant rodents. Four or more litters, of up to six young, are produced each year. Bank Voles occur on many islands where some have evolved into distinctive subspecies, such as the Skomer Vole which is twice as heavy as those found on the mainland. The Bank Vole was unknown in Ireland prior to 1964, and was almost certainly introduced by man.

Field Vole
Microtus agrestis
Head and body 9–14cm, tail 2.8–5.2cm. Compared with related voles, this species has long, shaggy fur and slightly darker colouration; the tail is darker above than below. It is found in a wide variety of habitats, but particularly in grasslands. It feeds on grasses, roots and other vegetation, and in winter it often eats bark. Populations are cyclic, and it is an important food source for several predators, such as foxes and Short-eared Owls. This is one of the most abundant voles in Europe but it is absent from Ireland and most of the Mediterranean area. It produces litters of 4–6 young between spring and autumn.

Snow Vole
Microtus nivalis
Head and body 8.5–14cm, tail 4–7.5cm. This large vole has long, soft, light-grey fur that becomes pale with age, and a distinctive whitish tail. It lives in meadows at altitudes above the tree line, mostly among rocky screes, and eats shrubs and alpine plants. This vole does not normally tunnel, but makes runs among rocks, on which it is occasionally seen sunning itself. Its distribution is fragmented but it occurs in many mountain ranges of central and southern Europe, from as high as 4000m in the Alps, down to 120m along the sheer coastal rocks of Yugoslavia. Up to two litters a year are born, each containing 1–5 young.

THE MUSK RAT'S LODGE

A cross-section through the Musk Rat's lodge. The entrance is under water, so that from the ground the lodge just looks like a heap of rotting vegetation.

Common Pine Vole
Pitymys subterraneus
Head and body 8–10.2cm, tail 2–4cm. This vole's fur is more reddish and its ears slightly smaller than other voles. Generally confined to areas with light soils, it lives in small colonies and burrows extensively. The colonies can often be detected by the presence of burrows and spoil heaps of dirt. It is the most widespread of the voles but, because it is largely nocturnal and usually underground, it is rarely seen. Although its range is discontinuous and fragmented, it occurs from France eastwards as far as the USSR. Up to nine litters, containing 2–3 young, are born each year.

⬤◐⬤✪❂⬛

Northern Water Vole
Arvicola terrestris
Head and body 12–20cm, tail 8–13cm. This large vole has colouring ranging from sandy brown to almost black. It usually occurs in wetland habitats, but is also found well away from water. It tunnels extensively in meadows and pastures, often throwing up tumps of soil resembling mole hills, although the soil is finer. Vegetable matter makes up the major part of its diet, as well as fish and carrion. Widespread over most of Europe except north-western France, most of Iberia and the southern Balkans. Occurs in Sicily but is absent from most other Mediterranean islands, and from Ireland.

🅑⬤✪

Musk Rat

Field Vole

Norway Lemming

Snow Vole

Wood Lemming

Common Pine Vole

Bank Vole

N Water Vole

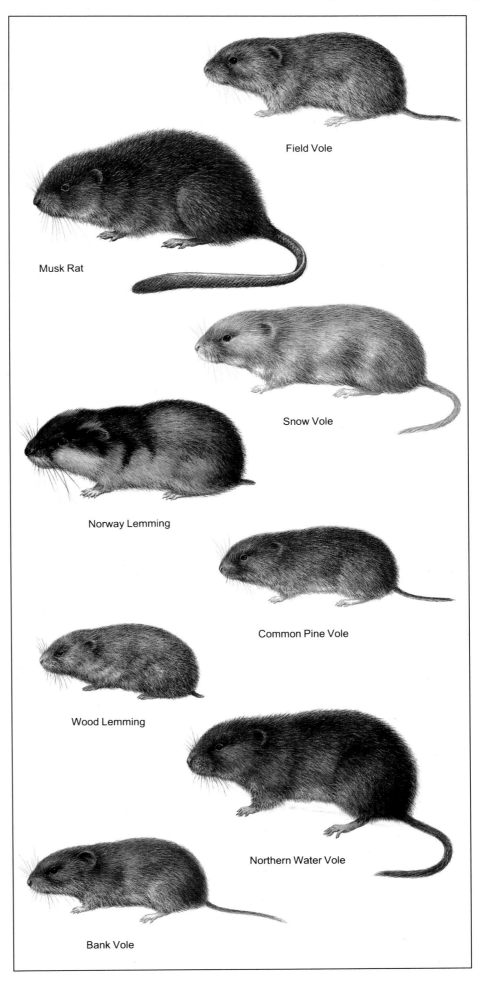

Field Vole

Musk Rat

Snow Vole

Norway Lemming

Common Pine Vole

Wood Lemming

Northern Water Vole

Bank Vole

RATS AND MICE

Over 450 species are known in this sub-family (Murinae), of which around 15 occur in Europe. They all have long, thin tails and feed largely on seeds, causing damage in grain stores. The Brown Rat and the house mice are found almost everywhere inhabited by man. It has been discovered that the house mouse comprises four or more separate species.

Brown Rat

Striped Field Mouse

Black Rat

Western House Mouse

Wood Mouse

Harvest Mouse

Y-necked Mouse

N Birch Mouse

Brown Rat
Rattus norvegicus
Head and body 20–28cm, tail 17–23cm. The fur, greasy in appearance, is usually dark above, paler below, but blackish animals are not uncommon. It is a serious pest, causing extensive damage to stored foods and carrying diseases transmissible to people and other animals. Highly adaptable, it prefers damp habitats, including sewers, and is a strong swimmer. Found throughout most of northern and central Europe, but is less widespread in the Mediterranean area, where it is replaced by the Black Rat.
Ⓑ ☻ ☗

Black Rat
Rattus rattus
Head and body 16–24cm, tail 18–26cm. Also known as the Ship Rat, its muzzle is more pointed and the ears and eyes larger than those of the Brown Rat. The fur is usually blackish, but sometimes it is sandy brown above and greyish below. Unlike the Brown Rat, it lives above ground and is frequently found in attics and sometimes in trees. It is omnivorous, eating fruits, crops, stored foodstuffs and refuse. Although the Black Rat is found throughout the

A Brown Rat with young. Although born naked, blind and helpless, by the time they are about a week old their fur is developing and they are increasingly active, becoming independent in 3–4 weeks.

Mediterranean region, northern European populations are becoming increasingly fragmented and it is endangered in Scandinavia and Britain. Scattered, isolated populations also occur in eastern Europe.
Ⓑ ☗ ⊗

Wood Mouse
Apodemus sylvaticus
Head and body 7.5–11cm, tail 7–11cm. This small mouse has large eyes and ears and a long slender tail. Usually sandy-brown above and white below, it is mainly nocturnal and extremely agile. Found in hedgerows, woodland and gardens, it also enters houses, particularly in

autumn. It feeds mainly on seeds, berries and other vegetable material but will also eat grubs and small invertebrates. It is common throughout Europe, except north-eastern regions, and also occurs on most islands.
Ⓑ ✿ ☗

Yellow-necked Mouse
Apodemus flavicollis
Head and body 9–12cm, tail 9–13cm. Similar to the Wood Mouse but slightly larger, it has a yellowish-brown bar or patch on the throat, extending across the chest. It is found mainly in wooded habitats, including orchards and gardens, but it also frequently enters houses. This mouse is widespread in

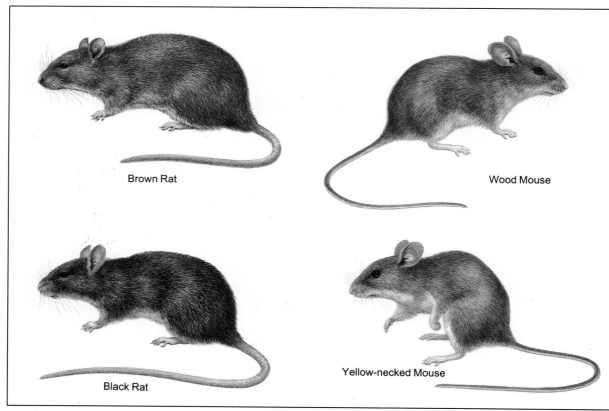
Brown Rat

Wood Mouse

Black Rat

Yellow-necked Mouse

AGGRESSION IN HARVEST MICE

When disputing territory, Harvest Mice are surprisingly aggressive, making a range of squealing noises.

eastern and central Europe but does not occur in most of France and the Low Countries, and is generally confined to mountainous regions of the Mediterranean. It has a patchy distribution throughout England and Wales.

Ⓑ❍❹❸🐞

Striped Field Mouse
Apodemus agrarius
Head and body 7–12.5cm, tail 6.5–9cm. This wood mouse is best distinguished by the black stripe down the middle of its back. The ears are smaller than those of the Wood Mouse. The tail is shorter than the head and body, distinguishing it from the similarly striped birch

mice which have much longer tails. Found mostly in dense vegetation, often along rivers, it feeds chiefly on seeds, but also on insects and their grubs. It lives in burrows, usually in small groups, and in winter frequently invades houses. Although widespread in the USSR and eastern Europe, its distribution becomes more fragmented across western and southern Europe.

❍❸🐞

Western House Mouse
Mus domesticus
Head and body 7.4–9.5cm, tail 7–9.5cm. In recent years it has become evident that there is more than one species of house mouse in

Europe. Unfortunately they cannot be distinguished with certainty in the field. House mice are darker and greyer than any other European mice, being generally brownish grey. They occur in a wide range of habitats, mostly close to human habitations, and will devour practically anything digestible, often spoiling stored foods. The Western House Mouse is found west of a line joining the western Baltic and the Adriatic.

Ⓑ❍❷❍❹❸❺🐞

Harvest Mouse
Micromys minutus
Head and body 5–7.8cm, tail 4–7.5cm. This is the smallest European rodent, with very small ears, reddish upperparts and white underside; the tail is prehensile. Active by day and night, it climbs stems and branches with agility and builds its nest of loosely woven grasses around the tall stems of grasses, reeds or cereals in late summer. In winter and early summer it spends much time in burrows. It feeds mostly on seeds and insects. Each litter contains 4–6 young. The Harvest Mouse occurs over much of Europe, but is absent from most of Greece and Yugoslavia.

Ⓑ❸🐞

BIRCH MICE

About 17 species are known in this family (Zapodidae), all occurring in grasslands and forests of the northern hemisphere. Birch mice are superficially like wood mice but have even longer tails. The two European birch mice are rather slender, often arboreal animals, with prehensile tails. They hibernate throughout winter.

Northern Birch Mouse
Sicista betulina
Head and body 5–7.8cm, tail 7–10.5cm. This is a slender mouse with a very long, prehensile tail. The upper parts are yellowish brown with a black stripe running from the back of the head to the base of the tail. Found in forests and in damp areas such as bogs and mountain meadows with dense vegetation, it is often associated with birch. This species is an agile climber, using its prehensile tail for support. From late summer to spring it hibernates. The centre of its patchy range is in the western USSR and southern Finland.

❍❷❍❹❸🐞

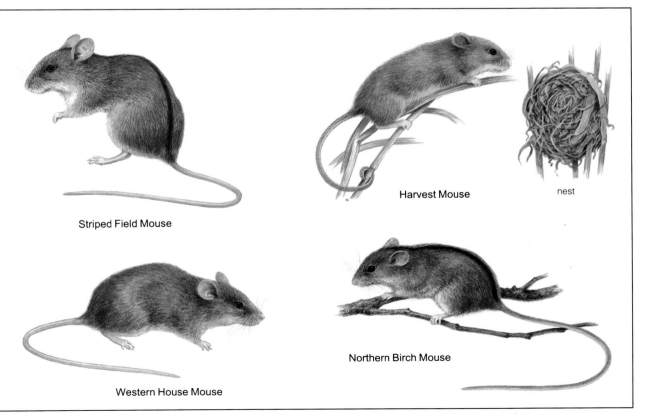

Striped Field Mouse

Harvest Mouse

nest

Northern Birch Mouse

Western House Mouse

The play of Brown Bears often involves mock fights. When disputing territory, however, the contests are quite serious.

Carnivores

The Order Carnivora contains about 235 species world-wide, of which 25 occur in Europe. The European species are diverse, ranging from the bears to the Weasel, which is often no bigger than mice. Carnivores have large carnassial teeth, which they use for shearing through flesh. Most species are predators, adapted especially for capturing and feeding upon relatively large prey. Many, however, are omnivorous, and some are even herbivorous.

BEARS

Of the eight species in the Family Ursidae, two are found in Europe: the Polar Bear and the Brown Bear. The former is confined to the extreme north. Both species are large and often walk on their hind feet. Their tails are generally invisible. Bears are the largest carnivores in Europe and are unlikely to be confused with other large European mammals.

Brown Bear
Ursus arctos
Head and body up to 2m, tail vestigial. This large bear has colouring that varies from chocolate brown to pale fawn. Although classed as a carnivore, it is omnivorous, feeding on a wide variety of plant matter as well as carrion, small mammals, honey and occasionally domestic livestock. The 3–6 tiny cubs, born in January or February, do not become independent until their second summer. Normally shy, bears can become aggressive in defence of cubs. Once found throughout most of Europe, including Britain, only a few isolated populations of the Brown Bear remain, mostly in mountainous areas.
◔◉◓◉◈◉

DOGS, WOLVES AND FOXES

This family (Canidae) contains about 35 species, of which six, including the feral populations of the domestic dog, occur in Europe. They are fast runners, with long legs, long muzzles and prominent ears. Most prey on animals, but some species scavenge and others take fruit.

Wolf
Canis lupus
Head and body 1–1.6m, tail 35–50cm. The ancestor of the Domestic Dog, with which it freely interbreeds, it feeds chiefly on wild mammals such as deer, but occasionally takes domestic livestock. Attacks on humans are virtually unknown and, after centuries of persecution, it has become extremely shy and usually nocturnal. Once widespread over almost all of Europe, including the British Isles, it has been exterminated in all but a few areas.
◔◉◓◉◈◉

Jackal
Canis aureus
Head and body 71–85cm, tail 20–30cm. The Jackal is similar in appearance to a small, lean German Shepherd Dog, with a shortish tail. It is found mostly around the outskirts of villages and small towns, where it is a scavenger. It also feeds on carrion and raids poultry and crops. There are normally 4–5 cubs in a litter and they are cared for by both parents. The Jackal is confined to south-eastern Europe and little is known of its current status – it may be declining or extinct in many parts of its range.
◉⊗

Red Fox
Vulpes vulpes
Head and body 60–90cm, tail 40–60cm. The red fox is generally a rufous red above and white below, with a white-tipped tail. The backs of the ears, the paws and lower limbs are blackish. Found in a wide variety of covered habitats, it feeds mainly on rodents but also on larger animals as well as soft fruits. It also occurs in urban areas, where it raids dustbins. This species has the widest range of any European mammal, occurring from the Mediterranean region to the Arctic.
Ⓑ◉◓◉◈◉◉⊛�🔟

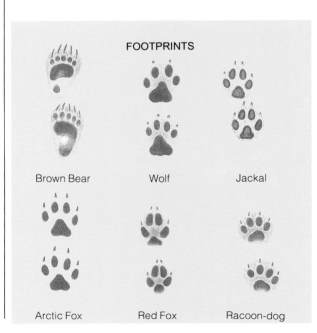

FOOTPRINTS

Brown Bear   Wolf   Jackal

Arctic Fox   Red Fox   Racoon-dog

Arctic Fox

Alopex lagopus
Head and body 50–85cm, tail 22–55cm. This fox occurs in two distinct colour phases, often found side by side. In one the fur is brownish above and pale below in summer, turning white in winter; in the other, less common phase, it is brownish grey in summer and bluish grey in winter. Active by day and night, the Arctic Fox wanders over long distances. Dens are extensive, often communal, and are made either by digging or in natural fissures in rocks. They may be used for several centuries, and the vegetation that grows on the soil enriched by the droppings often differs from that of the surrounding area. It is widespread and often abundant in the Arctic, usually above the tree-line; it also occurs on islands, including Iceland.

Raccoon-dog

Nyctereutes procyonoides
Head and body 50–80cm, tail 10–26cm. This species is similar in size to the Red Fox, but stockier, with a more shaggy appearance and a short bushy tail. It occurs in a wide variety of habitats, but prefers deciduous woodland with thick undergrowth. Its diet consists of almost any small animal as well as fruits and other plant matter. The footprints are dog-like, but more rounded than a fox's, and the trails are often interrupted, not continuous like those of a fox. Escapes from fur farms, together with introductions to the USSR, have extended its range to cover much of northern and eastern Europe.

Brown Bear

Red Fox

Wolf

Arctic Fox

Jackal

Raccoon-dog

Brown Bear

dropping

Red Fox

Wolf

summer

blue form

winter

Arctic Fox

Jackal

Raccoon-like Dog

WEASELS

The 64 or so species in the Weasel Family (Mustelidae) are characterized by their considerable diversity. In Europe they range from the often tiny Weasel to the large, robust Badger and the almost bear-like Wolverine. Most have anal glands that produce pungent scents, and some can moult into a white pelage in winter. Most species have been hunted for their pelts.

Stoat

Polecat

Weasel

Steppe Polecat

European Mink

Pine Marten

American Mink

Beech Marten

Stoat
Mustela erminea
Head and body 17.5–31cm, tail 5.7–14cm. This species is usually dark, reddish brown above and creamy white below, with a black-tipped tail. In the northern parts of its range (including Britain) it turns white in winter, except for the tail-tip, when it is known as Ermine. Found in a wide variety of habitats usually in or near woodlands, it feeds mainly on mammals up to the size of small rabbits. One of the most common and widespread predators in Europe, it is absent only from the south.
Ⓑⵔ⬮⬯⬤⬥⬦⬧

Weasel
Mustela nivalis
Head and body 11–26cm, tail 13–87mm. The smallest European carnivore, it also varies in size more than almost any other mammal. Typically reddish brown above, and white below, some animals turn white in winter. It is found in a wide variety of habitats, particularly near woodland, where it preys mostly on mice and voles. Weasels are prolific, in some areas breeding almost all year round. They are widespread throughout most of Europe.
Ⓑⵔ⬮⬯⬤⬥⬦⬧

Weasels are often seen along road verges, where they will prey on small birds, such as this House Sparrow, killed or injured by cars.

European Mink
Mustela lutreola
Head and body 28–43cm, tail 12–19cm. This creature is very similar to the domesticated (American) mink but smaller. The fur is usually dark blackish-brown, with a small amount of white on the muzzle and occasionally on the throat. Found mainly in aquatic habitats, it feeds mostly on small birds and mammals, and also fish. Its range is contracting and it is now extinct or endangered throughout its European range. It occurs in western France and possibly in north-western Spain, and in eastern Europe from Romania to Finland.
⬤⊗

American Mink
Mustela vison
Head and body 31–45cm, tail 12–25cm. This mink is considerably larger than the European Mink and is further distinguished from that species by having a small amount of white on the lower lip only. The American Mink occurs as an escape from fur farms. Naturally dark brown, it has been bred commercially in a variety of colours, which are now found in the wild. Able to swim and climb well, it can adapt to most habitats. It feeds on small mammals, birds and fish and will also take poultry and waterfowl. It has colonized Europe, and is now more widespread than the native species.
Ⓑⵔ⬮⬯⬤⬥⬦⬧

winter
partially moulted
winter
summer
Stoat

winter
(north of
range only)
Weasel

European Mink

dropping

European   American

domesticated
colour variants

wild
form

American Mink

FOOTPRINTS

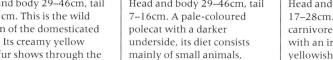

Stoat · European Mink · Polecat · Pine Marten · Weasel · American Mink · Steppe Polecat · Beech Marten

markers. Although widespread over most of Europe, the Pine Marten has been exterminated in most parts of the British Isles and is now found mainly in Scotland and Ireland. It occurs on Corsica, Sardinia and Sicily. One litter is produced in spring, usually containing three young.
Ⓑ◉◉◐④

Beech Marten
Martes foina
Head and body 44–54cm, tail 23–32cm. Similar in appearance to the Pine Marten, this species is slightly more heavily built, and has a pure white throat patch, which is usually smaller than in that species. The patch often has a dark strip down its centre. Also known as the Stone Marten, it frequents fairly open, rocky habitats, often close to human habitation and in a few areas it occurs in suburbs of towns, where it feeds on rats, mice, sparrows, berries and occasionally domestic fowl. It frequently makes its den in buildings, such as farm lofts and ruins. It is widespread over much of southern and central Europe, but is absent from Britain. One litter a year, consisting of 2–6 kittens, is born in spring.
◉◉◐④✪

Polecat
Mustela putorius
Head and body 29–46cm, tail 8.5–21cm. This is the wild relation of the domesticated Ferret. Its creamy yellow underfur shows through the longer, dark brown guard hairs, and it has a distinctive facial mask. It can produce a particularly strong and foul-smelling secretion, which it uses to mark territory and also releases when alarmed. The Polecat is mainly terrestrial, rarely climbing or swimming. Formerly widespread throughout much of Europe, its numbers declined drastically due to persecution. It is now protected and may be increasing in some areas.
Ⓑ◉◉◐④✪✪

Steppe Polecat
Mustela eversmanni
Head and body 29–46cm, tail 7–16cm. A pale-coloured polecat with a darker underside, its diet consists mainly of small animals, particularly rodents. The food remains and excrement near the entrances to its burrows have a foul smell. Grassland steppes are its main habitat, although these have been considerably reduced and its range fragmented. It has also declined due to hunting for its fur in the past. Found sporadically from Austria and Hungary, through Romania, Czechoslovakia, eastern Germany and Poland. It gives birth to one litter a year, of 8–11 blind young.
✪✪

Pine Marten
Martes martes
Head and body 35–58cm, tail 17–28cm. This cat-sized carnivore is rich brown above with an irregularly shaped yellowish throat patch. Normally found in well-wooded habitats, it is an agile climber and can move at great speed through treetops, usually building its den in a hollow tree or in a rocky crevice. It feeds on rodents and a wide variety of other small mammals and birds, as well as berries and fruits in autumn. Although generally nocturnal and shy, when not persecuted it frequently emerges during the day. It has a bounding gait. The droppings are often left on rocks or logs as territory

Ferret (dark form)

Ferret (albino form)

Polecat

Steppe Polecat

Pine Marten

dropping

Beech Marten

The European Lynx is spreading its range after centuries of persecution, and reintroductions have helped this process.

Wolverine
Gulo gulo
Head and body 70–86cm, tail 13–25cm. Also known as the Glutton, this bear-like animal has dark brown fur with a pale stripe across the flanks, and a bushy tail. The feet are furry, enabling it to run on firm snow. It eats a wide variety of animals and plants, taking mammals up to the size of the Reindeer. Formerly more widespread, it is now confined to Arctic Scandinavia and the USSR.
🌑🌑💧⊛⊗

Otter
Lutra lutra
Head and body 68–80cm, tail 35–47cm. This is a superbly streamlined creature, with a long tapering tail and webbed feet, and is most likely to be seen in or close to water. After centuries of persecution, it has become rather nocturnal and extremely shy. It is now rare or extinct over most of its former range, occurring in significant numbers only in Scandinavia, Scotland and Ireland.
Ⓑ🌑💧⊛⊘⊗

Badger
Meles meles
Head and body 67–87cm, tail 11–19cm. This species has quite unmistakable black and white facial markings. Found in a variety of habitats, it prefers woodland, where it excavates extensive burrows, known as setts. It is usually nocturnal and shy but, when not persecuted, it may emerge by day. It feeds on small invertebrates, but will also eat other animal and vegetable matter. It occurs over most of Europe except the extreme north and some islands.
Ⓑ🌱🌑⊛⊛💧

MONGOOSES

Of the 70 species in the Mongoose Family (Viverridae), only three are found in Europe. The Indian Grey Mongoose is restricted to a small area in Italy.

Egyptian Mongoose
Herpestes ichneumon
Head and body 50–55cm, tail 35–45cm. Rather marten-like but with a long tapering tail and a rather coarse, greyish coat, it prefers rocky habitats with thick scrub, and is partly nocturnal. It hunts singly or in pairs, feeding on small mammals and taking reptiles and their eggs. Originally from Africa, it has been introduced to Spain, Portugal, Italy and Yugoslavia.
🌑⊛🌑⊛

Genet
Genetta genetta
Head and body 47–60cm, tail 40–51cm. A slender, cat-like carnivore, it is heavily spotted and has a long, banded tail and prominent ears. It is an elusive, nocturnal animal that feeds on rodents and birds, and is rarely seen. Found in well-wooded and fairly marshy habitats, it climbs and jumps well and also swims. Thought to have been introduced into Europe from North Africa, it is widespread in the Iberian peninsula and France, where its range is spreading due to protection.
🌑⊛

RACCOONS

The Family Procyonidae contains 20 species, most of which are native to the New World.

Raccoon
Procyon lotor
Head and body 60–95cm, tail 19–40cm. This animal's banded tail and 'robber's mask' are distinctive. Originally from North America, it was introduced into Europe for its fur and is now firmly established in the wild. Found in a wide range of habitats, generally near water, it is extremely adaptable. It is also found scavenging in urban areas. The den is usually made in a hollow tree or rock cleft.
⊛🌑⊛

CATS

Of the 36 species in this family (Felidae), only two are native to Europe, although feral cats occur extensively and the Lion became extinct within historic times. Cats are arguably the most specialized predators, feeding largely on warm-blooded prey that they kill themselves. They are relatively long-legged and agile, often with attractively marked fur. The head is usually rounded and the eyes have a vertical pupil that contracts to a slit in sunlight. Most species can retract their sharp claws in order to protect them when walking.

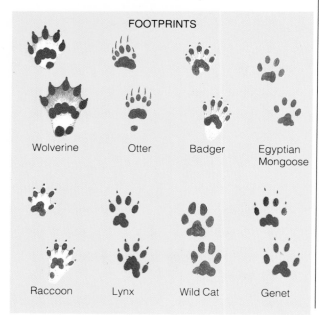

FOOTPRINTS

Wolverine   Otter   Badger   Egyptian Mongoose

Raccoon   Lynx   Wild Cat   Genet

Lynx

Lynx lynx
Head and body 80cm–1.3m, tail 11–25cm. A large cat, with a short tail and prominent ear tufts, its coat pattern is variable. It feeds on a wide range of prey, up to the size of young Reindeer, suffocating large prey with a bite in the throat. It makes a lair in a hollow tree or rock cleft. Once widespread over much of continental Europe, it is now extinct throughout most of its former range, being confined largely to the northern forests, Spain and a few mountainous areas in southern and eastern Europe. Reintroduction programmes have been successful in several areas but the Spanish population continues to decline.

Wild Cat

Felis sylvestris
Head and body 51–75cm, tail 23–36cm. This is generally larger, with a proportionally shorter, bushier tail than the feral Domestic Cat (*F. catus*), although the two species can interbreed. Found in forests, woodland and open clearings, it hunts mainly at night, feeding on a variety of mammals and birds as well as carrion. It makes a lair among rocks or under logs. Once widespread throughout most of central and southern Europe, and Scotland, its range is now considerably reduced, but is thought to be spreading in some parts of France and Scotland.

Wolverine

Raccoon

Otter   Lynx

Badger   Wild Cat

Mongoose   Genet

Wolverine

Raccoon

spraint

spraint

Otter

Lynx

Iberian race

variety of feral cats

Wild Cat

Badger

Genet

Egyptian Mongoose

Hoofed Mammals

There are two orders of hoofed mammals, or ungulates. The even-toed ungulates (Artiodactyla), including pigs, sheep, cattle and deer, have two or four hoofs per foot. The odd-toed ungulates (Perissodactyla), which include horses, tapirs and rhinoceroses, have one or three hoofs on each foot.

PIGS

The eight species in the Pig Family (Suidae) are native to the Old World. The Boar is the ancestor of the domestic pig.

Wild Boar
Sus scrofa
Head and body 1–1.5m, tail 15–25cm. The Wild Boar is similar to the domestic pig, but with thick hair and a long snout; males have tusks. It prefers mixed woodlands. The young have pale stripes. Once widespread throughout Europe, it is extinct in Britain, most of Scandinavia and parts of central Europe.
⬤◑✦✿⊞

CATTLE, SHEEP, AND GOATS

This family (Bovidae) contains about 127 species, ranging in size from the massive Bison to the tiny antelopes. They all have complex stomachs and ruminate – chew the cud – in order to digest cellulose. Most species carry horns, which consist of a horny covering to a bony core, growing from the skull. All the European species are gregarious, usually living in herds.

Mouflon
Ovis musimon
Head and body 0.8–1.25m, tail 7–15cm. The Mouflon is an ancestor of the Domestic Sheep and was probably introduced into Europe by man. Lacking the woolly fleece of domestic sheep, its coat is generally brown above and pale below. Adult males carry heavy, curled horns. The single lamb is born in spring and is independent at six months. Its European range is restricted to Corsica and Sardinia but it has been successfully introduced into many parts of the European mainland.
⬤◑✿⊞

A ram Mouflon resting its massive horns. When two rams are fighting over territory the clash of their horns can be heard a kilometre away.

Chamois
Rupicapra rupicapra
Head and body 0.9–1.4m, tail 3–8cm. This species is reddish brown in summer, but in winter the fur turns blackish. It has short horns which are unusual in pointing forwards. An agile, goat-like inhabitant of alpine meadows, it generally lives above the tree line in summer, descending in winter. Males usually live separately, but females gather together in herds, which in winter may contain over 100 animals. Threatened throughout its range, it survives only in a few isolated mountain ranges of Europe.
◑⊗

Alpine Ibex
Capra ibex
Head and body 1.15–1.7m, tail 10–20cm. Both sexes carry horns, which in the males can be over 1m long. During the winter breeding season, males charge headlong at each other and clash horns. Very agile, it is found in precipitous mountain habitats. Although once reduced to a single population in the Gran Paradiso National Park, Italy, it has been re-established in several parts of the Alps. The Pyrenean Ibex (*C. pyrenaicus*) is very similar, differing mainly in horn shape.
◑⊗

Wild Boar

summer   winter

Chamois

♂ winter   ♀ summer

Mouflon

♂   ♀   Pyrenean Ibex

Alpine Ibex

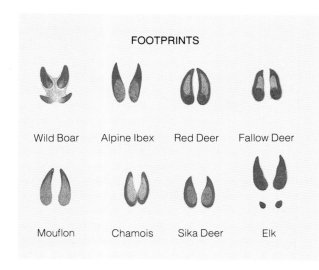

FOOTPRINTS

Wild Boar   Alpine Ibex   Red Deer   Fallow Deer

Mouflon   Chamois   Sika Deer   Elk

DEER

About 53 species of deer (Family Cervidae) are recognized, ten of which occur in Europe. Like the bovids, their range has changed due to hunting and introductions. The males of most species carry antlers, as does the female Reindeer, which are shed after the breeding season (rut). During the breeding season the males of several species defend territories and they are often vocal. All deer are ruminants that browse or graze.

Red Deer
Cervus elaphus
Head and body 1.7–2.6m, tail 12–15cm. The Red Deer is greyish brown in winter, reddish brown in summer. The stag carries large branching antlers and develops a shaggy mane during the rutting season. Found in a variety of habitats, including woodland and open moorland, it often lives close to human habitation, where it becomes nocturnal. One or two spotted calves are born in early summer. Although abundant over much of Europe, in many areas its populations are fragmented.

Sika Deer
Cervus nippon
Head and body 1–1.55m, tail 17–27cm. This species is similar in size to a small Red Deer, but spotted in summer and dark in winter. The stag has relatively short antlers with fewer branches than the Red. The two species occasionally interbreed. The Sika Deer prefers woodland, parkland and similar habitats, where it browses on leaves and shoots. Native to Asia, it has been widely introduced into many parts of Europe, and is now well established.

Fallow Deer
Cervus dama
Head and body 1.3–2.3m, tail 15–20cm. Mostly seen in parkland, this species has become partly domesticated. Wild populations are usually buff-brown with prominent whitish spots on the back, but more uniform colouring, ranging from white to blackish, is common. The tail has a black line down the centre. The stag's antlers are flattened. Probably native to the Mediterranean region, it has been introduced extensively since Roman times and is now established throughout Europe.

Elk
Alces alces
Head and body 2–3.1m, tail 5cm. This is a heavily-built deer, with a large muzzle; males have flat antlers. The Elk is found in forest habitats, usually near water, where it frequently wades, feeding on aquatic vegetation and tree shoots. Less gregarious than other deer, it is usually seen singly or in family groups. The rut is in autumn, when the males have a bugling call and fight with other males.

Wild Boar

Red Deer

Mouflon

Sika Deer

Chamois

Fallow Deer

Alpine Ibex

Elk

winter   summer
droppings

♂ winter   ♀ summer

Red Deer

colour variants

♀ winter

Fallow Deer   ♂ late summer

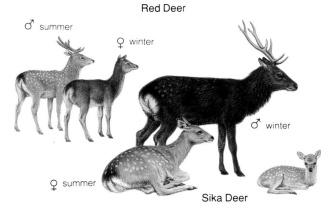

♂ summer   ♀ winter

♂ winter

♀ summer

Sika Deer

♀   ♂

Elk

LIFE in the MOUNTAINS

Climbing in the Alps or the Pyrenees – Europe's main mountain masses – is rather like travelling from the Mediterranean to the Arctic. Starting off in the deciduous forest zone, or even in the Mediterranean forest, the traveller passes through coniferous forests and emerges into a zone of stunted and sprawling shrubs very similar to those fringing the northern edge of the taiga. The shrubs give way to flower-rich grassland and, as one gets higher, the flowers and grasses thin out to leave large areas of lichen-covered rock. Frost shattering on the highest slopes leads to the formation of unstable screes where few plants can survive. Some of the highest peaks are permanently snow-covered, and even many of the lower ones carry snow for nine or ten months of the year.

True mountain life – commonly called alpine life – is that group of plants and animals living above the tree line. The height of this boundary varies with latitude, being about 1800 metres above sea level in the southern parts of the Alps, but only 300 metres in southern Scandinavia.

Ground-hugging Plants

The temperature drops on average just over 0.5°C for every 100 metres of altitude – mainly because of the thinner air – so the alpine zone is cold. It is also very windy and the air is dry. The plants form ground-hugging mats and cushions, just as they do on the arctic tundra (see p.246). In fact, the two habitats are very similar and have many species in common. Low growth keeps the plants out of the full force of the wind and helps them to maintain warmth and moisture. The temperature in the centre of a cushion may be twice as high as the air outside. Hairy or waxy leaves help to reduce water loss. Many flowers have vibrant colours that absorb harmful ultra-violet rays – especially strong in the clean mountain air – and it is these colours that make alpine flowers so popular for rock gardens. Collecting has endangered several species.

Annuals are rare in the alpine zone because the growing season is so short – sometimes less than two months on the upper slopes and often shorter than on the tundra because the mountains lack the benefit of continuous daylight during the summer.

ABOVE: *The broad wings of the Golden Eagle provide the lift necessary to battle against strong mountain winds.*
RIGHT: *The grasshopper* Podisma pedestris *occurs in the Alps from July to October, and is sometimes found at altitudes of up to 3000 metres. One of several flightless mountain species, its wings are almost absent.*

Growth is always slow and even some perennials don't flower every year – they need a rest to enable them to build up their food reserves again. In order to make use of the short growing season, many plants bloom as soon as the snow melts. Glacier Crowfoot, which grows higher up than any other plant, flowers right at the edge of the melting snow fields. In some years it is not uncovered at all and it can survive under the snow for up to three years. The Alpine Snowbell flowers even before the snow melts. Its leaves release heat, which melts the surrounding snow so that the flowers can poke up through the white carpet.

Sure-footed Grazers

Mountain birds are usually large and powerful and they include many birds of prey, which feed on small mammals such as marmots and hares. There are also vultures, including the Lammergeier, which feed on the remains of larger animals such as Ibex and Chamois. These are the

Colourful clumps of alpenrose form thickets up to a metre high near the tree-line on the scree-covered slopes of the Alps.

Mountain Wildlife
1 Alpine Ibex
2 Spring Gentian
3 Mountain Avens
4 Purple Saxifrage
5 Chamois
6 Glacier Crowfoot
7 Lichen
8 Alpine Marmot
9 Apollo Butterfly
10 Alpine Stonecrop
11 Lammergeier
12 Alpine Chough
13 Moss Campion

largest mammals of the alpine zone. Sure-footed, they graze the rocky slopes in the summer, but move lower down to more sheltered pastures for the winter. These upland mammals have fewer young than their lowland relatives – usually only one at a time. This allows the young to stay longer in the womb and thus grow larger and better able to withstand the rigours of alpine life.

Mountain Insects

Butterflies, notably ringlets of the genus *Erebia*, are common on the alpine pastures and several species are restricted to just one or two neighbouring peaks where they have evolved since the ice age. Mountain insects are often darker than their lowland relatives, for better

absorption of heat and harmful ultra-violet rays. The Mountain Clouded Yellow is a good example. Mountain insects rarely fly far above the ground, for they would be blown away by the strong winds. Many species, especially among the grasshoppers and bush-crickets, have short or almost absent wings and do not fly at all. Some springtails actually live on the snow fields, eating pollen and debris blown there by the wind. They are so numerous that they turn the snow brown, black or red.

Reindeer
Rangifer tarandus
Head and body 1.7–2.2m, tail 7–18cm. Unlike other deer, both sexes of the Reindeer carry antlers, although those of the female are smaller. The forward branch of the antlers divides again, unlike any other deer. It is gregarious and often lives in large herds. Feeding on lichens, shoots, grasses, sedges and leaves, it uses its hooves in winter to dig in the snow to expose plants. Its range is reduced to scattered populations in Scandinavia and eastwards through the USSR. It has been introduced into Iceland and Scotland. Domestic Reindeer are widespread in northern Scandinavia and there is one herd in the Cairngorms, Scotland. They are smaller and more variable in colouration than the wild variety.

Reindeer   Muntjac Deer

Roe Deer   Water Deer

FOOTPRINTS

Reindeer   Muntjac Deer

Roe Deer   Chinese Water Deer

A Roe Deer, photographed here in its reddish summer pelage. When pursued this species can clear a two metre obstacle.

Roe Deer
Capreolus capreolus
Head and body 0.9–1.3m, tail 2.5–3.5cm. This is the smallest native European deer. Its coat is a rich reddish brown in summer, and greyer in winter. The males carry short, branched antlers, but both sexes have almost no tail. The young are heavily spotted. It is found in woodland where it browses on bushes, usually feeding at dusk. If undisturbed, though, it may be diurnal. The rut is in mid-summer. The Roe Deer occurs throughout much of Europe, but is absent from most islands.

Muntjac Deer
Muntiacus reevesi
Head and body 75–90cm, tail up to 12cm. A diminutive deer. The male has short antlers and small tusks. The short tail conceals a white rump, exposed only when fleeing. The young are heavily spotted. It is also known as Barking Deer because of its loud bark. Secretive by nature, it is found in wooded habitats with dense cover, often near urban areas. Native to Asia, and introduced to France and England. It is now widespread in central and southern England.

Chinese Water Deer
Hydropotes inermis
Head and body 75–105cm, tail 5–8cm. A small deer, standing less than 60cm at the shoulder. Neither sex has antlers, but the male has clearly visible tusks. Generally nocturnal, it is usually solitary and lives in woodland, marshes and more open areas. It feeds on shoots, leaves and grasses and the male uses its tusks for digging up tubers. During the rut the male makes a whistling call. Introduced to Britain from Asia, it has since the 1940s become established in central and eastern England.

Reindeer

Muntjac Deer

Roe Deer

Chinese Water Deer

Marine Mammals

Two orders of mammals are found in European seas: the Pinnipedia and the Cetacea. The 34 species of pinnipeds include fur seals, sea lions, elephant seals, true seals and the Walrus. Only the true seals and the Walrus are found in European waters. The 77 species of cetaceans include dolphins, whales and porpoises. The pinnipeds have to return to land to breed, although in some cases the young can swim after a few hours. The cetaceans give birth at sea and never voluntarily come on to the land, although individuals may be stranded on the shore. They are quite helpless out of the water. Several marine mammals occur in land-locked freshwater. Many of the cetaceans migrate to spend different seasons in different parts of the oceans. Many marine mammals are threatened and most cetaceans are endangered, by hunting and pollution.

Seals

Most European seals (Order Pinnipedia) occur in the northern seas. The exceptions are the Monk Seal, which is found in the Mediterranean, and the Ringed Seal, which inhabits lakes in Finland. Seals have hair, insulating blubber, nostrils that can be closed under water, and whiskers. Their limbs are modified into flippers. They feed on fish and crustaceans, as well as squid and octopuses. European seals belong to the Family Phocidae.

Common Seal
Phoca vitulina
Head and body 1.2–1.6m. This smallish seal has a shorter, more rounded head and a less prominent nose than the Grey Seal. Also known as the Harbour Seal, it is often seen in and around estuaries. The single pup is born in mid-summer, and is able to swim within a few hours of birth. It is gregarious, hauling out in groups of up to 100. It is widely distributed along the coasts of Europe, and protected, but declining in many areas.
Ⓑ 😵

Monk Seal
Monachus monachus
Head and body 1.9–3.8m. The adults are generally dark brown above, and paler below. The single pup is born with chocolate-brown fur. Generally extremely shy and rarely seen, it breeds on remote beaches on uninhabited islands or in sea caves. Highly vocal, it barks, howls, yelps and 'sneezes'. Probably now numbering less than 1000 animals, populations have undergone catastrophic declines and it is now almost extinct in the western Mediterranean and extremely localized in the eastern Mediterranean. One of the largest populations survives in the Northern Sporades, in the Aegean Sea.
😵 😵 ⊗

Grey Seal
Halichoerus grypus
Head and body 1.65–2.3m. This is a large seal with a distinctive, dog-like head. Its colouration is extremely variable, females being generally paler. The single pup is born in autumn and has a whitish coat, which it moults when about one month old. The Grey Seal is very gregarious, and densely packed groups often haul out on islands and rocky shores, making a variety of barking calls. Although abundant around the British Isles, its European populations are scattered and, despite protection, it is decreasing in some parts of its range.
Ⓑ 😵

Ringed Seal
Phoca hispida
Head and body 1.35–1.85m. A small seal, named for the distinctive pattern of rings on its back; the fur colour is greyish brown, darker than the Common Seal. In winter it often lives below the ice, keeping holes open for breathing, and can dive for up to 20 minutes. The pups, born in early spring, are white and thickly furred. This is one of the few seals to occur in freshwater, being found in lakes in the Gulf of Finland. It is also present in the Baltic and Arctic waters.
😵 😵

Common Seal | Grey Seal

Monk Seal | Ringed Seal

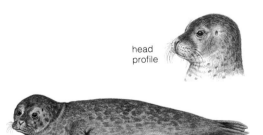

head profile

Common Seal

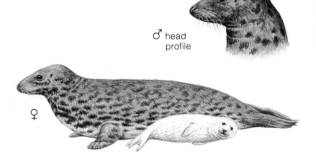

♂ head profile
♀

Grey Seal

Monk Seal

Ringed Seal

Whales, Dolphins and Porpoises

The whales (Order Cetacea) are divided into two sub-orders: the Mysticeti, or baleen whales, and the Odontoceti, or toothed whales, which include the sperm whales, dolphins and porpoises. All species are severely depleted in European waters. Their front limbs are modified into paddles and they are almost completely hairless but have thick layers of blubber. They breathe through a blowhole. Most of the cetaceans use sounds for echolocation and for communication.

BALEEN WHALES

Baleen whales (Family Balaenopteridae) are mostly large cetaceans (up to 30m). They feed by using huge sieve-like plates of horny baleen to strain plankton and fish from the sea.

Fin Whale
Balaenoptera physalis
Head and body up to 26.8m. One of the largest whales, belonging to a group known as the rorquals, it is slender with prominent throat grooves and a small dorsal fin set well back on the body. It

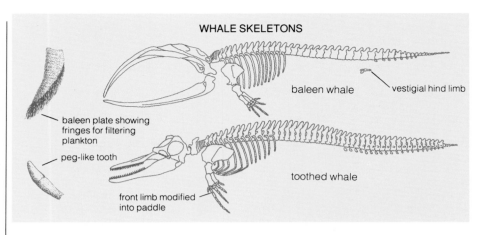

WHALE SKELETONS

baleen whale

vestigial hind limb

baleen plate showing fringes for filtering plankton

peg-like tooth

toothed whale

front limb modified into paddle

has unusual, asymmetrical colouring: the right hand side of the lower jaw, baleen plates and tongue are pale, whereas those on the left side are dark. It usually swims in groups (pods) of 6–15. Although found in all European seas and oceans, especially the north-eastern Atlantic, populations have been severely depleted.
Ⓑ 🌊

Minke Whale
Balaenoptera acutorostrata
Head and body up to 9.4m. Also known as the Little Piked Whale or Lesser Rorqual, this is the smallest of the rorquals. The head is narrow and pointed, and it has a white band on the upper side of the flippers. It swims singly or in small groups, and feeds on fish. Widespread in the north, particularly in Scottish, Norwegian and Icelandic waters, it occurs more often in estuaries and coastal waters than other rorquals.
Ⓑ 🌊

DOLPHINS

Most of the 32 species in the Family Delphinidae are small, swift, fish-eating dolphins, with a prominent back fin, a narrow beak, and numerous sharp teeth in both jaws. Some species, however, reach a length of over 9m and are referred to as whales.

Killer Whale
Orcinus orca
Head and body up to 9.75m. This whale, also called the Orca, is a medium-sized cetacean with black and white markings and a shark-like, triangular dorsal fin, which can be up to 2m high in males. Carnivorous, with long, sharp teeth, it often hunts in packs of up to 30 whales, preying on other cetaceans, as well as sea birds, squid and fish. This species occurs in all oceans, but is most often seen in the Atlantic and the North Sea.
Ⓑ 🌊

Long-Finned Pilot Whale
Globicephala melaena
Head and body up to 8.5m. Recognized by its bulbous head, long thin flippers and distinctive dorsal fin, this whale is almost entirely black or dark grey with a paler patch behind the fin, and white underneath. It is highly gregarious, travelling in schools of up to 200. This, and the fact that it tries to help the injured, makes it an easy target for whale-hunters. Although widespread throughout European waters, populations have collapsed due to hunting.
Ⓑ 🌊

Bottle-nosed Dolphin
Tursiops truncatus
Head and body up to 4m. A relatively large dolphin, bluish-grey above and paler below, with a prominent beak. Often forming large schools, it is very playful. Although primarily marine, it also occurs in coastal lagoons and bays, and sometimes even swims up river. It is also regularly stranded. Found in all European seas, it is most common in the Atlantic and Mediterranean and is the species most often exhibited in zoos and aquaria.
Ⓑ 🌊

Common Dolphin
Delphinus delphus
Head and body up to 2.6m. A streamlined dolphin, this species is distinctively patterned, with a prominent beak. Extremely active, it swims very fast, often near the surface, and rarely dives for more than a few minutes.

A Common Dolphin, showing its characteristic 'hour-glass' patterning as it leaps over the bow wave of a boat.

It once occurred in schools of up to 250,000, (notably in the Black Sea) but due to extensive hunting is now much depleted. It is found in all European seas.
Ⓑ 😵

Risso's Dolphin
Grampus griseus
Head and body up to 4m. Also known as the Grampus, this dolphin is superficially similar to the Long-finned Pilot Whale, but is greyer, with shorter flippers and a taller fin. It has a bulbous forehead and no beak. The body is usually extensively scarred. It lives in groups of 25 or more, and occasionally several hundred may gather, often in association with other cetaceans. Found mainly in deeper waters, it frequently follows ships. It feeds primarily on squid, as well as fish. It is one of the more frequently stranded species. Widespread in the seas around Europe, including the Mediterranean and possibly the Black Sea.
Ⓑ 😵

PORPOISES

The six species in the Porpoise Family (Phocoenidae) resemble small, stocky dolphins but have no beaks. Some have a small back fin. One species occurs in Europe.

Common Porpoise
Phocoena phocoena
Head and body up to 1.8m. Frequently observed in shallow coastal waters and estuaries, the Common Porpoise often swims up rivers. A slow swimmer, it has a characteristic style, rolling forwards to expose the short dorsal fin. Groups usually number 2–10 animals but they occasionally travel together in schools of 100 or more. It feeds on fish and crustaceans. Although populations have declined dramatically due to hunting, drowning in fishing gear and pesticide pollution, it is still one of the most widespread of European cetaceans.
Ⓑ 😵

Fin Whale

Bottle-nosed Dolphin

Killer Whale

Common Dolphin

Minke Whale

Risso's Dolphin

L-f Pilot Whale

Porpoise

Fin Whale

Bottle-nosed Dolphin

Killer Whale

Common Dolphin

Minke Whale

Risso's Dolphin

Long-Finned Pilot Whale

Common Porpoise

BIRDS

All birds belong to the Class Aves, which is one of the main divisions of the vertebrate, or backboned, animals. They are the only animals with feathers. Other distinguishing features are the beak, and the modification of the front limbs into wings. There are about 9000 species of birds.
Many bird species with wide distributions have populations in different areas that differ slightly from one another in plumage, size, bill size and so on. These are called races or subspecies. Only races that can be distinguished in the field are included in this book. Some species also have distinct colour phases. Where these occur, they are mentioned in the text or illustrated.

LEFT: *The handsome Green Woodpecker is seen here in a characteristic pose, with its stiff tail feathers providing stable support for its body as it clings to an almost vertical surface.*

A Jay in flight clearly shows the large primary flight feathers which provide the forward thrust.

Bird Groups

Living birds are divided into 28–30 orders. The orders, in turn, are divided into about 163 families. The descriptions of the orders and families in this book will help you familiarize yourself with the different groups of birds.

Habitats

Birds are highly adaptable animals, found in all habitats from the polar regions to the tropics, and from the mountains to the oceans. Knowledge of a bird's habitats is useful in identification. For example, you would be unlikely to see a Sky Lark in a forest, or a Tawny Owl in open grassland.

Flight and Feathers

The structure of a bird reflects its adaptation for flight. The skeleton is very light, consisting of hollow bones and a lightweight beak. Flying birds have powerful wing muscles, which may form 25 per cent of the bird's weight.

Feathers are modified scales, inherited by the first birds from their reptile ancestors 150 million years ago. Their original function was to provide a downy insulating layer. In the course of evolution, the feathered front limbs were used for gliding and they eventually evolved into wings for flight.

Birds renew worn feathers by moulting, and some birds moult from a breeding plumage into a different winter plumage. In some species the male ♂ and female ♀ differ markedly. Also, some young birds pass through different plumages before reaching maturity. Plumage patterns and colours are useful for identification.

A male Chaffinch, showing the main areas used when describing birds.

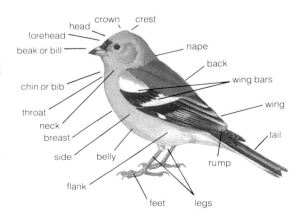

Wings and Tails

The shape of the wings can be very helpful in distinguishing between the various families of birds. The long broad wings of a pelican are very different from the very short narrow wings of an auk.

Tails also vary; they can be forked, like a tern's or a swallow's; long and slim, like a wagtail's; or notched, like a finch's. The wedge-shaped tail of the Northern Raven helps to distinguish it from the square-tailed Carrion Crow, while the Grey Wagtail has a much longer tail than the Yellow Wagtail.

Bills and Feet

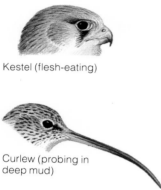

Robin (insects)

Kestel (flesh-eating)

Curlew (probing in deep mud)

A variety of birds' beaks, each adapted to a particular diet or feeding method.

Redshank (probing in shallow mud)

Swallow (opens wide for catching insects in flight)

Greenfinch (seeds)

Bills and feet reveal much about birds' lifestyles and especially their diets, as they depend on their bills, often working in conjunction with their feet, for gathering and eating food. For instance, birds of prey have strong feet with sharp talons for killing prey, and powerful, hooked bills for tearing it up. Many waders have long legs for wading and long, slender bills for probing into mud to reach invertebrates. Other specialized bills include the short, conical bills of finches for crushing seeds, and the chisel-like bills of woodpeckers. Specialized feet include the webbed feet of divers, cormorants, ducks and auks, which swim or dive, and the feet of woodpeckers, with two toes pointing forward and two back, which provide a stable support.

A bird's bill can be a useful aid to identification. There is a clear difference between the long, dagger-shaped bill of a heron and the small, fine bill of a warbler. In some families, bill length and shape can also help to identify species. Finches' bills, for instance, vary from the delicate bill of the Goldfinch to the massive bill of the Hawfinch.

Breeding

Instead of carrying their developing young inside them, which would make it impossible to fly, all birds lay eggs. The incubation period varies from 10 days in small songbirds to over 70 days in large albatrosses.

The downy chicks of many ground-nesting birds, such as ducks, gamebirds and waders, can run around and find their own food almost straight after hatching. At the other extreme, the chicks of perching birds are naked, blind and helpless on hatching and depend completely on their parents to keep them warm and bring them food.

The dense plumage of the adult Snowy Owl provides plenty of warmth for the chicks during their five weeks in the nest.

Habits

Birds have evolved a wide range of different forms of behaviour, and these too can be useful for identification. Starlings, for instance, walk on the ground, whereas sparrows hop. Wagtails constantly wag their tails, while shrikes fan them and swing them from side to side. Woodpeckers climb up trees in short jerks, whereas treecreepers ascend them in spirals, and the European Nuthatch is able to climb downwards as well as upwards, without the stiff tail prop of the other two.

Feeding behaviour, too, is often distinctive. Amongst the waders, for example, the godwits probe deeply into the mud, while the Marsh Sandpiper picks food delicately from the surface, and the Sanderling runs up and down beaches ahead of the breaking waves in its search for food.

A bird's behaviour can often provide clues to its identity. Sparrows hop, Sanderlings run along the shore in front of the waves, Meadow Pipits walk, and Turnstones turn over stones.

House Sparrow

Meadow Pipit

Sanderling

Turnstone

Calls and Song

Bird calls and song are valuable aids to identification. Most calls are short, simple and produced by either sex at any time, and have various functions, such as announcing alarm, threat, intention to fly or some stage in courtship. Songs, on the other hand, are long and complex. They are produced by males during the breeding season to advertise ownership of a territory to rivals and to attract mates. The text uses phonetic rendering and description to give an idea of the main calls and songs of each species.

Bird Movements

Birds include the greatest of all migrants, such as the Arctic Tern, which may travel from the Arctic to the Antarctic and back each year. Other birds may make local journeys, but they do not normally leave the breeding range all year. Birds such as these are called residents.

Many species, such as swallows, are summer visitors to Europe, breeding here and then migrating to spend winter in warmer southern countries. Others, such as many ducks and waders, are winter visitors to most of Europe, breeding far to the north in Scandinavia and Russia and spending winter in our milder climate. Some birds, such as the Blackbird, are partial migrants, with only some populations or parts of a population migrating.

The maps accompanying the illustrations show where in Europe each species can normally be found and at which time of year. The breeding range of summer visitors is shown in yellow, and wintering areas are shown in blue. A green area indicates where the bird is resident all year round.

In spring and autumn, huge number of migrant birds pass through Europe on their way to and from their winter quarters. In some cases, birds occur in Europe only as passage migrants. Large areas occupied by passage migrants are shown as grey areas on the maps.

Knowledge of a bird's seasonal and daily activities are of great value in identification. You are just as unlikely to see a Brent Goose in Britain in summer, when this species is on its Arctic breeding grounds, as to see a Lesser Whitethroat in winter in Europe, when the species is in Africa.

KEY TO MAPS

Breeding range

Winter range

Resident

Measurements

The sizes given in the texts are average lengths. Measurements of birds are taken from bill tip to tail tip, and are usually made using dead specimens. In life the apparent size may differ according to the bird's posture.

Divers

The divers (Order Gaviiformes) are elongated, goose-sized waterbirds with long pointed bills. They catch fish, crustaceans, frogs and leeches underwater. Rarely seen out of water, they are very awkward on land as their webbed feet are set far back on the body where they serve as efficient paddles. The sexes are similar. The nest is a mound of vegetation on a lake shore. The chicks soon leave the nest and are brooded on their parents' backs. There is only one family (Gaviidae).

Red-throated Diver
Gavia stellata
50–60cm. The smallest of the divers, this species has a distinctive, slender, uptilted beak. It breeds on small lochs and freshwater pools in moorland and winters on coastal waters. The nest is typical of divers, comprising a shallow pad of water plants. As a result, the 1–2 eggs are vulnerable to flooding. In summer, Red-throated Divers are more likely to be seen in flight than other divers, when they travel between their nest and coastal feeding sites, giving loud goose-like cackling calls.
Ⓑ☻☻

Black-throated Diver
Gavia arctica
60–70cm. This species breeds on large remote lochs and winters along coasts. In winter, the dark crown extends below the eye, giving a masked effect. The white flank patch, often obvious, distinguishes it from other divers. Like other divers, it is very vulnerable to disturbance at its breeding sites. During the breeding season, pairs perform elaborate displays and utter rhythmic wailing calls. It lays two olive-brown eggs, blotched with black. The average dive lasts 45 seconds, but birds sometimes stay underwater for two minutes in their pursuit of fish.
Ⓑ☻☻

Great Northern Diver
Gavia immer
70–80cm. This is the largest of the common European divers (only the rare White-billed Diver is larger). It has a thick neck and a stout, powerful bill, adapted for seizing large fish and cracking the shells of molluscs and crabs. It beats its wings more slowly than other divers. Like the Black-throated Diver, it needs a large territory to provide it with enough food and prefers large, deep lakes with islets for breeding. In winter, like other divers, it can be seen in small flocks on coastal waters.
Ⓑ☻☻

A pair of Black-necked Grebes in breeding plumage. These beautiful birds are expanding their range northwards and westwards: about 30 pairs breed annually in Britain.

Grebes

The grebe group (Order Podicipediformes) are totally aquatic birds that are smaller than divers, with relatively large but shorter bills, longer necks and very short tails. They dive underwater to catch fish, insects, molluscs and crustaceans. Their lobed feet are placed so far back on the body that the birds can hardly stand. The sexes are alike. Grebes build floating nests of aquatic plants. As with divers, the chicks ride on their parents' backs. This order contains only one family (Podicipedidae).

Little Grebe
Tachybaptus ruficollis
27cm. The smallest and shortest-billed of the grebes, this bird is also the most numerous and widespread member of the family. It breeds on slow rivers, ponds and various lakes – from remote moorland lochs to city park lakes – wherever there is plentiful emergent vegetation. In winter, it may move to estuaries or coastal waters. It dives frequently, often emerging hidden among dense aquatic vegetation. It is heard as often as it is seen, especially during the breeding season when it frequently utters a loud whinnying trill. It lays 4–6 white eggs in a nest of floating vegetation and often raises two broods. A very dumpy bird, it has a broad rear end and a yellow patch at the base of its bill.
Ⓑ☻☻

Great Crested Grebe
Podiceps ruficollis
48cm. The largest European grebe. Like other grebes, it has a dramatic courtship display, in which its splendid breeding plumage is shown off to advantage. The double black crest and the chestnut and black ear ruffs are raised in display. The pair also dive for weed and, holding this in their bills, rear up breast to breast, waggling their heads in a courtship 'dance'. In winter, the black cap remains above the eye and the foreneck is white. In the 19th century, it was killed in huge numbers for its dense white breast feathers, used in the hat trade. Today, however, it is a widespread breeder on lakes, flooded gravel pits and reservoirs. The black and white striped juveniles are fed fish by the diving adults. The birds often winter on sheltered coasts.
Ⓑ☻☻

Red-necked Grebe
Podiceps grisegena
Slightly smaller and stouter than the Great Crested Grebe, this grebe has a thicker neck, a heavier head with a black cap to below the eye and a thicker, yellow-based bill. In winter it has a dusky foreneck. It breeds among reeds beside freshwater and is a scarce winter visitor to the coast. The female lays 4–5 white eggs on a floating nest platform. As with other grebes and divers the young are carried on their parents' backs. Adults eat their own feathers and feed them to their young to aid digestion and help rid their stomachs of parasites.
Ⓑ☻☻

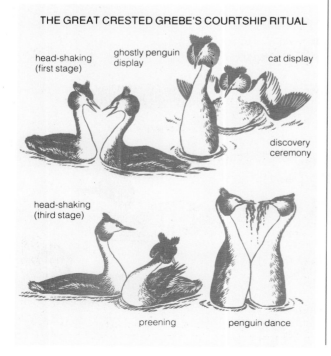

THE GREAT CRESTED GREBE'S COURTSHIP RITUAL

head-shaking (first stage)

ghostly penguin display

cat display

discovery ceremony

head-shaking (third stage)

preening

penguin dance

Slavonian Grebe

Podiceps auritus

33cm. Squat and round-bodied, the Slavonian Grebe has a shortish, rather stout bill, a clear-cut black cap and a white foreneck in winter. A rare breeder in the British Isles, it has an elaborate courtship display. It breeds on shallow pools and small lakes, building a nest comprising a floating mound of vegetation anchored to waterweed. The 4–5 white eggs are soon stained by the damp vegetation with which the parent covers them when it leaves to go fishing. In winter, this species occurs in small flocks in sheltered bays and estuaries.

Ⓑ ☻ ☻

Black-necked Grebe

Podiceps nigricollis

30cm. This species is very similar to the Slavonian Grebe in its winter plumage, but it has a rounder, peaked head, a thinner, upturned bill, a more indistinct, deeper, dusky cap and grey smudges on its foreneck. Unlike other grebes, this species usually nests in colonies. It favours well vegetated, shallow lakes. Like other grebes and divers, it feeds by diving from the surface of the water. A rare breeder in the British Isles, in winter it turns up mainly on lakes and reservoirs, though some visit sheltered southern coasts.

Ⓑ ☻ ☻

Red-throated Diver

Great Crested Grebe

Black-throated Diver

Red-necked Grebe

Great Northern Diver

Slavonian Grebe

Little Grebe

Bk-necked Grebe

Red-throated Diver — summer / winter

Great Crested Grebe — juvenile / summer / winter

Black-throated Diver — summer / winter

Red-necked Grebe — juvenile / summer / winter

Great Northern Diver — summer / winter

Slavonian Grebe — summer / winter

Little Grebe — summer / winter

Black-necked Grebe — summer / winter

Fulmars, Shearwaters and Storm-Petrels

The tubenoses (Order Procellariiformes) are named for their external, tube-shaped nostrils, from which they excrete excess salt. All have webbed feet and are armed with hooked bills, with which they catch fish, squid, crustaceans and other marine life. The sexes are alike. Fulmars and shearwaters (Family Procellariidae) soar low over the sea, with occasional stiff wingbeats. Storm-petrels (Family Hydrobatidae), the smallest seabirds, have a fluttering flight low over the waves.

Northern Fulmar
Fulmarus glacialis
45–50cm. Although superficially gull-like, closer observation reveals this bird's stiff straight wings, short thick neck, dark smudge around each eye and tube-nosed bill. It breeds in colonies on sea cliffs and sometimes on ruined buildings and screes, laying its single white egg on a bare ledge. The bird shakes its head, bows and growls and cackles when greeting a mate or warning off rivals. Both adults and young defend themselves by spitting out a stream of foul-smelling oil. This bird has expanded its range dramatically over the last 200 years, spreading south from Iceland.
Ⓑ☻

Cory's Shearwater
Calonectris diomedea
46cm. This shearwater has a grey-brown head and hindneck with paler upperparts. It has the regular habit of following fishing boats. A strong flyer, it has a wing action rather like that of the Northern Fulmar. It breeds in the Mediterranean and on various Atlantic islands, dispersing widely in autumn over the Atlantic. Like other shearwaters, it is a colonial nester, laying its single white egg in a burrow or beneath a rock.
Ⓑ☻

Manx Shearwater
Puffinus puffinus
35cm. The North Atlantic race of this shearwater flashes black and white as it tilts from side to side above the waves. It breeds in Iceland and the western British Isles, congregating on favoured islands, and filling the summer nights with its wailing and cackling calls. The western Mediterranean race (*mauretanicus*) is browner above and duller below. It moves west and north after breeding, and occurs off British coasts in late summer. After breeding, the adults abandon their chicks in the nest burrows; the young birds find their own way to the winter quarters 8000km away, off the coast of South America.
Ⓑ☻

European Storm-Petrel
Hydrobates pelagicus
14–18cm. This sparrow-sized seabird, with a white rump, has a fluttering, bat-like flight over the open sea. Its tail is cut square and its feet patter on the water as it dips down into the waves to pick up tiny fish, plankton and fatty or oily scraps of offal with its bill. It often follows ships. Like shearwaters, storm-petrels are truly birds of the open ocean, braving fierce gales and crashing waves and returning to land solely to breed. It nests colonially among rocks, in walls, or in rabbit burrows on small islands. It visits the breeding sites only by night to avoid predators such as large gulls. It lays a single white egg.
Ⓑ☻

Leach's Storm-Petrel
Oceanodroma leucorhoa
20cm. This petrel has a forked tail, a dark central stripe on its white rump, and a pale stripe on the upperside of each wing. It also lacks the white underwing bar of the European Storm-Petrel. Its flight resembles that of the shearwaters, bounding with short glides between periods of slow flapping; it occasionally hovers as it takes food from the ocean surface. It breeds on remote islands off Iceland, Scotland and Norway, and winters at sea, in tropical areas of the Atlantic Ocean.
Ⓑ☻

Northern Gannets at their breeding colony. Although a few individuals breed in their fourth year, most do not do so until their sixth year.

Gannets, Cormorants and Pelicans

There are six families within the Order Pelecaniformes, three of which occur regularly in Europe. They are large waterbirds with all four toes connected by webs. The sexes are alike and they nest on cliffs, on the ground or in trees. The exclusively marine gannets and boobies (Family Sulidae), with one species in Europe, plunge into the sea from a height to catch fish and squid with their long dagger-like bills. The cormorants (Family Phalacrocoracidae) catch fish by diving from the surface. The pelicans (Family Pelecanidae) also feed from the surface, trapping fish in their capacious pouches.

Northern Gannet
Sula bassana
90cm. Plunging like a great gleaming white arrow from heights of 10m or more into the ocean with a dramatic splash to seize fish and squid, this is one of the most exciting of all seabirds to watch. It breeds in large, noisy colonies on offshore islands and cliffs in the North Atlantic, with some 160,000 pairs in 14 colonies in the British Isles that comprise 72 per cent of the European population and 61 per cent of the world total.
Ⓑ☻

Great Cormorant
Phalacrocorax carbo
90cm. This waterbird typically breeds on coasts, although in eastern Europe it also nests inland. The nest is a mound of seaweed, usually on a cliff ledge but sometimes in a tree. The female lays 3–4 pale blue eggs. Wintering birds occur along most coasts and also inland on rivers and lakes. The continental race differs from the North Atlantic race in having more extensive white on its head and neck. Swimming low in the water, with its head tilted upwards, it dives frequently to catch fish. Its plumage is modified so that it becomes waterlogged easily to make diving easier. This means the bird must dry its plumage by standing on a rock or other perch with its wings outstretched.
Ⓑ☻☻☻

Shag
Phalacrocorax aristotelis
76cm. Smaller and more slender than the Great Cormorant, the Shag has dark shiny green plumage and a much thinner bill. In summer, adult birds also sport a distinctive crest. Unlike its larger relative, it is rarely seen inland. It nests along rocky coasts, on sheltered ledges, among boulders or in sea caves. Like other cormorants, it usually nests in colonies. Over 1,000 pairs may nest together but colonies are normally smaller. Young birds are brown with a white chin, while those of the Mediterranean race share the white bellies of young Great Cormorants.
Ⓑ☻

Pygmy Cormorant

Phalacrocorax pygmeus
48cm. This is by far the
smallest European cormorant.
It has a long tail, short neck,
small head and very short bill.
Adults have glossy greenish
black breeding plumage,
peppered with white spots,
and a reddish-brown head.
They soon lose the white
spots and acquire a white
throat and reddish-brown
breast. The young are
browner and duller. This
species lives in freshwater
marshes and reed beds but it
visits coasts in winter.

Dalmatian Pelican

Pelecanus crispus
160–180cm. This huge bird is
dull silvery white when adult,
with a yellowish breast patch
and a ragged crest in the
breeding season. A declining
species, it now breeds in only
a few colonies in marshes and
reedbeds in southeastern
Europe. Many move to
sheltered coasts in winter.
The similar White Pelican
(*P. onocrotalus*) is a purer
white with more contrasting
underwings – black flight
feathers on otherwise white
wings – and pinkish legs.

Northern Fulmar   Northern Gannet

Cory's Shearwater   Great Cormorant

Manx Shearwater   Shag

European Storm-
petrel   Pygmy Cormorant

L's Storm-petrel   Dmn Pelican

Northern Fulmar

Great Cormorant
summer   first winter
winter

Cory's Shearwater

Shag
summer   first winter
winter

Manx Shearwater

Pygmy Cormorant
spring   juvenile
winter

European Storm-petrel

Dalmatian Pelican
juvenile
summer

Leach's Storm-petrel

Northern Gannet
juvenile
first summer   second summer   third summer

201

Herons, Storks and Relatives

The members of the Order Ciconiiformes are elegant waterbirds that use their long legs to wade in shallow water, marshes or wet fields in search of food. Most species nest in trees, among reedbeds or on cliffs, and the sexes are alike. Herons, bitterns and egrets (Family Ardeidae) and storks (Family Ciconiidae) catch fish, frogs and other prey by suddenly darting out their long necks and seizing their prey in their long, pointed bills. Spoonbills (Family Threskiornithidae) and flamingos (Family Phoenicopteridae) have highly specialized bills, and eat small prey which they trap or sieve from the water.

Bittern

Botaurus stellaris
74cm. The shy, skulking Bittern is a bird of dense reed beds. It is more often heard than seen, as its distinctive loud booming calls may carry for up to 5km. When alarmed, it stands erect with head and bill pointing skywards, so that its striped plumage camouflages it superbly against the reeds. The Bittern is declining due to habitat loss. In Britain it is now a rare breeder, found at only a few sites. Males are sometimes polygamous. The female incubates the clutch of 4–6 eggs and may receive no help from the male in feeding the young. The Little Bittern, a widespread breeder in Europe south of Denmark, and a rare vagrant to the British Isles, is 35cm long. Males are a striking black and buff, while females and young are streaked brown.

Black-crowned Night Heron

Nycticorax nycticorax
60cm. The Night Heron breeds in dense riverside vegetation. It is a rare vagrant to the British Isles, mainly in spring. A colonial nester, it builds its untidy nest of twigs and reeds in bushes, low trees or reeds. The young are streaked brown in contrast to the strikingly plumaged adults. True to its name, the Black-crowned Night Heron is mainly nocturnal, although parent birds often hunt during the daytime when feeding young. Feeding by night avoids competition with day-feeding herons. The prey includes frogs, toads, fish, chicks, small mammals and crustaceans.

Squacco Heron

Ardeola ralloides
45cm. This heron is well camouflaged by its buff plumage as it skulks among marsh vegetation, but when it takes flight its white wings, rump and tail are revealed. It breeds in mixed colonies with other herons in freshwater marshes, swamps and the vegetated edges of lakes. As with many other herons and egrets, breeding birds acquire a crest and plumes on the back. It winters in Africa south of the Sahara and is a rare vagrant to the British Isles, mainly in the south. It eats mainly insects.

Cattle Egret

Bubulcus ibis
50cm. Although this species nests in freshwater wetlands, it often feeds on dry grassland with cattle and other farm animals, seizing insects and lizards disturbed by the grazing animals. It is a highly gregarious bird, breeding in colonies so dense that there may be as many as 100 nests in a single tree. It feeds in large groups too. Some birds fly south to winter in northwest Africa. This species is a rare vagrant to the British Isles, chiefly in the south. The European population of this once purely African species has expanded northwards from Spain since 1950.

Little Egret

Egretta garzetta
58cm. This bird's beautiful breeding plumage, with its 25cm head and breast plumes, was nearly its downfall. For, during the last century, it was nearly wiped out from much of Europe to supply the hat trade with feathers. Fortunately, it is now widespread in southern Europe, nesting in colonies in trees and feeding in open water. The 89cm Great Egret is a scarce summer visitor to a few marshes in central and south-eastern Europe. Both species are rare vagrants to the British Isles.

BITTERN CAMOUFLAGE

With its striped plumage, an alarmed Bittern can merge in with the reeds

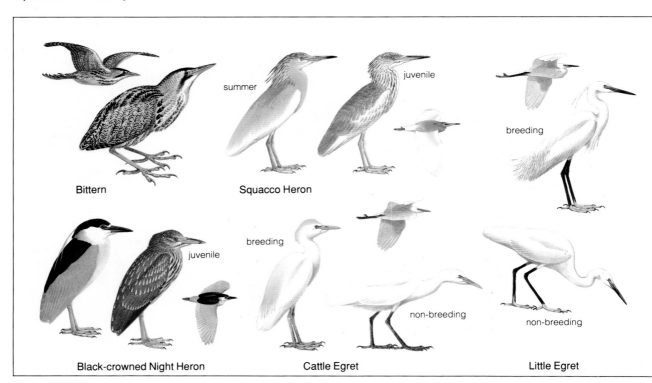

Bittern

summer   juvenile

Squacco Heron

breeding

Little Egret

juvenile

Black-crowned Night Heron

breeding   non-breeding

Cattle Egret

non-breeding

Little Egret

A White Spoonbill feeds one of its young at the nest. In its breeding plumage, the adult has a droopy crest and a yellowish neck band.

Grey Heron
Ardea cinerea
90cm. The most common large heron throughout Europe, the Grey Heron nests colonially in tall trees up to 25m above ground. It can be seen patiently stalking its prey in a wide range of freshwater habitats, as well as in fields. Its diet is chiefly fish, but also includes frogs, small mammals, reptiles and insects. It also occurs on estuaries. In flight, the Grey Heron beats its broad wings slowly and may utter a loud, harsh *fraank* call.
Ⓑ😊🐟😊🐛

Purple Heron
Ardea purpurea
80cm. The Purple Heron is largely restricted to reedbeds or other dense aquatic vegetation. It feeds mainly at dusk and dawn, roosting communally by day and night. It has a different flight silhouette from the Grey Heron, with a more strongly kinked neck, narrower body and wings. It also flies less ponderously and its large feet extend further behind its tail. It is a scarce vagrant to Britain, arriving mainly from the Netherlands, chiefly in the spring.
😊

White Stork
Ciconia ciconia
110cm. The natural nest sites of this large, easily identified bird are cliff-ledges and trees, but most European breeders build their huge nests of sticks on houses and other man-made structures. Once widespread in continental Europe, the White Stork has declined in many areas due to habitat loss and the effects of pesticides. It feeds on marshes, farmland and other open country, eating mainly amphibians, small mammals and insects. It is a rare vagrant to Britain. The 97cm Black Stork is a very rare vagrant to Britain.
😊😊🐟🐛

White Spoonbill
Platalea leucorodia
86cm. The most remarkable feature of this bird is the large spoon-shaped bill after which it is named. It feeds by scything its bill through shallow water, with the spoon-shaped tip below the surface. The mandibles are held slightly open to trap crustaceans, molluscs, insects and fish. The White Spoonbill nests colonially in dense reeds, bushes or trees. Although it bred in Britain until the 17th century, it is now only a scarce visitor to southern England and extreme southern Ireland.
😊😊

Greater Flamingo
Phoenicopterus ruber
125–145cm. In Europe, this unmistakable bird breeds only in the Camargue and at 3 sites in southern Spain. Highly gregarious, it breeds on saline or alkaline lakes, lagoons and deltas. The pink and red pigments of the adults are obtained from their food. When feeding, the flamingo holds its head upside down in the water and swings it to and fro. A pumping action of the tongue forces mud and water through comb-like plates on either side of the bill, which strain out the tiny crustaceans.
😊😊😊

Bittern

Grey Heron

Black-crowned Night Heron

Purple Heron

Squacco Heron

White Stork

Cattle Egret

White Spoonbill

Little Egret

Greater Flamingo

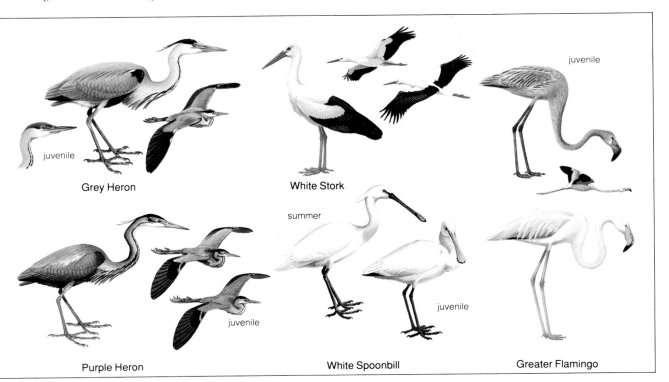

Grey Heron

White Stork

Purple Heron

White Spoonbill

Greater Flamingo

Wildfowl

The wildfowl are aquatic birds with webbed feet, medium to long necks, short legs and narrow, pointed wings. They have flattened, broad bills covered with a thin layer of skin and ending in a horny 'nail', often slightly hooked. Most species build their nests on the ground amongst vegetation, although some nest on rocky ledges or in tree holes. Newly hatched young are covered in down and can walk and swim just after hatching. All wildfowl belong to the Family Anatidae, the only family in the Order Anseriformes.

SWANS

The largest of the wildfowl, the swans (Family Anatidae) have very long necks. All three European species are white, with a distinctive bill pattern; the young are greyish-brown. Often noisy, they are clumsy on land and have to run across the water for a long way to become airborne. The sexes differ slightly in the Mute Swan. Swans upend to tear off aquatic vegetation in their strong bills and also graze on land. Like geese, they are strong flyers, capable of making long migrations between their northern breeding grounds and wintering quarters.

Mute Swan
Cygnus olor
150cm. This once domestic bird is now found on lakes, rivers, estuaries, sheltered coasts and nearby fields. It is one of the world's heaviest birds, walking with a rolling gait. Its wings make a powerful rhythmic singing noise in flight. On land and in the water it holds its neck in an S-shape. Belying its name, it sometimes utters quiet hisses and grunts. The male (cob) has a larger black knob on its bill than the female (pen). Cygnets are pale brown with pale pink and black bills.
Ⓑ🦆🏹☻〜

Bewick's Swan
Cygnus columbianus
120cm. This is the smallest of the three European swans. Bewick's Swan has a rather short neck, which it often holds straight, a smaller bill and a concave forehead. Although the pattern of yellow and black on the bill varies from individual to individual the area of yellow is characteristically rounded in shape. Its faster wingbeats and musical goose-like honking help distinguish it from other swans. Breeding on the tundras of Arctic Russia, it is a local winter visitor to freshwater marshes, estuaries and flooded fields, where it feeds on grass and aquatic vegetation.
Ⓑ🦆☻〜

Whooper Swan
Cygnus cygnus
150cm. Breeding on the tundra, this swan winters chiefly on lakes, rivers, floodlands, arable fields, estuaries and sea coasts. The same size as the Mute Swan, it is easily distinguished by its usually straight neck and yellow and black bill. Unlike the smaller Bewick's Swan, it has a longer neck, a flat profiled forehead and a longer bill with a larger triangular area of yellow at the base. Its wingbeats make a whistling sound and it also utters loud whooping and bugling calls after which it is named.
Ⓑ🦆🏹☻〜

GEESE

Intermediate in size between swans and ducks, the geese (Family Anatidae) are more terrestrial than either. Their legs are set well forward on their bodies, enabling them to walk much more easily, while their short, blunt bills have horny 'teeth' along the edges of the upper mandible for grazing vegetation. The sexes are alike. On their long migrations, geese usually adopt distinctive V-shaped flight patterns. There are two groups of geese, the mainly grey-brown 'grey' geese and the 'black' geese, which mostly have black and white heads and necks.

Whooper Swans have longer, narrower wings than Mute Swans, with a wingspan that measures up to 2.4 metres.

Bean Goose
Anser fabalis
75cm. This dark grey goose has a large dark head, orange on its relatively large bill, a long neck and orange-yellow legs. In flight it shows a uniform dark brown upper-wing. It is often less noisy than other geese, but when it calls its voice is a series of deep, low *ung-unks*. The Bean Goose breeds in Scandinavia and Arctic Russia, and is a scarce winter visitor to pastures and arable land in scattered areas of western Europe, including a few sites in Britain.
Ⓑ🦆☻〜

Pink-footed Goose
Anser brachyrhynchus
70cm. Like a smaller version of the Bean Goose, this species has a smaller head and bill, pink on the bill and legs rather than orange, and a greyer back. It may have some white around the bill. When it flies, it reveals a large grey forewing. This is a very vocal goose, with high-pitched, harsh *ung-unk* and *wink-wink-wink* honking notes. In winter it feeds mainly on arable land, on grass, spilled grain and waste potatoes, and roosts on coastal salt-marshes, mudflats and sandbanks.
Ⓑ🦆☻🏹☻〜

White-fronted Goose
Anser albifrons
75cm. Adults of this goose can be recognized by the broad white base to the bill and bold dark bars on the belly. Birds of the pale coloured, pink-billed Russian race visit England, the Netherlands, France, central Europe, Greece and Romania, while orange-billed Greenland birds winter in Ireland, west Scotland and west Wales. They are found on low-lying fields and freshwater and coastal marshes.
Ⓑ🦆☻🏹☻〜

Greylag Goose
Anser anser
80cm. The largest of the 'grey' geese, the Greylag Goose has a large pale head and neck, a large orange bill, pink legs and a prominent pale grey forewing in flight. The race in Eastern Europe has a pink bill. The Greylag is a noisy bird, uttering deep, loud, cackling *aahng-ung-ung* calls in flight. Small numbers of wild Greylags breed in north-western Scotland, while introduced birds, now living wild, are found in many parts of England. This goose is more widespread as a winter visitor, feeding on marshy ground and arable fields. The Greylag is the ancestor of most domestic geese.
Ⓑ🦆☻🏹〜

Canada Goose
Branta canadensis
95cm. The largest of the 'black' geese, this species was first introduced to Europe from North America in the 17th century. Since then it has become a familiar bird of ponds, lakes, gravel-pits and reservoirs in town and country in England, where it is widespread. Small scattered populations are found elsewhere. Its large bill, black head and neck with a white chin patch, and its brown body and wings distinguish it from other 'black' geese. It has loud, trumpet-like honking calls, often alerting one to a skein flying over. It forms large flocks at the end of summer for the moult.
Ⓑ🦆🏹

Barnacle Goose

Branta leucopsis

63cm. This is the only 'black' goose with an all-white face. It is also distinguished by its small bill and grey back and wings. Birds breeding in Greenland winter mainly in western Ireland and Scotland, those breeding in Spitzbergen winter on the Solway Firth, Scotland, while Siberian breeders winter chiefly in the Netherlands. Barnacle Geese utter short, sharp, puppy-like barks and deeper growls.

Ⓑ ⬤ ⚥ 😊 🐛

Brent Goose

Branta bernicla

58cm. The smallest of the three 'black' geese, the Brent Goose is also the darkest. It has a white marking on each side of the neck. Two races occur regularly in Europe as winter visitors to coastal mudflats. The pale-bellied race winters in northeastern England and Ireland, the dark-bellied race winters chiefly in southern England and the Continent. Brent Geese feed mainly on eelgrass and salt-marsh plants, but also on grass and cereals. They fly in straggling lines, giving soft, growling calls.

Ⓑ ⬤ ⚥ 😊

Mute Swan

Bewick's Swan

White-fronted Goose

Whooper Swan

Greylag Goose

Bean Goose

Barnacle Goose

Pink-ftd Goose

Brent Goose

Mute Swan
juvenile
♂
♂

Bewick's Swan
juvenile

Whooper Swan
juvenile

juvenile
Greenland race
Russian race
White-fronted Goose

Greylag Goose

Canada Goose

Barnacle Goose

Bean Goose

Pink-footed Goose

dark-bellied race
pale-bellied race
Brent Goose

SHELDUCKS, DABBLING DUCKS AND DIVING DUCKS

Shelducks are large and rather goose-like, with the sexes similar. They feed by scything their bills through mud and sand to sift molluscs and crustaceans. Dabbling ducks feed on the surface by upending, straining out seeds and small invertebrates on comb-like lamellae along the sides of their bills. Both sexes have a glossy, brightly coloured patch of wing feathers called the speculum – useful for species identification. Diving ducks dive from the surface to feed on invertebrates and plants. All three types of duck belong to the Family Anatidae.

Common Shelduck
Tadorna tadorna
62cm. This large, boldly marked duck is goose-like both in appearance and posture. Males are somewhat brighter than females and have a prominent knob at the base of the bill. The Common Shelduck nests in old rabbit burrows, tree holes, haystacks and other holes, mainly near the coast, where it favours shallow muddy and sandy shores and estuaries. The male defends a feeding territory on the shore where the female can feed unchallenged during the brief periods she leaves the eggs. Most of the north-west European population migrates in late summer to moult on the Waddenzee, off the coast of north Germany, leaving the young in large creches under the care of a few adults.
Ⓑ🦆🐟🐦🦆

Eurasian Wigeon
Anas penelope
46cm. The male of this species has a distinctive chestnut head and golden crown, and reveals bold white wing patches in flight. The female is more rufous than other female dabbling ducks. Both sexes have short, silver-grey bills and white bellies. Males utter high-pitched whistling *whee-ooo* calls; females make low growls. The Wigeon nests chiefly by large shallow freshwaters, taking off from water or land. Only small numbers nest in Britain. It is a widespread winter visitor, occurring mainly on coastal mud and sand flats and salt-marshes, but also on inland waters and flooded fields. It grazes in dense flocks, often with geese, on grass, eelgrass and aquatic vegetation.
Ⓑ🦆🦆🦆🐦🦆🦆▥

Gadwall
Anas strepera
51cm. The Gadwall is a rather shy and inconspicuous duck. The male is a mottled grey and brown bird, superficially resembling females of other dabbling ducks, while the female is similar to the female Mallard. Both sexes are distinguished by a white belly and white on the speculum, both visible in flight. The Gadwall nests among vegetation by reedy marshes, pools, lakes and slow rivers, but is more abundant as a winter visitor. It was introduced into Britain in the 1850s and is now a regular breeder in England.
Ⓑ🦆🐦🦆

Green-winged Teal
Anas crecca
35cm. This is the smallest common European duck. The male has a distinct head pattern and yellowish undertail and the female has a green speculum. These teal are agile flyers, springing off the water and twisting and turning in unison like waders. They breed near well-vegetated freshwaters and even on moorland some distance from water, and winter on coastal marshes, estuaries, shallow lakes and flooded fields. They are very shy birds.
Ⓑ🦆🦆🐦🦆🦆

Mallard
Anas platyrhynchos
50cm. The most common and widespread European duck, the familiar Mallard is also the ancestor of most farmyard ducks and sometimes interbreeds with them to produce oddly marked hybrids. The Mallard is an adaptable bird which varies from being a tame, hand-fed bird of city lakes to a wild and wary inhabitant of remote marshes, estuaries and seashores. Its range extends from the tundra to the subtropics. Natural nest sites are usually sited among dense vegetation near water but birds in built-up areas will nest in holes in trees and both in and on buildings.
Ⓑ🦆🦆🐦🦆

Northern Pintail
Anas acuta
56cm. This slim and handsome duck breeds by shallow waters in grassland, moorland or near the coast. In the British Isles it nests only rarely. It is also a winter visitor, mainly to estuaries, locally in large numbers. The male has long tail streamers, very noticeable white neck stripes and a chocolate brown head. The female's slim neck, grey bill and shorter but pointed tail are also distinctive. The Pintail's long neck enables it to reach deeper than other dabbling ducks when up-ending for plants and invertebrates. It also feeds by night on stubble and potato fields.
Ⓑ🦆🦆

Garganey
Anas querquedula
38cm. The male Garganey can be identified by his red-brown head and bold white eyebrow, while the female has a distinctly striped face; both sexes show a blue-grey forewing in flight. The male's call is a curious crackling rattle, while the female utters short, sharp quacks. The Garganey breeds on shallow reedy pools and marshes. It is the only duck to visit Britain in summer, wintering in Africa. Only small numbers breed in Britain, mainly in southern and eastern England. Like other ducks, they raise only one brood.
Ⓑ🦆

Northern Shoveler
Anas clypeata
51cm. The Shoveler's unmistakably huge, spoon-shaped bill is a very efficient filter, able to strain invertebrates and seeds from the water. When feeding, the duck half submerges its bill and sweeps it from side to side while swimming forwards. It breeds on reed-fringed marshes and lakes. It is more abundant as a winter visitor to open shallow lakes, reservoirs and estuaries. In flight the bird's long neck makes its wings appear set far back on the body and the blue-grey forewing is a very obvious feature.
Ⓑ🦆🦆

This male Mallard stretching shows the speculum, the patch of brightly coloured wing feathers that is useful for identifying dabbling ducks.

DUCK TYPES IN SILHOUETTE

dabbling duck upending

dabbling duck feeding at surface

dabbling duck

Shelduck

Red-crested Pochard
Netta rufina

56cm. The male has a very large, bright chestnut head with a paler erectile crest and a bright red bill, contrasting with his black breast and white flanks. The brown female has a dark cap and pale cheeks. Both sexes have a bold white wing panel. Found on fresh waters, outside its breeding colonies it occurs as a rare vagrant, but many birds are escapes from wildfowl collections.

Common Pochard
Aythya ferina

46cm. This diving duck breeds on reedy freshwaters and coastal marshes. An uncommon breeding bird in Britain, it is a more abundant winter visitor to reservoirs, lakes and estuaries. The female has blotchy cheeks and a light grey-brown back. Common Pochards have a distinctive profile, with a short neck, steep sloping forehead and large bill, and reveal a pale grey wing bar in flight. The female lays 8–10 greenish eggs on a mound of vegetation and down. She alone incubates the eggs.

Common Shelduck

Northern Pintail

Eurasian Wigeon

Garganey

Gadwall

Northern Shoveler

Green-winged Teal

Common Pochard

Mallard

Rd-crstd Pochard

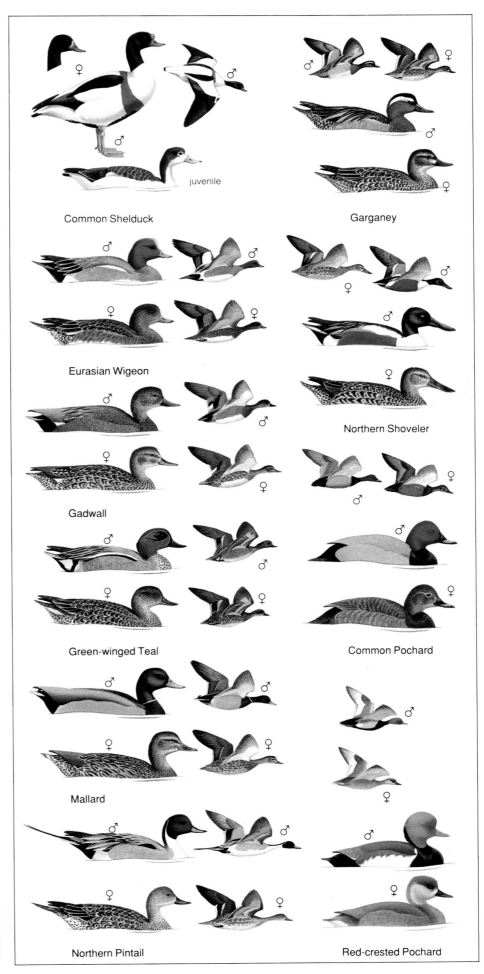

Common Shelduck

juvenile

Garganey

♂ ♀

♂

♀

Eurasian Wigeon

♂

♂

♀

♂

Northern Shoveler

♂

♀

♀

Gadwall

♀

♀

♂

♂

♀

Green-winged Teal

♂

♀

♂

♀

Common Pochard

♂

♀

Mallard

♂

♀

♀

Northern Pintail

♂

♂

♀

♀

♂

♀

Red-crested Pochard

Tufted Duck
Aythya fuligula
43cm. The most widespread European diving duck, the Tufted Duck is mainly a freshwater species. It breeds by a wide variety of lowland waters, from ponds in city parks to reservoirs, lakes and slow rivers, and winters on similar sites as well as on sheltered estuaries. Some females have white at the base of the bill, but never as large an area as that of a female Greater Scaup. Hybrids between this species and Greater Scaup or Common Pochard are quite common. Like most ducks, the female alone incubates the eggs and raises the young.
🅑🅔🅞🅔

Greater Scaup
Aythya marila
48cm. Although similar to the Tufted Duck, the Greater Scaup is slightly larger. The male also differs in having a green gloss on his head and a pale grey back, while the female has a large white area at the base of her bill; both sexes also lack the crest of the Tufted Duck. The Greater Scaup breeds by freshwaters. It breeds in northern Europe and occasionally in Scotland. In winter, it is found almost exclusively on coastal waters and estuaries, with the largest flocks gathering in northern European waters.
🅑🅔🅔🅔

SEA DUCKS, SAWBILLS AND STIFFTAILS

Like the diving ducks that live mainly on fresh waters, sea ducks (Family Anatidae) also dive for their food. They use their large, strong bills to crush the shells of crabs and molluscs. Although, as their name implies, sea ducks spend much of the year on the sea, many species breed by fresh waters, as do the closely related sawbills. Sawbills dive to pursue fish, which they seize in their narrow, toothed bills. Stifftails are small, dumpy freshwater ducks with stiff tails used for steering underwater. They are highly aquatic and very clumsy on land.

Common Eider
Somateria mollissima
58cm. This large sea duck has a heavy body and short neck, with a long, sloping head and bill profile. Exclusively marine, it dives from 2 to 20m deep to catch molluscs and crustaceans. It is a gregarious bird, breeding in groups which may number over a thousand, mainly on small coastal islands. In Iceland and Norway, eider down is harvested from the nest for filling sleeping bags, duvets and pillows.
🅑🅔

Common Scoter
Melanitta nigra
48cm. The male of this sea duck is the only all-black duck. It has a yellow bill, with a black knob at its base. The female is dark brown with pale sides to her face and a grey bill. It nests on tundra and moorland, usually by freshwater. It is a winter visitor to coastal waters, usually in flocks of 100 to 1000 or more. Like other sea ducks, auks and other seabirds, the Common Scoter is very vulnerable to the effects of oil spills and overfishing of its prey.
🅑🅔🅔🅔🅔

Common Goldeneye
Bucephala clangula
56cm This sea duck has a peaked fore crown and a sloping hind crown. The white spot between the eye and the bill of the male stands out at a distance, as does his black and white plumage. Both sexes have prominent yellow eyes and show white on the inner wing in flight. The Common Goldeneye breeds in tree holes and nest boxes by freshwaters in forests. It is a widespread winter visitor to both coastal and inland waters.
🅑🅔🅔🅔

Long-tailed Duck
Clangula hyemalis
42cm. This sea duck is unique among ducks in having eight distinct adult plumages: both sexes have different spring, summer, autumn and winter plumages. The small head, steep forehead, short upturned bill, triangular uniform brown wings in flight, together with the long tail and loud yodelling calls of the male, are all good identification clues. Long-tailed Ducks breed on tundra pools and by the coast. They occur in large flocks on coastal waters in winter. They are superb divers, reaching depths of up to 55m.
🅑🅔🅔🅔

Smew
Mergus albellus
41cm. This beautiful duck is the smallest of the sawbills, with a much shorter bill than its relatives. It nests in tree holes near freshwater on the tundra and in northern coniferous or mixed forests. It winters chiefly on freshwaters, especially on reservoirs, and on sheltered estuaries. Numbers of Smew wintering in Britain have declined considerably since the 1950s. Like other sawbills, the Smew dives to catch its prey, eating mainly small fish in winter and catching more insects in summer.
🅑🅔🅞🅔🅔🅔

Red-breasted Merganser
Mergus serrator
55cm. This sawbill is a long, slim bird with a long, thin bill and a wispy double crest. It breeds along coasts and sea lochs but also by wooded rivers and lakes. It hides its nest hollow among tree roots or rocks on the ground. It is a widespread winter visitor to coasts and estuaries. Like the Goosander, it feeds by diving mainly for fish, which it seizes in its saw-edged bill. The male performs a spectacular head-shaking display and other courtship rituals, especially in late winter and early spring.
🅑🅔🅔

A handsome drake Smew. Females and immature birds tend to winter further south than most of the males.

DUCK TYPES IN SILHOUETTE
dabbling duck
diving/sea duck
take-off abrupt, almost vertical
need a long run across the water to become airborne
Sawbill (Merganser)
diving/sea ducks

Goosander
Mergus merganser
62cm. Largest of the three European sawbills, the Goosander is bulkier than the Red-breasted Merganser, with a thicker neck and a larger head. The Goosander also sports a larger spiky crest, which in the male may touch the back. Unlike the Red-breasted Merganser, the Goosander is chiefly a bird of freshwaters, breeding by wooded lakes and rivers, nesting in tree holes or on the ground. In winter it is found in small flocks, mainly on large lakes and reservoirs.
Ⓑ🦆🌊⛰️🌊

Ruddy Duck
Oxyura jamaicensis
41cm. This dumpy, large-headed duck belongs to a group called the stifftails. Its long stiff tail may be cocked at an angle or held flat along the surface of the water. This duck was introduced from North America into England, where it has bred in the wild since 1960 on shallow lakes and reservoirs. It is slowly spreading eastwards. Large flocks of Ruddy Ducks gather on freshwaters in winter. It eats plants and insects.
Ⓑ🦆

Tufted Duck	Long-tailed Duck
Scaup	Smew
Common Eider	Red-breasted Merganser
Common Scoter	Goosander
Cmn Goldeneye	Ruddy Duck

Tufted Duck

Scaup

Common Eider

Common Scoter

Common Goldeneye

Long-tailed Duck

Smew

Red-breasted Merganser

Goosander

Ruddy Duck

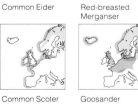

209

Birds of Prey

This large group (also known as raptors) forms the Order Falconiformes. Most are active predators which hunt by day, using their powerful clawed feet to seize and kill their prey, and their strong, hooked bills to tear its flesh. All birds of prey are superb flyers, typically making a short series of wingbeats followed by a glide. The larger species in particular make use of warm rising air currents (thermals) to soar in spirals. Most raptors build large nests of sticks in trees and on cliffs but some use old stick nests of other birds. The sexes are usually alike, but females are bigger.

OSPREYS

There is only one species of Osprey in the world. It is classified in a family of its own (Pandionidae) because it is so highly specialized for fish-eating, with a reversible outer toe and sharp spines beneath its feet for gripping its slippery, wriggling prey.

Osprey
Pandion haliaetus
55cm. This bird lives by lakes, rivers, estuaries and coastal waters, often with tall trees. It makes dramatic feet-first dives to catch fish, often after hovering overhead. With its pale underparts and bowed wings, it resembles a large gull in flight, but its small head with a dark eye stripe, long neck and black patches at the bend of the wings on their undersides, help to distinguish it. The Osprey has become extinct in most of Europe, due to shooting and egg collecting. Birds from the species' Scandinavian stronghold recolonized Scotland in 1954 and a small population now breeds there. Shooting and egg collection are still a problem but careful protection of nests has helped the population expand. It is also seen on passage to and from its winter quarters in Africa.

KITES, EAGLES, VULTURES, HARRIERS AND BUZZARDS

These birds (Family Accipitridae) typically spend their time in soaring flight, searching for food below. Many take live prey, from wasp larvae to snakes, mammals and birds, but some take carrion. The vultures are almost exclusively carrion eaters. Most vultures have unfeathered necks that dry off and clean up easily after being plunged into carcases. Harriers, unlike most other raptors, roost and nest on the ground, and the male and female plumages are very different. Sparrowhawks have short rounded wings and longish tails.

Honey Buzzard
Pernis apivorus
53cm. This bird superficially resembles true buzzards, but has a smaller head, weaker bill, longer and thinner neck, longer and slimmer wings 'pinched in' to the body, and a longer tail, typically with a single broad band at the tip and two narrow bands near the base. Also, it soars on flat wings, never in a shallow 'V' like the Common Buzzard. Its plumage is very variable, ranging from pale to dark. Though a widespread summer visitor to Europe, it is a very rare breeder in Britain. The name refers to its habit of raiding bee and wasp nests for adults, pupae and larvae; it also eats small mammals, birds and amphibians.

Black Kite
Milvus migrans
56cm. Smaller and less elegant than the Red Kite, this bird has shorter wings and only a shallow fork to its tail. It eats carrion, small mammals, birds and fish, swooping down with amazing dexterity to snatch morsels from the ground or water, or even from other birds in mid-air. It is a highly gregarious species outside the breeding season. A widespread summer visitor to Europe, it is a very rare vagrant to Britain, chiefly in spring.

A Red Kite brings food to its well-grown young at its treetop nest. Bad weather can result in many chicks dying.

Red Kite
Milvus milvus
61cm. The Red Kite is a declining species, even in its strongholds of Spain and Germany. It was once common, even in towns, but persecution, habitat destruction and improved sanitation led to its extinction in many places. Today, it favours open country with scattered woodland. A tiny isolated population of Red Kites is resident in Wales, and a reintroduction scheme is underway elsewhere. It has a deeply forked tail which it twists as a rudder as it banks.

White-tailed Eagle
Haliaeetus albicilla
70–90cm. With its massive deep bill, huge broad vulture-like wings and short wedge-shaped tail (white in adults), this bird is Europe's largest eagle. A scarce and local breeder, it lives along rocky sea coasts, lakes and large rivers. It feeds mainly on fish, waterbirds and carrion. It also takes some mammals and often robs other birds, especially Ospreys, of their prey. Extinct in Britain by 1918, a reintroduction scheme has led to a few pairs nesting in northwestern Scotland. Some winter in western Europe.

Lammergeier
Gypaetus barbatus
110cm. Also known as the Bearded Vulture, this bird has longer, narrower and more pointed wings than other large vultures and a longer, wedge-shaped tail. In Europe, this is a rare and declining breeder, now limited to just a few remote mountain regions. It does not compete with other vultures, specializing in eating bones and meat from freshly killed mammals and birds. Smaller bones are swallowed whole but the bird drops larger ones from a height so that they break and it can eat the marrow within.

Egyptian Vulture
Neophron percnopterus
62cm. The smallest European vulture, this dingy white bird with black wingtips has a short, wedge-shaped tail and a tiny head with a long, thin bill. The weakness of its bill means that it cannot compete with the larger vultures and is the last to feed at a large carcase. It eats the remains of small animals, insects, offal and human and animal waste of all sorts, often congregating at rubbish tips. Like other European vultures, this species has declined greatly. The European population winters in Africa.

Griffon Vulture
Gyps fulvus
1m. This vulture has a wingspan of almost 3m. It spends most of the day soaring in groups on its great broad wings, which have curved trailing edges and are held in a shallow 'V'. The Griffon is now restricted to wild, remote mountains, where it breeds colonially on ledges or in caves, though it visits plains to feed.

Black Vulture

Aegypius monachus
104cm. Even larger than the Griffon Vulture, the Black Vulture has entirely dark brown plumage, which looks black at a distance. Its short, bare bluish-pink neck is swathed in a dark neck ruff of feathers. When soaring it holds its wings flat, or even a little downwardly bowed, and not in a 'V'. It has a slightly wedge-shaped tail. It needs wild hill and mountain forest habitat for breeding. A rare and seriously threatened bird in Europe.

Short-toed Eagle

Circaetus gallicus
66cm. This raptor has a large head and a sturdy body. Its plumage is very variable, though most birds have a dark head and breast. Compared with the Osprey, which also has pale underparts, the Short-toed Eagle has broader wings and a larger head and lacks dark patches at the bend of the wing. It often hovers to search for its prey, which consists chiefly of reptiles, especially snakes. It winters in northern tropical Africa.

Osprey

Lammergeier

Honey Buzzard

Egyptian Vulture

Black Kite

Griffon Vulture

Red Kite

Black Vulture

W-tailed Eagle

Short-toed Eagle

Osprey

Lammergeier

pale phase

pale phase

dark phase

Honey Buzzard

Egyptian Vulture

Griffon Vulture

Black Kite

Black Vulture

Red Kite

Short-toed Eagle

juvenile

White-tailed Eagle

211

Marsh Harrier
Circus aeruginosus
52cm. This bird is usually seen over marshes and reedbeds. Though bulkier and broader-winged than other harriers, it shares their graceful flight low over the ground, a few leisurely flaps followed by a long glide on half-raised wings as it searches for prey. This consists of small mammals, birds, eggs, snakes, frogs and fish. It also eats carrion. In Britain, it became extinct by 1900 through persecution, but it later recolonized East Anglia and its numbers are slowly increasing. The nest is in an extensive reedbed. The female lays 4–5 eggs and incubates them. It is also a passage migrant and a winter visitor to parts of Britain.

Hen Harrier
Circus cyaneus
47cm. The Hen Harrier breeds on moorland, in young conifer plantations and in open country, and is also found on marshes and farmland in winter. It feeds mainly on voles and other small mammals and small birds. The male performs dramatic 'roller-coaster' flights over the breeding territory. In common with other harriers, the male brings food to the female while she is incubating the eggs and brooding the chicks, dropping the prey to his mate who catches it in mid-air, turning over neatly on her back to receive the food in her talons. In winter, 10 or more birds may roost together on the ground.

the same size. The best distinctions are the Goshawk's deeper chest, more protruding head, more pointed wings and broader tail. Goshawks also have a darker cap, whiter eyestripe and bold white undertail coverts. Females have similar plumage to the males. In Britain this species is a rare but increasing breeder. It nests in a high fork of a tree in extensive woodlands.

Northern Sparrowhawk
Accipiter nisus
Male 30cm; female 40cm. This predator feeds almost entirely on small birds. It catches them after a dashing flight through the trees and bushes, twisting and turning before shooting out a long leg to seize them, or by a swift attack from a concealed perch or by surprising them as it suddenly flies low over a hedge. Although decimated by pesticide pollution in the 1960s, it is now a widespread breeder in woodlands within open country.

Common Buzzard
Buteo buteo
54cm. The commonest of the larger raptors, this buzzard has very variable plumage, from mainly dark to mainly white. Its tail is usually strongly barred or whitish, and it always has dark patches on the 'wrist' joints of its wings and a dark breast. It spends much of its time soaring high overhead, its broad wings held in a shallow 'V'. It has a wide diet, feeding chiefly on small mammals, especially rabbits and voles, earthworms, birds and carrion. It nests in tall trees in woods and moorland and on cliffs. It often utters a ringing *pee-oo* call.

Rough-legged Buzzard
Buteo lagopus
55cm. Unlike the Common Buzzard, this raptor holds its longer wings flat when soaring and hovers much more often. It usually has dark patches on flanks and belly and more of a contrast between dark and light. The best distinction is the longer white tail with a broad black subterminal band. The underwings are whitish with dark patches at the 'wrist' joints. This is the buzzard of the far north, breeding on the tundra and in coniferous forests, though it winters to the south, including Britain, where it is a regular but scarce visitor to east coasts.

Golden Eagle
Aquila chrysaetos
80cm. This raptor is named for the tawny-gold crown and nape of the adult. Young birds have white wing flashes and white at the base of the tail. When soaring and gliding, it holds its wings in a shallow 'V'; active flight is powerful, with deep wingbeats. It feeds mainly on mammals such as hares and rabbits and birds such as grouse and ducks, also carrion. It builds its twig nest, huge when used year after year, on a cliff ledge or tall tree. The Scottish population is one of the largest in Europe, but this magnificent bird is threatened by deliberate poisoning, egg collectors and afforestation.

Booted Eagle
Hieraaetus pennatus
50cm. Although a little smaller than a buzzard, this bird has a more prominent head, longer wings and a longer, square-ended tail. It occurs in two colour phases, a pale phase (whitish with black flight feathers and a

Common Buzzards contesting a kill in winter. Sometimes rivals strike one another with their talons, and occasionally fight to the death.

Montagu's Harrier
Circus pygargus
44cm. The smallest and most slender of the harriers, this bird is a summer visitor to Europe. Though quite common in parts of Europe, in Britain it is a rare breeder. The male differs from the male Hen Harrier in having a dark line across the upper wings, black bars on the underwings, chestnut streaks on the dirty grey underparts and no white rump. Females of the two species are very similar, though Montagu's has slenderer wing tips, a narrower white rump and bolder cheek patch. Young Montagu's are easier to separate, having unmarked rufous underparts. Like other harriers, it has acute hearing which helps it detect prey.

Northern Goshawk
Accipiter gentilis
Male 50cm; female 62cm. Resembling a huge sparrowhawk, the Northern Goshawk has a similar method of hunting to its relative, but catches mainly larger birds. Though males are slightly larger than female sparrowhawks, they can look

THE SPARROWHAWK'S HUNTING TECHNIQUE

A hunting Sparrowhawk often flies low, continually slipping from one side of a hedge to the other, then surprising its prey as it suddenly sweeps over the hedge.

pale tail, when seen in flight from below), much more common in Europe, and a dark phase (dark brown with a pale tail). In both there is a pale wedge-shaped patch on the underside of the wings near the tips. Booted Eagles soar on level wings, with quicker wingbeats than the Common Buzzard. They are seldom far from trees, usually breeding on wooded hillsides, and winter in Africa.
○⊛

Bonelli's Eagle
Hieraaetus fasciatus
70cm. This eagle usually has grey-brown upperparts, with a distinctive white patch on the back. The underparts are sparsely streaked white or cream and, when seen in flight from below, contrast with the long, narrow, dark wings. The underwings have a broad black bar across them and there is a broad black band at the end of the tail. Juveniles are reddish-buff, with no contrast between wings and body, only traces of the dark underwing bar and a closely barred tail. The adult plumage is acquired gradually over 3–4 years. Numbers are low in Europe.
◕◔◑◓○⊛◍⊞

Marsh Harrier

Common Buzzard

Hen Harrier

Rough-legged Buzzard

Montagu's Harrier

Golden Eagle

Northern Goshawk

Booted Eagle

Sparrowhawk

Bonelli's Eagle

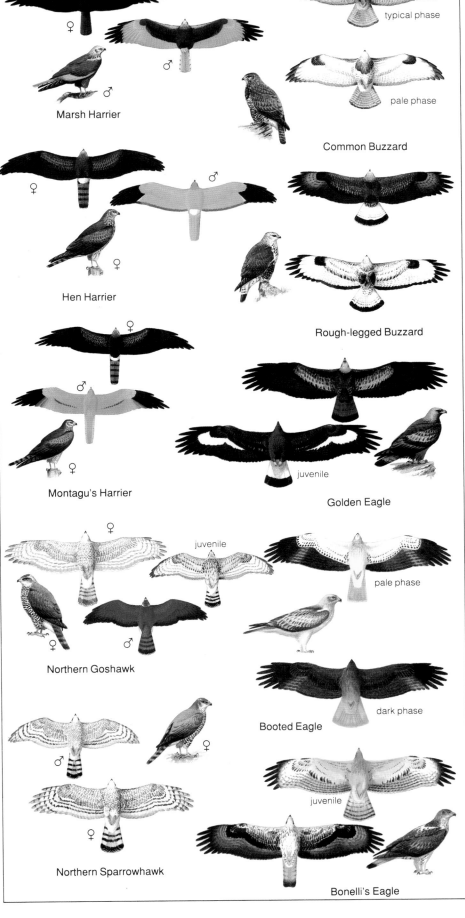

Marsh Harrier

Common Buzzard
typical phase
pale phase

Hen Harrier

Rough-legged Buzzard

Montagu's Harrier

Golden Eagle
juvenile

Northern Goshawk
juvenile

Booted Eagle
pale phase
dark phase
juvenile

Northern Sparrowhawk

Bonelli's Eagle

FALCONS

Falcons (Family Falconidae) are generally smaller than other birds of prey. They are distinguished by their long, pointed wings, longish tails and fast, dashing flight, although they also soar frequently. Many of the species are specialized aerial predators of birds and insects, diving on or chasing their prey with great ferocity. They lay their eggs on the ground, on cliff ledges or in the abandoned nests of other birds such as crows. In some species the sexes differ in plumage. Falconers train falcons to hunt and bring their prey back to them.

A Peregrine Falcon at its cliff-ledge nest site with its chicks. The young birds leave the nest after about five weeks.

Lesser Kestrel
Falco naumanni
30cm. This slender falcon is gregarious and hovers less than the Common Kestrel, feeding chiefly on insects in mid-air. The male is brighter, with unspotted rich chestnut-red upperparts, a bluer head and tail, no moustache stripe and very pale, little spotted underparts and a blue-grey patch on the wings in flight. The female and young are similar to Common Kestrels, but are paler below and, like the male, have whitish claws. Many breeding colonies are in towns. It is suffering from the effects of pesticides on its insect food.

Common Kestrel
Falco tinnunculus
34cm. The most common European raptor, often seen hovering, head to the wind, as it scans the ground for prey. In flight the long tail and long, pointed wings are distinctive. It feeds chiefly on voles and other small mammals, though urban kestrels eat mainly small birds. It occurs in a variety of habitats, from wild moorland and coastal dunes to motorway verges, city parks and wasteland. Its usual call is a loud, shrill *kee-kee-kee*.

Red-footed Falcon
Falco vespertinus
30cm. This small, gregarious, insect-eating falcon occurs in small numbers in western Europe, mainly in spring. The male is dark blue-grey with bright chestnut thighs and undertail coverts. The female has barred grey upperparts and tail, with rich buff underparts and underwing coverts and a pale head, with a dark eyestripe and small 'moustache' streak. The legs, bill base and eye-ring are red in the male and orange in the female.

Merlin
Falco columbarius
Male 27cm; female 32cm. The Merlin is a bird of open country, which dashes after small birds low over the ground. The male is blue-grey above and reddish with streaks beneath, with a black band at the end of his tail, while the female is dark brown above and pale brown and streaked below, with a many-barred tail.

Northern Hobby
Falco subbuteo
34cm. This elegant, long-winged, short-tailed falcon has prominent chestnut thighs and undertail coverts. A summer visitor that winters in Africa, it is a superb flyer, chasing and killing birds and insects in flight. It often hunts at dusk, taking birds from their roosts. It is a scarce but increasing breeder in southern Britain.

Eleonora's Falcon
Falco eleonorae
30–40cm. Similar to the Northern Hobby in build, nearer the Peregrine Falcon in size, this gregarious falcon has longer wings and a longer tail than either. In its paler phase it resembles a very dark Northern Hobby, but is larger, with a dark-streaked, deep buff breast and dark, unbarred underwings, with paler flight feathers. Dark phase birds are entirely dark brown or even black. It breeds late in the season to feed its young on small autumn migrant birds, before migrating to winter in East Africa and Madagascar.

Lanner Falcon
Falco biarmicus
37–50cm. This bird resembles the bulkier Peregrine Falcon, but is paler above with a buff or rufous crown and nape, a much thinner moustache stripe and lightly streaked, white underparts. From below, it appears a very pale bird, with no contrast between body and wings. From above, the tail shows numerous black bars. Young birds are browner above and more heavily streaked below, dark body and underwing coverts contrast with paler flight feathers. Now a rare European breeder, it is still abundant in Africa.

Saker Falcon
Falco cherrug
45–55cm. This bird resembles a larger, much browner version of the Peregrine Falcon. Adults have a whitish, streaked head, with only a trace of a moustache stripe at most and distinctly dark eyebrows. They have dark brown upperparts and white underparts, most heavily streaked or spotted on the flanks. The underwing coverts are often streaked, in contrast to the pale flight feathers. The tail is faintly barred below; above it bears white spots on the outer edges. Scarce in Europe, it is a bird of open country and woodland.

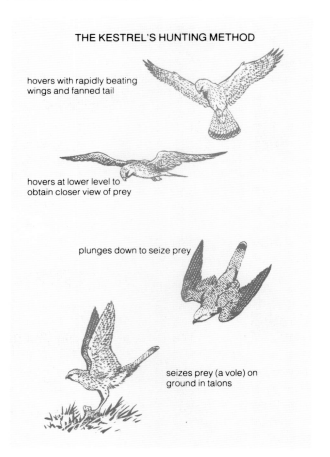

THE KESTREL'S HUNTING METHOD

hovers with rapidly beating wings and fanned tail

hovers at lower level to obtain closer view of prey

plunges down to seize prey

seizes prey (a vole) on ground in talons

Gyr Falcon
Falco rusticolus
Male 53cm; female 62cm.
Largest of all the falcons, the
Gyr Falcon breeds in the
Arctic. It is a rare vagrant
south of Scandinavia, but
visits Shetland. It is bulkier
than the Peregrine, with
broader-based, blunter wings.
Plumage varies from mainly
dark grey to almost pure
white. It catches birds after a
chase or by seizing them on
the ground or water.

Peregrine Falcon
Falco peregrinus
Male 40cm; female 46cm.
This large, powerful falcon
usually catches its prey –
mainly medium-sized birds
such as pigeons, ducks,
seabirds, waders and grouse –
by 'stooping' almost vertically
at very high speeds, striking
the victim with a foot and
killing it or knocking it
unconscious so that it falls to
the ground where it can be
retrieved. The male and
female are very similar, with
prominent 'moustaches'. The
Peregrine was badly hit by
pesticide pollution in the
1960s but has since recovered
in many areas.

Lesser Kestrel

Eleonora's Falcon

Common Kestrel

Saker Falcon

Red-footed Falcon

Lanner Falcon

Merlin

Gyr Falcon

Northern Hobby

Peregrine Falcon

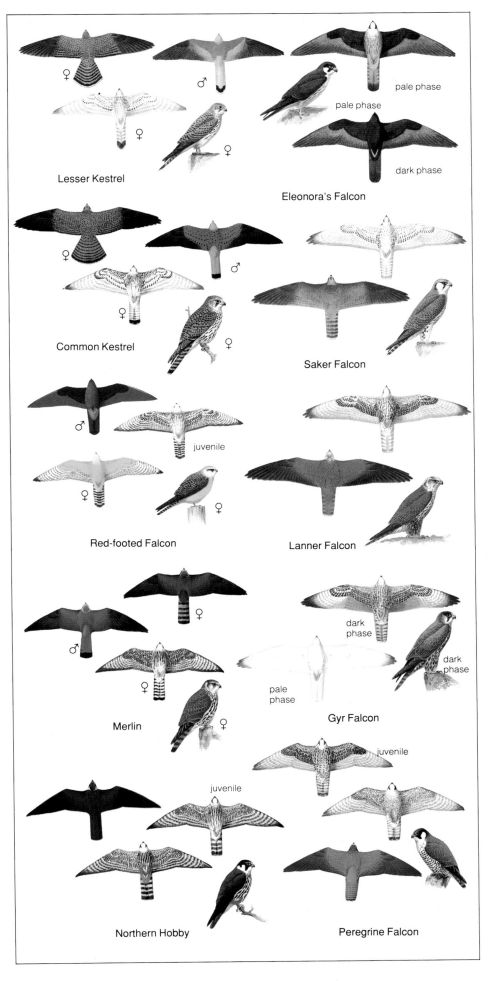

Lesser Kestrel

Eleonora's Falcon

Common Kestrel

Saker Falcon

Red-footed Falcon

Lanner Falcon

Merlin

Gyr Falcon

Northern Hobby

Peregrine Falcon

Gamebirds

The members of the Order Galliformes are plump, chicken-like birds which spend much of the time on the ground, where they nest. Gamebirds are mainly vegetarian, though the chicks are fed on insects. They are reluctant flyers.

GROUSE

The grouse (Family Tetraonidae) are northern or upland birds, with feathered legs for warmth in winter. Most have red wattles. The sexes often differ, as do their summer and winter plumages.

Hazel Grouse
Bonasa bonasia
35cm. The smallest European grouse, the Hazel Grouse (or Hazel Hen) prefers damp, dense spruce woods. It feeds on buds and leaves. Well camouflaged, it reveals itself by high-pitched whistles and wing-beating displays. In flight, the black band on the tail is noticeable.
♀ ⬆

Willow/Red Grouse
Lagopus lagopus
40cm. The Willow Grouse is a widespread resident breeder in Scandinavia, found in arctic willow bogs, tundra and moorland. The British Isles race is called the Red Grouse. Unlike the Willow Grouse, it does not become all white in winter and its wings are never white. It is found on heather moors in northern England and eastern Scotland where its habitat is managed for shooting. Its calls are a loud, harsh *go-back, go-back back-back-back* and a rapid cackling *ko-ko-ko.*
Ⓑ ● ◗

Ptarmigan
Lagopus mutus
35cm. This bird replaces the Willow/Red Grouse at higher altitudes. Most common in Iceland and Scandinavia: it is more local on mountains of Scotland, the Alps and the Pyrenees. In summer, it is mottled grey-brown; in winter, all white except for a black tail. Ptarmigan gather in large flocks in autumn and winter. They give a quiet, rattling *karra-karrrk* of alarm and a harsh belching *aar-aar-ha-ha-ha* in flight.
Ⓑ ● ● ◗

Black Grouse
Tetrao tetrix
Male 54cm; female 41cm. The male has a distinctive, lyre-shaped tail and a white wingbar in flight; the female, unlike other grouse, has a slightly forked tail and a faint pale wingbar. Blackcock are birds of woodland edges and rough pasture and of moorland with trees. Up to 40 or more males gather at dawn and dusk at traditional sites (leks) to display. They flaunt their tails and utter dove-like bubbling songs.
Ⓑ ◗ ✿

A male Capercaillie is an imposing sight as he performs his territorial display in spring. He may give this from the ground or from a tree.

Capercaillie
Tetrao urogallus
Male 90cm; female 60cm. The largest of the grouse, the Capercaillie is a bird mainly of old coniferous forests, where it spends much of the summer on the ground, eating leaves, stems and berries, and the winter in the trees, feeding mainly on pine needles and pine seeds. The unmistakable male is the size of a turkey. Capercaillies burst out of cover with loud beats of their rounded wings, but often remain elusive.
Ⓑ ♀ ⬆

Hazel Grouse ♂ ♀

Black Grouse ♂ ♂ ♀

Red Grouse ♂ ♀

Willow Grouse ♀ summer ♂ summer ♂ winter

Ptarmigan ♂ summer ♀ winter ♂ winter

Capercaillie

PHEASANTS, PARTRIDGES AND QUAIL

These birds (Family Phasianidae) have unfeathered legs and feet, with strong heavy claws adapted for scratching for food on the ground. Pheasants are large birds of woodland, including open woodland, with long tails; the sexes differ in plumage. Several exotic species have escaped from parks and now breed in the wild. Partridges and quails are birds of open country. They are smaller and plumper than pheasants, with very short tails. The sexes are alike.

Rock Partridge
Alectoris graeca
33cm. This bird is very similar to the Red-legged Partridge, but the black lower border to its white throat is clear-cut, and its occurs further east. An even more similar species, found further east again, is the Chukar Partridge. This has the black through the eye touching only the uppermost part of the bill base and fewer, bolder flank bars. The Rock Partridge has loud *whit whit* alarm calls and a staccato, grating *chuck-chuck-chuck-per-chuck-per-chuck-chuckara* song.

Red-legged Partridge
Alectoris rufa
34cm. This bird is larger and more upright than the Grey Partridge, with a distinctive facial pattern, bolder flank markings and red legs. It prefers drier, stonier habitats, especially arable fields, heathland and dunes. It is much more reluctant to fly than the Grey Partridge and runs faster. If hard pressed, it flies off on whirring wings, then planes down to land and run off into cover. It often perches on walls and other objects, unlike the Grey Partridge. Flocks tend to scatter when disturbed. Its voice is very different from that of the Grey Partridge: a harsh, grating *chuk-chuk-chuk-chukar*; males utter mechanical-sounding *go-chack-chack-chacks* like a steam engine. Introduced from the late 18th century to Britain it is now common in east and south Britain.

Grey Partridge
Perdix perdix
30cm. This plump gamebird lives in a wide range of open habitats including farmland. It has an orange face and less striking barring on the flanks than other partridges. Males have a dark horseshoe-shaped mark on the upper belly, absent or reduced to a few blotches in females. It is gregarious in autumn and winter, when flocks (coveys) number up to about 20 birds. Its usual calls are a creaky, grating *keerr-r-r-ik* and a slowing cackle *krikrikri-kri-kriùùkri*. Its severe long term decline in numbers is due to increased predation resulting from loss of hedges and to the effects of farm chemicals on insects which chicks eat.

Common Quail
Coturnix coturnix
18cm. Resembling a tiny partridge with short legs, the Common Quail is the only migratory gamebird, wintering in Africa. Males arrive first and utter their loud, liquid, 'wet-me-lips' calls. The birds are rarely seen and will not fly until almost trodden on, when they whirr and glide on long, pointed wings before fluttering into cover. They breed in rough pastures, cereal fields and downland. Climatic changes cause huge year-to-year fluctuations in the numbers that reach Europe. There has been a decline in many areas. In Britain, where it bred commonly until the early 19th century, the Common Quail is now a scarce visitor and rare breeder.

Common Pheasant
Phasianus colchicus
Male 75–90cm; female 52–64cm. The most common and widespread gamebird of woods, hedgerows and fields, this bird was introduced into much of western Europe from Asia around 500–800 AD and is today reared for shooting. Many birds have escaped and become wild. Plumage is very variable, but males often have a prominent white neck ring. The long tail is distinctive. This bird prefers to run swiftly or hide by crouching but, when it flies, it explodes into the air with powerful, noisy wingbeats. Males have a loud, crowing *kok-kok* call and females a husky *kia kia* and purring calls.

Rock Partridge

Grey Partridge

Red-legged Partridge

Common Quail

Common Pheasant

variants

Hazel Grouse

Rock Partridge

Willow Grouse
Red Grouse

Red-legged Partridge

Ptarmigan

Grey Partridge

Black Grouse

Common Quail

Capercaillie

Cmn Pheasant

Rails, Cranes and Bustards

Birds of the Order Gruiformes have long legs and many live in freshwater marshes and other wetland habitats. Rails (Family Rallidae), which include crakes, gallinules and coots, are mainly secretive birds that rarely fly. When they do, their dangling legs are distinctive. The sexes are similar. Cranes (Family Gruidae) are very tall, dagger-billed birds of open country. They fly with their long necks outstretched. The sexes are similar. Bustards (Family Otididae) are large, stately birds of open country. Like cranes, they are very wary. The sexes differ.

Water Rail
Rallus aquaticus
28cm. Highly secretive, this bird slips easily through dense aquatic vegetation, thanks to its very narrow body. It utters a bizarre cacophony of groans and pig-like grunts and squeals, often at night. It is distinguished from other crakes by its long, red, slightly downcurved bill. The barred black-and-white flanks and pure white undertail coverts beneath its short cocked tail are noticeable. It is active mainly at dawn and dusk, but during freezing weather may be forced to feed by day. It will kill and eat small birds and mammals; more typical items are worms, molluscs, insects and plant matter.
Ⓑ ☻

Spotted Crake
Porzana porzana
23cm. This bird is like a small Water Rail but has a much shorter bill and yellow-green legs. It is usually located by its frequently repeated breeding season call, a far-carrying, liquid *whitt whitt whitt*, rather like a whiplash. At a distance this sounds like a tap dripping into a bowl of water. It is a localized breeder, affected by drainage or natural lowering of water levels. This crake is a rare summer visitor to Britain, breeding very occasionally.
Ⓑ ☻

Baillon's Crake
Porzana pusilla
18cm. This tiny crake is a scarce summer visitor to parts of continental Europe. It probably winters mainly in Africa. Adults have heavily barred flanks, brownish or pinkish legs and a plain green bill. The young have white spots scattered on the wings. The very similar Little Crake (*P. parva*), which breeds mainly in eastern Europe, has less strongly barred flanks, green legs and a red bill base; females are not grey below.
☻

Corn Crake
Crex crex
27cm. The Corn Crake is the only European crake to occur regularly in dry habitats, chiefly in hay meadows with clumps of taller vegetation for nesting. It is active mainly at dusk and at night, when the male utters his far-carrying *crek crek* call. If flushed, its chestnut wings and long trailing legs help identify it; the barred tail and undertail coverts are also distinctive. It has declined greatly, due to earlier, mechanized harvesting, which destroys incubating adults, eggs and young. In the British Isles, it now breeds regularly only in northwestern Scotland, the Hebrides and Ireland.
Ⓑ ✪ ⊞

Common Moorhen
Gallinula chloropus
31–35cm. This abundant, widespread and well-known bird is found on freshwaters of all sizes, in country and urban areas alike, and often leaves the water to feed on surrounding grassland. Despite its unlobed feet, it swims well and spends much time on the water. Unlike the Common Coot, it holds its tail high, revealing its prominent white undertail coverts. Its white flank streaks are also distinctive, as are its red and yellow bill and red frontal shield. It has various calls, including a harsh, penetrating *kitt-ik*, an abrupt, rippling *prrrrk* and a loud, metallic *kaak* and *kik-kik-kik*.
Ⓑ ☻ ✪

Purple Gallinule
Porphyrio porphyrio
48cm. This waterbird is very distinctive, with its dark purplish-blue plumage and white undertail coverts. The very deep bill and frontal shield and huge feet and legs are bright red. Living in marshes at the edge of lakes, it spends most of its time in reedbeds. It utters loud, hooting, trumpeting, shrieking and snoring sounds. Most numerous in the Coto Doñana, southern Spain, it is declining over most of its small European range.
☻ ☻

Common Cranes are gregarious outside the breeding season, migrating and wintering in flocks of up to several thousand individuals.

Common Coot
Fulica atra
36–40cm. Found on lowland lakes and slow rivers, requiring both large areas of open water for feeding and dense vegetation for nesting. Some 6–10 eggs are laid in a broad cup of dead vegetation. In winter it forms large flocks on lakes, reservoirs, sheltered bays and estuaries. Although it feeds on wet grassland near water, it spends most of its time swimming with its big lobed feet. It generally runs over the water rather than flying: when it does fly, it does so strongly on broad rounded wings with its long legs trailing. It dives frequently to feed, mainly on water plants. It also feeds on the surface or by upending. Its calls include a hard explosive *pik* and a loud *kowk*.
Ⓑ ☻ ☻

Common Crane
Grus grus
115cm. This bird has a striking black-and-white head pattern and elongated wing feathers forming a drooping blackish 'tail' (the true tail is very short). Groups of cranes perform dramatic courtship dances accompanied by wild, strident trumpeting calls. They breed in lightly wooded wet swamps, wet bogs and reedbeds. Before and after breeding, Common Cranes concentrate in the south Baltic before moving to their wintering areas, where they live by large lakes and open fields. They are rare but increasing vagrants to the British Isles, mainly in autumn to south and east England, and a few have nested recently.
Ⓑ ☻ ✪ ⊞

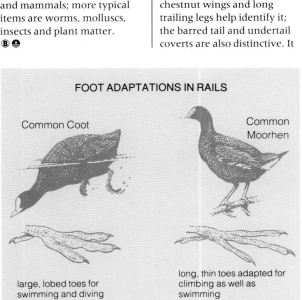

FOOT ADAPTATIONS IN RAILS

Common Coot

Common Moorhen

large, lobed toes for swimming and diving

long, thin toes adapted for climbing as well as swimming

Little Bustard
Tetrax tetrax
44cm. A scarce breeder on large grassy plains and open fields, including crops, this bird is a rare vagrant to Britain. It lives in small flocks. It has a fast flight, with neck outstretched and shallow, flicking wingbeats. Females and winter males are mainly speckled brown; breeding males have a striking black-and-white neck pattern. In his courtship display, the male of this species utters frog-like *prett* calls as well as leaping into the air.
Ⓑ ✦ ▥

Great Bustard
Otis tarda
Male 90cm; female 74cm. The Great Bustard is one of the world's heaviest flying birds: males weigh up to 18 kg. It is a rare and local breeder on grassy steppes and open treeless plains, usually found in small flocks. It is a rare vagrant to Britain. In flight its slowly beating wings appear mainly white. In their spring display, males inflate their necks like balloons, thrust their long white 'moustaches' into the air and turn their wings forward.
✦ ▥

Water Rail

Purple Gallinule

Spotted Crake

Common Coot

Baillon's Crake

Common Crane

Corn Crake

Little Bustard

Cmn Moorhen

Great Bustard

Water Rail

Purple Gallinule

juvenile

summer

Spotted Crake

juvenile

Common Coot

juvenile

Baillon's Crake

juvenile

♂

Common Crane

juvenile

Corn Crake

Little Bustard

♂ summer

♀

♂ summer

Common Moorhen

juvenile

♂

Great Bustard

♂

♀

Waders, Gulls and Relatives

This very large order of birds (Charadriiformes) includes over 300 species in 18 families. All have a close association with water for at least part of their lives. The order is subdivided into three suborders: the waders (Suborder Charadrii); the skuas, gulls and terns (Lari); and the auks (Alcae). The sexes are alike in almost all species.

OYSTERCATCHERS

Oystercatchers (Family Haematopodidae) are large, mainly coastal waders. They have only three slightly webbed toes. One species occurs in Europe.

Eurasian Oystercatcher
Haematopus ostralegus
43cm. This heavily built wader has bold, pied plumage, a stout straight orange-red bill, orange-red eye-ring and shortish pink legs. In winter adults are duller black with a narrow, white throat-band and a dusky bill tip. Young birds are duller still. It is found on rocky, sandy and muddy shores, also on wet grasslands and freshwater marshes near the coast, and sometimes breeds inland along river banks. Flocks of several thousand can occur. It utters loud, shrill, *kleep* and *kleep-ka-kleep* and *pik* calls.
ⓑ☻✪☻

STILTS AND AVOCETS

These birds (Family Recurvirostridae) are elegant waders of coastal and inland waters. They wade through shallow water and swim in deeper water. Avocets catch invertebrates by sweeping their bills from side to side or by upending. Stilts feed on invertebrates by snapping them up with their bills.

Black-winged Stilt
Himantopus himantopus
38cm. This slender, long-necked wader has a long, needle-like black bill, a white body with black back and wings and long, slender legs, which trail in flight. The male has a dusky hind crown, nape and rear neck. This species breeds in small groups by shallow fresh or brackish water. It winters in the Coto Doñana, Spain. It has nested a few times in Britain, where it is otherwise a rare vagrant. Its voice includes shrill *kyik-kyik-kyik* calls.
ⓑ☻☻☻

Pied Avocet
Recurvirostra avosetta
43cm. This graceful bird has mainly shining white plumage with black markings on head, neck and wings and long grey-blue legs. Its most distinctive feature is its slender, strongly upcurved bill. It is a scarce and local breeder in quite large, loose colonies by bays, coastal lagoons and river deltas. Its call is a repeated, high-pitched, fluty *'kluititititititit'*.
ⓑ☻☻

A flock of Eurasian Oystercatchers resting. Like other waders, they cannot feed at high tide and fly to traditional roost sites.

PLOVERS

Plovers (Family Charadriidae) are plump, boldly patterned waders with short bills. They are found in dry as well as freshwater and coastal habitats. They feed by running a few paces then picking up invertebrates from the surface. Lapwings are a subgroup of plovers. One species breeds in Europe.

Ringed Plover
Charadrius hiaticula
19cm. This dumpy plover has a large rounded head, a short stubby bill, orange with a black tip, and a white line above a black eye patch. Its main call is a melodious *too-lee* with a rising pitch. The song is a very rapid sequence of *kroo-ee* notes. The Little Ringed Plover (*C. dubius*) has a black bill and a white crown bar. It is a scarce summer visitor to inland freshwaters.
ⓑ☻☻☻⬛

Kentish Plover
Charadrius alexandrinus
16cm. This plover is paler than the Ringed Plover, with a black bill and legs. Summer males have a sandy-golden crown with black at the front; in winter this is brown as in females and young. Adults have an incomplete breast band. Although common in southern Europe, it has declined in west and central Europe. It is a rare passage migrant to England.
ⓑ☻☻

Eurasian Dotterel
Charadrius morinellus
22cm. This plover is a scarce summer visitor to tundras and high mountains. It is a scarce breeder in Britain, almost entirely in Scotland. It also occurs as a scarce migrant to fields, heathland or coastal areas. In breeding plumage, the white band separating the breast and belly with a black patch are distinctive. Winter plumage is duller. The male incubates the eggs and cares for the young.
ⓑ☻☻☻✪☻☻

European Golden Plover
Pluvialis apricaria
27cm. In summer this plover has speckled black and gold upperparts and a black belly, separated by white. It breeds on moorland and is declining in some areas, but is still abundant as a winter visitor, occurring in large flocks on grassland, arable land and marshes. The usual call of this species is a melodious, whistling *tluee*.
ⓑ☻☻☻

Grey Plover
Charadrius squatarola
29cm. The Grey Plover breeds in the Arctic, occurring in Europe as a passage migrant and winter visitor to coasts. Birds in summer plumage have speckled grey and white upperparts, a black belly and face and white side patches. Winter plumage is duller. Its usual call is a plaintive *tleee-oo-ee*.
ⓑ☻

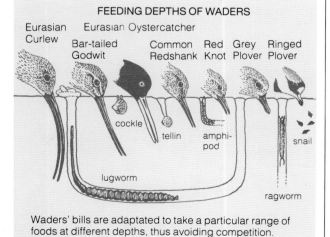

FEEDING DEPTHS OF WADERS

Eurasian Curlew Eurasian Oystercatcher
Bar-tailed Godwit Common Redshank Red Knot Grey Plover Ringed Plover

cockle
tellin amphi-pod snail
lugworm
ragworm

Waders' bills are adapted to take a particular range of foods at different depths, thus avoiding competition.

Northern Lapwing

Vanellus vanellus
29–32cm. Seen close to, this abundant plover has glossy green and bronze-purple highlights to its upperparts, a long wispy crest and orange undertail coverts. In winter, the throat and upper breast of adults turns white. It usually occurs in large flocks outside the breeding season. Its call is a loud, plaintive, nasal *peewit*.
Ⓑ 🐦 🌊 ⚤ 😀

STONE CURLEWS

Stone Curlews (Family Burhinidae) are also known as thick-knees, from the swelling at the ankle. There is one species in Europe.

Stone Curlew

Burhinus oedicnemus
40cm. This wary bird is active mainly at dawn and dusk, feeding mainly on insects and worms. Distinctive features are its large, yellow eyes, pale yellow base to its short bill, bold black-and-white wing bars and longish tail in flight. It has declined in many parts of Europe; it is now a rare summer visitor to England.
Ⓑ 🐦 ⚤ 🌐

Eurasian Oystercatcher

Black-winged Stilt

Pied Avocet

Eurasian Dotterel / European Golden Plover

Ringed Plover / Grey Plover

Kentish Plover / Northern Lapwing / Stone Curlew

Eurasian Oystercatcher

Black-winged Stilt

Pied Avocet

Ringed Plover

Kentish Plover

Eurasian Dotterel

European Golden Plover

Grey Plover

Northern Lapwing

Stone Curlew

SANDPIPERS AND SNIPES

Sandpipers and Snipes (Family Scolopacidae) are the largest and most varied family of waders. They feed by probing for invertebrates. These birds breed on tundra, moorland and marshes. Outside the breeding season, they occur mainly on coasts, especially estuaries; then they are highly gregarious, and flocks perform spectacular aerobatic displays.

Little Stint
Calidris minuta
13cm. The stints are the smallest European waders. This species looks like a miniature Dunlin, from which it differs in its shorter legs and short, straight bill. It feeds rapidly, running along and picking food from the surface in quick jabs. As a passage migrant to coasts, estuaries and inland freshwaters, it is more numerous in autumn than in spring when most birds are juveniles, identifiable by the double white 'V' on the back.
ⓑ◑◔

Red Knot
Calidris canutus
25cm. This stocky wader has relatively short legs and a straight, shortish bill. In flight it shows a distinctive pale rump and tail with a darker terminal band and a faint white wingbar. Its call notes are a low, hoarse, *knut* and a whistling *twit-twit* in flight. In winter, huge flocks perform spectacular manoeuvres, moving in unison like clouds of smoke. On passage, it may be seen in its rich chestnut-pink and mottled black-and-rufous breeding plumage.
ⓑ◑◔

Sanderling
Calidris alba
20cm. The Sanderling has a distinctive feeding method, racing madly across the beach after the waves like a clockwork toy. In winter, when it is widespread on sandy shores, the Sanderling is the palest of the small waders, with pale grey upperparts and white head and underparts. The black smudge on the 'shoulder' is also distinctive. Compared to the Dunlin, it has a shorter bill and a bolder white wingbar in flight.
ⓑ◔

The barred patterning of the Eurasian Woodcock helps it to merge into the background of dead leaves, thus escaping the notice of predators.

Purple Sandpiper
Calidris maritima
21cm. This is a dumpy, thick-necked wader with short yellow legs and a stout-based, medium-length bill that has a distinctive yellow base. In winter, it is the darkest of the smaller waders, with a contrasting white chin and eye-ring. Its breeding plumage is browner, scaly on the back and more streaked below. In flight, it shows a narrow white wingbar. It is the most maritime of all waders, rarely seen away from rocky shores in winter.
ⓑ◑◔

Curlew Sandpiper
Calidris ferruginea
19cm. This wader is a regular passage migrant, more abundant in autumn. Early autumn birds are mainly adults, still with some of their chestnut breeding plumage on the breast; later arrivals are mostly young birds, which have scaly upperparts and an unstreaked, pale buff breast. Slightly larger and more elegant than the Dunlin, the Curlew Sandpiper has a more strongly and evenly down-curved bill, a longer neck and legs and a bolder eyestripe.
◑◔

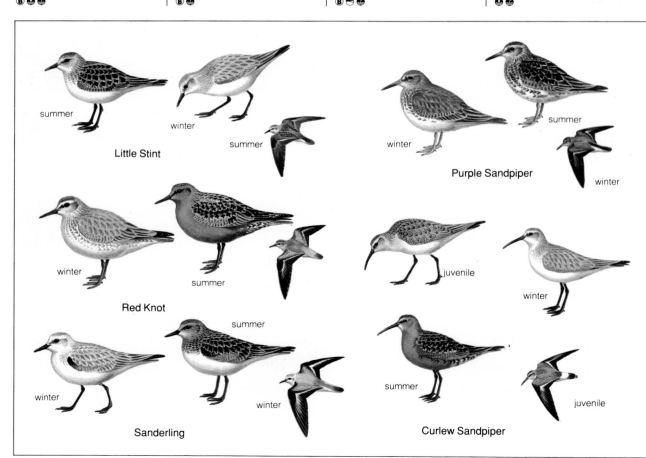

222

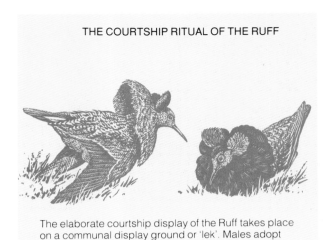

THE COURTSHIP RITUAL OF THE RUFF

The elaborate courtship display of the Ruff takes place on a communal display ground or 'lek'. Males adopt aggressive postures, erecting their ear tufts and ruffs.

Dunlin
Calidris alpina
18cm. This wader has a dumpy, 'round-shouldered' appearance, with medium-length black legs and a longish bill, slightly downcurved towards its tip. In breeding plumage, they are the only waders with a black belly patch. In winter, the plumage is grey above and white below. Dunlin show a white wingbar and white tail patches in flight. Young birds have brown, buff-edged upperparts and a heavily streaked buff breast. The Dunlin breeds on tundra and moorland; on passage and in winter it is the commonest small wader of coastal mudflats and estuaries, often occurring in huge flocks.
Ⓑ●◑🌰😊

Ruff
Philomachus pugnax
Male 29cm; female 23cm. The male has a bare, warty reddish face and sports an extravagant ruff of multicoloured plumes on his head and neck. The female is much smaller and slimmer, with a bold scalloped pattern of buff-tipped brown feathers on her back. The male in winter resembles the female, as do young birds, which have even more scalloped upperparts and a uniform buff-pink breast. The longish legs vary from orange-red to green and yellow, and the small head, long neck, fine, medium-length, slightly downcurved bill, and erect stance are all distinctive. In flight, the dark tail shows conspicuous oval white side patches.
Ⓑ●😊

Common Snipe
Gallinago gallingo
27cm. This secretive wader has a very long, straight bill and mottled and streaked plumage. Its head is striped and there is a 'V'-shaped pattern of golden-buff stripes on the back. The tail shows a little white on its outer edges. When disturbed, this Snipe flies off with a rapid, towering, zig-zag flight, often ascending high into the distance before landing, and utters distinctive harsh *schraep* calls. In the breeding season, the male performs a diving display flight over his territory, in which the stiff outer tail feathers make a loud bleating sound.
Ⓑ◑😊😊

Jack Snipe
Lymnocryptes minimus
19cm. Compared to the more abundant Common Snipe, this wader is smaller and has a shorter bill. It also has more contrasting upperparts, with brighter golden back stripes, and in flight reveals shorter, more rounded wings. It shuns open areas, feeding among reeds. It also rarely flies until almost trodden on and then flies slowly, straight and low, soon dropping noiselessly into cover.
Ⓑ😊😊

Eurasian Woodcock
Scolopax rusticola
34cm. This plump, mainly nocturnal bird is usually found in moist woodlands. It is rarely seen on the ground because its barred plumage blends in well with dead leaves and other ground cover. When disturbed, it flies off fast with noisy wingbeats. The male performs a distinctive display flight in the breeding season. With exaggeratedly slow beats of his broad, rounded wings and long bill pointing downwards, he utters deep, frog-like croaking notes and a wheezy *tissick*.
Ⓑ🔾🌲

juvenile
winter
summer
Dunlin
variants
♂ winter
♂ summer
♀
Ruff

Common Snipe
Jack Snipe
juvenile
Eurasian Woodcock

Little Stint

Dunlin

Red Knot

Ruff

Sanderling

Common Snipe

Purple Sandpiper

Jack Snipe

Clw Sandpiper

Woodcock

Black-tailed Godwit
Limosa limosa
41cm. In flight, this large wader shows a bold black and white pattern on its wings and a square white rump and tail with a black terminal band. Adults lose their chestnut heads and breasts in winter, when they have much greyer upperparts. Young birds have scalloped brown upperparts and a buff breast. This wader gives loud *kee-wick* and *wicka-wicka* calls in its powerful flight; at the breeding site, it gives a noisy *krrru-wit-kew* song in a display flight.
Ⓑ🦢🐟👤🦢

Bar-tailed Godwit
Limosa lapponica
38cm. This wader differs from its Black-tailed relative in having a shorter, slightly upcurved bill, no wingbar, a long white 'V' extending upwards from its rump, several black bars on its tail, and shorter legs. In winter, its upperparts are browner and more streaked and spangled than the Black-tailed Godwit. In summer, it has all-chestnut underparts and boldly patterned black and chestnut upperparts. It is generally silent, but may utter a sharp *kirrick* alarm call.
Ⓑ🦢🦢

Whimbrel
Numenius phaeopus
41cm. Like a small Eurasian Curlew, but has a shorter bill, downcurved only near the tip, and a distinctly striped crown. Its call is also very different: a rapid sequence of about seven evenly emphasized high-pitched whistling notes. It has faster wingbeats than the Eurasian Curlew, with little contrast in shade between its inner and outer wing. In Britain it is mainly a spring and autumn passage migrant although a few pairs breed in northern Scotland, mainly in Shetland.
Ⓑ🦢🦢🦢

Eurasian Curlew
Numenius arquata
55cm. The largest of the European waders, this species has a very long, evenly downcurved bill. Like the Whimbrel, it has a barred tail and a long white 'V' up its back. It can look rather gull-like in flight, with leisurely wingbeats. Its distinctive calls include a clear, ringing *coourlee* and variants and a low *whaup*; it has a harsh *kvi-kvi-kvi-kvi* alarm call. Its most beautiful song is a series of liquid, rippling *coourlee* notes, accelerating to a bubbling crescendo.
Ⓑ🦢👤🌀🦢

Like those of most other waders, Ruddy Turnstone chicks leave the nest just after hatching and are superbly camouflaged, helping them escape the attention of predators.

Spotted Redshank
Tringa erythropus
30cm. More delicate than the Common Redshank, this elegant wader has a long, thin neck and a long, thin, dark bill. Its long legs are dark red in summer and orange in winter. It is unmistakable in summer, with its all-black plumage spangled with white above. In winter it is paler and greyer than the Common Redshank, with a more prominent white eyebrow. In flight it can be distinguished from its relative by its lack of white trailing edges to its wings. Its distinctive call is a loud, clear *choo-it*. A winter visitor to the British Isles.
Ⓑ🦢🌀🔺🦢🦢

Common Redshank
Tringa totanus
27cm. The nervous head-bobbing and ringing, melancholy *tyew* and *tyew-yew-yew* calls of this wader at the approach of danger often serve as a warning to other birds, earning it the nickname 'watchdog of the marshes'. Its orange-red legs are shorter than those of the Spotted Redshank's, as is its orange-red bill. In flight, it reveals a distinctive, very broad white trailing edge to the wings. One of the commonest coastal waders in winter, it breeds on wet meadows, bogs and moorland.
Ⓑ🦢🦢👤🦢

winter

winter

winter

summer

Black-tailed Godwit

summer

Spotted Redshank

winter

Whimbrel

winter

summer

winter

Bar-tailed Godwit

Eurasian Curlew

summer

winter

Common Redshank

Common Greenshank
Tringa nebularia
30cm. The largest and most elegant of the 'shanks', the Common Greenshank has a long, grey, slightly upturned bill and long greenish legs that trail well behind its tail in flight. Its uniformly dark grey wings contrast sharply with the white rump and 'V'-shaped wedge up its back. Its markings are more distinct in summer. It has a distinctive flight call, a loud, ringing *teu-teu-teu* and, on the moors, bogs and forest edges where it breeds, a repeated, ringing *tew-ee*.
Ⓑ🦆🌙🌳🌊🌊

Green Sandpiper
Tringa ochropus
23cm. This wary wader looks black and white at any distance, with its dark upper and under wings contrasting with the pure white rump. It takes flight with a rather snipe-like zig-zag action before towering up with jerky wingbeats. The dark brown upperparts are peppered with pale spots, the breast is speckled and the olive green legs are quite short. It bobs and sways its body when on the ground. Its calls are a loud rippling *tit-loo-eet* and a ringing *weet tweet weet weet*.
Ⓑ🌙🌳🌊

Common Sandpiper
Tringa hypoleucos
20cm. This wader has olive-brown upperparts and white underparts, with the streaked brown smudges on either side of the breast separated from the wing by a clear white wedge. Its tail projects beyond the wings when at rest. It constantly bobs its head as it runs about on its somewhat short, green legs. Its flight is distinctive, the rapid, shallow, flicking beats of its stiff bowed wings alternating with brief glides. It has a white wingbar and white sides to its tail. Its alarm call is a shrill, staccato *twee-see-see* and its song a rapid *titti-weeti, titti-weeti*.
Ⓑ🌊🌊

Wood Sandpiper
Tringa glareola
20cm. This bird is smaller and slimmer than the Green Sandpiper, with longer, pale green-yellow legs, paler upperparts, much more mottled with white, and a more distinct white eyebrow. In flight, it never appears black and white and has a much paler underwing; its legs extend well beyond the tail. It does not usually fly high before dropping back to the ground. Its alarm call is a high, rapid *chiff-chiff-chiff*.
Ⓑ🌙🌳🌊

Ruddy Turnstone
Arenaria interpres
23cm. With its portly body, very short neck, short, wedge-shaped bill and short orange legs this wader is quite distinctive. In summer, it has black, white and rich chestnut upperparts, a unique black and white head pattern and a black breast band. In winter, it is much duller. In flight it has black and white bars and stripes on the wings and two black tail bands. It feeds among stones and seaweeds, turning them over with its head and bill. Its call is a metallic, staccato twittering.
Ⓑ🌊🌊

Red-necked Phalarope
Phalaropus lobatus
17cm. Smaller than the Grey Phalarope, this dainty wader has a longer, thinner bill and a more delicate build. In the breeding season it also has a white throat and a bright orange patch down the side of the neck. Unlike other waders, phalaropes have partly webbed feet that enable them to spend much of their time swimming at sea. Their feeding action is very distinctive – they spin around rapidly, stirring up small aquatic creatures which they snatch with their bills.
Ⓑ🌊🌊🌊

Black-tailed Godwit

Common Greenshank

Bar-tailed Godwit

Green Sandpiper

Whimbrel

Common Sandpiper

Eurasian Curlew

Wood Sandpiper

Spotted Redshank

Ruddy Turnstone

Common Redshank

Phalarope

Common Greenshank — winter, summer, winter

Common Sandpiper

Ruddy Turnstone — winter, summer, winter

Green Sandpiper

Wood Sandpiper

Red-necked Phalarope — winter, winter, ♀ summer, juvenile

SKUAS

Skuas (Family Stercorariidae) resemble gulls, but have brown adult plumage and a faster, more agile flight. Most species are pirates, chasing other seabirds and forcing them to disgorge their food. They also catch prey, including small birds, and will take eggs.

Pomarine Skua
Stercorarius pomarinus
43–53cm. This skua is similar to the Arctic Skua, but larger, broader-winged and deeper-breasted, with a heavier bill. In spring, the central tail feathers of adults are longer, blunt and twisted. There are

two colour phases, pale and dark. Like other skuas, it spends most of its time at sea but is seen in inshore waters as a scarce passage migrant in spring and autumn.
Ⓑ 😎

Arctic Skua
Stercorarius parasiticus
38–48cm. The most frequently seen European skua, and a regular passage migrant to western coasts. It occurs in light and dark phases. In spring, adults have the two central tail feathers elongated and pointed. A slenderer bird than the Pomarine Skua, with a more agile, dashing flight, the Arctic is heavier and less graceful than the Long-tailed Skua.
Ⓑ 😑 😎 😎

The Black-headed Gull, once rare in many parts of Europe, has increased dramatically in range and numbers over the last 100 years.

Long-tailed Skua
Stercorarius longicaudus
38–50cm. The most graceful skua, it is almost tern-like in flight, with very long pointed central tail feathers in spring adults, which are lacking in autumn and sub-adult birds. It occurs only in the pale phase and is the rarest of the four species in Europe. Outside its breeding grounds, it is a scarce passage migrant to western coasts in spring and autumn. It is paler and greyer above than the other skuas, with much smaller wing flashes, and a highly contrasting dark cap. Young birds are more buff than the young of other species.
Ⓑ 😑 😎

Great Skua
Stercorarius skua
58cm. The Great Skua is the largest of the skuas, with entirely brown plumage, except for the prominent large white wing flashes.

Compared with large young gulls, its wings look broader and its head and bill smaller. Its flight is also more buoyant and dashing, especially when it is chasing seabirds for food. A bold predator of birds and their eggs, it also eats fish and carrion. It is a scarce breeder in the north and a passage migrant to western coasts. It winters at sea as far north as France and Spain.
Ⓑ 😑 😎

GULLS

Gulls (Family Laridae) are omnivores, feeding on fish, worms and insects as well as carrion and refuse. The larger species also take the eggs and young of other birds and small mammals. The smaller species take about eighteen months and the larger ones about four years to change from the mottled brownish juvenile plumage to the grey, black and white of the adult. Some species occur far inland. Sexes are similar. They nest on the ground, cliff ledges and buildings, often in colonies.

Mediterranean Gull
Larus melanocephalus
39cm. Superficially similar to the Black-headed Gull, this species is stouter, with a heavier, drooping scarlet bill with a black band. It also has no contrasting white leading edge to the pale grey wings, which look completely white at the tips, and white underwings. In summer, it has a black, not dark brown, hood, which extends down the back of the neck, and a prominent broken white eye-ring. In winter, the black hood is lost, and there is a dark smudge behind the eye. Juvenile birds resemble young Common Gulls, but with a paler central wing panel. A scarce passage migrant and winter visitor to the British Isles; a few breed.
Ⓑ 😑 😎

Little Gull
Larus minutus
28cm. The smallest of the world's gulls, this species has a buoyant, tern-like flight, often swooping low over the

water and picking off insects with its tiny bill. Its uniformly grey wings lack black tips and the underwings are very dark grey. In summer it has a black hood, replaced in winter by a dark hind crown and a spot behind the eye. Young birds show an inverted black 'W' across the upperwings in flight. Calls include a low *kek-kek-kek* and repeated *kay-eee*. A passage migrant and winter visitor to the British Isles.
Ⓑ 😑 😎 😎

Sabine's Gull
Larus sabini
33cm. This small, graceful gull is a vagrant to western European waters in autumn, sometimes blown inshore by gales, and rarely encountered in its handsome grey-hooded breeding plumage. Most birds seen here are juveniles, which are brown where the adults are grey, but share the adults' strongly forked tails and the striking black and white pattern on their wings. The young birds have a broad black band at the tip of the tail, an all-black bill and pale pinkish legs. It breeds on Arctic coasts and islands and winters on the open sea.
Ⓑ 😑 😎

Black-headed Gull
Larus ridibundus
36cm. The most common gull of the region, this species is found both on coasts and far inland. Breeding birds have a chocolate brown hood that does not extend down the back of the neck; this is lost in winter, when there are blackish smudges behind and in front of the eye. At all times, it has prominent white leading edges to its pointed wings in flight. A noisy bird, its usual calls are a harsh *kvarrr*, a short *kwup* and a repeated *kuk-kuk*.
Ⓑ 😑 😑 😑 😎

THE PIRATICAL SKUA

skua chases tern
with fish in bill

tern is eventually
forced to drop
prey

skua dives down
to pick up fish

Slender-billed Gull
Larus genei
43cm. This bird looks like a bulky Black-headed Gull, with a similar white forewing in flight, but with more black on the trailing edge of the wing tips and an all-white head in all adult plumages. Juveniles have a vague ear spot. Its long, red, down-tilted bill appears even longer because of its sloping forehead and long neck, giving it an odd, front-heavy appearance in flight. Its calls include a high, nasal *yep yep* and high chattering notes.

Audouin's Gull
Larus audouinii
50cm. This rare gull is less bulky than a Herring Gull, with narrower, more pointed wings, which have extensive black tips with only tiny white spots. It also has a long flattish head and a large, downward-tilted red bill with a black band and a yellow tip. The dark eyes have red rims and the legs are greenish. Young birds have brownish upperparts, a pale grey crown, a dark mark behind the eye and a broad black wedge across the wings.

Pomarine Skua

Little Gull

Arctic Skua

Sabine's Gull

Long-tailed Skua

Black-headed Gull

Great Skua

Slender-billed Gull

Mdtn Gull

Audouin's Gull

dark phase | pale phase | juvenile
Pomarine Skua

winter
summer
Little Gull
first winter

dark phase | pale phase | juvenile
Arctic Skua

juvenile
summer
summer
Sabine's Gull

juvenile
Long-tailed Skua

winter
summer
Black-headed Gull
first winter

Great Skua

first winter
Slender-billed Gull

summer
first winter
first summer | winter
first winter
summer
Mediterranean Gull
Audouin's Gull

Common Gull
Larus canus
41cm. This gull resembles a small Herring Gull, but is much smaller and longer-winged, with slightly darker upperparts. It has a smaller head and a more delicate greenish-yellow bill, which give it a gentler appearance, and smaller greenish-yellow legs. In winter, its head is more strongly streaked with grey than the Herring Gull's. Young birds show a dark trailing edge to the secondary wing feathers in flight and a pale greyish central wing panel. Despite its name, it is not generally the most common gull.

Lesser Black-backed Gull
Larus fuscus
55cm. Almost as large as a Herring Gull, this bird has a much darker grey back (black in the Scandinavian race, which occurs further south in winter). It differs from the much larger Great Black-backed Gull in having yellow legs and a much slimmer bill. Young birds are very similar to young Herring Gulls but have paler edges to their upperparts, bolder spots on their underparts and a more distinct dark trailing edge to their wings. Its calls are similar to those of the Herring Gull but deeper.

Herring Gull
Larus argentatus
60cm. This is the most common gull of sea coasts and is often seen inland. It is the largest gull with grey upperparts and black wingtips. It has a heavier bill than the Common Gull, yellow with a red spot, and pink legs (yellow in the Mediterranean race). In winter the head has dark streaks. Immature birds generally have paler backs than immature Lesser Black-backed Gulls. Its calls include a repeated, harsh *kee-yow*, a staccato *ga-ga-ga* of alarm and a variety of barking, laughing and mewing notes.

Iceland Gull
Larus glaucoides
60cm. About the size of a Herring Gull, this gull is a smaller, slimmer, much scarcer version of the Glaucous Gull. It has a much shorter, less heavy bill and a smaller, more rounded head, giving it a more benign expression. Its wings are proportionately longer and the tips project beyond the tail at rest. Young birds are pale brown above (greyer than young Glaucous Gulls) and have pinkish, black-tipped bills. Its voice is similar to that of the Herring Gull but much shriller.

Glaucous Gull
Larus hyperboreus
58–69cm. This fierce-looking gull can be as big as a Great Black-backed Gull, but has very pale grey upperparts. It shares the Herring Gull's pink legs and yellow bill with a red spot – but its bill is both longer and heavier. It also differs in that its wingtips are all-white, and not black with white spots. Young birds are similar to young Iceland Gulls, but their wingtips are even whiter. Its voice is similar to that of the Herring Gull, but hoarser.

Great Black-backed Gull
Larus marinus
69cm. Much larger than the Lesser Black-backed and Herring Gulls, the Great Black-backed Gull has a large head and a much thicker bill. It can be distinguished from Lesser Black-backed Gulls by its size and pale, pinkish-grey legs. It is fiercely predatory, feeding on other seabirds, rabbits and fish, as well as carrion. In flight, it beats its broad, powerful wings slowly. It breeds on rocky coasts, and is mainly coastal in winter. Typical calls are a deep, harsh *owk* and a gruff *uk-uk-uk*.

Black-legged Kittiwake
Rissa tridactyla
41cm. This seabird superficially resembles the Common Gull, but is rarely seen inland and has darker grey upperparts, much shorter, black legs, longer, narrower wings with black tips lacking any white spots, and a slightly forked tail. Young birds have a black bar on the neck and an inverted black 'W' across the upperwings visible in flight, like that of young Little Gulls. It breeds in large colonies on cliffs and increasingly on seaside buildings. The usual call is a loud, nasal, repeated *kitti-wa-aak*.

Black-legged Kittiwakes build their neat drum-shaped nests of seaweed on precariously narrow cliff-ledges, safe from land-based predators.

TERNS

The terns (Family Sternidae) have slender bodies, narrow wings and forked tails. In flight, they are more aerobatic than gulls. Terns have pale grey and white plumage with a black cap, partly lost in winter. Most hover, then plunge into the water to catch fish. A few species – the marsh terns – are much darker and feed mainly on insects picked from the surface of the water, from mid-air or even on the ground.

Gull-billed Tern
Gelochelidon nilotica
38cm. The Gull-billed Tern is heavier bodied and broader winged than the Sandwich Tern. It also has a shorter, far stouter bill, a much less forked grey tail and, in winter, a whiter head. Its black legs are longer than those of other terns. Young birds can be distinguished by their buffish crowns with a dark patch around the eye. It seldom plunges into the water, but often hawks for flying insects over land and may snatch prey from the ground. Its throaty, rasping *kahak kahak* and *za-za-za* calls and rapid laughing notes are also distinctive.

Sandwich Tern
Sterna sandvicensis
43cm. One of the larger terns, the Sandwich Tern has particularly long wings, a short forked tail, a long black,

FEEDING METHODS OF TERNS

Hovers above water to spot prey

dives into water when prey is seen

plunges under water to seize fish in bill

yellow-tipped bill and short black legs. It is much paler than other terns, except for the Gull-billed and Roseate Terns. In summer, the black cap has elongated feathers at the back of the crown, forming a ragged crest. In winter, the crown is mainly white, with a streaky black crest. It is found on coasts and estuaries; rarely inland. Its call is a harsh *kirrick*. Like other terns, it usually lays two eggs in a scrape on a sand or shingle beach.
Ⓑ 😎

Roseate Tern
Sterna dougallii
38cm. This supremely elegant tern can be picked out in a flock of Common or Arctic Terns by its much whiter colouring, shorter wings, and long tail which protrudes beyond its wings when it is at rest. In flight its wingbeats are characteristically shallow and fast. Its bill is black with a red base in summer, when its breast takes on a pinkish tinge. It has distinctive calls – a soft *chu-ick* and a long, rasping *aaaaak*. This is the rarest of European breeding terns and may nest with Arctic or Common Terns.
Ⓑ 😎

Common Gull

Great Black-backed Gull

Lesser Black-backed Gull

Black-legged Kittiwake

Herring Gull

Gull-billed Tern

Iceland Gull

Sandwich Tern

Glaucous Gull

Roseate Tern

Common Gull

Great Black-backed Gull

Lesser Black-backed Gull

Black-legged Kittiwake

Herring Gull

Gull-billed Tern

Iceland Gull

Sandwich Tern

Glaucous Gull

Roseate Tern

Common Tern
Sterna hirundo
35cm. The most abundant and widespread of the terns. Its bill is typically orange-red with a black tip, but may be all-red; in autumn, it becomes blackish. Unlike the Arctic Tern, this tern has a dark wedge on the primary flight feathers of the upperwing, and only the inner primaries are translucent from below. Typical calls are a fairly deep, rasping *keee-aarr* and *kek-kek-kek*. It winters in Africa. Around 15,000 to 20,000 pairs nest in the British Isles, mainly on the coast but they take readily to islands and rafts in lakes and reservoirs. The 2–3 eggs are cream to brown with brown or black blotches.
Ⓑ😊😰

Arctic Tern
Sterna paradisaea
35cm. Very similar to the Common Tern, this species differs in having a shorter, blood-red bill in summer (never with a black tip), shorter legs, a longer tail and shorter, narrower wings, whose primary feathers look uniformly grey from above and translucent from below. Calls include a brief *key-rr*.

This bird migrates further than any other, breeding mainly north of the Arctic Circle and migrating to spend winter as far south as the Antarctic – a round trip of up to 36,000km. The oldest-known Arctic Tern made this double journey for 34 years. Birds will nest with Common Terns. Nesting in a colony provides these ground nesters with some protection against predators such as foxes. Arctic Terns vigorously divebomb intruders, including humans, and may strike them with their beaks.
Ⓑ😊😰

Little Tern
Sterna albifrons
24cm. This dainty tern flies fast with flickering beats of its long narrow wings. It also hovers, suddenly dropping to a lower level as it searches for fish before diving. Unlike other terns, its forehead is white at all times of year. It breeds on shingle and sandy beaches in Britain and Ireland; elsewhere it also nests on river banks. Marine developments and disturbance by tourists have forced it to abandon many sites. It winters in Africa.
Ⓑ😊😰

Atlantic Puffins stand on their feet alone, and move about quite fast, unlike other auks, which shuffle clumsily using their legs and feet.

Whiskered Tern
Chlidonias hybrida
24cm. The stockiest and palest of the three *Chlidonias* or 'marsh' terns, which are all characterized by the short fork to their tails. In winter, it differs from the Black Tern in having a pure white breast and from the White-winged Black Tern by its grey rump, longer bill and lack of a white collar. Like other marsh terns, this species builds a floating nest of vegetation anchored to water plants. All species lay three brown or green eggs with dark markings. Its call is a rasping *krrrt*. It is a rare vagrant to Britain and winters mainly in Africa.
😊👤

Black Tern
Chlidonias niger
23cm. Black and grey in summer, this tern is grey above and white below in winter, with a white forehead to the black cap and a dark smudge at the sides of the breast. The White-winged Black Tern (*C. leucopterus*) breeds in eastern Europe and is a scarce passage migrant in the west. In summer, its almost white wings and white tail contrast with its jet black body; in winter it has a faint cap and no dark breast smudge. It has a dry *keersch* call, harsher than the Black Tern's squeaky *kreek*. Both species winter in Africa.
Ⓑ😊👤😰

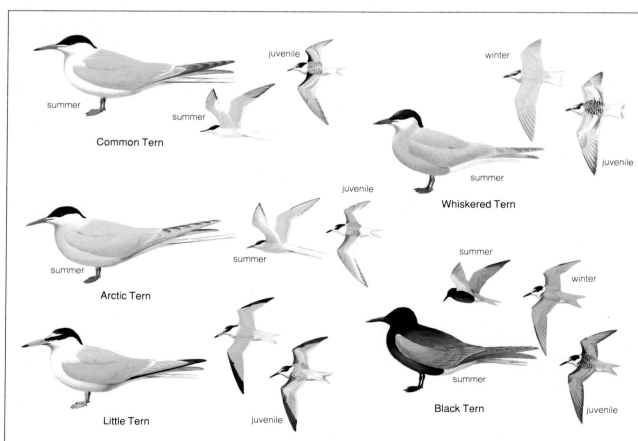

summer
Common Tern
summer
juvenile

winter
juvenile

Arctic Tern
summer
summer

juvenile
Whiskered Tern
summer

Little Tern
juvenile
summer
winter

Black Tern
summer
juvenile

ADAPTATIONS OF AUKS TO DEEP DIVING

Common Guillemot

specially modified ribs

fish prey

The ribcages of auks have evolved special overlapping processes, which forms them into rigid baskets. This helps the birds to withstand high pressures underwater.

AUKS

Auks (Family Alcidae) are black and white seabirds that nest on cliff ledges or in burrows and are found only in the northern hemisphere. Their short legs are set far back on their bodies and they have very short, narrow wings. Auks stand erect and, like the penguins, which they superficially resemble, dive underwater to catch fish. Unlike penguins, they can fly, with fast whirring wingbeats. They spend most of their lives at sea, visiting land only to breed.

Common Guillemot
Uria aalge
42cm. Birds of the northern races are almost black above, while those of the southern race are browner. In winter, the sides of the face and neck are white. Most numerous in the north, the bridled form has thin white 'spectacles' in summer. The more northerly Brunnich's Guillemot (*U. lomvia*), which breeds in Iceland and Norway, has a thicker, shorter bill with a whitish line along its base. In winter it lacks a dark line on the face and the black cap extends below the eye. Like most other auks, these guillemots lay just one egg.
Ⓑ 😎

Razorbill
Alca torda
41cm. Jet black above, this bird has a square, deep, laterally flattened bill, with a white vertical line near its tip, and a thick, short neck. When swimming, its long, pointed tail is usually held raised. In flight, it shows much more white on the sides of the rump than the Common Guillemot and its tail conceals its feet. It nests on ledges or in crevices. Some 70 per cent of the world population breeds in the British Isles.
Ⓑ 😎

Black Guillemot
Cepphus grylle
34cm. Often seen close inshore, this auk is unmistakable in summer. In winter, it is mottled grey above and white below, but still has the white wing patches. The inside of its black bill is brilliant red, as are its legs. Juveniles are darker and brownish above, while first summer birds can look all black. It is very vocal when courting, uttering far-carrying, high, whistling calls, sometimes rapidly repeated as a trill. It nests in caves, crevices and under boulders.
Ⓑ 😎

Little Auk
Alle alle
20cm. One of the world's most abundant birds in its Arctic breeding colonies, it is elsewhere a scarce autumn visitor, most numerous after severe storms. It is a dumpy little bird with a tiny, stubby bill. The small white marks on its 'shoulders' are noticeable at long range. It can be distinguished from young Razorbills and Guillemots by its smaller, shorter bill and blackish underwings, and from Puffins by its bill shape.
😎

Atlantic Puffin
Fratercula arctica
30cm. This comical-looking bird has a large head and a very deep bill, which in summer is brightly coloured; this becomes smaller and duller in winter as the plates from which it is made are moulted. In flight, this auk looks very big-headed and its bright orange legs are also prominent. It nests in clifftop burrows which it excavates or takes over from rabbits. Aided by hooks inside the bill, adult birds can carry 10 or more fish in their bills to their single chick.
Ⓑ 😎

summer
'bridled' form
winter
Common Guillemot

summer
winter
Little Auk

summer
winter
Razorbill

summer
winter
Atlantic Puffin

summer
winter
Black Guillemot

Common Tern

Common Guillemot

Arctic Tern

Razorbill

Little Tern

Black Guillemot

Whiskered Tern

Little Auk

Black Tern

Atlantic Puffin

231

Sandgrouse

The sandgrouse are placed in a single family (Pteroclididae) in the Order Pteroclidiformes. They are pigeon-like, ground-dwelling and ground-nesting birds of dry, open country, with long, pointed wings and tails and very rapid flight. Adult males have specially absorbent belly feathers that serve as a sponge for carrying water back to their chicks. The sexes differ slightly. They are only rare vagrants to the British Isles.

Black-bellied Sandgrouse
Pterocles orientalis

34cm. A very gregarious bird, which flies in flocks to and from water sources in the morning and evening. It is a seed-eating bird, able to survive in areas of semi-desert. It has a large area of black on its belly and pointed but not elongated central tail feathers. Its usual call is a deep, gruff, bubbling *churr-urr-urr*. The larger Pallas's Sandgrouse (*Syrrhaptes paradoxus*), which occasionally overflows from Asia into western Europe (the last major irruption was in 1908; a small one occurred in 1975), has a much smaller black belly patch, and extremely long central tail feathers. Following irruptions in the 19th century, it bred occasionally in Britain.

Pin-tailed Sandgrouse
Pterocles alchata

37cm. This sandgrouse has long, needle-pointed central tail feathers, a white belly and more white on the underwing than the Black-bellied Sandgrouse. In winter, the male resembles the female but lacks the lavender barring on her back. It usually occurs in much larger flocks than the Black-bellied Sandgrouse, and performs coordinated aerobatics. Its characteristic calls comprise loud, guttural *katar katar* notes which are often heard from flocks in flight. Like other European sandgrouse, it lays 2–3 cream to buff eggs with dark streaking.

Pigeons

The Order Columbiformes contains a single family, the Columbidae. The name 'pigeon' is usually used for the larger species and 'dove' for the smaller ones. Swift flyers, their wings often make a clattering noise when they take off, perhaps to convey alarm to others of their own kind. The sexes are similar and they nest in trees and holes. Pigeons are unusual in drinking by sucking up water, rather than taking a beakful and tipping the head back. They are also remarkable in feeding their young on 'milk' that is secreted from their crops.

Rock Dove/Feral Pigeon
Columba livia

33cm. The Rock Dove is now restricted to cliffs in the extreme north-west and south. Elsewhere, it has interbred with feral pigeons – domesticated Rock Doves that have established themselves in the wild. Some look just like their wild relative, pale grey with two black wing bars, a white rump and an iridescent green and purple patch on the neck. Others range from white to reddish-brown. The call of feral and wild birds alike is a series of muffled *oo-roo-coo* notes.

Common Stock Dove
Columba oenas

33cm. Smaller and darker than the Wood Pigeon, this dove lacks white patches on the wings and neck. Compared to the same-sized Rock Dove, it has smaller double black wing bars, no white on the rump, a bold black border to almost the entire wing, and a blue-grey underwing. It has a deep, grunting *ooh-ah* call, with the accent on the second syllable. It nests in holes in trees, cliffs, buildings and in disused rabbit burrows.

Common Wood Pigeon
Columba palumbus

41cm. The largest European pigeon, it has a prominent white patch on its neck, with glossy green and purple feathers above, and a broad white wing bar, which is conspicuous in flight. It is often seen in huge flocks in winter. It bursts noisily from cover when disturbed, clattering its wings. Its call is a muffled, repeated cooing, *coo-coo-coo-cu-coo*. Its nest is a platform of twigs in a tree.

Most pairs of Western Turtle Doves raise two broods and some three in their untidy twig nests in a hedge or tree.

Collared Dove
Streptopelia decaocto

32cm. This dove has sandy-buff upperparts and is faintly pinkish below. It has a broad white undertail. Its name derives from the narrow black half collar (lacking in young birds) around the back of the neck. Its call is a monotonous, deep *cooo-cooo-coop*, with the emphasis on the second syllable, repeated for long periods, and a nasal, cat-like *mair* flight note. Over the past 60 years, this bird has had a phenomenal expansion in range north-westwards from south-central Asia.

Western Turtle Dove
Streptopelia turtur

27cm. This small, slender pigeon has a pinkish breast and a distinctive turtleshell pattern of black and rich brown feathers on its upperparts. Its tail is dark above with white edges and black below with a narrow white tip. Adult birds have a black and white neck patch. It has swift, direct flight with stiff, jerky wingbeats, and a soft, purring call in summer. In autumn huge flocks gather to migrate to West Africa; many are shot on the way.

Parrots

Although not native to Europe, one introduced species of these colourful, fruit and seed eating, tropical birds (Order Psittaciformes, Family Psittacidae) is established in the wild.

Rose-ringed Parakeet
Psittacula krameri

41cm. This parrot was brought to Europe from India in the 1960s. Since then, escaped birds have established themselves in the wild, mainly in suburban gardens, parks and fields. It is now spreading from southern England to northern England, Wales, Scotland, and in the Low Countries and Germany. Its red hooked bill, brilliant green plumage and very long tail make it easy to identify. It has a loud, screeching *keeo-keeo* call. It nests in tree holes and visits bird tables.

Cuckoos

Cuckoos are mostly slender, long-tailed birds with two toes pointing forwards and two backwards. They are classified in the single Family Cuculidae within the Order Cuculiformes. The sexes are usually similar. Two species breed in Europe: both lay their eggs in other birds' nests so that the hosts incubate the cuckoos' eggs and rear their young.

Great Spotted Cuckoo

Clamator glandarius

40cm. This bird has a pale grey head with an erectile crest and a bright orange eye-ring. Young birds show large chestnut wing patches and have blackish caps without a crest. It is conspicuous and noisy when breeding, in olive groves and open wooded habitats. It has a loud, repeated *kittera* and a crow-like *kark* alarm call. It parasitizes crows, often laying several eggs in a nest. It is a rare vagrant outside the Mediterranean region.

Eurasian Cuckoo

Cuculus canorus

33cm. The call of the male is well known, but the female has a different, long bubbling call. With long tail and wings, it can look like a small raptor in flight, but appears uneasy when perched. Young birds have upperparts of either red-brown with dark bars or grey-brown with faint bars; both types have a white nape patch. The hepatic phase female is rare. Each female specializes in a particular host species, laying a single egg in several nests.

Black-bellied Sandgrouse

Collared Dove

Pin-tailed Sandgrouse

Western Turtle Dove

Rock Dove

Rose-ringed Parakeet

Common Stock Dove

Great Spotted Cuckoo

Wood Pigeon

Eurasian Cuckoo

♀ summer

♂ summer

♂

Black-bellied Sandgrouse

Collared Dove

♀ summer

♂

♂ summer

Pin-tailed Sandgrouse

Western Turtle Dove

Rock Dove

♀   ♂

Rose-ringed Parakeet

juvenile

Common Stock Dove

Great Spotted Cuckoo

juvenile   juvenile

Common Wood Pigeon

♀ hepatic phase

Eurasian Cuckoo

Owls

The owls (Order Strigiformes) are mainly nocturnal, predatory birds, quite unrelated to the diurnal birds of prey. They have big, rounded heads and large, forward-facing eyes set in a flattened facial disc, whose feathers partly conceal the short, hooked bill. Hunting adaptations include soft, sound muffling feathers, strong, sharp claws, and superb vision and hearing. The sexes are usually alike in plumage; females are larger. All species lay white eggs. There are two families within the order. The Barn Owl is the only European member of the Family Tytonidae. All other European owls are placed in the Family Strigidae.

The ghostly shape of a Barn Owl floats towards its nest site in an old barn, bearing a shrew for its young.

Barn Owl
Tyto alba
35cm. Mainly nocturnal, this owl usually hunts for rodents at dusk but sometimes flies by day in winter. It has a light, buoyant flight, frequently changing direction and periodically hovering. It utters long, blood-curdling shrieks, and at the nest may hiss or snore. It has suffered a decline in many countries, due to the loss of nesting sites in farm buildings, disturbance and pesticides. If voles are plentiful, it rears two broods. The dark-breasted race occurs in central Europe.
Ⓑ ◑ ✿ ⊞

European Scops Owl
Otus scops
19cm. This diminutive owl is a strictly nocturnal hunter, not often seen, but often heard. Its far-carrying, monotonous, plaintive *piu ... piu ... piu* call resembles that of the Midwife Toad and is a typical sound of Mediterranean summer nights. Its slender shape, very upright posture, broad, horn-like ear tufts and less flat head distinguish it from the Little Owl; feeds mainly on insects and migrates to Africa for the winter.
◑ ◑ ✿ ✿ ⊞

Northern Eagle Owl
Bubo bubo
65–70cm. One of the world's largest owls, it has orange eyes and dark eyebrows that join up with large ear tufts. It can prey on mammals as large as young Roe Deer and regularly kills raptors such as buzzards as well as other owls. This is a bird of remote, wild country, especially areas with rocky outcrops for nesting, though it also nests in hollow trees and in the old nests of raptors. Its call is a deep *ooo-hoo*, which can be audible for over 1km.
◑ ◑ ✿ ⊞

Snowy Owl
Nyctea scandiaca
55–65 cm. This large, white northern owl hunts mainly during the day, preying chiefly on lemmings but also taking prey as large as Mountain Hares and Common Eider ducks. The much larger female is heavily spotted with black on her upperparts and has barred lower underparts, in contrast to the almost pure white male. When the lemming population suddenly plummets, every four years or so, Snowy Owls migrate southwards. They have bred in Shetland. The nest is a scrape on the ground.
Ⓑ ◔ ◑

Northern Hawk Owl
Surnia ulula
35–40 cm. The daytime habits, long tail, relatively pointed wings and barred underparts of this owl give it a decidedly hawk-like appearance. It often perches conspicuously on a treetop or telegraph pole in an inclined posture, twitching its tail. Its white facial disc with blazing yellow eyes is bordered by broad black 'sideburns' and white 'eyebrows'. Its alarm call is a shrill, hawk-like *qui-qui-qui-qui* and its song, heard mainly at night, is a long, loud, bubbling trill.
◔ ✿

Eurasian Pygmy Owl
Glaucidium passerinum
16cm. Although little bigger than a sparrow, this owl is a bold, fierce predator which kills small birds up to the size of thrushes in flight and also preys on mammals, including shrews, rodents and weasels. It hunts mainly at twilight. It has a rotund shape, with a rather small head and prominent short white 'eyebrows'. Its flight is fast and bounding. It usually perches at an angle and frequently fidgets, flicking its tail upwards or waving it from side to side. Its call is a monotonously repeated, flute-like *du*.
✿

Little Owl
Athene noctua
22cm. The small size, long legs and flat-headed appearance of this owl are distinctive, and its glaring yellow eyes, beneath low, bold, white 'eyebrows' give it a fierce, frowning expression. Often seen in broad daylight, perched upright on a fence-post or telegraph wire, it bobs its head and jerks its body from side to side comically when suspicious. Preying mainly on insects and small mammals, its flight is deeply undulating. It was introduced to Britain from the Continent in the late 19th century.
Ⓑ ◔ ✿ ⊞

Tawny Owl
Strix aluco
38cm. Best known for the long, quavering hoots, usually uttered by the male, this strictly nocturnal owl also has a loud, harsh *kewick* call. The most common and widespread of the European owls, it can be found in the largest towns and cities, where it feeds mainly on birds. Rodents are its chief prey in rural areas. Distinctive features are the large rounded head, with a prominent facial disc and large dark eyes.
Ⓑ ◔ ◔ ✿ ✿

OWL ADAPTATIONS FOR HUNTING

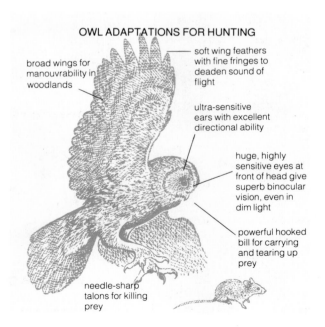

broad wings for manouvrability in woodlands

soft wing feathers with fine fringes to deaden sound of flight

ultra-sensitive ears with excellent directional ability

huge, highly sensitive eyes at front of head give superb binocular vision, even in dim light

powerful hooked bill for carrying and tearing up prey

needle-sharp talons for killing prey

Ural Owl
Strix uralensis
60cm. This owl has a long tail that gives it a hawk-like appearance in flight. It has a rather plain facial disc and relatively small dark eyes. It generally hunts small mammals and birds at night, but is also active by day in the breeding season. It has a deeper hoot than the Tawny Owl, beginning softly and often rising in volume and pitch. It gives a gruff *kawveck* and barking alarm calls.
◐ ✦

Great Grey Owl
Strix nebulosa
65–70 cm. This huge, dusky grey owl can be as large as a Eurasian Eagle Owl, but is less bulky. Its very large head has concentric bars around the relatively small yellow eyes, white 'eyebrows' and 'moustaches' and a black 'beard', and looks 'sawn off' vertically in profile when it flies. In flight, a pale patch becomes visible towards the wingtip, and the dark band at the end of the tail becomes conspicuous. It often hunts during daytime. Its call is a very deep, rapidly repeated series of hoots.
✦

Barn Owl

Eurasian Pygmy Owl

European Scops Owl

Little Owl

Northern Eagle Owl

Tawny Owl

Snowy Owl

Ural Owl

Hawk Owl

Great Grey Owl

light-breasted race

dark-breasted race

Barn Owl

Eurasian Pygmy Owl

grey phase

rufous phase

rufous phase

European Scops Owl

alert posture

resting posture

Little Owl

Northern Eagle Owl

Tawny Owl

♀

♀

♂

Snowy Owl

Ural Owl

Northern Hawk Owl

Great Grey Owl

Long-eared Owl

Asio otus

36cm. Communal winter roosts provide the best chance of seeing this strictly nocturnal, extremely secretive owl. When alarmed, it has a very slim, upright posture with ear tufts fully erect; at other times and in flight the ear tufts are invisible. This owl's song is a series of low, quiet *ooh* notes. The young are noisier, with a food-begging call like a rusty hinge on a swinging gate.
Ⓑ◐⊕

Short-eared Owl

Asio flammeus

38cm. This owl hunts for rodents mainly by day, quartering open country like a harrier, with a few wingbeats followed by long, wavering glides, its wings held in a shallow 'V'. It nests on the ground. The short ear tufts are rarely visible and its piercing yellow eyes give it a fierce expression. It looks similar to the Long-eared Owl in flight, but it has a pale belly, a more contrasting black patch on the bend of the wing and a more strongly barred tail.
Ⓑ◐⊕✿⊕▥

Tengmalm's Owl

Aegolius funereus

25cm. A strictly nocturnal forest owl with a deep, pale facial disc with bold black margins, black beneath the yellow eyes and permanently raised white 'eyebrows'. This gives it a surprised expression. It looks rather like a smaller version of the Northern Hawk Owl without the long tail. Its call consists of three to six rapid, soft but far-carrying *poo-poo-poo* notes, usually repeated five or six times, and it also has a *cha-week* alarm call. It is a very rare vagrant to Britain.
◐⊕

Nightjars

The nightjars (Family Caprimulgidae, Order Caprimulgiformes) are nocturnal, insect-eating, ground-nesting summer visitors. The sexes differ slightly.

European Nightjar

Caprimulgus europaeus

27cm. On heaths and in open woods the male's far-carrying, churring song can be heard at dusk and at night in summer. Both sexes also have a frog-like *kooick* flight call. In display flights, the male claps his wings above his head and hovers and glides, wings raised and tail spread, to show off the white spots near his wingtips and on the outer edges of his tail.
Ⓑ◔◐⊕

Swifts

The swifts (Family Apodidae, Order Apodiformes) feed on flying insects and mate and sleep on the wing. They land only when nesting. Sexes are alike. They winter in Africa.

Eurasian Swift

Apus apus

16cm. This bird is easily distinguished from swallows and martins by its entirely blackish-brown plumage, relieved only by a vague whitish patch on the chin. It flies on very long, narrow, stiffly-held, sickle-shaped wings, which are beaten in rapid succession several times prior to each glide. The Pallid Swift (*A. pallidus*) is similar but paler and is restricted to the Mediterranean. Both species have high-pitched, screaming calls and nest in roofs and holes in cliffs.
Ⓑ◔◐✿▥

A Hoopoe brings an insect larva to its young hidden within its tree-hole nest. The young are fed by their parents until after they have fledged.

Alpine Swift

Apus melba

22cm. By far the largest European swift, this bird has a stocky body with a white chin and underparts separated by a brown breast band. Its wingbeats are slower but its flight is faster than its relatives. It often holds its wings below the horizontal when gliding. Like other swifts, it is a very gregarious bird. It breeds on cliffs and even buildings. It has a loud, whistling trill.
◔◐✿

Kingfishers and Relatives

The Order Coraciiformes includes four European breeders: kingfishers (Family Alcedinidae), bee-eaters (Family Meropidae), rollers (Family Coraciidae) and the Hoopoe (Family Upupidae).

River Kingfisher

Alcedo atthis

16cm. This brilliantly coloured little bird is usually only glimpsed flashing past low over the rivers and streams where it nests in burrows which it excavates up to 90cm long in the banks. It feeds on fish, which it catches by diving from a perch or after hovering. Many birds die of starvation in hard winters when the water freezes, but others move to coastal marshes and estuaries where they can continue to feed. The population recovers quickly as birds lay 5–7 eggs and rear 2–3 broods. The call is a loud, shrill, whistling *chee* or *chee-kee*, rapidly repeated when excited.
Ⓑ◔▥

European Bee-eater

Merops apiaster

28cm. This unmistakable, vividly coloured, gregarious bird has a fast, aerobatic flight and glides frequently; its wings are pointed and rich reddish-brown beneath. It feeds on bees, dragonflies and other large flying insects. It often perches on telegraph wires and has a distinctive, far-carrying, liquid *prrupp* call. It excavates a nesting tunnel up to 2m long, in a bank or in the ground. North of its breeding range, as in Britain, it is a vagrant which occasionally breeds. It winters in Africa, some birds flying as far as 16,000km.
◔◐✿⊕▥

THE KINGFISHER'S NEST

Kingfishers feed their young for the 25 days they remain in the nest. The leftovers of their fish diet create such a stinking mess that the adults bathe after each visit.

European Roller
Coracias garrulus
31cm. This stocky bird of open woods has a large head and heavy bill. It flies with rapid wingbeats, revealing luminous blue forewings and black flight feathers. During its display flight it rolls from side to side. It sits on exposed perches, from where it can pounce on large insects. It utters harsh, chattering calls and deep, crow-like *krak-ak* and *krrrak* calls. It nests in tree holes.

Hoopoe
Upupa epops
28cm. With its distinctive plumage and long black-tipped erectile crest, this bird is unmistakable. It looks rather like a huge butterfly as it flits lazily across an olive grove with a slow open-and-shut action of its broad wings. Using its long bill it probes the soil or tree crevices for large insects. It nests in holes in trees or old buildings, or among rocks. Its name comes from its distinctive *poo-poo-poo* call. It is a scarce visitor north of its breeding range, mainly in spring, but breeds sometimes in Britain.

Long-eared Owl

Alpine Swift

Short-eared Owl

River Kingfisher

Tengmalm's Owl

European Bee-eater

European Nightjar

European Roller

Eurasian Swift   Hoopoe

Long-eared Owl

Alpine Swift

Short-eared Owl

River Kingfisher

Tengmalm's Owl

European Bee-eater

♂

♀
European Nightjar

European Roller

Eurasian Swift

Hoopoe

Woodpeckers

The woodpeckers (Family Picidae) are the only European members of the Order Piciformes. Most true woodpeckers (Subfamily Picinae) are boldly plumaged birds in which the sexes differ in their head markings. They use their bills to hack into trees for insects, to excavate nests and to communicate by drumming on dead wood. Adaptations for tree-climbing are strong feet, usually with two toes pointing forward and two backward, and a prop of stiff tail feathers. The single European wryneck (Subfamily Jynginae) has dull plumage, with sexes alike, and behaves more like a perching bird.

Northern Wryneck
Jynx torquilla
16cm. This secretive little bird spends much time on the ground, hopping along with its tail raised. Its crown feathers can be erected as a crest, and its short bill and long tail make it look more like a large warbler than a woodpecker. It has a clear, ringing *kyee-kyee-kyee* call. Its common name comes from its habit of twisting and turning its neck when alarmed. This species is declining in many countries.
Ⓑ🔾⊕✪

Grey-headed Woodpecker
Picus canus
27cm. This slightly smaller, duller and shorter-billed version of the Green Woodpecker is more scarce than that species, found at higher altitudes and spends more time in trees. In the lowland parts of its range, it prefers smaller woods. Its head and neck are grey with a narrow black stripe through the eye, and a narrow black moustache stripe. The female lacks the male's red crown. Young birds are only slightly barred. The voice of this species is similar to that of the Green Woodpecker, but more whistling, less laughing, slowing down and becoming lower pitched towards the end of the call.
🔾⊕✪

Green Woodpecker
Picus viridis
30cm. Seen in strong sunlight, this woodpecker can look almost tropical, with its bright green upperparts and yellow rump, and may then be mistaken for the Golden Oriole. Adults have red crowns and a moustache stripe that is red in the male and black in the female. Young birds also have red crowns, but are barred above and below. This bird spends much of its time on the ground, feeding on ants. Unlike other woodpeckers, it rarely drums but proclaims its territorial rights with loud, ringing, laughing *keu-keu-keu* calls.
Ⓑ🔾🔾⊕✪

Black Woodpecker
Dryocopus martius
46cm. The largest European woodpecker, this almost crow-sized bird prefers mature beech or mixed beech and conifer forests, where it hacks large craters in the tree trunks in its search for ants. Its black colouring makes it difficult to see. The voice of this species is a loud, ringing *kree-kree-kree-kree* laugh, more liquid than that of the Green Woodpecker, and without a fall in pitch at the end. In flight, the irregular flaps of its wings, followed by partial closure, give it a jay-like, unsteady action, not undulating as in other woodpeckers.
🔾⊕

Great Spotted Woodpecker
Dendrocopos major
23cm. The most common and widespread black-and-white woodpecker in Europe, this species has white cheeks, a white neck patch and two large white ovals on its back. The female lacks the male's red nape. Young birds have a large red crown patch. The underparts are buffish-white and there is a large red patch under the tail. This bird often visits bird tables. It has a loud, sharp *tchick* call.
Ⓑ🔾⊕✪

Syrian Woodpecker
Dendrocopos syriacus
23cm. This bird is very similar to the Great Spotted Woodpecker, but lacks the black bar joining the crown and moustache stripe. Males have a red nape and young birds a large red crown patch. Over the last 100 years, this species has expanded its range north and west, reaching Austria and Poland. Its calls are like the Great Spotted Woodpecker's. It is found mainly in lowlands.
🔾⊕✪

Middle Spotted Woodpecker
Dendrocopos medius
22cm. This woodpecker has white ovals on its back, smaller than the Great Spotted Woodpecker's, and black markings on its head which do not connect with the bill or nape. Males, females and young have an all-red crown. The flanks are lightly streaked and the undertail is pale pink. The bill is small and weak and used more for probing than hacking. This bird gives a series of *kik* notes, and a slow, nasal *wait-wait* call in spring.
🔾

A male Great Spotted Woodpecker flies away from the nest hole he is excavating with a beakful of wood chippings.

White-backed Woodpecker
Dendrocopos leucotos
25cm. The largest, longest-necked and longest-billed of the black-and-white woodpeckers. It has boldly streaked underparts and pink undertail coverts. In flight, its white rump and lower back are clearly visible. The male has a red crown and young birds a trace of one. Found mainly in mature deciduous forests in mountains, this is a scarce and declining species, as it needs a regular supply of decaying timber – rarely provided in sufficient quantity by the tracts of managed forestry. It has a deep, quiet *kiuk* call.
🔾⊕

Lesser Spotted Woodpecker
Dendrocopos minor
14cm. Only the size of a sparrow, this is the smallest European woodpecker. It lives in large gardens and

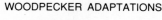

WOODPECKER ADAPTATIONS

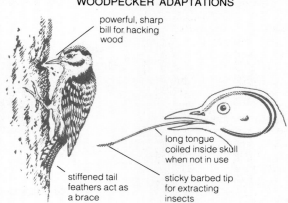

powerful, sharp bill for hacking wood

long tongue coiled inside skull when not in use

stiffened tail feathers act as a brace

sticky barbed tip for extracting insects

hedgerows as well as woods. Most of its time is spent among the smallest, highest branches, feeding with a sewing machine-like action of its short bill. It is barred, not spotted, above and it has no red under the tail. Females have a whitish-buff crown, males a dull red one; young birds have duller underparts and a trace of red on the crown. Calls are a shrill, weak *pee-pee-pee-pee-pee* and a feeble *tchick*.

ⒷⓄ◆✪

Northern Three-toed Woodpecker

Picoides tridactylus
22cm. Much darker than the other black-and-white woodpeckers, this species is distinguished by its black head marked by two narrow white stripes, mainly black wings and heavily-barred flanks. Its white rump and back are much more obvious than in the White-backed Woodpecker. Adult males have a golden-yellow crown patch. As its name suggests, it has only three toes. It often feeds low down on trees and is usually quite tame. It sometimes utters quiet, deep *kik* or *kyuk* calls.

◆

Northern Wryneck

Syrian Woodpecker

Grey-headed Woodpecker

Middle Spotted Woodpecker

Green Woodpecker

White-backed Woodpecker

Black Woodpecker

Lesser Spotted Woodpecker

Gt S Woodpecker

N 3-td Woodpecker

239

Perching Birds

The perching birds or passerines form the largest order of birds – the Passeriformes – containing about 60 per cent of all bird species, classified in over 70 families. They have three toes pointing forward and one backward, which enables them to perch easily. Passerines are found in all habitats and range in size from the 9cm Goldcrest and Firecrest, Europe's smallest birds, to the 65cm Northern Raven, the world's largest passerine.

LARKS

Larks (Family Alaudidae) are small, fast-running birds of treeless habitats. Most are brown and streaked. They are stockier than pipits, with shorter, thicker bills, broader wings and shorter tails. They mostly have an undulating flight and are often gregarious. The sexes are similar and they generally nest on the ground. Their songs are distinctive and often given in a characteristic song flight.

Calandra Lark
Melanocorypha calandra
19cm. The largest European lark, this heavily built bird has a stout yellowish bill and black neck patches. It has a very buoyant, undulating flight, in which it appears neckless and shows a white rear edge to the wings. Its song is louder than that of the Sky Lark, with frequent trills and mimicking of other birds' songs, given in a high, circling flight, often with a silent final dive. A very rare vagrant to Britain.

Short-toed Lark
Calandrella brachydactyla
14cm. This lark has very pale underparts, a short, pointed yellowish bill and a darkish bar across the closed wing. The dark smudge on the neck is variable. Western birds have sandy-buff upperparts; eastern races are greyer. The song consists of high-pitched twittering notes, repeated at short intervals during a high song flight, in which the bird bobs up and down like a yo-yo. It winters in Africa and is a rare vagrant to Britain.

Crested Lark
Galerida cristata
17cm. This lark has a long, spiky crest, a long, slightly downcurved bill and a short tail with reddish-buff outer feathers. Unlike the Sky Lark, it has no white on the trailing edge of its broad, rounded wings. Its song of short, repeated phrases is sometimes delivered in the air, though never in a soaring display flight, but often from a perch or the ground. A very rare vagrant to Britain.

Wood Lark
Lullula arborea
15cm. This species has a very short tail without white sides, only the hint of a crest, prominent pale eyebrows meeting at the nape and a black-and-white mark at the bend of the wing. It breeds on heaths and similar areas, nesting in patches of taller vegetation, and uses scattered trees from which to make its song flights. Its lovely song, in a descending scale, is a series of short melodious phrases interspersed with trilling *lu-lu-lu* and *tee-oo* notes.

Sky Lark
Alauda arvensis
18cm. The most common European lark, found in a wide variety of habitats. It has a short, but usually distinct, rounded crest and a longish tail with bold white outer tail feathers. Its long, pointed wings show white hind edges in flight. It gives its loud, clear, very rapid warbling song in flight, while ascending, hovering and descending, but its final plummet to the ground is silent. It also has a liquid *chirrup* flight call.

Shore Lark
Eremophila alpestris
16cm. Breeding on tundra and mountains, and wintering on seashores and saltmarshes, this lark is well camouflaged, but at close range reveals its distinctive black and yellow head and breast pattern, and two small black 'horns' on top of the head. Its flight call is a thin, shrill *tseep* or *tseep-tseep* and its song is similar to that of the Sky Lark but higher pitched. It usually sings from a low perch but sometimes in a high circling display flight.

The Sky Lark has benefited from the increase in farmland, which provides it with the open terrain it needs for feeding and breeding.

SWALLOWS AND MARTINS

Swallows and martins (Family Hirundinidae) are gregarious birds, with streamlined bodies, long, pointed wings and usually with forked tails. Agile in flight, they catch flying insects in the wide gape of their bills. The sexes are similar and most species build nests of mud on rocks and buildings. Most make long migrations southwards for winter.

Sand Martin
Riparia riparia
12cm. The Sand Martin is distinguished by its brown breast band on white underparts. It has a shallowly forked tail, sharply angled wings and a jerky, flicking flight. It nests colonially in burrows which it excavates in sand banks, often near water. It has greatly declined since the mid-1980s, due to drought in the African Sahel region, where it winters.

Crag Martin
Hirundo rupestris
14cm. This martin is the only member of its family to spend the whole year in Europe. It breeds on inland cliffs and on old buildings, often in mountains, and winters along coastal cliffs. It is buff, not white, below and lacks a breast band. When spread, its almost square-ended tail shows a row of white marks. It is stouter than its relatives, with a more gliding flight.

NESTS OF SWALLOWS AND MARTINS

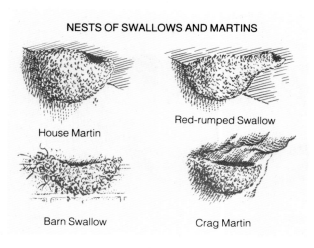

House Martin

Red-rumped Swallow

Barn Swallow

Crag Martin

Barn Swallow
Hirundo rustica
16–22cm. This common summer visitor has dark metallic blue upperparts, a chestnut-red forehead and throat bordered by a dark blue breast band, and creamy-white to pinkish-buff underparts. The deeply forked tail shows a row of white spots when spread. The outer tail feathers are greatly elongated, especially in males. It often hawks for flying insects over open country, swooping low on flicking wings. Calls include a high-pitched *tswit tswit*.
Ⓑ 🐦 🌳 🕊 🐛 📏

House Martin
Delichon urbica
12cm. A common and widespread summer visitor, it is smaller and more compact than the Barn Swallow. Its upper wings and short forked tail are black and its underparts are pure white without a breast band. Its most distinguishing feature, visible even at long range, is its white rump. It has a more fluttering flight than the swallow, with long glides. Its calls are a dry *tchirrip* and a shrill *tseep* of alarm.
Ⓑ 🌳 🕊 🐛

Calandra Lark	Shore Lark

Short-toed Lark	Sand Martin

Crested Lark	Crag Martin

Wood Lark	Barn Swallow

Sky Lark	House Martin

Calandra Lark

Shore Lark
♂ winter
♂ summer

eastern race
Short-toed Lark
western race

Sand Martin

Crested Lark

Crag Martin

Wood Lark

Barn Swallow
♂
♂

Sky Lark

House Martin

PIPITS AND WAGTAILS

Pipits and wagtails (Family Motacillidae) are small, slender, generally terrestrial, long-tailed and long-toed, chiefly insect-eating birds. Most pipits have streaked brown plumage which is paler below. Wagtails are much more boldly coloured, either with pied plumage or with a combination of yellow, grey, bluish or greenish feathers. They have much longer tails than pipits, and wag them up and down. Pipits and wagtails nest on the ground or in crevices. The sexes differ slightly in wagtails, but are alike in pipits.

Tawny Pipit
Anthus campestris
16.5cm. This large but slender pipit is more wagtail-like in appearance than other pipits. It has unstreaked underparts, a distinctive line of dark spots forming a bar across the 'shoulders' and a conspicuous pale 'eyebrow'. Its call is a wagtail-like *tsweep*, as well as a sparrow-like *chee-up* and its

song, given in a high song flight, is a repeated, metallic *chivee*. This pipit is a migrant, wintering in Africa and Arabia. Its nest is a well-hidden cup of grass, lined with hair. It is a regular visitor to British coasts, chiefly in autumn.

Tree Pipit
Anthus trivialis
15cm. Similar in appearance to the Meadow Pipit, this bird has a yellowish-buff breast and white flanks with clearer streaks, and a conspicuous buff 'eyebrow'. It is found in woodland edges, young conifer plantations, tree-scattered heaths and other open habitats that provide it with perches from which to launch out on its parachuting song flights, descending to a nearby perch or the ground on stiff wings like a paper aeroplane. Its call is a harsh *tees*. It is a summer visitor, wintering in Africa.

Meadow Pipit
Anthus pratensis
14.5cm. This little bird is a common inhabitant of a wide range of open habitats. It has a shuffling, rather mouse-like

The Grey Wagtail builds its nest of grasses and moss, lined with hair, close to fast-flowing water.

gait as it searches the ground for insects and small seeds. When disturbed, it flies off, uttering thin high-pitched *tseep* notes, usually repeated two or three times. Its wingbeats are erratic and its flight rises and falls in jerky steps. It delivers its rather quiet song, a series of thin piping notes gradually accelerating into a musical trill, during a brief parachuting song flight up from the ground. Like other pipits, it builds a concealed grass cup on the ground.

Red-throated Pipit
Anthus cervinus
14.5cm. This pipit has a strongly streaked rump and underparts. The rusty-pink colour on the throat and upper breast is variable, and is replaced by bold streaks in winter. Distinctive calls are a long, thin, hoarse, hissing *tzeeez* and a soft, explosive *chup*. From Scandinavia and Russia it migrates via the eastern Mediterranean to winter in Africa, and is a rare vagrant to western Europe, including Britain.

Tawny Pipit

Water Pipit

Tree Pipit

Yellow Wagtail

Meadow Pipit

Grey Wagtail

Red-throated Pipit

Pied Wagtail

Rock Pipit

Waxwing

Tawny Pipit

juvenile moulting to first winter

Meadow Pipit

Tree Pipit

summer

winter

Red-throated Pipit

Rock Pipit
Anthus petrosus
17cm. This is normally a coastal species, and is noticeably larger and greyer than the Meadow and Tree Pipits, with a longer bill, dark legs and grey-buff outer tail feathers. It breeds on rocky coasts, and winters on other coasts and estuaries, too. Its call is a clear *pheeest*, less high-pitched than that of the Meadow Pipit and rarely uttered in twos and threes. Its song is like that of the Meadow Pipit but is louder, harsher and more chirruping. It has a similar song flight.
Ⓑ🐛

Water Pipit
Anthus spinoletta
17cm. This bird is distinctive in summer, with a peach or buff coloured breast and no streaks. In winter the white breast is finely streaked. The combination of unstreaked back, prominent 'eyebrow' and white outer tail feathers distinguish it from other pipits. It breeds on high mountains, on moist alpine meadows or moorland, of central and southern Europe. It winters mainly on marshes, flooded meadows, by lakes and in other freshwater habitats. Both its calls and song resemble those of the Rock Pipit. It is a rare passage migrant and winter visitor to the British Isles.
Ⓑ🌀🍃🐛

Yellow Wagtail
Motacilla flava
17cm. This small, neat wagtail with a distinctive combination of greenish back and yellow underparts has a shorter tail than its relatives and occurs in a variety of geographical races, differing mainly in the pattern of colours on the male's head in springtime. The race *flavissima* breeds in Britain; other races also turn up in small numbers on passage. It is often seen in damp meadows, where it feeds among cattle, making brisk fluttering runs and short aerial chases after flies. Its call is a loud *tsweep*, and its song is a brief trill.
Ⓑ🐛🦗🐛🕸

Grey Wagtail
Motacilla cinerea
19cm. This is the largest and most elegant of the European wagtails, with the longest tail. It is also the most attached to water, breeding along fast-running streams and rivers, chiefly in uplands, and wintering more widely in freshwater habitats, including reservoirs and lakes. In all plumages, it has a blue-grey back, in contrast to the greenish back of the Yellow Wagtail. The male is distinguished by his black bib in summer. Its calls are a loud, sharp, metallic *tzitzi, tzik* and *tsee*. It has a brief warbling *tsee tsee tsee* song.
Ⓑ🐛

Pied Wagtail
Motacilla alba
18cm. This is the only European wagtail that regularly occurs in a wide range of open habitats away from as well as near water, from remote tundra and semi-desert to farmyards and town centres. Females of the race *yarellii*, which breeds in Britain, are greyer above and have less black on the head and chest than males, especially in summer, but both have a distinctive black rump. Young birds have grey backs. The race *alba*, often known as the White Wagtail, which breeds on the Continent, is pale grey above and has a white rump. The main calls are a loud, harsh *chizz-ick* and *tchick*.
Ⓑ🐛🦗🐛🕸

WAXWINGS

Only one species of the waxwing family (Bombycillidae) occurs in Europe. Waxwings are highly nomadic birds that feed mainly on the flesh of berries, but eat insects in summer. They build cup-shaped nests in conifers. The sexes are alike.

Bohemian Waxwing
Bombycilla garrulus
20cm. This handsome bird resembles a starling in shape, size and flight silhouette, but its pinkish brown plumage and smart crest readily distinguish it. It takes its name from the waxy red and yellow spots on its wings. Breeding in Europe only in northern Scandinavia and Russian conifer forests and birch woods, it disperses in winter, sometimes in large numbers, about every five to six years, as far west as Britain and France. Then it appears in more open country, seeking out berry-bearing bushes and trees in hedges, parks and gardens, mostly in the coastal areas of the region.
Ⓑ🌀🍂🦗

British race — Scandinavian race — spring
Rock Pipit

French race — Balkan race — Italian/Albanian race — British race — ♂ — ♀ — juvenile
Yellow Wagtail

White ♂ — summer — winter — Pied ♂ — winter — summer
Pied Wagtail

summer — winter
Water Pipit

♂ summer — winter
Grey Wagtail

Bohemian Waxwing

DIPPERS

Dippers (Family Cinclidae) are the only perching birds that can move about underwater in search of insects. The name comes from the birds' habit of bobbing their whole bodies up and down. They are plump and have very short, often slightly cocked tails, and build large spherical nests above running water. There is a single species in Europe and the sexes are alike.

White-throated Dipper
Cinclus cinclus
18cm. Typically seen bobbing on a boulder in a rapidly flowing upland stream, this instantly recognizable bird blinks, flashing its white eyelids and showing off its pure white throat and breast. It flies fast and low over the water, giving sharp metallic *clink-clink* calls; It also produces a distinctive, loud *zit zit zit* call and the song is a sweet, rippling trill. This bird wades or plunges into the water and can swim well, despite having unwebbed feet, using its wings. Thick body feathers enable it to continue feeding in winter.
ⓑⓔ

WRENS

Europe has only one species of wren (Family Troglodytidae), the remaining 60 species being confined to the New World. Wrens are small, rotund, chiefly insect-eating birds with erect tails and whirring flight on short, rounded wings. They build roofed nests with a side entrance among thick vegetation, in holes or beneath overhangs. The sexes are alike.

Northern Wren
Troglodytes troglodytes
12cm. With its short tail cocked, this bird pours out its surprisingly loud warbling song, or scolds the observer with harsh, repeated *tic-tic* calls. This is one of the most abundant and widespread of European birds, found in many habitats, from rocky

islands, dense reedbeds and high mountains to hedges and gardens. Males are polygamous and each builds a series of nests and tries to attract several females to lay their eggs in them.
ⓑⓔⓞⓠⓐⓧⓚⓦⓜ

ACCENTORS

There are two species of accentor (Family Prunellidae) in Europe. They are mostly soberly plumaged, insect-eating birds with a shuffling walk, a fine pointed bill and a complex mating system in which more than one male may share a territory with a female. They build open cup-shaped nests in low vegetation or crevices, or on the ground. The sexes are alike.

Hedge Accentor
Prunella modularis
14cm. Shuffling along on the ground like a mouse, frequently flicking its wings, this tame, sparrow-sized bird, also known as the Dunnock, is common in gardens and woodlands. Although it may appear superficially like a female House Sparrow, its thin bill and grey face readily distinguish it. It generally remains in cover, though it may use a prominent perch to deliver its song, a thin, high, staccato warble, rather like the song of the Northern Wren, but slower and quieter, without trills. The main call is a loud, shrill, piping *tseep*. It feeds on seeds in winter.
ⓑⓔⓞⓐⓧⓜ

Alpine Accentor
Prunella collaris
18cm. This much larger, more brightly coloured version of the Hedge Accentor breeds in the high mountains of southern and central Europe, favouring patches of alpine grassland with boulders or scree. In winter, it usually descends to the foothills and can then sometimes be seen in villages, or around ski-lifts. Its main call is a rippled, liquid *tchirrrip* and it has a song like that of the Hedge Accentor, but lower in pitch and more musical. It is a very rare vagrant to the rest of Europe, including Britain.
ⓞⓧ

A male Common Redstart is most likely to feed by diving out from a tree branch, while females feed more often on the ground.

CHATS AND THRUSHES

Chats and thrushes (Family Turdidae) are small to medium-sized, insect- and fruit-eating birds that feed mainly on the ground. The chats (including robins, nightingales, redstarts, wheatears and rock thrushes) are smaller and proportionately longer-legged than the true thrushes, which generally have less bold plumage. In many chats the sexes differ; they are alike in most European true thrushes. All have cup-shaped nests; those of the true thrushes are strengthened with mud.

Rufous Scrub-Robin
Cercotrichas galactotes
15cm. This sprightly bird of arid scrubland, vineyards and gardens has a conspicuous rufous tail, with striking black and white markings on its outer tips, which it frequently cocks like a wren. It delivers its song, a musical series of clear, flute-like notes with an even rhythm, from a perch or in a parachuting flight. Calls include a harsh *check check* and a sweet, fluty *piu*. It winters in Africa and is a rare vagrant to Britain.
ⓔⓔⓧ

European Robin
Erithacus rubecula
14cm. This very familiar bird is tame and confident only in Britain: it is often shy and elusive on the Continent. It is aggressive, and territorial disputes are frequent. The bird shows off its red breast and sometimes even fights to

the death. Both male and female defend their territories by singing their beautiful, clear, warbling song throughout the year. They sing at night in areas with street lights. The chief call is a loud, sharp *tic*, often repeated.
ⓑⓞⓐⓧⓜ

Common Nightingale
Luscinia megarhynchos
16.5cm. This rich brown bird is justly famed for its superb, loud song, consisting of repeated phrases of rich, liquid trills, deep bubbling *chook chook chook* and slow *piu piu piu* notes, rising to a crescendo, uttered by day as well as night. It is a very secretive bird, but a glimpse of its rounded, rusty red tail, often cocked, and its large black eyes provides clues to its identity. Calls include a liquid *hooeet*, a loud, harsh *tac* and a harsh *kerr* of alarm. It winters in Africa.
ⓑⓞⓐⓧ

Bluethroat
Luscinia svecica
14cm. The prominent white 'eyebrow' is distinctive in all plumages, as are the rusty red patches at the base of the tail. Males of the race *cyanecula*, which breeds in central and southern Europe, have a white spot in the centre of their cornflower blue breasts. Those of the race *svecica*, which breeds in Scandinavia and Russia, have a red breast spot. The song is varied and musical, a loud, high-pitched series of tinkling notes, mixed with mimicry of birds and even train whistles. A regular but scarce passage migrant to Britain, it winters around the Mediterranean.
ⓑⓔⓞⓠⓞⓔⓔ

Black Redstart

Phoenicurus ochruros
14cm. In his dapper breeding plumage, the male is unmistakable. Winter males and females, though less striking, are still relatively easy to distinguish from the much paler Common Redstart. The song is a brief, fast warbling followed by a rattle. Calls include a brief *tsip*, often followed by a hard, scolding *tuck tuck*. Inland it breeds among rocks and in buildings. Along the coast it breeds on cliffs. This is a scarce breeder in Britain, and a regular passage migrant.
Ⓑ ⦾ ⦿ ⦿

Common Redstart

Phoenicurus phoenicurus
14cm. Despite his striking plumage, the male is often hard to see as these birds perch and feed mainly among trees. Both sexes have a brick-red tail, which they constantly flicker up and down. It nests in tree holes and nestboxes, and is a summer visitor wintering in Africa. The main calls are a plaintive *hueet* and distinctive *huee-tucc-tucc*. The song is a short jingle of weak, hurried, robin-like notes.
Ⓑ ⦾ ⦿ ⦿ ⦿

White-throated Dipper

European Robin

Northern Wren

Common Nightingale

Hedge Accentor

Bluethroat

Alpine Accentor

Black Redstart

Scrub-Robin

Redstart

White-throated Dipper

juvenile

European Robin

Common Nightingale

juvenile

Northern Wren

♂ summer
white-spotted race
red-spotted race
♂ summer
♀

Bluethroat

Hedge Accentor

♂ summer
♀

Black Redstart

Alpine Accentor

Rufous Scrub-Robin

♂ summer
♂
♀

Common Redstart

245

The NORTHERN TUNDRA

The tundra is a cold, windswept habitat covering the most northerly areas of the land surface. In Europe it skirts the northern tip of Scandinavia and extends south along the mountains of Norway and Sweden. It also covers much of Iceland. Winter temperatures often fall to about –40°C and the tundra is covered with snow for much of the year – up to nine months in some areas – but the snow is rarely more than about 40cm deep and many exposed areas are kept almost clear of snow by the wind. In terms of precipitation, the tundra is a desert, but much of it turns into a swamp during the short summer due to the permafrost – the permanently frozen soil just below the surface. The surface layers melt in the summer, when temperatures rise to about 10°C, but the water cannot drain away through the frozen sub-soil and the tundra becomes covered with small pools. There are also many permanent lakes.

Colourful Flowers
Tundra vegetation is dominated by lichens, mosses, and sedges. There are also many flowers, such as Moss Campion, Arctic Poppy, and numerous saxifrages, which put on a brilliant show during the short summer. Most of these plants form dense mats which hug the ground to avoid the wind. Dwarf shrubs, notably willows and heathers, grow here and there. Some are over 100 years old, but their creeping stems are no thicker than a pencil. The height of these plants is controlled by the snow depth, for anything that pokes its head above the snow is quickly killed by the bitter winds. Shrubs are rarely more than 30cm high. Temperatures are higher in the southern part of the tundra and the snow is deeper. The shrubs grow taller here and this zone is often called the forest tundra. It gradually merges with the taiga.

Pollination of the flowers is effected by bumble bees, butterflies, and small flies. The Arctic bumble bees form

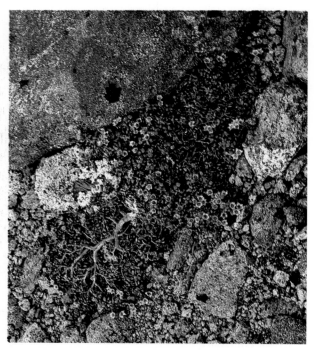

The pencil-thin stem of this trailing azalea creeping over the stony tundra may well be over 100 years old.

only small colonies, for they do not have time to build up large numbers during the short summer. Some of the most northerly species produce no workers: there is time to rear only one brood and these must be males and queens to ensure the species survives. Because of the cold, many Arctic butterflies take two years to reach the adult stage.

Birds by the Million
The flies of the tundra include blood-sucking mosquitoes and blackflies and numerous other midges that grow up in the pools and the waterlogged soil. Wading birds arriving to breed on the tundra feed on the fly larvae, but they make little impression on the population and the adult

ABOVE: *The Icelandic tundra, sparsely clothed with grass and moss, at the southern edge of the Vatnajokull glacier.*
RIGHT: *The Northern Clouded Yellow butterfly survives sub-zero temperatures for most of the year.*

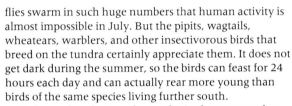

Tundra Mammals

The Norway Lemming is one of the few mammals confined to the tundra and it plays a vital role in the ecology of the habitat, being a staple in the diets of the Snowy Owl and Arctic Fox. The lemming is famous for its population fluctuations, which are followed closely by changes in the numbers of its predators. Several voles also live on the tundra, as do various small carnivores such as the Stoat. Reindeer once roamed all over the tundra in summer and moved south into the forest for the winter, but there are now few truly wild Reindeer.

The harsh climate of the tundra is largely responsible for its scanty plant and animal life, but it is also a very new habitat, having been exposed by the retreating glaciers less than 10,000 years ago. With time many more species may adapt to the harsh conditions, and become permanent residents – unless, of course, a new ice age begins.

flies swarm in such huge numbers that human activity is almost impossible in July. But the pipits, wagtails, wheatears, warblers, and other insectivorous birds that breed on the tundra certainly appreciate them. It does not get dark during the summer, so the birds can feast for 24 hours each day and can actually rear more young than birds of the same species living further south.

Birds are abundant on the tundra in the summer, but they are nearly all summer visitors. Among the few hardy resident species are the Willow Grouse and Ptarmigan – both of which turn white for the winter – the Snowy Owl, and the Common Raven. The first two are vegetarians, but the Snowy Owl feeds on lemmings and the Common Raven eats whatever it finds – raiding birds' nests, killing lemmings, or taking carrion.

The Mountain Hare is more sociable than the Brown Hare and sometimes occurs in large groups.

Tundra Wildlife
1 Arctic Fox
2 Ptarmigan
3 Arctic Fritillary
4 Bilberry
5 White Wagtail
6 Lichens
7 Reindeer
8 Arctic Saxifrage
9 Matted Cassiope
10 Grasses
11 Arctic Poppy
12 Reindeer Moss
13 Norway Lemming
14 Snowy Owl
15 Alpine Catchfly
16 Dwarf Willow
17 Purple Saxifrage

Whinchat
Saxicola rubetra
12.5cm. Unlike its close relative the Common Stonechat, this bird is exclusively a summer visitor which winters in Africa. It has a distinctive white 'eyebrow', contrasting with dark ear coverts, white patches on the wings and a white patch on either side of the base of the tail. Breeding males are brighter than females, with pale orange underparts and larger white wing patches. In winter males become duller. Its very variable, brief, sweet warbling song includes mimicry of other bird species. Its commonest calls are *tuee-tick-tick* and a short hard rattling *churr* of alarm.
ⓑ😊🐦😊🐛

Common Stonechat
Saxicola torquata
12.5cm. This bold little bird perches bolt upright on a bush-top or post, constantly flicking its wings and tail as it scolds passers-by with *hwee-tsak-tsak* calls, the last two notes sounding like a couple of pebbles knocked together, and accounting for its name. In the breeding season, the male has a large-looking black head, a prominent white half collar and a white rump, though he is duller in winter, resembling the female. The male uses a prominent perch as a songpost or launches into a dancing, hovering song flight to utter his squeaky warbling song. Often found in gorse habitats. The female lays 5–6 eggs in a low nest.
ⓑⒷ😊🐦😊

Northern Wheatear
Oenanthe oenanthe
15cm. Often seen flitting fast and low over open ground, this bird flaunts its conspicuous white rump and

tail sides. It is very restless, often bobbing its body and fanning its tail; it usually stands upright. This species makes impressive migrations: even those birds breeding in Siberia and western Alaska winter in Africa. Calls are a hard *chack chack* and *wheet chack chack*. The song is a melodious series of warbling notes linked by creaking, rattling notes and often contains mimicry of other birds. The nest is in a rock crevice or a burrow.
ⓑ😊🐦😊😊🐛

Blue Rock Thrush
Monticola solitarius
20cm. The male's handsome dark blue body can appear almost black, as can the drabber female. Shy and secretive, it shoots off with soft wingbeats to disappear behind a mountain boulder. The melancholy song is a series of short, soft, fluty phrases. The Mountain Rock Thrush (*M. saxatilis*) is a scarce summer visitor to Mediterranean mountains, generally at higher altitudes than its resident relative. The male has a striking orange-chestnut body and tail, a blue head and neck and a blackish back. The female is much paler than the female Blue Rock Thrush, and has an orange tail, not a dark one. It winters in Africa. Both species feed on insects and berries, and nest in a rock crevice.
😊😊

Ring Ouzel
Turdus torquatus
24cm. This mainly summer visitor to mountains and moorlands is a shy and wary bird. It likes dense cover, but shows its silvery wings as it swoops swiftly and erratically over the rocks. The white breast crescent, which helps

to distinguish it from the Blackbird, is most noticeable in the breeding male: in winter it becomes browner with scaly markings, like the female. It feeds on berries and insects. Calls include a hard, rattling *tac-tac-tac* and clear piping *peee-u* notes. The song is a loud, short, simple and melancholy series of sweet, fluty double or treble notes separated by pauses. It winters in south-western and south-eastern Europe and in North Africa.
ⓑ😊😊

Blackbird
Turdus merula
25cm. This is a very common bird of many habitats, from wild bushy moorland to farm hedges and city gardens. The male is the only thrush with an entirely jet black body, and his yellow eye-ring and bill are also distinctive. Young birds are browner and more speckled below than females, but share the adults' shape and posture. Albinos are quite common, some with white on the breast like a Ring Ouzel. A noisy, excitable bird, it gives low *chook* notes of mild alarm, hysterical harsh rattling or chattering of full alarm and a chorus of *chinks* heard at dawn and dusk. The song is a rich, mellow, fluty warbling of great beauty. The nest is an untidy cup of grass, moss and mud.
ⓑ🅾️😊🐦😊🐛

Fieldfare
Turdus pilaris
26cm. The grey head and nape, chestnut back and boldly speckled orange-buff breast and white flanks identify this large thrush. In

A Song Thrush brings a worm to its brood of hungry chicks. Young Song Thrushes have boldly speckled upperparts.

flight, the grey rump and black tail are distinctive. In winter, Scandinavian and eastern European breeders migrate to western Europe. It nests colonially in woodland edges, and on the ground above the tree line. A few pairs breed in Scotland. The flight call is a chattering *tchak-tchak-tchak* and its song is a rapid sequence of chuckling notes and feeble squeaks.
ⓑ😊😊🅾️😊🐛😊

Song Thrush
Turdus philomelos
23cm. This common thrush has a warm brown back and a yellowish-buff wash on its neatly spotted breast. In its strong, direct flight, it shows an area of pale orange-buff on the underwing. As well as worms, insects, fruit and berries, it eats many snails, whose shells it breaks open on an 'anvil' – a large stone or patch of concrete. The song is very distinctive, featuring a variety of clear, ringing phrases each repeated two to four times, with a brief pause between. The most common call of the Song Thrush is a short *sip*. The alarm call is a repeated *tchuk tchuk*. The nest has a neat mud lining.
ⓑ😊🅾️😊🐛😊

Redwing
Turdus iliacus
21cm. This small thrush has a prominent pale 'eyebrow' and a patch of rust-red on the flanks, which extends up on to the underwings and is visible in flight. Its facial markings give it a distinctive 'cross' expression. In winter, it is gregarious and is often seen with Fieldfares in open country. The flight call is a

THE SONG THRUSH'S ANVIL

Song Thrushes have mastered the art of breaking open snail shells on stones, paths or other hard surfaces to eat the nutritious body within.

long, soft but penetrating *seeeip*, often heard from birds overhead on migration at night. About 100 pairs breed in Scotland. The song is very variable – typically a repeated phrase of four to six fluty notes, rising and falling, ending with a weak warbling. Like other thrushes, winter birds feed mainly on berries but also take fallen fruit, insects and worms.
Ⓑ◐○●⊗▥

Mistle Thrush
Turdus viscivorus
27cm. Largest of the European thrushes, this bird is much greyer and paler than the Song Thrush, with larger spots on its underparts. It has a distinctive undulating flight, in which the white underwing and white tips to the outer tail feathers are noticeable. It is a rather aggressive bird, which will defend berry-bearing trees from other birds in winter. The usual call is a distinctive loud rattling, like that made by a football rattle. The song is similar to that of the Blackbird, but louder, simpler and more monotonous, with a much wilder quality. It nests as early as February.
Ⓑ◑○⊗

Whinchat

Blackbird

Common Stonechat

Fieldfare

Northern Wheatear

Song Thrush

Blue Rock Thrush

Redwing

Ring Ousel

Mistle Thrush

Whinchat

Blackbird

Common Stonechat

Fieldfare

Northern Wheatear

Song Thrush

Blue Rock Thrush

Redwing

Ring Ousel

Mistle Thrush

WARBLERS

The warblers (Family Sylviidae) are a large family of small, generally shy and skulking, mainly insect-eating birds with slender bills. Most species are long-distance migrants, wintering in Africa. The sexes are similar in appearance and most species build cup-shaped nests on the ground or in vegetation not far above it. Reed Warblers' nests are particularly deep and are woven among vertical stems, while the leaf warblers build domed nests with a side entrance. Two species the Goldcrest and Firecrest, are residents that build tiny, deeply cup-shaped nests, using moss and spiders' webs, at the tips of conifer branches. Warblers produce a variety of often distinctive songs.

The Reed Warbler builds a deep, cup-shaped nest of dried grass, intricately woven around the reed stems.

Cetti's Warbler
Cettia cetti
14cm. This secretive bird of reed beds and other aquatic vegetation can be located by its loud, explosive song of repeated *settee* and *cheweeoo* notes. It is dark rufous-brown above, with a pale 'eyebrow', a whitish breast and a long rounded tail, often spread and sometimes flicked upwards to reveal the barred undertail coverts. This resident warbler is expanding its range northwards.
Ⓑ☻

Grasshopper Warbler
Locustella naevia
13cm. A continuous, mechanical clicking song – similar to the sound made by the reel of a fishing rod – is usually the only evidence of this shy warbler, in tangled vegetation in dense, wet and dry grassy habitats, or in conifer plantations. Savi's Warbler (*L. luscinioides*), which lacks the streaked back of this species, has a similar reeling song, but it is shorter. It is a rare breeder in reed beds in southeastern England.
Ⓑ☻☻☻

Sedge Warbler
Acrocephalus schoenobaenus
13cm. The narrow black eyestripe, broad creamy 'eyebrow' and dark-streaked crown give this common summer visitor a distinctive head pattern. The brown back is heavily streaked with black; the rump is orange-brown and unstreaked. This bird spends much time in cover but emerges to sing from a perch or in a brief vertical display flight. Its song consists of an uneven, loud, rapid torrent of harsh chattering notes, alternating with sweet musical phrases and long trills.
Ⓑ☻

Marsh Warbler
Acrocephalus palustris
12.5cm. This small warbler looks very like the Reed Warbler and is best identified by its song – an extremely varied and musical mixture of harsh *chirrups*, canary-like trills, rich warbling phrases, a distinctive nasal *tsawee* note and a remarkable range of mimicry of other bird calls. If seen, its more prominent 'eyebrow', more olive upperparts, olive-brown rump, paler underparts, longer wings and pinkish legs also help separate it from the Reed Warbler. It is now a very rare breeder in Britain.
Ⓑ☻☻☻

Reed Warbler
Acrocephalus scirpaceus
12.5cm. Very similar to the Marsh Warbler, this bird is rustier brown above with a slightly rufous rump and buff flanks, a more sloping forehead, a longer bill and darker legs. Its song is like that of the Sedge Warbler, but with an even pace and harsh phrases, (including *jug jug jug*), interspersed with more liquid notes. The Great Reed Warbler (*A. arundinaceus*) is a much larger version of the Reed Warbler; it is a rare vagrant to Britain.
Ⓑ☻☻

Melodious Warbler
Hippolais polyglotta
13cm. This round-headed warbler has a long, babbling song, including chirrups and mimicry, with little repetition of phrases. The Icterine Warbler (*H. icterina*) is very similar, but brighter above and paler below and has a pale wing panel and longer wings. Its song is a loud, long jumble of harsh and melodious notes. The Icterine Warbler is a summer visitor to eastern and central Europe and a vagrant to the west, including Britain.
Ⓞ☻

Sardinian Warbler
Sylvia melanocephala
13.5cm. This skulking warbler is a common resident of dry, open maquis scrubland, and is also found in thickets and open woodland. The longish, blackish tail is frequently cocked and has broad white edges and a white tip. Its song is a fast gabble of musical notes interspersed with harsh chattering like the alarm call, given in a short display flight or from a perch, but mostly from dense undergrowth. A rare vagrant to Britain.
☻☻Ⓞ

Dartford Warbler
Sylvia undata
12.5cm. This tiny warbler utters its scratchy warbling song from a prominent perch or in a dancing display flight but otherwise it is very elusive, skulking in dense cover. It has very dark plumage, a ruby-red eye-ring and a long, often cocked or fanned tail. The brighter male frequently raises his crown feathers. This is one of the few resident European warblers and suffers heavy mortality in hard winters, though a much greater threat is the destruction of its heathland habitat.
Ⓑ☻

Lesser Whitethroat
Sylvia curruca
13.5cm. An agile, secretive inhabitant of thick scrub, tall overgrown hedges and young conifers, this species resembles the Common

---

THE STEALTHY GRASSHOPPER WARBLER

When alarmed, the Grasshopper Warbler creeps quietly away through the undergrowth rather than taking flight.

Whitethroat but is neater, more compact and shorter-tailed. It is greyer above, with a dark face mask, lacks chestnut in the wings and has dark grey legs. Its song is a rapid repetition of a single note, preceded by a short warble. The Orphean Warbler (*S. hortensis*) of Mediterranean woods, orchards and scrub is larger, with pale yellow eyes and a dark face in the male. Ⓑ▲❶

Common Whitethroat
Sylvia communis
14cm. This common warbler of heaths, commons, scrub and hedgerows has a prominent white throat and rusty wings. Its short scratchy warbling song is delivered from an exposed perch or in a brief dancing display flight. Otherwise, the bird spends much time hidden, giving hard *tak tak* calls or a harsh, scolding *charr*. The Spectacled Warbler (*S. conspicillata*) is similar but smaller; the male has a dark mask and the plumage is browner. The Subalpine Warbler (*S. cantillans*) is much smaller and brighter. Both species are Mediterranean. Ⓑ◐❶▥

Cetti's Warbler

Grasshopper Warbler

Sedge Warbler

Marsh Warbler   Dartford Warbler

Reed Warbler

Cmn Whitethroat

Melodious Warbler

Cetti's Warbler

Melodious Warbler

Grasshopper Warbler

Sardinian Warbler

juvenile

♂

♀

Sedge Warbler

Dartford Warbler

♂

♀

spring

first autumn

Marsh Warbler

Lesser Whitethroat

♂

♀

Reed Warbler

Common Whitethroat

Garden Warbler
Sylvia borin
14cm. This plump-bodied, secretive, very plain-looking warbler has a rounded head, a faint eye-ring and a short, thickish bill. A common summer visitor, it prefers broadleaved and mixed woodland with dense undergrowth, including large gardens. It is also found in tall scrub and young conifers. Its warbling song has the same mellow babbling quality as that of the Blackcap, but is usually longer, quieter, more flowing and more even.

Blackcap
Sylvia atricapilla
14cm. Only the male Blackcap deserves the name, as the cap of the female and the young is rust-coloured. This species is resident in the Mediterranean, and regularly winters in Britain in small but growing numbers, which often visit bird tables aggressively. Although secretive, it will sing from a relatively exposed perch. Its song is a rich warbling, usually louder, more varied and fluting than that of the Garden Warbler. It is a good mimic of birds, including the Garden Warbler.

Bonelli's Warbler
Phylloscopus bonelli
11.5cm. When in breeding plumage, the greyish upperparts, gleaming white underparts, yellow edges to the wing and tail feathers and bold yellow rump of this warbler are distinctive. Otherwise it is duller and very similar to other *Phylloscopus* warblers. It breeds chiefly in wooded mountain regions, preferring pine and cork oak forests. Its calls are a loud *hoo-eet* and *chee chee*; birds of the southeastern race have a loud, hard, short *tsiff* call. The song is a rather slow, single-note trill. This is a rare but regular autumn vagrant to Britain.

Wood Warbler
Phylloscopus sibilatrix
12.5cm. The largest of the European leaf warblers, it has yellowish-green upperparts, a sulphur yellow throat and breast and a pure white belly. Its bold yellow 'eyebrow' is also distinctive. This is a bird of mature woods, especially beech. It has two songs – a sad, piping *peeu*, repeated up to 20 times, and a repeated, explosive *stipp*, accelerating to a shivering trill, like a coin spinning on a table.

The Willow Warbler breeds throughout northern Eurasia in woods and scrub of all types.

Chiffchaff
Phylloscopus collybita
11cm. This common warbler looks extremely similar to the Willow Warbler. Its song is a distinctive repetition of notes in irregular order. The main call is a soft *hueeet*, less disyllabic than the call of the Willow Warbler. Although most northern breeders migrate to the Mediterranean and northern Africa for winter, small numbers winter in southwestern Britain and Ireland.

Willow Warbler
Phylloscopus trochilus
11cm. This abundant, widespread summer visitor is best distinguished from the Chiffchaff by its song. This is a flowing series of sweet, melancholy notes, descending in pitch. Its call is a soft, distinctly disyllabic *hooeet*, with the accent on the first syllable. Like other *Phylloscopus* warblers, it is very active, flitting about among the foliage to pick off insects and spiders.

Goldcrest
Regulus regulus
9cm. Together with the Firecrest, this is Europe's smallest bird. It searches for insects among foliage, especially conifers. Calls include a repeated *zee-zee-zee* and *tzit*. The song is a rapid series of thin notes, ending in a short flourish. The male has an orange centre to the yellow crown; young birds have no crown.
Ⓑ◔◬

Firecrest
Regulus ignicapillus
9cm. This bird differs from the Goldcrest in having a black eyestripe and white 'eyebrow'. This species is less tied to conifer. Its song is harsher, often ending abruptly. In Britain, it is a scarce breeder, passage migrant and winter visitor in the south.
Ⓑ◔◬

FLYCATCHERS

Flycatchers (Family Muscicapidae) are small birds that catch flying insects. All European species are summer visitors. They nest in holes in trees or walls. The sexes often differ.

Red-breasted Flycatcher
Ficedula parva
11.5cm. The male resembles a tiny Robin, but has a grey face and, like the female, a pale eye ring and a black tail with white sides, which it flicks and cocks frequently. Its call is a sharp *zeek* and its quiet song an accelerating series of notes descending in pitch. Young birds are scarce but regular autumn vagrants to western European coasts.
Ⓑ◔🍂

Pied Flycatcher
Ficedula hypoleuca
13cm. In autumn and winter the male resembles the drabber female, as do young birds. Its calls are a persistent, short *whit* and a sharp *tac* and the song a series of mellow *zee-vree* double notes sometimes ending in a short trill. A tree-hole nester, it readily takes to nest boxes. In Britain, it is found mainly in deciduous woodland in the west and north.
Ⓑ◔◬✿

Spotted Flycatcher
Muscicapa striata
14cm. This bird has a streaked breast and forehead. It likes open woodland and large gardens where it may be seen frequently flicking its wings and tail. Its calls are a hoarse, thin *tzee* and a quiet, sharp *tzee-tchuck*, and its song is a series of five or six faint thin, squeaky notes. It nests in creepers against a wall or tree but will use old birds' nests and nestboxes.
Ⓑ◔◬✿

PARROTBILLS

Only the Bearded Parrotbill (Family Paradoxornithidae) occurs in Europe; the remainder are mostly in China. This bird is related to the babblers, a mainly Asian family.

Bearded Parrotbill
Panurus biarmicus
11cm. Commonly known as the Bearded Tit, this is a tit-like little bird with a very long tail. It spends much time in dense reedbeds, where it breeds and winters. Flocks fly rather weakly but directly, on short whirring wings low over the reeds, uttering loud, pinging calls. The nest, low among the reeds, is a cup of reed leaves lined with reed flowers. A local bird, its decline in many areas, including Britain, is due to the drainage of wetlands.
Ⓑ🍂

Garden Warbler

Goldcrest

Blackcap

Firecrest

Bonelli's Warbler

Red-breasted Flycatcher

Chiffchaff

Pied Flycatcher

Wood Warbler

Bearded Parrotbill

Willow Warbler

Sptd Flycatcher

Goldcrest — ♀ — juvenile — ♂

Red-breasted Flycatcher — ♂ summer — ♀

Bearded Parrotbill — ♂ — ♀

Firecrest — ♀ — juvenile — ♂

Pied Flycatcher — ♂ — ♀/autumn ♂

Spotted Flycatcher — juvenile

LONG-TAILED TITS

Long-tailed Tits (Family Aegithalidae) are not closely related to the true tits. These insect-eaters have short bills and slender legs. Sexes are alike. The nests are intricate domes, lined with many feathers.

Long-tailed Tit
Aegithalos caudatus
14cm. Flocks of these gregarious little birds are very distinctive as they move acrobatically through trees and hedges and cross open spaces in single file with weak, laboured flight. It is usually the constantly uttered calls that are noticed before the birds themselves: a weak, high pitched *tzee tzee*, a repeated, trilling *tzirrup* and a low *trrup*. The northern race has an all-white head.
ⒷⒺ◐④❻

TITS

Tits (Family Paridae) are small, plump-bodied, round-headed, short-billed, woodland and garden birds. They are very agile and acrobatic, hanging upside down from the smallest twigs to feed on insects, seeds, nuts and berries. They are easily attracted to bird feeders. Outside the breeding season, mixed flocks of tits roam woodlands, often with other birds. Most species are tree-hole nesters, and readily use nestboxes. The sexes are alike.

Marsh Tit
Parus palustris
11.5cm. Despite its name, this bird is rarely found in marshes, but occurs in open deciduous woodland. The very similar Willow Tit (*P. montanus*) lives mainly in damper woodland, where the females excavate their own nest holes. The northern race of the Willow Tit is much greyer above and white below. Calls are distinctive: the Marsh Tit has a loud explosive *pitchew* and *chickadee-dee-dee*, while the Willow Tit utters a buzzing *eez eez eez* and a very high *zi zi zi*, often followed by *tchay*.
Ⓑ◐④❻

Great Tit
Parus major
14cm. This is a widespread and abundant species. The bold black band running from the throat and yellow breast to the lower belly is broader and blacker in the male. It is aggressive, driving off other birds at bird tables. It has a huge vocabulary of calls, but the most common are a loud, ringing *chink*, a *tsee*, often repeated, and a scolding, nasal *cha-cha-cha*. The commonest song is a loud *teacher teacher*.
ⒷⒺ◐④❷❻

Crested Tit
Parus cristatus
11.5cm. The only European tit with a crest. In Britain, it is restricted to mature pine forests in northeastern Scotland but, elsewhere in Europe, it is found among other conifers. It rarely moves far from its breeding area where it excavates its nest in the decaying stump of a tree. The crest is streaked black and white and there is a distinct black stripe over the eye. It has a trilling song and a soft, purring alarm call.
Ⓑ④

Coal Tit
Parus ater
11cm. This is the smallest European tit, with a big head, glossy black crown and a stumpy tail. It is readily distinguished by the white patch on its nape but also has two white wing bars. It is most commonly found in coniferous woodland, but also occurs in mature broadleaved woods. Its calls include a thin, Goldcrest-like *zee zee zee*, while its *pee-choo pee-choo pee-choo* song is more piping than that of the Great Tit.
ⒷⒺ◐④❻

Blue Tit
Parus caeruleus
11.5cm. This is the commonest of the tits throughout most of Europe, especially in broadleaved woodland. The narrow black line down the centre of the breast is not always visible. Calls include a clear *tsee tsee*, often ending with a *tsit* and a rapid scolding *churr*. The usual song is two long, thin notes followed by a rapid trill. Each pair produces a brood of about 11 young.
ⒷⒺ◐④❷❻

The intricate nest of the Long-tailed Tit is built of moss and spiders' webs, lined with up to 2000 feathers and camouflaged with lichens.

PENDULINE TITS

Penduline Tits (Family Remizidae) share many characteristics with the true tits, but are more acrobatic, often moving upside down along the undersides of twigs. Sexes are similar. Most build hanging, bag-like nests with a 'spout'.

Penduline Tit
Remiz pendulinus
11cm. This tiny bird frequently flicks its prominent tail as it hangs from stems in marshland and reedbed thickets. The distinctive call is a plaintive, soft, thin, drawn-out *ptseee* and the song a quiet, brief series of *zeeu-seewut* phrases. It is extending its range westwards and has recently started breeding in the Netherlands. It is a very rare vagrant to Britain.
Ⓔ

NUTHATCHES

Nuthatches (Family Sittidae) are mostly found in woodland, although two European species, the Western Rock Nuthatch and the Wallcreeper, live among rocks. These are very agile birds, with short legs and strong feet. They climb hanging from the higher foot and using the lower foot for support; they are the only birds able to climb down trees as well as up them. They are all hole or crevice nesters. The sexes differ slightly.

European Nuthatch
Sitta europaea
14cm. This bird picks insects out of tree crevices with its dagger-like bill. It also eats seeds and, in the autumn, takes large amounts of acorns, beechmast and hazel nuts, wedging them in the bark and hacking them open. Its chief calls are a loud, liquid, high-pitched *chwit chwit*, a loud, repeated, clear piping *twee* and a sharp repeated *tsit*. Its song is a loud, whistling trill. It does not excavate its own nest hole, but it may reduce existing holes by plastering up their entrances with mud. The Western Rock Nuthatch (*S. neumayer*) looks similar but lives among cliffs, rocks and old ruins in Greece and Yugoslavia. It sometimes winters in woodland.
ⒷⒺ◐❻

Wallcreeper
Tichodroma muraria
16.5cm. This striking bird is restricted to high mountains. In Europe, it breeds sparsely in the centre and south, at up to 2500m, though it feeds at up to 4800m. It winters at lower altitudes. A very elusive bird but, once seen, it is unforgettable. It frequently flicks its wings, even while climbing sheer rock faces, to expose the broad crimson forewing patches and white spots on the flight feathers. Its black chin becomes grey or white in winter. In flight it resembles a huge butterfly. It nests in a deep crevice among rocks. The Wallcreeper's call is a plaintive, slow, thin *pee pee pee*. It is a very rare vagrant to Britain.
❻

TREECREEPERS

Treecreepers (Family Certhiidae) are aptly named, for they creep in spirals up the trunks and branches of trees, supported by their stiff tail feathers. As they climb, they constantly search for insect food in cracks in the bark, which they winkle out with their long, downcurved bills. They nest behind loose bark, or among ivy. The sexes are alike.

Common Treecreeper
Certhia familiaris
12.5cm. This little bird is usually heard before it is seen, uttering high-pitched *tsee* or *tsit* calls. Its song is a series of weak, high-pitched *tsee* notes accelerating and ending in a flourish. It prefers coniferous woods on the Continent and, in central and southern Europe, is restricted to woods above 1000m. The very similar Short-toed Treecreeper (*C. brachydactyla*), which is a rare vagrant to Britain, lives from 1500m to sea level. It has two calls, a shrill piping *zeet* and a penetrating *chink*.
Ⓑ🌓◗⬆️👤

Long-tailed Tit

Blue Tit

Marsh Tit

Great Tit

Penduline Tit

European Nuthatch

Crested Tit

Wallcreeper

Coal Tit

Cmn Treecreeper

Northern race

juvenile

juvenile

Long-tailed Tit

Blue Tit

Marsh Tit

♂

juvenile

Penduline Tit

Great Tit

juvenile

Scandinavian race

European Nuthatch

Crested Tit

♂ summer

winter

Wallcreeper

Coal Tit

Common Treecreeper

ORIOLES

Only one of the 26 orioles (Family Oriolidae) occurs in Europe: the Golden Oriole. Like its relatives, its woven, cup-shaped nest is slung, hammock-fashion, between two twigs. The sexes differ.

Golden Oriole
Oriolus oriolus
24cm. Despite the male's striking plumage, this bird is difficult to see, spending

The Eurasian Jay plays a vital role in oakwood regeneration: it fails to find many of the acorns it buries in autumn, and these grow into trees.

most of its time in the dappled light beneath the foliage of broadleaved trees where it feeds on fruit and insects. It is a very scarce spring visitor to southern England, with a tiny breeding population. When flying from tree to tree, this bird has a deeply bounding flight, swooping upwards into cover. The male's flute-like *weela-weeo* whistling song is very distinctive and both sexes produce cat-like mewings and a variety of *churrs* and *chacks*.
Ⓑ🖝🔾🐾

SHRIKES

Like miniature birds of prey, shrikes (Family Laniidae) have strong, hooked bills. Swooping from a perch or hovering, they catch large insects, small lizards, birds and mammals. They store prey on thorns or barbed wire. Shrikes live in open, shrubby country, building cup-shaped nests in trees or thorny bushes. The songs are a mixture of harsh notes and musical warblings.

Red-backed Shrike
Lanius collurio
17cm. This is the only European shrike with a chestnut back and no white in the wings. Its call is a harsh *tchack*. This species has been declining in western Europe, and in Britain is now virtually extinct as a breeding bird. This is due to the changing climate affecting its diet, and also to habitat loss and egg collecting. It winters in Africa.
Ⓑ🖝🐾

Lesser Grey Shrike
Lanius minor
20cm. This species is smaller than the Great Grey Shrike, with a shorter tail. The black facial mask of adult birds also extends to the forehead and there is no white 'eyebrow'. Its flight is much less undulating than that of the Great Grey Shrike, and it perches more upright. Its usual call is a harsh *check*. It winters in Africa and is a scarce passage migrant to the east coast of Britain.
🖝🐾

Great Grey Shrike
Lanius excubitor
24cm. This is the largest European shrike. It is a solitary bird, fond of exposed perches, and occupies a large territory even in winter. Scandinavian breeders fly south in winter and small numbers turn up regularly in Britain. Like other shrikes, it often swings its tail from side to side. Its calls are a *shek shek*, sometimes becoming a rattle, and a grating *schaeeg*.
Ⓑ🖝🐾

Woodchat Shrike
Lanius senator
17cm. This big-headed bird is the commonest shrike in the western Mediterranean. It winters in Africa and is a rare vagrant to Britain. The white patches on its shoulders form two distinct ovals and the white rump is apparent in flight. Calls include harsh chattering and *chip* notes. The races found on the islands of the western Mediterranean lack white wing-bars. It mimics other birds' phrases.
🖝🐾

Masked Shrike
Lanius nubicus
17cm. This small shrike breeds in south-eastern Europe, in orchards and other semi-open country. It has a longer tail than other small shrikes, peach coloured flanks and large, oval white wing patches, more prominent on the male. Females have the upperparts grey where the male's are black. Young birds are greyer than those of other small shrikes. The song is a series of subdued, scratchy notes and the call a plaintive, repeated *keer*.
🖝🔾🐾

CROWS

Crows (Family Corvidae) are a widespread and successful group. They have powerful legs, feet and bills. Most species have wide diets. They are gregarious, and usually have harsh calls. The sexes are alike. The nest is often a cup of twigs in a tree, but some nest in holes or on cliffs.

Eurasian Jay
Garrulus glandarius
34cm. This beautiful woodland crow is more often heard than seen, as it utters its harsh *skaak* alarm call. Its flight is fast, low and undulating into cover when disturbed, but more leisurely and laboured when flying high over the treetops. When seen in flight from above, the barred blue and white patches at the front of the wings and the white rump contrasting with a black tail are distinctive. It favours broadleaved woodland and especially oakwoods. Its chief food is acorns, which it collects and buries in autumn.
Ⓑ🔾🍂🐾

Siberian Jay
Perisoreus infaustus
31cm. This subtly-plumaged bird is adapted to life in the cold northern forests. Slightly smaller than the Eurasian Jay, it inhabits forests of birches and conifers, where it feeds on the seeds in the cones. Shy in summer, it can be quite tame when searching for food around houses in winter. The dusky brown crown and wings and rust-red wing patches, underwing feathers, rump and outer tail feathers are distinctive. Its calls include a harsh *chair*, a brisk *kook-kook* and *whisk-eee*.
🍂🐾

Azure-winged Magpie
Cyanopica cyana
34cm. This shy, handsome bird has striking blue wings and a long blue tail. It is gregarious, roosting and feeding together and nesting in small, loose colonies in which each bird builds its

---

THE SHRIKE'S LARDER

Many shrikes, such as this Great Grey Shrike, store their prey in a 'larder' on thorns or barbed wire.

untidy, cup-shaped nest in a separate tree or shrub. It is a noisy bird, making cat-like cries and harsher, crow-like calls. It feeds on seeds, berries and insects, and avoids flying in the open. It has a rather odd distribution: in Europe it is restricted to southern Spain and Portugal and elsewhere is found only in eastern Asia, 5000km or more away.

Black-billed Magpie
Pica pica
46cm. This well known, common resident has increased in numbers in Britain and many other parts of Europe, with its dramatic expansion into suburban and urban areas. Although frequently accused of decimating songbird populations, it eats relatively few young birds or eggs. Its usual call is a harsh cackling *chak-chak*, often repeated. It builds its distinctive, large, untidy, domed, mud-lined nest of sticks in a tree or shrub, often a hawthorn. The female lays one clutch of 5–7 eggs. It has a characteristic flight, with a series of rapid, fluttering wingbeats alternated with short glides.

Golden Oriole | Masked Shrike

Red-backed Shrike | Eurasian Jay

Lesser Grey Shrike | Siberian Jay

Great Grey Shrike | Azure-winged Magpie

Woodchat Shrike | Bk-billed Magpie

Golden Oriole

Masked Shrike

Red-backed Shrike

juvenile

Lesser Grey Shrike

Eurasian Jay

Great Grey Shrike

juvenile

Siberian Jay

Azure-winged Magpie

Woodchat Shrike

Black-billed Magpie

257

Nutcracker
Nucifraga caryocatactes
32cm. This boldly spotted crow lives in conifer forests, in the lowlands of Scandinavia and Russia and in the mountains of central and eastern Europe. It hides pine seeds and nuts, finding them later under the snow. In its undulating flight, the wings appear blackish and very broad. The white undertail is conspicuous. Its calls are a harsh *kror* and a loud, rasping *krair*, often repeated. In years when the crop of pine cones fail, Nutcrackers wander far and wide reaching western Europe, including Britain.

Alpine Chough
Pyrrhocorax graculus
38cm. This gregarious bird is a high mountain dweller, found up to the snowline, though it descends in winter. At close range, it can be readily distinguished from the Red-billed Chough by its much shorter, straighter yellow bill (young Red-billed Choughs have orange bills which are longer and more curved). Its behaviour and aerobatic flight are similar, but its wings are narrower, with more swept-back primary feathers at their tips when gliding. Its calls are a shrill explosive *tchiupp*, a rippling *chirrish* and harsh crow-like notes.

Red-billed Chough
Pyrrhocorax pyrrhocorax
40cm. This gregarious crow breeds in mountains and along steep rocky coasts, but is generally declining in numbers, with less than 300 breeding pairs in Britain. It is threatened mainly by changes in agriculture. It is a superb flier, diving headlong at top speed with wings folded, then suddenly pulling out of the dive, buoyed up on its broad wings. Its call is a ringing *chow* – probably the original pronunciation of its name, now pronounced 'chuff'.

Western Jackdaw
Corvus monedula
33cm. This small crow has a distinctive grey nape and white eye and a short, stubby bill. Very gregarious, it breeds in holes on cliffs, in tree holes and in ruins, churches and chimneys. It regularly performs aerobatic displays around its breeding sites. It is often seen with Rooks feeding on farmland, but is easily distinguishable by its smaller size and quicker wingbeats. Its main calls are a high-pitched *chak*, often repeated, and a ringing *kya*.

Rook
Corvus frugilegus
46cm. This very gregarious bird feeds and roosts in flocks. It also nests colonially, siting its rookeries in clumps of tall trees. Adult birds can be distinguished from Carrion Crows by their bare whitish faces, peaked crowns, more slender, pointed greyish bills and baggy thigh feathers. Young birds are duller and have fully feathered faces, but they still differ from Carrion Crows in having slimmer bills. Most frequent calls are a flat, nasal *kaaa* or *kaw*.

Common Starlings often nest in tree-holes, especially old woodpecker holes, but are adaptable, also breeding in holes in cliffs and walls.

Carrion Crow/Hooded Crow
Corvus corone
47cm. These birds are generally seen singly or in pairs, and they do not nest colonially. In winter, though, they may form large flocks. They are the most widespread of the crows, ranging from remote islands and moorland to city parks. The all-black race, the Carrion Crow, is found throughout western Europe, including much of Britain. Two races of the Hooded Crow, with a grey body, live in northwest Scotland, Ireland, the Isle of Man and Scandinavia, and in eastern and southeastern Europe. They will pair with Carrion Crows. The usual call is a hoarse *kraar*, harsher than the cawing of the Rook.

Common Raven
Corvus corax
64cm. This is the biggest crow – indeed, it is the largest of all perching birds. It has a massive, powerful bill, shaggy throat feathers, long wings and a long, wedge-shaped tail. It is a superb flier, fond of soaring high in the air and performing aerobatics. A bird of wild mountains, woodlands, moorlands and rocky coasts, it is a solitary breeder, and lays its eggs in February or even earlier. It eats grain and carrion but will kill small birds and rabbits. Chief calls are a deep, resonant *pruk pruk* and a high, metallic *tok*.

STARLINGS

Starlings (Family Sturnidae) are small to medium sized birds with strong bills and legs. Found throughout the Old World, only three species occur in Europe. Most starlings are highly gregarious. They walk and run rather than hop on the ground, and most are omnivorous, eating mainly fruit and insects. They have unmelodious songs, including wheezing and whistling notes, and mimic other birds. The sexes are generally alike.

Common Starling
Sturnus vulgaris
21cm. Jaunty, quarrelsome and noisy, this bird is a familiar visitor to fields and gardens. Like the other starlings, it nests in holes. Outside the breeding season, it is very gregarious, with huge flocks assembling at communal roosts, in woods, reedbeds and on buildings in city centres. The young are greyish-buff with a white chin. Its main call is a harsh, descending *tcheer* and the song is a long, rambling medley of descending whistles, rattles, chuckles and clicks, often incorporating mimicry of other birds and even imitations of barking dogs and ringing telephones. Winter birds have more spots. Many birds from the Continent winter in Britain.

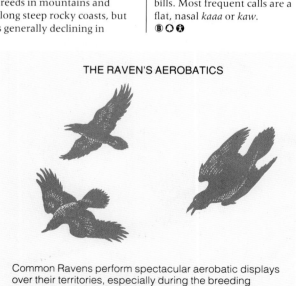

THE RAVEN'S AEROBATICS

Common Ravens perform spectacular aerobatic displays over their territories, especially during the breeding season, soaring, diving and rolling over onto their backs.

Spotless Starling

Sturnus unicolor

21cm. This starling is resident in southwestern Europe, where the Common Starling is only a winter visitor. In summer it is distinguished by its less glossy black plumage which lacks spots, while in winter it has just a few, dull, small spots. It nests in holes in trees, rocks and buildings. Young birds are darker than Common Starlings. The calls are shriller than those of the Common Starling, including a whistling *seee-oooo*.

Rose-coloured Starling

Sturnus roseus

21cm. Adult birds of this species are unmistakable with their bold plumage and shaggy crests. Young birds are similar to those of Common and Spotless Starlings, but are paler. The bill is shorter and blunter than that of its relatives. It normally breeds no further west than southwest USSR, and winters in India. Occasionally, it irrupts westward, when it may breed in southeast Europe for a year or two. It is a rare visitor to northwest Europe, mostly in summer.

Nutcracker

Carrion Crow

Alpine Chough

Common Raven

Red-billed Chough

Common Starling

Western Jackdaw

Spotless Starling

Rook

Rose-clrd Starling

Nutcracker

Hooded Crow

Carrion Crow

Alpine Chough

Common Raven

Red-billed Chough

summer
winter
juvenile
Common Starling

Western Jackdaw

♂ summer
♀ winter
Spotless Starling

juvenile
Rook

summer
juvenile
Rose-coloured Starling

259

SPARROWS, ROCK SPARROWS AND SNOW FINCHES

Sparrows and their relatives (Family Passeridae) are small, mainly streaked, brown birds with thick bills and unforked tails. They are gregarious and build untidy domed nests of grass, often in holes in buildings, shrubs, trees or among rocks. They are chiefly seed eaters. The sexes usually differ.

House Sparrow
Passer domesticus
14.5cm. Among the most familiar of all birds, this sparrow is found wherever there are people, from remote farms to city centres. The male is distinguished by his grey crown and large black bib. Females and young are drabber brown and buff, streaked above, with a pale 'eyebrow', faint wingbar and stout bill. Males of the Italian Sparrow (race *italiae*), found in Italy, Corsica and Greece, have an all-chestnut crown and whiter cheeks. Its calls include a wide variety of *cheeps* and *chirrups*.

Spanish Sparrow
Passer hispaniolensis
14.5cm. This scarce sparrow is far less associated with human habitation than the House Sparrow, occurring in scrubland, hedgerows and woodland edges. The females are similar to female House Sparrows, but have pale streaks on breast and flanks. Males have the back heavily streaked with black, white cheeks, a large black bib extending as streaks onto the flanks, and an all-chestnut crown. Its calls are similar to those of the House Sparrow, but are deeper.

Tree Sparrow
Passer montanus
14cm. A smaller, neater bird than the other sparrows, this species prefers farmland and open woodland to built-up areas, although it does occur around habitations in southern and eastern Europe. The sexes look alike. Both have an all-chestnut crown, a white half-collar, a small, neat black bib and a neat black oval on the white cheeks. Its distinctive calls are a high-pitched *chup chup* flight call and a hard *tek tek*.

Streaked Rock Sparrow
Petronia petronia
14cm. This bird of rocky mountainsides, arid country, fields and villages looks rather like a female House Sparrow, but is paler, with a distinctly striped head, a large pale bill and pale spots near the tip of the tail, most visible in flight. The small yellow spot on the chin is noticeable only when the bird is seen at close range with its breast feathers puffed out. Its calls include various sparrow-like chirrups and a distinctive, squeaky *pey-ee*.

White-winged Snowfinch
Montifringilla nivalis
18cm. This high-mountain specialist breeds in southern Europe at up to 3700m or more. It is often seen near houses and, in winter, flocks move down the mountains. It perches upright and frequently jerks its tail. In flight, it shows its black-tipped, white wings and white tail with a black centre. Its chief calls are a hoarse, metallic *tsweek* and a purring *chrrt* of alarm. The song is a high-pitched, jerky repetition of *sitti-cher* notes.

FINCHES

Finches (Family Fringillidae) are small birds, often with slightly forked tails. They have short, heavy bills, with conical grooves inside for shelling seeds. Finches are gregarious in winter, roaming the countryside in large mixed flocks of several species. Most species have attractive songs. Finches build cup-shaped nests of grass, moss and other vegetation in trees and bushes. The sexes usually differ.

European Serin
Serinus serinus
11.5cm. This tiny, dumpy, streaked, yellow finch has a stout bill and a distinctive yellow rump in all plumages. The flight call is a fast, trilling *tui-tui-tui* and the song, delivered from a tree-top, telegraph wire or in a display flight, is a loud, musical tinkling. A common resident in the Mediterranean region, it is a summer visitor further north, where its range has been spreading. A few pairs breed in southern England.

House Sparrow

European Serin

Spanish Sparrow

Common Chaffinch

Tree Sparrow

Brambling

Streaked Rock Sparrow

Citril Finch

Snow Finch

Greenfinch

Italian Sparrow

House Sparrow
♂

♀

Spanish Sparrow
♀

♂

Tree Sparrow

Streaked Rock Sparrow

summer

winter

White-winged Snow Finch

A male White-winged Snowfinch feeds its offspring. Both parents care for the young.

broom and heather. The grey crown and nape are distinctive, the dark wings have a bold double yellow wingbar and the rump is variably yellowish-green. Young birds are browner. Its calls include a plaintive *tsi-i* and a metallic *chwick*. The song, often given in a circling display flight, is a rapid mixture of musical twitters and creaking notes.
🐦🕊

Common Chaffinch
Fringilla coelebs
15cm. This is the most common finch and one of the most abundant and widespread of European birds. The bold white double wingbar, white outer tail feathers and greenish rump are particularly noticeable as the birds fly up from the ground. In winter, males and females often roam the countryside in separate flocks. Its main calls are a loud, repeated *pink*, an insistent *whit* and a quiet *choop* in flight. The cheerful song is a vigorous series of about a dozen notes, speeding up and ending in a flourish. The nest, in low vegetation, is a neatly woven cup of grass, covered with lichens and lined with hair and feathers. The female lays 4–5 eggs.
Ⓑ🐚🍂🕊🌼🐜🐛

Brambling
Fringilla montifringilla
14.5cm. This northern relative of the Common Chaffinch is best distinguished by its white rump, orange double wingbars and black tail. It winters in areas south of its breeding range, including Britain, in varying numbers – most occur in years when beechmast, its chief food, is abundant. A few pairs breed in northern Britain. Its calls are a metallic *tsweek* and a hard *tchik*, repeated as a flight call. Its song is a monotonous series of *dzeee* notes, interspersed with a few very weak *chips*.
Ⓑ🐚🍂🕊🌼🐜🐛

Citril Finch
Serinus citrinella
12cm. This little yellowish-green finch lives in areas of scattered conifers on mountainsides, above 1500m in summer but lower in winter. On Corsica and Sardinia, it breeds among

Western Greenfinch
Carduelis chloris
14.5cm. This heavily built finch has a stout whitish bill, which enables it to feed on larger seeds. It is a familiar garden bird, often seen driving away other small birds from bird feeders. Its flight is deeply undulating, and the flight call a series of musical *chup* notes, often run together into a rolling trill. The song, delivered from a prominent perch or in a circular butterfly-like display flight, is a monotonous, wheezy, nasal *dzjeeer*, often mixed with a powerful trilling.
Ⓑ🐚🍂🕊🐚🐜🐛

European Serin
♂ ♀

♂ summer ♀

♂ winter

♂ winter

Brambling

Common Chaffinch
♀ ♂ ♂

Citril Finch
♀ ♂

Western Greenfinch
♀ ♂

European Goldfinch
Carduelis carduelis
12cm. The streaked grey-brown young lack the unmistakable face pattern of this exotic-looking finch but still have the bold yellow wingbars. The white rump is noticeable in the bird's dancing flight. Often seen in flocks and family parties, this finch feeds on thistles, teasels and other composite weeds, hanging and tweezering out the seeds with its pointed bill. The nest is a neat cup of grass and wool, lined with hair or down, often at the end of a tree branch. The eggs are bluish with dark markings. Its chief calls are a high-pitched, liquid *switt-witt-witt-witt* in flight and a soft *ah-i* of anxiety. The song is a canary-like, liquid twittering based on the call notes.
Ⓑ🌰🌀🍂🐾🕸

Eurasian Siskin
Carduelis spinus
12cm. This little finch is found chiefly in damp woods, where it nests high in the outer branches of conifers. It feeds in flocks on birch and alder seeds in winter and also visits gardens, where it is attracted to nuts in red net bags, feeding with tit-like agility. It forms mixed flocks with Common Redpolls in winter. Its flight is fast and undulating. Males have a black cap and bib. Its bold yellow rump and wingbars are distinctive, and the deeply forked black tail has yellow sides. Its calls are a shrill, wheezy *tsu-weet* and a high, squeaky *tsy-zi*. The song is a long, rapid, nasal twitter, given in a circling song flight.
Ⓑ🌰🌀🍂🐾

Common Linnet
Carduelis cannabina
13.5cm. This is a common breeding bird of open country with bushes. It often nests in loose colonies, usually raising two broods. In winter, it roams in huge flocks over farmland, waste ground and coastal marshes. Breeding males have red on the forehead and breast and a chestnut back. The edges of the forked tail and of the wing feathers are white. Its calls are a rapid twittering during the strongly undulating flight, and a nasal *tsoeet*. The song, delivered from a perch, is a pleasant, varied twitter, interspersed with pure and nasal notes.
Ⓑ🌰🍂😊🌾

Twite
Carduelis flavirostris
13.5cm. This bird replaces the Common Linnet as a breeder in northern uplands. In winter, it roams in flocks, often mixed with Common Linnets, mainly in coastal areas. Its distinctive features are a warm buff throat and a greyish-yellow bill which is yellow in winter adults and young. It is always a more heavily streaked bird than the Common Linnet. The summer male's pink rump is difficult to see. Its voice is similar to the Common Linnet's, but harder and more nasal, its song a dry, hoarse, twanging twitter.
Ⓑ🌀🌰😊🍂🐾😖

Common Redpoll
Carduelis flammea
13.5cm. This small streaked finch feeds in the treetops, hanging acrobatically, tit-like, at the very tips of branches to

THE CROSSBILL'S FEEDING ADAPTATIONS

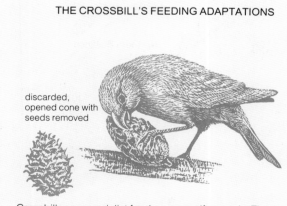

discarded, opened cone with seeds removed

Crossbills are specialist feeders on conifer seeds. They cut off a cone with the powerful bill and prise apart the scales with the crossed mandibles to expose the seeds.

A male Northern Bullfinch feeds on dock seeds. Bullfinches prefer to feed directly from their food plants rather than on the ground.

extract seeds from birch, alder and other trees. Its call is a metallic, rattling *chichichichi*, given in its very bounding flight, and a song containing a mixture of the flight call with dry, buzzing, nasal trills. The tiny cup nest, usually in a small tree, is often covered with lichens. The Arctic Redpoll (*C. hornemanni*), which replaces the Common Redpoll in the far north, is similar with a white rump, but much paler. It is a vagrant to Britain.
Ⓑ🌰🌀🍂🐾

Common Crossbill
Loxia curvirostra
16.5cm. This finch feeds mainly on spruce seeds. Gregarious and tame, it is a large-headed, stoutly built bird with a short forked tail. Failure of the seed crop every few years leads to large irruptions southwards and westwards. The Scottish Crossbill (*L. scotica*), with a thicker bill adapted for feeding on pine seeds, is Britain's only endemic bird species and is restricted to the ancient Caledonian pine forest of the Scottish Highlands. The Parrot Crossbill (*L. pytyopsittacus*), with a thicker bill still, also feeds on pine seeds. Breeding in Scandinavia and Russia, it occasionally irrupts southwards and westwards together with Common Crossbills.
Ⓑ🍂

Common Rosefinch
Carpodacus erythrinus
14.5cm. Formerly known as the Scarlet Grosbeak or Scarlet Rosefinch, this dumpy finch is a summer visitor to eastern Europe and Asia. It has recently colonized Scandinavia as a breeder and

has bred in Britain, though it is more usually a rare vagrant. It winters in India and Southeast Asia. In his bright spring plumage, the male is easily recognized, but female and first year birds are usually rather nondescript in colour and are best identified by their pale, heavy, conical bills, beady black eyes and faint double wingbars. The call is a quiet, pure *weet* and the song is a far-carrying, whistling *switti-sweetoo*. It feeds on seeds.
🌰🌀🍂😊🐾

Pine Grosbeak
Pinicola enucleator
20cm. This very large, heavy finch, the size of a starling, has a long forked black tail, bold double white wingbars on its black wings and a stout, slightly hooked bill. It breeds throughout the coniferous forests of northern Scandinavia and Siberia. Mainly resident, some birds migrate south in winter and occasionally irrupt westwards. It is a rare vagrant to Britain. Small flocks are tame and easily approached when gorging themselves on rowan and other berries. Its chief call is a high, clear, piping *tee-tee-tu* and its song is a rapid mixture of loud, whistling and twanging notes.
🌀🍂

Northern Bullfinch
Pyrrhula pyrrhula
15cm. This plump, bull-necked finch is usually seen singly or in pairs slipping secretively through dense cover. The stubby black bill, broad white wingbar and bold square white rump, which contrasts with the black tails, are distinctive. In spring, these birds eat many buds – at a rate of up to 30 a minute

– and can be a pest in fruit orchards. The call is a soft, piping *deu* and the rarely heard song is a brief, quiet, creaky warbling. Two broods of 4–6 young are raised in a root-lined twig cup. Young birds lack the black crown.

Ⓑ🔽Ⓞ🔆🔆

Hawfinch
Coccothraustes coccothraustes
18cm. This stout finch has a massive grey bill worked by powerful muscles, capable of cracking cherry stones. In flight, its large head, thick neck, stocky body, short, white-tipped tail and broad white wingbars are distinctive. The female is duller, with a grey wing panel. Young birds are yellow-brown and streaked, but have the white wingbars. This finch is notoriously wary and elusive, often perching immobile for long periods among the foliage high in mature hornbeam and other deciduous trees. It feeds mainly on the seeds of hornbeam, elm and beech. Its calls include a very hard, explosive *ptik* and a thin *tzeeip* and it has a rarely heard, Bullfinch-like song.

Ⓑ Ⓞ 🔆

European Goldfinch   Common Crossbill

Eurasian Siskin

Common Rosefinch

Common Linnet   Pine Grosbeak

Twite   Northern Bullfinch

Common Redpoll   Hawfinch

juvenile

European Goldfinch

♀ Common Crossbill

♂

♂ Eurasian Siskin ♀

♀ Common Rosefinch

♂ spring

♂ Common Linnet ♀

♀ Pine Grosbeak

♂ winter

♂

Twite

♂ summer

Northern Bullfinch

♀

♂

juvenile

♂ summer

Common Redpoll

♀

Hawfinch

Although adult Yellowhammers feed mainly on seeds, they also eat some fruits and also insects, which they give to their young.

BUNTINGS

Buntings (Family Emberizidae) are small finch-like birds, mostly found in open country. They have stout bills with a hump in the roof of the mouth for crushing seeds. Their tails are often slightly forked and are usually longer than those of finches. Many species rear their young on insects and other invertebrates. Most buntings have streaked brown plumage. The sexes usually differ in appearance, breeding males having distinctive head markings that are useful in identification. Many species also have musical songs. Most buntings are gregarious in the winter months.

Lapland Bunting
Calcarius lapponicus
15cm. This summer visitor to Scandinavia and Russia migrates south to the southern USSR in winter, and in smaller numbers to North Sea coasts. Winter males, females and young differ from female Reed Buntings in their pale crown stripe, yellower bill, chestnut wings and (in the male) chestnut nape. A ground dweller, it will also perch on boulders. Its calls include a short *chu* and a hard, dry *prrt*. The song, delivered in a parachuting display flight, is a short, jingling lark-like warble. The Lapland Bunting sometimes breeds in Scotland in small numbers.

Snow Bunting
Plectrophenax nivalis
16.5cm. This bunting breeds farther north than any other landbird, nesting in northern Greenland. It breeds on high mountains, hiding its nest deep in a rock crevice or beneath a boulder. Up to 30 pairs breed on the highest mountains of the Scottish Highlands. It winters on the coasts of northern and central Europe, where large flocks gather along seashores to feed on seeds. Feeding flocks move fast, with individual birds leap-frogging over the flock in brief flights, displaying large white wing and tail patches, and uttering frequent rippling calls. The Snow Buntings plumages are a mixture of brown, black and white.

Yellowhammer
Emberiza citrinella
16.5cm. This is a common bird of fields and hedgerows, heaths, downs, woodland edges and conifer plantations, typically seen perched atop a branch or telegraph wire, uttering its familiar song. This is often described as 'little-bit-of-bread-and-no-cheese'. The final 'cheese' may be higher or lower pitched or may be omitted. This is a large, rather slim bunting, with a long, notched tail. The best identification feature in all plumages is the rust-coloured rump. In winter, this species forms flocks, often mixed with other buntings, finches and sparrows, to feed on stubble fields. The nest, usually constructed in or under a bush, is a grass cup, often lined with hair.

Cirl Bunting
Emberiza cirlus
16.5cm. This is primarily a bird of warm sheltered valleys with bushes, old hedgerows and dry Mediterranean hillsides. In Britain it is on the extreme northern edge of its range. Never common, it was once much more widespread. Today, a declining population of about 100 pairs breeds only in south Devon. The male has a bold black and yellow head and a greenish breast band. The female is buff rather than yellow; both sexes have an olive rump. The chief call is a thin *sip* and the song a monotonous, rattling repetition of a single note.

Rock Bunting
Emberiza cia
16cm. This is a bird mainly of rocky mountainsides, with scattered shrubs or trees. In winter it descends to lower levels. It is a rare vagrant to northern Europe, including Britain. Distinctive features are the buffish-chestnut underparts, bold head pattern, unstreaked chestnut rump and pale grey throat. It often flicks its tail open to reveal white edges. Its calls are a very high, whistling *seeea* and a thin, weak *zeet*, and the song is a brief, weak, squeaky *zi-zi-zi-zirr*, the last note often missing.

Ortolan Bunting
Emberiza hortulana
16.5cm. This bird breeds in open, cultivated lowlands in the north and on open hillsides in the south. The male has a grey-green head with pale yellow moustache and throat. Winter males and females are duller but all birds have a pinkish bill and pale eye-ring. Most migrate to winter in southern Arabia and Africa. It is a regular autumn visitor in small numbers to northwestern Europe, including Britain. The main call is a soft *tsee-ip* and the song a series of six to eight rich, clear *tsee* or *tseu* notes, often in a song flight.

Little Bunting
Emberiza pusilla
13.5cm. This bunting has a pointed bill, short tail and distinctive head pattern, with a dark crown stripe and chestnut cheeks bordered with black, and pale pink legs. The main call is a short, thin *tick* and the song a rich jingle. The Rustic Bunting (*E. rustica*) breeds in Finland and Russia. It has a distinct crest, a whitish 'eyebrow' and bolder head pattern, black and white in the breeding male. Both species winter in China and are rare vagrants to western Europe.

Reed Bunting
Emberiza schoeniclus
15cm. In summer, the male has a distinctive white 'moustache' and collar on his jet black hood. In winter, his head becomes duller and he resembles the female. This bunting frequently flicks its wings and its long, deeply notched tail, showing off its white outer feathers. A common breeder in marshlands and reedbeds it has spread to drier habitats, including farmland, conifer plantations and gardens. Its calls are a loud *tseek*, a plaintive *tseu* and a metallic *chink*. Its song is a monotonous and jerky *tseek-tseek-tseek-tississisk*.

THE DISPLAY FLIGHT OF THE CORN BUNTING

The male Corn Bunting performs a short upward display flight then hovers with his legs dangling near the female.

Black-headed Bunting
Emberiza melanocephala
16.5cm. The underparts of both sexes of this bunting are unstreaked, the undertail coverts are yellow, and there is no white in the tail. It breeds on the coasts of Italy and the Balkans, on hillsides and grassland with scattered trees and shrubs. It winters in India. It is a rare visitor to western Europe, including Britain. The main call is a short, loud *zitt*. The attractive song has two to five buzzing notes followed by a short, quick, subdued warbling.

Corn Bunting
Miliaria calandra
18cm. This portly, almost neckless bunting likes open grassland and arable farmland with bushes. Both sexes have a large round head and a big, stubby bill. There is no white in wings or tail and the streaks on the breast form a dark patch. It often perches on posts and wires, throwing back its head and uttering its song, like the jangling of a bunch of little keys. Its calls are a harsh, sharp *quit* and *tsee*. Both males and females mate with several partners.

Lapland Bunting Ortolan Bunting

Snow Bunting

Little Bunting

Yellowhammer Reed Bunting

Cirl Bunting Black-headed Bunting

Rock Bunting Corn Bunting

Lapland Bunting
Ortolan Bunting
Snow Bunting
Little Bunting
Yellowhammer
Reed Bunting
Cirl Bunting
Black-headed Bunting
Rock Bunting
Corn Bunting

REPTILES AND AMPHIBIANS

The reptiles and amphibians are backboned animals belonging to the Classes Reptilia and Amphibia respectively. Both groups are cold-blooded, meaning that their body temperatures fluctuate with the surrounding air or water temperature instead of remaining more or less constant as in birds and mammals. They cannot stay active in very low temperatures, so, with the exception of a few Mediterranean species, European reptiles and amphibians go into hibernation during the colder months. In the most northerly areas this can mean sleeping for as much as seven or eight months of the year.

LEFT: A Sand Lizard flattens its abdomen and basks in the morning sunshine. Basking is the normal way of raising the temperature of the body to its working level.

Reptiles

The reptiles arose from some kind of amphibian about 300 million years ago. They are clothed with scales and, although several species live in water, they are generally much better able to cope with dry conditions than the amphibians. Of the four orders of reptiles alive today, only the Chelonia (tortoises and turtles) and the Squamata (snakes and lizards) occur in Europe. The Order Rynchocephalia is represented by a single living species, now confined to islands off New Zealand. The crocodilians (Order Crocodilia) are mostly confined to the tropics. The snakes and lizards account for over 5500 of the 6000 or so reptile species alive today.

The European chelonians belong to four families – two of marine turtles, one of land tortoises and one of terrapins. The Squamata contains the Sauria (lizards), Amphisbaenia (worm lizards) and Ophidia (snakes), which, despite superficial differences, are closely related with many intermediate forms.

Most European reptiles occur in the warmer, Mediterranean regions. However, despite their dependence on warmth, reptiles have managed to colonize all but the coldest regions of Europe, and the Adder is even found within the Arctic Circle. Reptiles maintain their temperature by basking in the sun to increase it and retreating into shade or burrows to cool down.

Most reptile species lay their eggs in cavities in the soil or in crevices in rocks, where they are normally incubated by the sun's rays or by the heat that is generated by rotting vegetation. A few species retain the eggs within the body cavity. They incubate the eggs by basking in the sun, and they either lay the eggs shortly before they hatch, or in some cases give birth to living young. This form of development is known as ovoviviparity. The marine turtles and the freshwater terrapins return to land to lay their eggs.

The Grass Snake often feigns death when alarmed, remaining motionless with its mouth open and thereby avoiding the attentions of various predators.

Most reptiles eat live animal prey, including insects, molluscs and small vertebrates. Snakes often feed on warm-blooded prey, including mice and nestling birds, and swallow it whole. Tortoises feed mainly on plant matter, including fruit, shoots and leaves, but will also eat carrion.

In the cooler regions all reptiles hibernate in winter, sometimes undertaking local migrations to favoured sites. In the warmer southern regions of Europe some reptiles become dormant or aestivate during the hottest months of the year.

Unlike mammals and birds, reptiles leave few signs. Their footprints are difficult to see, and their nests are simple excavations. However, all snakes and lizards regularly slough their skins. Reptile scales are distinctive and it is usually possible to identify the species from the cast skin.

Amphibians

The amphibians evolved from some kind of fish over 350 million years ago, and most of today's amphibians still return to the water to breed. There are three living orders within the Class Amphibia – Anura (tail-less frogs and toads), Caudata (newts and salamanders) and Apoda (limb-less, worm-like amphibians confined to the tropics). Like the reptiles, the amphibians favour warm climates. Most of the 4400 or so known species live in the tropics. Less than 50 are found in Europe. Amphibians are most abundant in wetland habitats, but some toads have managed to invade relatively dry places, including deserts, where they depend on seasonal rains for breeding and emerge only in the cool of the night.

Most amphibians are rather soft-skinned and they need to keep their skin moist. Although most species have lungs, the skin plays an important role in respiration. It is well supplied with small blood vessels, and oxygen can diffuse into the bloodstream from the air as long as the skin remains damp. A good deal of respiration also takes place through the lining of the mouth.

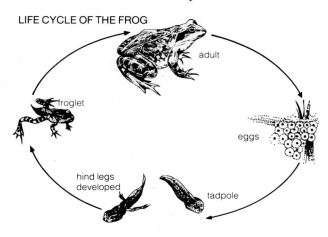

LIFE CYCLE OF THE FROG

adult

eggs

tadpole

hind legs developed

froglet

In the frog's life cycle the transition from egg to froglet takes about three months at normal temperatures, but is slowed down by cold. The froglet takes a further two or three years to mature.

All amphibians feed on living prey, although some tadpoles eat aquatic vegetation. Several toads and salamanders have evolved poison glands and the brilliant colours of some species act as warnings to predators.

There is considerable variation in the breeding habits of the European amphibians. Newts have an elaborate courtship in which the males dance in front of the females and display their crests. The male drops a packet of sperm, and if the female is stimulated by his dancing she picks it up in her genital region. The eggs are usually laid singly on water plants. Most salamanders perform their courtship on land. The males of most frogs and toads make calls to attract the females to breeding sites. The males embrace the females and fertilize the eggs as the females lay them. Most frogs and toads lay their eggs or spawn in jelly-coated clumps or strings in the water.

Amphibian eggs hatch into gill-breathing larvae called tadpoles. These are legless and fish-like at first, but gradually develop legs and metamorphose into miniature adults. There are, however, many variations on this basic life cycle. Some salamanders, for example, retain their eggs in their bodies and give birth to a few well-developed larvae or even to fully metamorphosed young. A few salamanders, such as the cave-dwelling Olm from the Adriatic region, never leave the water and retain their larval form throughout their lives, although they become sexually mature and able to breed.

Common Frogs often gather in their hundreds to mate and spawn in small ponds. The males are very noisy at this time.

Lizards

More than 3000 species of lizards (Sub-order Sauria) are known, of which over 50 occur in Europe. They all have scaly skins and relatively long, slender bodies and long, slender tails. Most have movable eyelids and four limbs; however, some species are legless. Although most species lay eggs, some incubate the eggs within the body and either give birth to live young, or lay the eggs on the point of hatching. Most lizards can shed their tails to escape predators.

Moorish Gecko
Tarentola mauritanica
Family Gekkonidae
Length up to 15cm, including tail. This sturdy gecko has visible adhesive pads on its toes which enable it to climb smooth, vertical surfaces with agility. It occurs in warm, dry areas. Mainly active at night, it is widespread in Spain and Portugal and coastal areas around the Mediterranean. ☻❀

Agama
Agama stellio
Family Agamidae
Length up to 30cm, including tail. This chunky, spiny lizard is the only European member of the 280 or so species in the Agama family. It has a habit of bobbing its head in a distinctive fashion. Like the chameleons, it can change its colour to suit its backgound. Insects make up the major part of its diet, but it also eats flowers and soft fruits. Although not rare, it has a very limited range, occurring mainly around Salonika on mainland Greece, and on some Greek islands, where it is often called the Rhodes Dragon. It may occur on other Mediterranean islands. ☻❀

Slow Worms are primarily ground-living reptiles, but can climb well when necessary – to avoid flooding, for example.

Slow Worm
Anguis fragilis
Family Anguidae
Length up to 50cm, including tail. Snake-like in appearance, this legless lizard is very smooth, shiny and usually silver or copper-coloured. Unlike a snake, it can close its eyelids. Its fragile tail is often broken, sometimes never regenerating. Found in wooded habitats, it mainly feeds on slugs. Widespread in Europe, but is absent from the far north, Ireland, southern Spain, and most islands. ⓑ❀☻○④❀🐛

European Glass Lizard
Ophisaurus apodus
Length up to 120cm, tail up to twice body length. A relative of the Slow Worm, this lizard closely resembles a snake. Its tiny limbs are usually concealed but, unlike a snake, it can close its eyelids. Uniformly yellowish-brown, it is well camouflaged in its dry, rocky habitat. It is rather secretive and is usually seen only after rainfall when it becomes more active. It is found only in the Balkans. Some 8–10 eggs are laid in a clutch and males fight fiercely during the breeding season. ☻❀🐛

Three-toed Skink
Chalcides chalcides
Family Scincidae
Length up to 40cm, about half of which is tail. This is a streamlined skink, which can move so quickly through grass as to be barely visible to the human eye. Superficially it resembles a snake but it can be identified by its tiny limbs. It is found in warm, damp habitats, mainly where there is a good covering of herbage in which it hides and burrows. It is distributed throughout southern Europe, including Italy and the south of France. The female gives birth to up to 23 live young in one brood. ○❀🐛

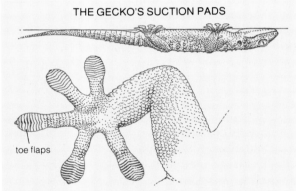

THE GECKO'S SUCTION PADS

toe flaps

The toes of the Gecko bear numerous flaps, each of which is clothed with thousands of adhesive hairs. These enable it to cling to ceilings and vertical surfaces.

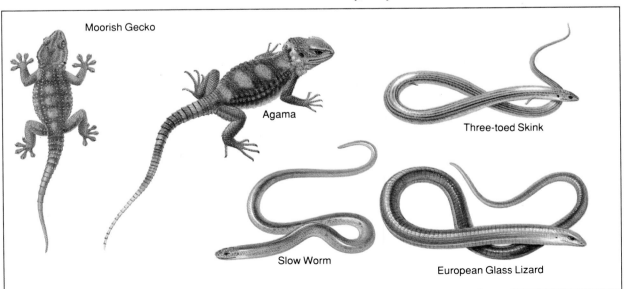

Moorish Gecko

Agama

Three-toed Skink

Slow Worm

European Glass Lizard

A Common Lizard struggles from its egg membrane. This usually happens when the eggs are laid, but may be delayed for a few days.

TYPICAL LIZARDS

There are about 180 species of typical lizards (Family Lacertidae) world-wide, of which around 38 occur in Europe, mostly in the south. They have well-developed limbs, clearly defined heads and long tails. The young of some species are quite different in colour from the adults. Lizards feed on insects and other animals up to the size of mice and fledgling birds. Most species also take some vegetable matter. Their habitats vary from moist woodlands to arid rocky areas. Most lizards lay eggs, though a few are ovo-viviparous – retaining the eggs in the body until they hatch and then giving birth immediately.

Large Psammodromus
Psammodromus algirus
Snout to vent up to 7.5cm, tail up to three times body length. Usually a metallic brownish colour, sometimes with vague spots or stripes, this lizard is well camouflaged for its woodland habitat. It digs its own burrow at the foot of trees and shrubs and spends most of its day hunting in leaf litter and brush. It comes out on to open ground to bask. When captured, it may squeak loudly. This species occurs only in Iberia and southern France, but is often abundant.

Ocellated Lizard
Lacerta lepida
Snout to vent 25cm, tail up to twice body length. This large, sun-loving, green lizard has a massive head, and the males often have spectacular blue spots on their flanks. Found in dry habitats, it frequents olive groves and vineyards as well as open woodland. Although an adept climber, it is mainly ground-dwelling and can be noisy as it crashes through undergrowth. Its diet consists mainly of insects, but it also takes birds' eggs, small vertebrates and fruit. The males are territorial and during the breeding period they are highly aggressive towards rival males. After mating, the female deposits her 6–16 eggs in a tree hollow. This lizard is widespread throughout Iberia, southern France and north-western Italy.

Green Lizard
Lacerta viridis
Snout to vent up to about 13cm, tail twice body length. The males of this lizard are usually uniformly bright green, with a blue throat when mature. The females often resemble the males but are sometimes brownish. Young lizards have two or four narrow stripes. This species prefers an open, wooded habitat with dense vegetation. It preys mainly on invertebrates, but also eats fruit and birds' eggs. In the morning and evening it may be seen basking out in the open. It is widespread over much of southern Europe, including the Channel Islands, but is endangered in Germany and other northern parts of its range. A number of different races have evolved on the various Mediterranean islands.

Wall Lizard
Podarcis muralis
Length up to 8cm, tail usually about twice body length. The colouring and pattern of this species is extremely variable, even within populations. It may be blackish or single-coloured, but more often is brownish or grey with black and white bars. Males are more brightly coloured than females. This lizard eats mainly insects and requires a warm, sunny climate and sheltered habitats in the north of its range. In the south it prefers damper places, and is often found in mountains. Occurring in most of central and southern Europe with the exception of much of Iberia, it may be encountered climbing on overgrown screes, cliff bases, walls and sunny slopes.

Lilford's Wall Lizard
Podarcis lilfordi
Up to 8cm, tail up to nearly twice body length. This is a robust lizard with highly variable patterning. It is most commonly brownish or greenish with broken stripes down the back and spotting on the throat. The scales are very fine and smooth and the sides may be reticulated. This lizard can withstand very hostile habitats with next to no vegetation, although its diet consists of a relatively high proportion of vegetable food. It is confined to rocky islets and larger islands in the Balearics.

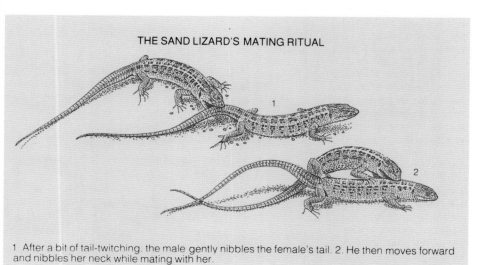

THE SAND LIZARD'S MATING RITUAL

1 After a bit of tail-twitching, the male gently nibbles the female's tail. 2. He then moves forward and nibbles her neck while mating with her.

Spiny-footed Lizard
Acanthodactylus erythrurus
Up to 7.5cm, tail up to twice
body length. A ground-
dwelling lizard with a large
head, its colouring varies
from grey to coppery-brown
above, usually with rows of
dark spots and blotches on
the back and sides. The
underside is whitish. The
young are characteristically
marked: black with white or
yellow stripes and a bright red
tail and thighs. It is found
mainly in shrubby vegetation
but, occasionally, in more
open, rocky habitats and on
beaches. It is confined to
Iberia, but is not found in its
extreme north.
◔✪

Sand Lizard
Lacerta agilis
Snout to vent up to 9cm, tail
one and a half times body
length. This stocky species has
a fairly broad and short-
snouted head. The colouring
is variable but the males
usually have green on the
flanks and the females are
brownish. Both sexes are
usually blotched or spotted.
Widely distributed across
most of central and eastern
Europe, it is thought to have
drastically declined in
numbers, largely because of
habitat loss. In Britain it
depends upon ever
diminishing heathland, and is
now confined to a small
region of southern and north-
western England.
Ⓑⴲ◔✿⊗

Viviparous Lizard
Lacerta vivipara
Snout to vent up to 6.5cm,
tail up to twice body length.
Usually terrestrial, this lizard
prefers dense undergrowth in
regions of high humidity. It
may also be found in more
open areas such as railway
embankments and even
gardens. Members of this
species often have a favourite
site on a log, stump or rocky
perch and return to it every
day to bask. They feed on
spiders and small insects. In
most of its range the female
gives birth to live, black-
coloured young, although in a
few montane areas eggs are
laid. Found throughout most
of Europe, except for
Mediterranean regions, its
population is thought to be
much depleted.
Ⓑⴲ◔✪✿⊛

Large Psammodromous

Ocellated Lizard

Green Lizard

Common Wall Lizard

Lilford's Wall Lizard

Spiny-footed Lizard

♂

♀ Sand Lizard

♂

♀ Viviparous Lizard

271

Snakes

Of a world total of over 2700 species of snake (Sub-order Ophidia), less than 30 occur in Europe. They are all elongated and legless, and they lack eyelids. All European snakes feed on living animals, from slugs, grasshoppers and various other invertebrates to mammals up to the size of rats. Snakes detect prey by scenting the air with their tongues. Constricting snakes suffocate their prey with the coils of their bodies (see below). Poisonous snakes kill by injecting venom from their fangs. Several European snakes are venomous, though most are not dangerous to people. Most species lay eggs, though a few bear live young. The young of many species are more brightly marked than the adults, sometimes dramatically so. One or more species of snake occur in almost all terrestrial habitats in Europe, except in the areas that are permanently frozen. Measurements given are total body lengths.

Sand Boa
Eryx jaculus
Family Boidae
Length up to 80cm. This is a stout snake with a short blunt tail. It has variable colouring, sometimes its skin is pale grey or buffish, at other times a reddish-brown shade with darker bars and blotching. It

is paler underneath. It feeds mainly on small rodents, lizards and young birds, constricting larger animals before it swallows them. Found only in Yugoslavia, Greece and a few coastal regions around the Black Sea, it tends to prefer dry, sandy habitats, where it frequently burrows. It gives birth to live young.

TYPICAL SNAKES

The largest family of snakes, the Colubridae, is distributed world-wide and comprises the most abundant group in Europe. The European species are typically diurnal, and most have round pupils. Three of the European species are venomous, but the fangs are at the rear of the jaw and consequently they are not considered to be dangerous to humans. The majority lay eggs, the size of the clutch varying from around 10 in some species to as many as 50 in others; one species is able to give birth to live young.

Montpelier Snake
Malpolon monspessulanus
Length up to 200cm. This snake has overhanging 'eyebrows' which give it a formidable expression. It is found in a variety of warm, dry habitats, usually with good ground cover, often near the sea. From fangs situated at the back of the jaw, venom is injected into

The Smooth Snake feeds mainly on lizards, which it quickly subdues by suffocating (constricting) them with the coils of its powerful body.

The Grass Snake has no venom, but the force of its bite is usually enough to subdue a struggling frog before it is swallowed alive.

the prey – usually lizards and small mammals – and kills them within minutes. Rather aggressive, this snake hisses loudly if cornered, but its venom is not dangerous to people. It is found throughout Iberia and the Mediterranean region, but is absent from most of Italy and the Mediterranean islands.

Grass Snake
Natrix natrix
Length up to 150cm. This snake occurs in many colourations, from greenish-grey to olive-brown with darker blotches. It prefers damp habitats and swims well, hunting for its prey of frogs and fish; it also takes small mammals and nestling birds. Its population has declined drastically over recent years, probably due partly to the disappearance of horses in agriculture as its eggs were often incubated in farmyard manure heaps. Harmless to people, it has still suffered the same persecution as other snakes. It occurs throughout Europe with the exception of Ireland, Scotland and parts of Scandinavia.

Viperine Snake
Natrix maura
Length up to 100cm. This boldly marked snake is usually yellowish or greyish-brown with staggered black blotches and occasionally a yellow or red belly. When this species is attacked, it flattens its head like a viper. Found in watery habitats from mountain streams to weedy ponds, it swims and dives extremely well. Its diet consists mainly of aquatic vertebrates, including frogs, toads, newts and fish. This

snake is commonly found in south-western Europe, as far east as Switzerland, and in north-western Italy and Sardinia.

Smooth Snake
Coronella austriaca
Length up to 80cm. The colouring of this species is variable, usually greyish or pinkish brown with rather indistinct markings. It is found in the warmer parts of Europe, particularly in regions of dense growth of heather and bushes. However, it is secretive and rarely encountered. Its diet consists of small mammals, lizards and small snakes. Prey is usually subdued by constriction. The Smooth Snake is England's rarest reptile. It has never been common and is now confined to a small area of heathland in the south. It produces 2–15 fully formed young, which mature at four years.

Ladder Snake
Elaphe scalaris
Length up to 160cm. This species is so-called because the young usually have a ladder pattern down the back. This becomes two parallel lines in the adult. Although mostly terrestrial, this snake climbs well and preys on a variety of small mammals including rodents, young rabbits and birds. Prey is constricted and, although aggressive when captured, this snake is not dangerous to people. Found throughout Iberia and southern France, its numbers are thought to be declining through loss of habitat and more intensified agriculture.

Horseshoe Whip Snake
Coluber hippocrepis
Length up to 1.5m. This slender snake has a pattern of dark-edged blotches on the back, and a 'V' or horseshoe-shaped marking on the head. The belly can be yellow, orange or red and has dark spots at the sides. It is usually found in dry habitats, sometimes around buildings, where it feeds on mammals, lizards and birds. It occurs in Spain, Portugal, and southern Sardinia.

Western Whip Snake
Coluber viridiflavus
Length up to 175cm. This snake is usually greenish-yellow with heavy, darker markings, but in some areas it can be almost entirely black. It has smooth scales and prominent eyes. Found in a variety of dry and overgrown habitats, its diet consists mainly of lizards and mammals. This is a very fast snake which, if captured, will bite hard. It occurs mainly in France and Italy.

Cat Snake
Telescopus fallax
Length up to 100cm. The body colour of this snake is brownish or greyish with a dark spot or band at the back of the head and dark blotches along the back. The pupils are vertical. Its name derives from the way it slowly stalks its prey rather like a cat. Feeding mainly on lizards, it injects prey with venom from fangs at the rear of the jaw. It is confined to south-eastern Europe.

Leopard Snake
Elaphe situla
Length up to 1m. This is an attractive snake with reddish or brownish stripes or blotches, dark-edged on a grey background. The underside is yellowish near the head, and blackish at the rear. It occurs in dry, rocky habitats and is usually diurnal. When adult it feeds mainly on small mammals, but the young feed on lizards. It is found in southern Italy and the Balkans.

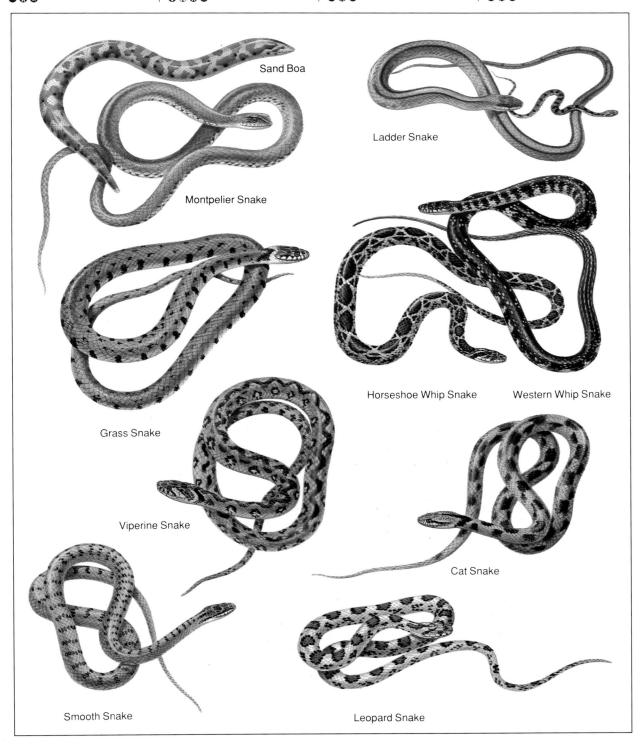

Sand Boa

Ladder Snake

Montpelier Snake

Horseshoe Whip Snake

Western Whip Snake

Grass Snake

Viperine Snake

Cat Snake

Smooth Snake

Leopard Snake

VIPERS

Over 40 species of viper (Family Viperidae) are found in the Old World, and about eight of them are found in Europe. At least one species is present in most parts of Europe, including northern regions and mountain tops. They are relatively heavy-bodied, ground-dwelling snakes and they all possess very well-developed hollow front fangs which can inject venom deep into the tissue of their prey. They have vertical pupils and although they are often diurnal, most are at least partially nocturnal, especially in the warmer regions. All but one of the European species give birth to living young, producing up to 20 in a brood. In some areas vipers may hibernate communally.

Adder
Vipera berus
Length up to 80cm. Also known as the Common Viper, this thick-bodied snake has a distinctive zig-zag stripe along its back. The male is usually greyish with a black zig-zag, and the female is brownish or reddish with a dark brown zig-zag. It is found in a wide variety of habitats including marshy meadows, open woods and, occasionally, mountain areas. Although largely diurnal, particularly in the north of its range, its pupils are vertical, which is a characteristic of many nocturnal animals. It will catch and eat most small mammals, as well as lizards. This species likes open places such as heaths and moors, and is sometimes found among sand-dunes. It is widespread throughout most of Europe, except the Mediterranean region.
Ⓑ🐭🦎☌◑④🕷🐛

Asp
Vipera aspis
Length up to 75cm. Similar to the Adder in appearance, and said to be more venomous, it can be distinguished by its upturned snout. It usually has a dark zig-zag down the back, although completely black snakes are sometimes encountered. Found in a variety of habitats from high, mountainous regions in the north of its range to more open, dry places in the south. Since it is sensitive to temperature extremes, it mainly limits its activities to the morning and late afternoon. Its diet is mainly voles, mice and lizards. It occurs from central France southwards through Switzerland, Italy and Sicily, and is also commonly found in northern Spain.
🐭🦎☌🕷🐛

Lataste's Viper
Vipera latasti
Length up to 75cm. This snake has the zig-zag pattern characteristic of most European vipers, and a small but distinct nose horn. It is generally found in dry rocky habitats, as well as open scrub and woodland. Mostly diurnal, adults prey on small mammals and occasionally birds; the young eat lizards and invertebrates. Confined to Iberia, it is the only viper present in most of the region but, in the north, its range overlaps with those of the Adder and the Asp.
☌◑🕷🐛

THE DANCE OF THE ADDERS

During the mating season male Adders sometimes fight over a female by rising up and trying to force each other to the ground in a strange 'dance'.

Tortoises and Terrapins

The term tortoise is used in Europe to describe the three terrestrial species in this order (Testudines), while terrapin is used for the three aquatic species. All tortoises and terrapins have domed shells, or carapaces, into which they can retract the head, legs and tail at the first approach of danger. They all lay eggs, which are preyed on by martens, hedgehogs and

Adder

Lataste's Viper

Asp

The European Pond Terrapin, seen here in its typical basking attitude, clearly shows its oval and rather flattened shell.

A carnivore, it feeds mainly on molluscs, amphibians and small fish. Found only in the Balkans, with a very closely-related species occurring in Iberia, its population is thought to be declining due to habitat destruction and as a result of over-collection.

European Pond Terrapin
Emys orbicularis
Carapace length up to 30cm, tail up to half carapace length. The carapace is flattened and is usually dark with yellowish markings. Found in sunny ponds, slow-moving brooks and ditches with dense vegetation where it basks at the water's edge, ready to dive into the water if disturbed. It is often called the Pond Tortoise. Unlike true tortoises, it is mostly carnivorous, feeding on a variety of aquatic life, including fish and amphibians. Females lay about 4–10 eggs in holes dug in the sandy banks. Although widespread over most of Europe, except the north, its population has declined dramatically because of the drainage of wetlands and over-collection.

other mammals. They feed on a wide range of plant and animal matter as well as carrion, although tortoises are mainly herbivorous and terrapins are mainly carnivorous. Their ranges are much reduced in Europe, because of the destruction of their habitats and over-collection.

Hermann's Tortoise
Testudo hermanni
Family Testudinidae
Carapace length up to 20cm. The carapace of this species is strongly domed and on occasion rather lumpy. Restricted to southern Europe, it can survive only in areas with hot summers and it prefers dry habitats with dense vegetation. This species has a fairly varied diet feeding on plants as well as small invertebrates. The female lays up to 12 white, hard-shelled eggs which can take up to three months to hatch. It is now endangered owing to over-collection for the pet trade, road casualties and habitat destruction over most of its range. The Spur-Thighed Tortoise (*T. graeca*) is similar but has spurred thighs.

Stripe-necked Terrapin
Mauremys caspica
Family Emydidae
Carapace length up to 25cm, tail up to half carapace length. The carapace of adults is usually greyish or greenish, but juveniles often have bright red or yellow markings. The neck stripes are clearly visible. It occurs in a variety of watery habitats from small pools to big rivers with plenty of vegetation and appears to be fairly tolerant of pollution. It strays only a short distance, and for brief periods, from the water, spending most of its time basking on banks in the sun.

Hermann's Tortoise

European Pond Terrapin

Stripe-necked Terrapin

Frogs and Toads

Around 25 of the 4000 or so frogs and toads (Order Anura) occur in Europe. The name frog is applied to those species which have smooth skins, while toad is applied to those with warty, often drier skins. Although this distinction is made in Europe, it is not always made elsewhere in the world. Most of the males are vocal during the breeding season; they have either a pair of vocal sacs on each side of the head, or a single one located under the chin. All frogs and toads feed on invertebrates and occasionally larger prey. They lay eggs, in clumps or strings, which hatch into tadpoles.

Midwife Toad
Alytes obstetricans
Family Discoglossidae
Length up to 5cm. This is a plump, short-legged toad with a disc-shaped tongue. It is so-called because the male carries strings of large eggs wrapped around his hind legs until they are ready to hatch, when he deposits them in shallow water. The male has a ringing call which gives it its alternative name of Bell Toad. Mainly nocturnal, it occurs in a variety of wooded and rocky habitats, usually on land. It is found in western Europe, and has also been introduced into Britain.

Yellow-bellied Toad
Bombina variegata
Length up to 5cm. A small toad, it is warty on the back, with a bright yellow or orange, black-blotched belly. It hibernates in holes or under rocks in winter, and frequents a variety of lowland and mountainous habitats wherever there is shallow water. Very aquatic, it is also highly sociable. Found mainly in central and southern Europe, it is absent from Iberia and Britain.

Painted Frog
Discoglossus pictus
Length up to 7cm. A sturdy frog, its skin is usually smooth and yellow-brown, grey or reddish with darker, spotted markings. The underside is whitish and sometimes speckled. Although the female lays several thousand eggs each year, they are laid singly and only a few at a time. Its distribution is limited to Iberia and south-western France. Similar species occur elsewhere.

Common Spadefoot
Pelobates fuscus
Family Pelobatidae
Length up to 8cm. This smooth-skinned toad has a pale-coloured tubercle (the spade) on its hind foot, which is used for burrowing. Its eyes have a vertical pupil. It is grey, brown or greenish with blotches and marbling. It is found in central Europe, as far north as Denmark and the Baltic States.

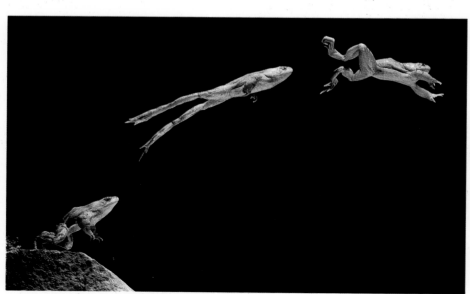

THE COMMON TOAD'S DEFENCE STRATEGY

To deter predators, such as this Grass Snake, the Common Toad raises and inflates its body.

Parsley Frog
Pelodytes punctatus
Length up to 5cm. Slender bodied, with a whitish underside, its rather warty back is mostly brownish or grey and speckled with green – as if decorated with parsley. It is very agile and it always lives in the vicinity of ponds. Usually nocturnal, but more diurnal during the breeding season, it is recognized by its distinctive croak which closely resembles the sound made by a squeaky shoe. It is found in western Europe, from Belgium southwards.

Common Toad
Bufo bufo
Family Bufonidae
Length up to 15cm. The largest European toad, this is usually brownish or greyish, with warty, sometimes almost spiny, skin. The pupils are horizontal. It hides by day and emerges at dusk, particularly after rain, to feed on slugs, worms and insects. Rarely leaping, this toad has a distinctive walking, crawling gait. The eggs are laid in long strings. It occurs across Europe, but not in northern Scandinavia, Ireland and some Mediterranean islands.

Natterjack Toad
Bufo calamita
Length up to 10cm. Usually with brownish or greenish blotches, this toad can be readily identified by the bright yellow stripe running along its back. It prefers sunny, but damp, sandy habitats, particularly near the sea. Hibernating until April, it is mostly nocturnal. Unlike other frogs and toads, it runs rather like a mouse in short, quick bursts. It commonly occurs in Ireland, south-western and central Europe but is endangered in Britain.

Green Toad
Bufo viridis
Length up to 10cm. This is a plump, rather warty toad with relatively short limbs. The colouring is distinctive, being grey or greenish with darker marbled markings. Normally nocturnal it lives in sandy habitats where it digs and burrows using its hind legs. The male has a long, trilling call which can be heard from a distance. It is most commonly found in eastern Europe.

Common Tree Frog
Hyla arborea
Family Hylidae
Length up to 5cm. This species is usually bright green all over, but occasionally yellow or blotchy brown, and

The explosive power of its muscular hind legs can send a frog leaping up to twelve times its own length through the air.

it has a narrow, darker stripe running from the nostrils along the side of the body. The toes have suction pads enabling this frog to climb well and it is often found in trees high above ground. The male has a vocal sac on his throat which, when he croaks during the breeding season, inflates and becomes spherical. It is found over much of southern and central Europe and attempts have been made to introduce it into Britain.

Common Frog
Rana temporaria
Family Ranidae
Length up to 10cm. This familiar amphibian is variable in colour, ranging from grey, brown and green to pink or yellow, usually with darker blotches. The most widespread European frog, it inhabits woods, meadows, fields and gardens. It is found as far north as the Arctic Circle, but is absent from the Mediterranean region and most of Iberia.

Edible Frog
Rana esculenta
Length up to 12cm. Often heavily spotted, particularly around the hind legs, this frog usually has a broadish pale yellow or green band along the back and whitish vocal sacs. Highly aquatic and often active by day, it can be seen basking in the sun. Despite its name, it is not unique in being edible. Widespread in southern and central Europe, it has been repeatedly introduced into Britain.

Marsh Frog
Rana ridibunda
Length up to 15cm. The largest native European frog, it is similar in colouring to the Edible Frog, but occasionally darker, and the vocal sacs are usually grey, not whitish. Highly vocal by day and night it produces a variety of calls often sounding like human laughter. Extremely aquatic, it is found in two separate areas in south-western and eastern Europe and south-eastern England.

Midwife Toad

eggs

Parsley Frog

Common Tree Frog

Yellow-bellied Toad

Common Toad

eggs

tadpole

eggs

Common Frog

Painted Frog

Natterjack Toad

Edible Frog

Common Spadefoot

Green Toad

Marsh Frog

277

Newts and Salamanders

There are over 300 species of newts and salamanders (Order Caudata), of which around 25 are found in Europe. They all have long bodies, long tails and soft, moist skin. Most have limbs with four toes on the forefeet and four or five on the hind feet. They all have larval forms (tadpoles) with external gills, but some species retain the young within the mother's body until they are metamorphosed, and so give birth to fully developed young. The term newt is applied to species which are aquatic during the breeding season, and in which the male develops a distinct breeding form, usually with elaborate fins. Some species are almost exclusively terrestrial, while others retain the larval stage throughout their lives, even when breeding. They all feed on invertebrates, especially worms and molluscs. They hunt mainly at night and particularly after rain. The species described below all belong to the Family Salamandridae.

Marbled Newt
Triturus marmoratus
Length up to 15cm, including tail. This extremely attractive newt has a bright red, yellow or orange stripe running along its vivid, velvety green and black mottled back. The breeding male develops a spectacular striped crest which is smooth-edged. Although it may occasionally spend all year in water, it usually becomes terrestrial outside the breeding season. During such times it may wander far from water, and is often found in fairly dry woods and on heathland. It breeds in ponds and ditches with good weed growth. Following fertilization, the female lays 200–300 eggs, attaching them singly to aquatic vegetation. This species occurs in Iberia and western France.

Warty Newt
Triturus cristatus
Length up to 17cm, including tail. A large, dark-bodied newt with a bright orange or yellow spotted belly and a warty skin. In many parts of its range, including Britain, it is often terrestrial outside the breeding season, and can be found hiding under rocks and logs. The breeding male develops a tall, spiked crest, which gives the species its alternative common name of Great Crested Newt. The courtship ritual (illustrated below) and breeding take place in slow-moving water, or still ponds, with dense vegetation. The eggs are attached singly to aquatic plants. This species can produce a poisonous secretion from glands along its back to deter potential predators. It occurs throughout most of Europe, except Iberia and Ireland, but is locally endangered in Britain.

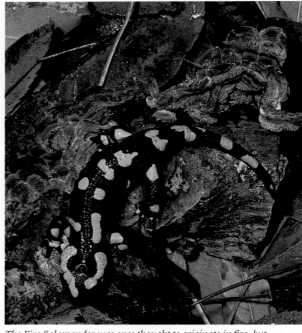

The Fire Salamander was once thought to originate in fire, but actually creeps out of logs when they are put on the fire.

Palmate Newt
Triturus helveticus
Length up to 9cm, including tail. This rather pale, smooth-skinned newt is olive or brownish and lightly spotted above, pale orange or yellow below. It is distinguishable from most other newt species by its dark, palmate feet and by the short filament at the end of the tail on the breeding male. During the breeding season it is found in a variety of watery habitats, including puddles and woodland ponds. Sometimes it even frequents brackish pools near the sea. At other times of year it is usually terrestrial. It is commonly found throughout western Europe, but not in Ireland, southern Iberia or Italy.

Smooth Newt
Triturus vulgaris
Length up to 11cm, including tail. The breeding male develops a wavy crest, and is grey-brown with dark spots on the back and sides, with an orange or reddish-spotted belly. During the breeding season, it occurs in still, shallow water, particularly in weedy ditches and ponds. At other times it is found in a variety of damp habitats, including gardens, woodland and cultivated land. It is found throughout Europe except the south-west and far north. Formerly common in Britain, it has declined in some areas because of the loss of breeding sites.

Alpine Newt
Triturus alpestris
Length up to 12cm, including tail. This attractive newt has a dark, mottled back and a uniformly orange belly and bluish spotted sides. Females are usually less brightly coloured. Very aquatic, it prefers clear pools and lakes. Usually found at altitudes of between 800 and 2000 metres, it is much more widely distributed than its name suggests – it occurs in central Europe, from Denmark and Brittany to northern Greece. An isolated population exists in north-western Spain and it has been introduced into England.

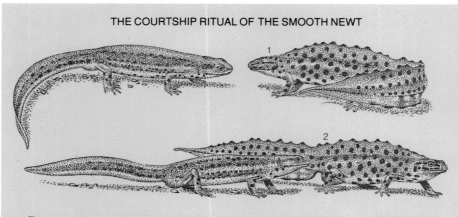

THE COURTSHIP RITUAL OF THE SMOOTH NEWT

1. The male displays his tail and wavy crest to the female. 2. He drops a packet of sperm and she moves forward to pick it up and inseminate herself. Males with the biggest crests are the most likely to stimulate the females.

Fire Salamander

Salamandra salamandra
Length up to 25cm, including tail. Powerfully built, the glossy body is spotted or blotched (or occasionally striped) with bright yellow or orange, and even red. The large glands on each side of the head contain a venomous secretion which irritates the mouth and eyes of predators. Preferring damp situations in hilly regions with deciduous forest, it is almost entirely terrestrial. Strictly nocturnal and slow-moving, it frequently emerges after rain to feed on a variety of invertebrates including worms, slugs and insects. The female does not enter the water until her eggs have hatched in her body; she then gives birth to well-developed tadpoles. It is found in central and southern Europe.

Spectacled Salamander

Salamandrina terdigitata
Length up to 11cm. A slim salamander with a ribbed appearance, its upperside is blackish or brown with a yellowish marking between the prominent eyes. The underside of the legs and tail are a bright, reddish pink. It is the only European salamander with four toes on the hind feet. Mainly nocturnal, it occurs close to streams with dense undergrowth. When captured, it may roll up its tail to expose the underside, or feign death. Its range is restricted to western Italy.

Alpine Salamander

Salamandra atra
Length up to 15cm, including tail. This species has some similarity to the Fire Salamander. Although uniformly glossy black, the glands at the back of the head are equally conspicuous. Found in wooded habitats in mountainous regions, it likes damp places but never enters water. Although primarily nocturnal, it may emerge during the day, especially after rain or when overcast. The female usually gives birth to two fully developed young, which can be up to 5cm long. Its distribution is restricted to the Alps and the mountains of western Yugoslavia.

Marbled Newt

Alpine Newt

Crested Newt

Fire Salamander

Palmate Newt

♂

Spectacled Salamander

tadpole

egg

Smooth Newt

♀

Alpine Salamander

279

FISHES

ishes are backboned animals that live in water and breathe by removing dissolved oxygen from the water with gills. There are about 22,000 species world-wide, making fishes more numerous than all the mammals, birds, reptiles and amphibians put together. Approximately 1000 species are found in European seas and freshwater.

LEFT: *The Dace is mainly a fish of the cool, fast-flowing river reaches, but it also occurs in estuaries.*

BELOW: *Most fish breathe with gills. Water enters the mouth, passes over the gills – where its oxygen is absorbed into the blood – and then escapes through the gill slits.*

Fish Groups

The term fishes covers four very different groups of aquatic animals: the lampreys and hagfishes (Superclass Agnatha), the sharks and rays (Class Chondrichthyes), the bony fishes (Class Osteichthyes) and the lobe-finned fishes (Class Sarcopterygii). The last three classes belong to the Superclass

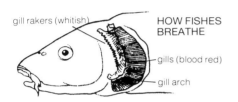
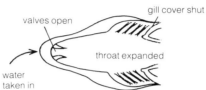
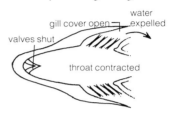

Gnathostomata. The lobe-finned fishes have fleshy lobes at the bases of some fins, with bony supports in them. These fishes include the lungfishes, but none lives in European waters and they are not covered in this book.

The lampreys have no jaws and they feed mostly by sucking the blood of prey. They have no vertebrae, the backbone being a cartilaginous rod known as a notochord. The rest of the skeleton is also composed of cartilage. The sharks and rays and the bony fishes have jaws and most feed by eating animals. Sharks and rays have no bone in their skeletons, which are made of cartilage. They have a series of separate gill slits.

Bony fishes have skeletons of real bone and their gills are concealed by a flap-like gill cover with a single opening at the rear. The lobe-finned fishes also have bony skeletons.

Salmon are powerful fish and can leap over small waterfalls when making their way upstream to their breeding sites.

Habitats

The fishes in this book are divided into those that occur in freshwater and those that occur in coastal habitats. Some fishes, however, can occur in both habitats, either all the time or according to the different stages of their life cycles.

The greatest variety of freshwater fishes live in rivers, reflecting the different habitats that a river offers as it flows from its source to its mouth. Other freshwater habitats include ponds and lakes.

The most important coastal habitats are the shallow inshore waters. These support a wide variety of fishes, which occupy various niches according to the flora and fauna found at different depths and to the different types of sea-bed. Other coastal habitats include rock pools and lagoons.

Estuaries are another important coastal habitat, containing brackish water which is neither strictly salt nor fresh. These too have their characteristic fishes, such as the Flounder, which is equally at home further up rivers and in the open sea.

Fins

Among the most distinctive features of a fish are its fins, which are primarily designed to assist in swimming, although some fins serve other functions. The primitive lampreys have only two simple fins – a flap of cartilage-supported tissue located on the back (the dorsal fin), and another under the tail (the anal fin). The fins of sharks are more complicated; there are often two dorsal fins and usually an anal fin, together with two pairs of fins at the sides – one pair situated behind the head (pectoral fins) and another pair on the belly (pelvic fins) – and a well-developed tail fin with the tail running up the upper lobe. All the fins carry cartilaginous supports in the sharks.

The Asp, showing the fins and other major features of a typical bony fish.

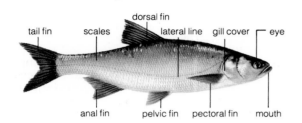

The fins of bony fishes are more complex still, although most of these fishes retain the dorsal, tail, anal, pectoral and pelvic fins seen in the sharks. Most fins are supported on bony rays, although some fishes have an adipose fin on the back without any skeleton. The fins are more mobile than among the sharks, but some bony fishes have lost certain fins during their evolution.

Scales

The scales are best developed in the bony fishes, although some species have none. The scales form a protective covering and they in turn are coated by a thin skin. This produces an antiseptic slime, which helps to prevent infection.

Senses

Many fishes have small holes in a series of scales along each side of the head and body or pores in the skin if they are scaleless. These lead to sense organs that can detect pressure changes in the water and alert the fish to prey or obstacles. This sensory system is called the lateral line.

The senses of smell, taste and touch are far more highly developed in fishes than in humans. Hearing is good in many species, and many can communicate by sound. Vision is good in fishes that live in shallow habitats.

Breeding

Most fishes reproduce by laying eggs. These are often scattered in the water and fertilized by the male after laying. Internal fertilization occurs in some species, notably the sharks and rays, and the female may lay eggs or bear live young. Most species abandon their eggs when they have laid them.

Salmon eggs and hatchlings. The latter each have a large yolk-sac, which keeps them supplied with food for the first few months of life.

Freshwater Fishes

LAMPREY FAMILY

Lampreys (Family Petromyzontidae) are primitive, fish-like vertebrates which lack many of the features of true fishes. They are eel-like in form but lack jaws and paired fins. They have a cartilaginous skeleton and a series of openings along the sides of the front of the body in place of gill arches. Instead of jaws they have a flat, sharply toothed disc on the underside of the head with which they inflict wounds on fishes and suck their blood. Lampreys live in the cool zones of the world, but they are most numerous in the northern hemisphere.

Eight species are found in Europe. All lampreys breed in freshwater but some migrate to the sea to feed and grow to maturity. Many species are parasitic on fishes as adults, others do not feed as adults.

Lampern
Lampetra fluviatilis
30–50cm. The Lampern is widespread in western and northern Europe, but it is now rare and endangered in much of its range. Most populations are migratory. The maturing adults live in estuarine and inshore seas, where they suck blood from fishes. Some populations substitute large lakes for the sea. The juveniles live buried in mud from which they feed by filtering out micro-organisms. Breeding takes place in spring on the stony beds of small rivers.
Ⓑ☻☻⊗

This Lamprey displays the sucker and the horny teeth around its mouth. The seven gill openings are also clearly visible.

Lamprey
Petromyzon marinus
Up to 91cm. This species is distributed widely throughout northern Europe both in rivers and seas. It is now very rare and locally extinct due to the obstruction and pollution of lower rivers. Breeding takes place in freshwater, where the young (prides) live buried in mud or weed beds, migrating to the sea at between three and five years. In estuaries and the sea it feeds as a parasite, sucking the blood from fishes.
Ⓑ☻☻⊗

STURGEON FAMILY

Sturgeons (Family Acipenseridae) are a group of primitive fishes found only in the northern hemisphere. They are large fishes with five lines of body plates along their sides, a small mouth with four barbels in front, and a body that turns upwards at the end to form the tail fin. Most sturgeons spawn in freshwater and migrate to the sea. Many of the 23 known species, including two of the three species found in Europe, are endangered due to pollution, obstruction of rivers and overfishing. The black eggs of the sturgeon are the highly prized caviar.

Sturgeon
Acipenser sturio
Female 3.5m, male 2m. This fish was once found in all European coastal waters from where it entered the larger rivers to spawn. Now highly endangered, it breeds only in the French rivers Garonne and Gironde, and is rarely seen north of the Bay of Biscay. Spawning takes place in spring in deep, gravel-bottomed rivers. Young fish eat insect larvae and small crustaceans; adults feed on bottom-living worms, molluscs and small fishes.
Ⓑ☻☻⊗

THE PARASITIC LAMPERN

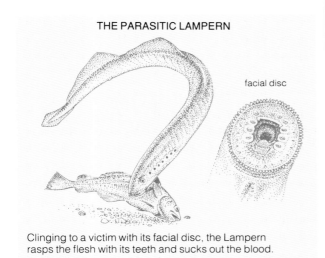

facial disc

Clinging to a victim with its facial disc, the Lampern rasps the flesh with its teeth and sucks out the blood.

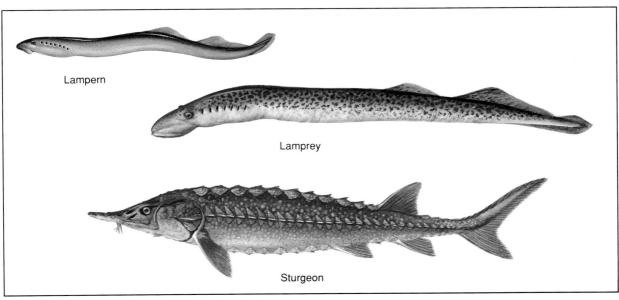

Lampern

Lamprey

Sturgeon

SALMON FAMILY

The Salmon Family (Salmonidae) comprises long-bodied, muscular fishes which all live in the cooler waters of the northern hemisphere. Salmon and trout have small scales; charr have minute scales, the whitefishes and grayling have large scales; all have a fleshy, adipose fin on the back between the rayed dorsal fin and the tail. Many species show considerable variation in colour and body form in response to their environment.

Salmon
Salmo salar
Up to 1.5m. Distributed widely from Scandinavia to northern Spain, it is now rare in the southern parts of its range. Many rivers are also stocked with hatchery fish. It breeds in fast-flowing rivers on upstream gravel beds in winter, the eggs being buried in gravel. Young fish live in streams, feeding on invertebrates, and gradually move downriver. As they grow they become silvery and migrate to the sea where they feed on crustaceans and fishes, returning to their native river to breed after a year or more. The seaward migration may take them to the Faroes, the Norwegian Sea and, in a few cases, to western Greenland.
ⓑ☻☻

Trout
Salmo trutta
23cm–1.4m. This species has a wide range in northern Europe, where it lives in lakes and often migrates to the sea. In southern Europe it is mostly confined to rivers and is non-migratory. Its colour and size vary. Sea trout migrate to the sea and are silvery in colour; brown trout are dark with red and orange spots, especially when living in small, overgrown streams. Small trout feed on insects and crustaceans; large trout often eat fishes. Breeding takes place in winter on gravel banks in rivers and lakes. It can be distinguished from the salmon by its upper jaw bone, which reaches beyond the eye, and by having a deeper tail in front of the fin.
ⓑ☻

Arctic Charr
Salvelinus alpinus
25cm–1m. It lives in isolated mountain lakes in northern Europe and in the Alps. Near the Arctic Circle it inhabits rivers from which it migrates to the sea. Migratory fish are larger than lake fish; all are brilliantly coloured with white spotted sides and bright red flanks and bellies. It feeds on small crustaceans, insects and fish. It breeds mostly in winter on gravel in lakes and rivers. The separate lake populations are very variable, having been isolated since the Ice Ages.
ⓑ☻

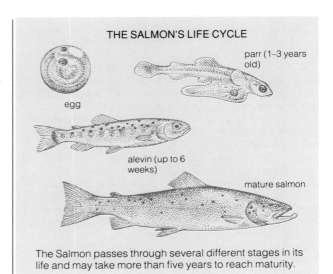

THE SALMON'S LIFE CYCLE

egg

alevin (up to 6 weeks)

parr (1–3 years old)

mature salmon

The Salmon passes through several different stages in its life and may take more than five years to reach maturity.

Powan
Coregonus lavaretus
30cm. This is one of several species of whitefish (*Coregonus*) found in northern Europe, where it lives in isolated lakes. In the Arctic, it may migrate to the sea. It feeds mostly on small, planktonic crustaceans and sometimes on bottom-living insect larvae. Many lake populations have become scarce, while others have been wiped out. Because of their isolation in lakes, many populations of whitefish are variable in body form.
ⓑ☻⊗

Vendace
Coregonus albula
Up to 26cm. Distributed widely in Scandinavia and western USSR, it is also found in Alpine lakes and in Britain, where it lives in only two lakes in the Lake District. It feeds on planktonic crustaceans and occasionally on larger invertebrates. Many of the northern Vendace populations migrate from lakes or the Baltic Sea to spawn in deep rivers.
ⓑ☻

Grayling
Thymallus thymallus
50cm. A river fish, it lives mainly in clean, cool, well-oxygenated water and is also found in lakes in mountainous regions. It is distributed across Europe from Wales eastwards but is not native to southern Europe. It feeds mainly on bottom-living insects, crustaceans and molluscs but sometimes eats surface flies and small fishes. Spawning occurs in spring.
ⓑ☻

Salmon

Powan

Trout

Vendace

Arctic Charr

Grayling

The Pike is well camouflaged as it lurks among the water plants of lakes and slow-moving rivers.

PIKE FAMILY

The family of pike (Esocidae) are long-bodied, predatory fish with a pointed head and large jaws. The lower jaw has a small number of large teeth, while the roof of the mouth is covered with small, backwardly curved teeth. All pike have the dorsal and anal fins close to the tail, making a powerful paddle. All five species live in the northern hemisphere; the single European species has a circumpolar distribution and is known in North America as the northern pike. Three further species occur in eastern North America and one species is found in Siberia.

Pike
Esox lucius
1.6m. Widespread throughout the British Isles and northern Europe, this fish has also been introduced to Spain. It lives in still or slow-flowing water, among water plants including rushes and tree-roots. The species can often be seen lying motionless near the surface. It feeds on insect larvae and small fishes when young, and on fish when adult. Water voles, ducklings and small aquatic birds may also be taken. It breeds in early spring, when the larger female may be accompanied by two or three smaller males over weed beds and flooded water meadows. The eggs stick to underwater leaves. Individuals can be identified by their unique body and tail markings.
Ⓑ ☻

CARP FAMILY

This enormous family (Cyprinidae) of freshwater fishes comprises about 2000 species which live in the northern hemisphere. Their body shape is varied but all have a single dorsal fin comprised of branched rays, and pelvic fins on the belly. They are usually fully scaled, except for the head, and with a distinct lateral line. They lack teeth in the jaws but crush their food by means of pharyngeal teeth in the back of the throat. Cyprinids are well adapted to life in turbid water. While their vision is good, they have exceptionally sensitive hearing, highly developed lateral line sense organs, and an acute sense of smell.

Roach
Rutilus rutilus
Up to 20cm but, very rarely, reaching 50cm. Distributed widely throughout Europe in slow-flowing rivers and still waters, this is a popular fish with anglers. As a result, it has been introduced to some hardly suitable waters. It eats insect larvae, crustaceans, snails and plants, including algae. By being an unselective feeder, it can survive in most freshwater locations. It breeds from April to June, shedding eggs on water plants, algae mats, and even fine tree-roots. The eggs are adhesive, hatching in 9–12 days; the juveniles hide amongst the weed. This species may live for up to 14 years and becomes sexually mature at 2–3 years. The Roach is an adaptable fish, able to cope with high and low temperatures, low oxygen and brackish water.
Ⓑ ☻

Rudd
Scardinius erythrophthalmus
Up to 30–45cm. This species is found in a wide range from Ireland, where it has been introduced, and eastern England to central Europe and south to Greece. It is, however, absent from the extreme north of Europe, including Scotland. Related local species are also found in Italian, Austrian and Greek lakes. It typically inhabits still waters, and backwaters of rivers, schooling near the surface and in mid-water. It feeds on surface-living insects, aquatic insect larvae, crustaceans and on plants. Spawning occurs from April to June on weed beds and amongst reeds; eggs stick to plants, hatching in 8–15 days. It often forms large populations of small, stunted fish, due to overcrowding, and may live up to 10 years. It favours mature, vegetated waters.
Ⓑ ☻

Dace
Leuciscus leuciscus
18–30cm. It occurs across northern Europe from England eastwards and from Sweden to France and the Balkans. It is a riverine fish, living in the middle reaches of rivers and in brooks, but is also found in lowland rivers. Most common in moderate-flowing waters, it feeds heavily on insects and arthropods which fall into the water from bankside vegetation, flying insects and insect larvae. It also eats plant food. This species usually spawns at night between mid-February and May, laying its eggs over gravel shallows. Eggs stick to the gravel and take three to four weeks to hatch. Dace are relatively short-lived, rarely surviving longer than 7 years.
Ⓑ ☻

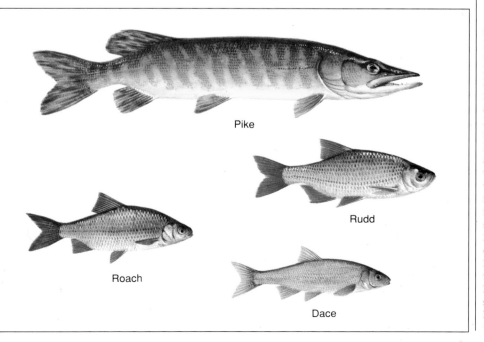

Pike

Rudd

Roach

Dace

285

FRESHWATER HABITATS

Much of the rain falling on the land runs over the surface and finds its way into the rivers. Most rivers originate in the uplands, where rainfall is high, and most of them have a number of well-defined zones or reaches, each with its characteristic assemblage of plant and animal life.

The Headstream
The headstream is the shallow, uppermost reach, where the water first gathers to form a distinct channel. The bed is rocky and flowering plants are unable to establish themselves on it. Stonefly and mayfly nymphs cling to mossy boulders, while the larvae of midges feed amongst the waterlogged mosses. Grey Wagtails find plenty to eat here, especially when the adult insects are on the wing.

The Troutbeck
The troutbeck is formed when several headstreams merge. The flow is much stronger here and sends quite large boulders tumbling along the bed. No plants can grow here. Swirling stones scour deep hollows in the bed, where trout are seen. Caddis larvae and other young insects live under the stones, especially near the edge, and feed on debris brought down by the current. Waterfalls are quite common in the troutbeck and the exposed rocks provide nesting sites for Dippers and Grey Wagtails. Ferns, mosses, and liverworts clothe the rocks.

The Grayling Reach
As the river continues its journey down from the hills, the slope decreases and the current slows. The river is now entering the grayling reach, so called because the Grayling is nearly always present. But the Grayling is not common in the British Isles, where this stretch of the river is often called the minnow reach – after another prominent inhabitant. Other fishes include Trout, Salmon, Lampreys, and the Bullhead or Miller's Thumb. The best-known bird of the grayling reach is the River Kingfisher, although few people see more than a

White Water-lilies flourish in most kinds of still and slow-moving water. Here they are growing in a strongly acidic moorland pool.

blue and orange blur as it streaks over the water. Each bird has a favourite perch from which it can survey a stretch of clear, shallow water.

Many grayling reaches are overhung by graceful alder trees. The trees produce dense mats of fine surface roots which help to reduce erosion of the banks, and alders are commonly planted on the riverside for this purpose. Monkeyflower, Brooklime and Watercress grow on the banks and in shallow water. The river bed is stony and gravel banks are common in mid-stream. They are often colonized by River Water-crowfoot, whose stems and hair-like leaves stream out with the current. Its white flowers carpet the water in summer and attract many insects. Female damselflies often settle on the carpets to lay their eggs in the submerged crowfoot stems. Many other dragonflies flourish in the grayling reach, along with numerous mayflies, stoneflies and caddis flies.

The Common Moorhen is abundant on lowland ponds and rivers, where it rears up to three broods between March and August.

The Lowland Reach

Below the grayling reach is the lowland or cyprinoid reach, so called because the dominant fish belong to the Carp Family – the Cyprinidae. They include Roach, Bream, and Barbel. Perch, Pike and Eels are also common. The river is slow-moving, quite deep, and rather muddy, with abundant vegetation at the water's edge. Herons wait patiently, while coots and moorhens squawk among the reeds. Dragonflies often dispute their territories, and damselflies perform courtship dances over the vegetation.

The Estuarine Reach

The estuarine reach is the lowest part of the river, which is much affected by the rise and fall of the tides. Wide mud banks are exposed at low tide, and salt-marshes (see p.310) fringe many estuaries. Ducks, waders and gulls forage for molluscs, worms and crustaceans in the mud. Few invertebrate species can tolerate estuarine conditions but those that can do so occur in extremely high concentrations. The fishes found in estuaries include both marine species that travel up river to feed, such as the Flounder – the most common fish occurring in estuaries – and certain freshwater species such as the European Eel which migrates out to sea to breed. Life is not easy for animals in the estuarine waters because of the changing salinity as the tides sweep in and out.

The Otter has declined nearly everywhere, mainly as a result of river pollution.

Lakes and Ponds

A natural lake develops where a river runs into a hollow and fills it before finding an escape route on the far side. Many upland lakes have developed where rivers have filled hollows left by melting glaciers. A current may run through the centre, but much of the lake water is still. Lowland lakes are generally very rich and support much the same wildlife as a river's lowland reach. Upland lakes are often barren because the hard rocks around them do not yield enough minerals to support a rich vegetation.

Ponds are small bodies of still water occupying natural or artificial hollows. Usually rich in vegetation and in invertebrate animals, they are also important habitats for amphibians. Many ponds have been lost in recent decades – sometimes deliberately filled in, but often lost to the natural processes of succession. Debris accumulates in the pond, allowing reeds and other marginal plants to encroach on the open water. They eventually fill it completely, turning it first into a swamp and finally into dry land. Even large lakes will be obliterated in this way – converted to dry land with the original river flowing through the middle.

The large Raft Spider inhabits fens, marshes and the edges of ponds and streams. It detects the vibrations of prey by resting its feet on the water.

Wildlife of the Grayling Reach
1 White-throated Dipper
2 Atlantic Salmon
3 Brown Trout
4 River Kingfisher
5 Monkeyflower
6 Alders

Chub
Leuciscus cephalus
Up to 60cm. This river fish is widespread across Europe, from England and southern Sweden to the Caspian Sea, and south to Spain, Greece and Turkey. It is most common in slow to moderate currents in the middle reaches of rivers, but also lives in the lakes of flood plains. It feeds on most aquatic insects, crustaceans (including crayfish), small fishes and even frogs. Breeding occurs from May to June in shallow water, the eggs sticking to plants and stones. They hatch in 8–10 days. Growth is relatively slow, but the lifespan may be up to 12 years. It forms small schools when young but these disperse after the first year to live a solitary life in deep pools.
Ⓑ ☻

Ide
Leuciscus idus
45cm–1m. It occurs across Europe from southern Scandinavia to the Black Sea. The golden variety, known as the Orfe, has been introduced into lakes and ponds in England. Found in the larger lowland and brackish rivers, it feeds on fishes and crustaceans; young fish eat insect larvae and planktonic crustaceans. Spawning takes place from April to May in shallow freshwater; the eggs stick to aquatic plants and gravel. It has become uncommon in parts of Europe due to pollution and obstructions in rivers.
☻

Bleak
Alburnus alburnus
Up to 15cm. This bright silvery fish is widespread throughout Europe but absent from the far south. It forms schools which live near the surface in slow-flowing lowland rivers. It is also common in canals and other stillwaters. It feeds on insects and arthropods that fall into the river from bankside trees, as well as on planktonic crustaceans and insects. Spawning takes place from May to June in shallow water among stones and plants. This species is an important source of food for larger fish, and birds such as Kingfishers.
Ⓑ ☻

Bream
Abramis brama
Up to 80cm. This species occurs from Ireland, where it has been introduced, to the Caspian Sea, and from Scandinavia to France. It is found in slow-flowing, deep rivers and lowland lakes, where it forms schools, generally in mid-water or near the bed. It feeds in a characteristic head-down posture, the protrusible mouth forming a tube to suck in worms, insect larvae and molluscs. It puffs mud away with mouthfuls of water until the food is exposed, its tail 'dimpling' the water surface as it does so. Breeding takes place from late spring to early summer, among dense plants. The yellowish eggs stick to weeds, and hatch in 3–12 days. This species may live for up to 15 years.
Ⓑ ☻

The prominent nostrils and the four barbels around the Carp's mouth help the fish to detect its food at night.

Silver Bream
Blicca bjoerkna
Up to 36cm. Found from eastern England to the Caspian Sea, and from southern Sweden to France, it is native to slow-flowing lowland rivers and still waters. It feeds amongst vegetation, mainly on insect larvae, but also on crustaceans and plants. The young feed on planktonic crustaceans. Spawning takes place in summer amongst plants. This species is very abundant in stagnant water such as drainage canals and peaty lakes.
Ⓑ ☻

Bitterling
Rhodeus sericeus
8cm. Native to the Danube basin, it has also been introduced to the Rhine basin and to England, where it is locally common. It is found in a variety of habitats, including deep, slow-flowing rivers, small lakes and ponds. It feeds on planktonic crustaceans. Breeding takes place in late spring, when both sexes become brilliantly coloured. This species has a very unusual method of spawning. The female develops a long tube from the genital aperture, which she uses to stimulate a Swan Mussel to open its shell. Some 10–25 eggs are then laid safely inside, hatching three to four weeks later.
Ⓑ ☻

Minnow
Phoxinus phoxinus
Up to 12cm. This species is native from England to the USSR, and from Sweden to the Pyrenees and Balkans, and introduced to Ireland, Scotland and Wales. It lives in rivers, often in mountainous regions, where it forms schools in shallow water. Its diet consists of small crustaceans, insects at the surface of the rivers, and small animals that drop off bankside vegetation. Spawning takes place in summer on gravel shallows; the eggs sticking to the stones and hatching in 5–10 days. Males are brilliantly coloured in the breeding season and have white flashes on the pectoral fins.
Ⓑ ☻

Gudgeon
Gobio gobio
20cm. Distributed widely across Europe from Britain to the USSR, and from southern Scandinavia to the south of France, it lives chiefly in slow-flowing to moderately fast rivers but may also be found in lakes. It usually stays close to the bottom, often over gravel shallows, but in winter it will occupy deeper pools. It feeds on bottom-living insect larvae, molluscs and crustaceans. Spawning takes place in early summer, in shallow water. The young form large schools.
Ⓑ ☻

THE BITTERLING'S STRANGE NURSERY

1. The male and female select a mussel as a nursery.
2. The female lays her eggs in the mussel, and the male fertilizes them. 3. In 3–4 weeks the larvae emerge.

Barbel
Barbus barbus
50–60cm. This is one of several related species found throughout all of Europe except the far north and far south. A bottom-living fish, found in the middle reaches of rivers, it feeds on invertebrates. Spawning occurs in late spring on gravel banks. The eggs stick to the stones or lodge between them, and hatch in 5–10 days. The adults usually migrate upstream to the spawning grounds, where they form small schools.
Ⓑ☻

Tench
Tinca tinca
45–70cm. This species is found across Europe, partly as a result of introductions. A fish of still waters, it lives in dense weed beds and on muddy bottoms. Its diet consists of molluscs, crustaceans, insect larvae and plants. Tolerant of low oxygen levels and high temperatures, it can live where few other fish would survive. Spawning takes place from late spring to early summer, the eggs sticking to leaves of water plants.
Ⓑ☻

Carp
Cyprinus carpio
Up to 70cm but can reach 1.5m. Native to the Danube basin and the northern Balkans, it is now found throughout Europe due to widespread introduction as a food or sport fish. Naturally suited to lowland rivers and large lakes, it favours weed beds. It can often be seen basking in the sun near the surface. This species feeds on plants and invertebrates. Breeding takes place in summer; the eggs are attached to plants, as are the young fish for several days.
Ⓑ☻

Nase
Chondrostoma nasus
Up to 50cm. This fish is distributed in Europe from France to the USSR. It lives in the swiftly flowing, middle reaches of rivers, in slow-flowing rivers below weirs and in turbulent water. It eats algae and other small plants. It spawns in spring on gravel in small tributaries.
☻

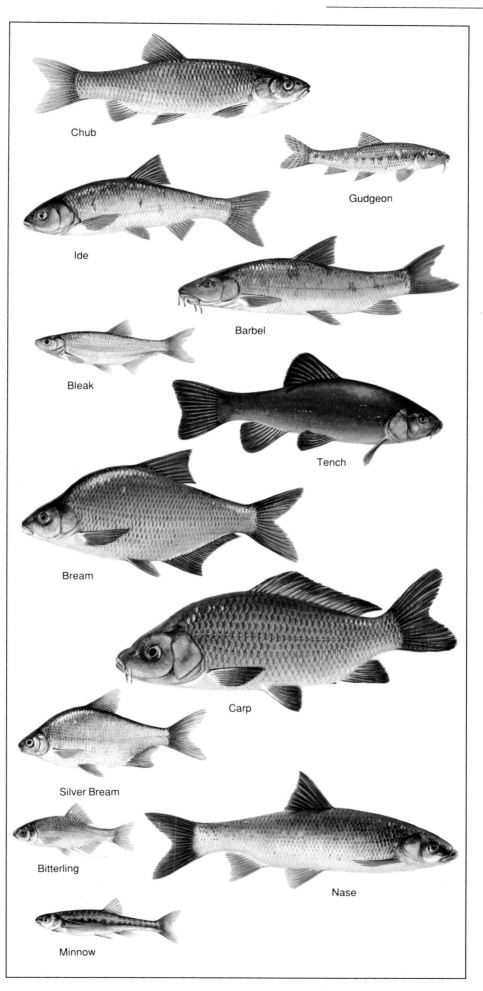

Chub

Gudgeon

Ide

Barbel

Bleak

Tench

Bream

Carp

Silver Bream

Bitterling

Nase

Minnow

LOACH FAMILY

Loaches are a family (Cobitidae) of generally small, freshwater fishes, found in Europe, Asia and northern Africa. Mostly they are elongate, even worm-like, and burrow into the river or lake bed, dense plant beds or under stones. Some have one pair of barbels on the lips, others have up to six. Three species occur in northern Europe.

Stone Loach
Nemacheilus barbatulus
10–15cm. Distributed throughout Europe, although rare in southern Sweden, it usually lives in small rivers but may also be found in shallow stretches of large rivers and stony-bottomed lakes. It forages on the bottom, feeding on small invertebrates. Spawning takes place from April to June; the eggs are shed amongst gravel. It is an important food for larger fish, birds, water shrews and other mammals.
Ⓑ ☻

Pond Loach
Misgurnus fossils
Up to 35cm, usually about 15cm. This fish is distributed in Europe throughout the Rhine and Danube basins, but is now rare in many places due to the destruction of its habitat. Those which remain live in overgrown, muddy, lowland ponds, marshes with patches of open water and ditches. Frequently, these areas are devoid of oxygen, forcing the fish to come to the surface to breath air which it absorbs through its gut. Breeding takes place from April to June, the eggs being shed over water-plants.
☻ ⊗

Spined Loach
Cobitis taenia
Up to 13.5cm, but mostly about 7cm. This and several closely related species occur throughout Europe, where they burrow in soft mud or filamentous algae in slow-flowing rivers and flood plain lakes. It searches for food such as small crustaceans, close to the bottom, mostly in the half-light or at night. It spawns from April to June.
Ⓑ ☻

CATFISH FAMILY

Species of this family of freshwater catfish (Siluridae) have characteristic mouth barbels, a very small dorsal fin and a rather long anal fin. The family is widely distributed across Europe and Asia, but there are only two species in Europe: the widespread Wels Catfish, and Aristotle's Catfish, which occurs only in Greece. At least two species of North American catfish (Family Ictaluridae) have been introduced to Europe. These aliens are distinguished by the strong spine in each pectoral fin and by their adipose fin on the back.

Wels
Silurus glanis
Usually up to 2m, but can sometimes reach 3m. This is native to the Danube and Rhine basins, but introduced to England, Spain, Italy and the south of France. It lives in slow-flowing, deep, lowland rivers and flood plain lakes and marshes. A rather secretive fish, it hides amongst weeds, and tree roots during daylight, but in turbid water it feeds at any time. Its diet includes bottom-living fishes, ducklings, water voles and amphibians. Spawning occurs from mid-May to mid-July, in a shallow depression excavated by the male. The eggs form a small mound in the nest which is guarded by the male.
Ⓑ ☻

EEL FAMILY

The freshwater eels (Family Anguillidae) breed in the sea but migrate as young fish into freshwater rivers and lakes, where they live for up to 20 years before returning to the sea to spawn. About 16 species are known throughout the world, but only one occurs in Europe. All are elongate and snake-like with long dorsal and anal fins, which meet at the tail. They have minute scales embedded in their skin.

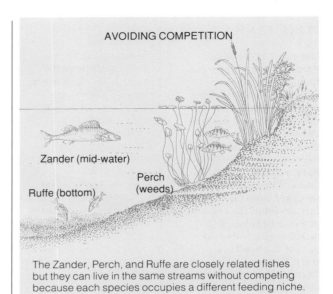

AVOIDING COMPETITION

Zander (mid-water)

Ruffe (bottom)

Perch (weeds)

The Zander, Perch, and Ruffe are closely related fishes but they can live in the same streams without competing because each species occupies a different feeding niche.

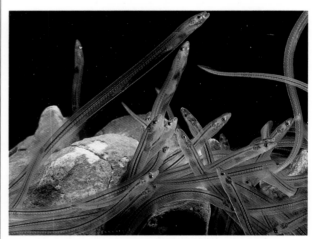

These young Eels (known as elvers) are only 6–7cm long, but they have already spent three years drifting across the Atlantic Ocean from their birthplace in the Sargasso Sea.

Eel
Anguilla anguilla
Female 1m, male up to 50cm. Distributed widely across Europe in freshwater, it also lives in coastal waters in northern Europe. It is found in rivers, except for the headwaters, and lakes into which it migrates. These may sometimes be reached overland on wet nights as this fish can breathe through its skin. 'Yellow' eels are the muddy-brown, freshwater stages which change to 'silver' eels on sexual maturity when they migrate downriver. They are believed to breed in the Sargasso Sea, near Bermuda, after which the young fish drift back across the Atlantic. They arrive in Britain from February to March and in Greece during May and June when they are aged about three years. They migrate seawards at 8–15 years.
Ⓑ ☻

COD FAMILY

The members of the Cod Family (Gadidae) are, with the exception of the Burbot, all marine fishes. They are long-bodied fishes, with one to three dorsal fins and a tail that merges into the fin; most have a chin barbel.

Burbot
Lota lota
Up to 1m, but mostly around 50cm. Widely distributed across northern Europe, this fish lives in lowland rivers and large lakes, hiding during daylight under tree roots and rocks or in weed beds. It feeds on bottom-living insect larvae, crustaceans, molluscs, and occasionally other fish. Spawning takes place in mid-winter, often under ice. The eggs are laid in mid-water and drop to the bed.
☻ ⊗

PERCH FAMILY

The perches (Family Percidae) are a large family of freshwater fishes found across the northern hemisphere in temperate waters. About 150 species are known, most of which occur in North America. They all have a sharply-spiny first dorsal fin (sometimes separate from the remainder of the fin) and one or two spines in the anal fin. The body and part of the head are scaly. Perch usually live in still water, although some inhabit fast-flowing brooks.

Perch
Perca fluviatilis
Up to 50cm, usually 35cm. Widely distributed across Europe, this fish lives mostly in slow-flowing rivers and lakes, usually in lowland regions. It feeds on insect larvae and small fish, including smaller perch. When young, it forms small, loose schools for protection. Adults usually school only prior to spawning in April and May. The eggs are wound in long strings around weeds, stems and tree roots. They hatch in about eight days. Solitary adults often dominate a stretch of water, and may live for up to 10 years.
ⓑ 😊

Zander
Stizostedion lucioperca
Up to 130cm, usually 60cm. This species is found across northern Europe from Germany to the Aral Sea. It has also been introduced successfully to the Rhine and to England. At home in lowland rivers and lakes, it prefers cloudy, turbid water, in which it hunts other fish in the twilight. Usually solitary when mature, young fish gather in small schools. It spawns from April to June over sandy or stony bottoms, or among plant roots, in shallow water. A single female may lay between 13,000 and 125,000 eggs.
ⓑ 😊

Ruffe
Gymnocephalus cernuus
Up to 30cm, usually 15cm. This fish occurs throughout Europe from England to Siberia but is absent from the Iberian, Italian and Balkan peninsulas. It inhabits turbid lowland rivers and lakes, and in places may become extremely abundant. It feeds in small schools during daylight, excavating bloodworms (the larvae of non-biting midges) and other buried insect larvae and may also take fish eggs. It breeds in spring, its eggs sticking to plants or stones. This species rarely lives to be older than five years.
ⓑ 😊

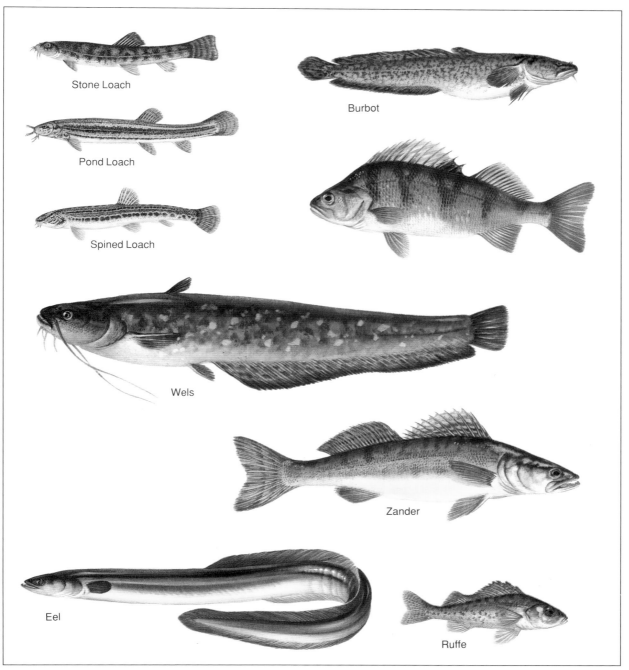

Stone Loach

Pond Loach

Spined Loach

Burbot

Wels

Zander

Eel

Ruffe

KILLIFISH FAMILY

Killifish (Family Cyprinodontidae) are small carp-like fishes with numerous tiny teeth. They live in fresh to brackish water in the coastal regions of warm temperate and tropical areas. Five species occur in Europe.

Spanish Toothcarp
Aphanius iberus
Female 5cm, male smaller. This small fish lives in the coastal regions of southern Spain. It feeds on insect larvae and small crustaceans. It spawns in summer, laying eggs among plants. This species is endangered by the drainage of wetlands and the introduction of a related North American livebearer.
😊💧⊗

South European Toothcarp
Aphanius fasciatus
Maximum length 6cm. This toothcarp inhabits lagoons, coastal marshes and also estuaries in the northern Mediterranean from France to western Turkey. Many of these habitats have been drained or developed and it is now much less common. It feeds on small crustaceans and insect larvae. Spawning occurs in spring and early summer in dense vegetation.
💧

SCULPIN FAMILY

Sculpins (Family Cottidae) are a widely distributed group whose members are found in both fresh and salt water. Most are small fish with spiny heads, no scales, and two dorsal fins. Only three species live in freshwater in Europe, but there are six marine sculpins.

Bullhead
Cottus gobio
10cm; rarely to 17cm. This abundant fish is absent only from the far north and far south. It is found in streams, small rivers and large lakes. It skulks under stones and boulders in shallow, fast-flowing water or hides in the dense weed beds of still waters. Active mostly at night, it feeds on freshwater shrimps and insect larvae. It spawns in early spring.
Ⓑ💧

STICKLEBACK FAMILY

The sticklebacks (Family Gasterosteidae) include about seven marine and freshwater species found throughout the northern hemisphere. Most are small, scaleless fishes with 3–16 spines along the back.

The spiny Bullhead or Miller's Thumb inhabits upland lakes and the well-aerated waters of the troutbeck and the grayling reaches.

Three-spined Stickleback
Gasterosteus aculeatus
Up to 5cm, occasionally 10cm. This species is widely distributed throughout most of Europe and is found in both fresh and salt water habitats. It occurs most often in lowland rivers and lakes, in shallow water close to weed beds where it feeds on minute crustaceans and insect larvae. It breeds in spring and summer, when the male develops a bright red throat. The eggs are laid in a small nest, which the male builds from plant fragments glued together with body secretions.
Ⓑ💧

Nine-spined Stickleback
Pungitius pungitius
Up to 7cm. This species occurs on the coastal plain of northern and central Europe, in lakes, ponds and small rivers. Less common than the Three-spined Stickleback, it often chooses to live in pools or ditches which are choked with vegetation and are often stagnant. It feeds on insects and their larvae as well as crustaceans. Spawning takes place in late spring and early summer. The male constructs a nest of plant fibres just above the bottom, and guards the eggs and young.
Ⓑ💧

♀

Spanish Toothcarp

♂

Bullhead

Three-spined Stickleback

South European Toothcarp

Nine-spined Stickleback

Coastal Fishes

DOGFISH FAMILY

The members of this family (Scyliorhinidae) are small sharks, with cartilaginous skeletons. They live in coastal waters in all temperate and tropical oceans. Most are bottom-living. About six species are found in European seas.

Lesser-spotted Dogfish
Scyliorhinus canicula
Up to 1m. This dogfish is found in all European seas. It prefers shallow water, but can occur down to depths of 100m. It is most common on sandy or fine gravel bottoms where it eats invertebrates. The female lays eggs in tough, light brown capsules which mingle with seaweed. The eggs hatch in 5–11 months.
Ⓑ 🐟

RAY FAMILY

This family (Rajidae) is related to the sharks and, like them, rays have cartilaginous skeletons. Adapted for sea-bed life, they have flattened bodies, with the mouth, nostrils and gill openings on their underside and the eyes on the back. Some 20 species live in European coastal waters.

Thornback Ray
Raja clavata
Up to 85cm, the female larger than the male. This ray is widely distributed from Norway south to Morocco and throughout the Mediterranean. It lives on gravel, sand and muddy bottoms in inshore waters down to 60m. Young fish eat small crustaceans, larger ones eat crabs and fishes. The eggs are laid in oblong capsules during the spring and summer.
Ⓑ 🐟

CONGER-EEL FAMILY

The Conger-eel Family (Congridae) contains about 100 species inhabiting temperate oceans. They are scaleless and have well-developed pectoral fins. Unlike freshwater eels they have the dorsal fin beginning right above the pectoral fins.

Conger-eel
Conger conger
Up to 2.75m, but usually much smaller. This eel is found along Atlantic, North Sea and Mediterranean coasts. It lives on rocky shores with deep pools and dense seaweeds, and is also found among the rocks of harbour walls and breakwaters. It feeds on fishes, crabs and octopuses. Adults migrate to breed in the tropical Atlantic, where the young live near the surface.
Ⓑ 🐟

PIPEFISH FAMILY

Pipefish (Family Syngnathidae) are mostly sea fishes, but in the tropics may also be found in freshwater. There are about 250 species in the shallow inshore waters of the Atlantic, Pacific and Indian Oceans. The male incubates the eggs, which are laid by the female in a pouch on the underside of his body.

Nilsson's Pipefish
Syngnathus rostellatus
Up to 17cm. This species occurs from southern Norway south to Biscay and all round the British coast. Preferring shallow waters, it may be found in sandy bays and the mouths of estuaries. It feeds on planktonic crustaceans and fish larvae. Males carry the eggs from June to August.
Ⓑ 🐟

Seahorse
Hippocampus ramulosus
Up to 15cm from top of crown to tail tip. The more common of the two European seahorses, this species occurs from the Hebrides southwards to the Mediterranean. It lives amongst eelgrass and seaweeds but is occasionally caught swimming near the surface in the open sea. It swims with its body held vertical, and its dorsal fin whirring like a propeller. Its tail is prehensile and is used to anchor the fish to vegetation. This species feeds on crustaceans and tiny plankton. Males with eggs have been found between May and August.
Ⓑ 🐟

COD-FISH FAMILY

Cod-fish (Family Gadidae) are a small family of about 50 species living in the cool temperate regions of the Atlantic and Pacific. Most have chin barbels, and three dorsal and two anal fins.

Five-bearded Rockling
Ciliata mustela
Up to 25cm. An abundant fish in rock pools or under stones on the shore and found down to 20m. It has five barbels on the front part of its head. It feeds on small crustaceans and fishes. Breeding takes place in late winter. The young fish are silvery with greenish backs and are very common in spring, when sea birds prey upon them heavily.
Ⓑ 🐟

Lesser-spotted Dogfish

Conger

Greater Pipefish

Seahorse

Thornback Ray

Five-bearded Rockling

WRASSE FAMILY

There are some 600 members of this group (Family Labridae), most of them tropical inshore fishes. Several kinds of wrasse are 'cleaner fish', which pick the parasites off other fishes; a few European species have this habit when young. Most wrasses are small and brightly coloured.

Cuckoo Wrasse
Labrus mixtus
Up to 35cm. This common European species is distributed from southern Norway and Shetland south to Morocco and across the Mediterranean. Young specimens swim just below low-tide mark, but the adults occur down to 150m. Young fish and females are orange with three brown blotches on the back. Males have brilliant blue heads and blue streaks on their sides over an orange background.
Ⓑ 😛

WEEVER FAMILY

There are about five species of Weever (Family Trachinidae) confined to European and west African coasts. They live in shallow water, buried, except for their eyes and back, in sand. They all have venomous spines on the gill covers and first dorsal fin, which can give a painful and often dangerous sting.

Lesser Weever
Echiichthys vipera
Up to 14cm. This species lives buried in clean, relatively coarse sand between tide marks at high water and in slightly deeper water. It moves up the beach with high tide to forage for bottom-living organisms, which burrow in the sand, such as sand hoppers and young shrimps. The black first dorsal fin is a warning sign.
Ⓑ 😛

GREY MULLET FAMILY

This is a large family (Mugilidae) of mostly tropical and warm temperate fishes which live mainly in coastal waters. They are slender-bodied with a broad head, and have a large stomach and a long gut, which allows them to digest algae and small animals which they pick up in the bottom mud.

Thick-lipped Grey Mullet
Chelon labrosus
Up to 75cm. This species is widely distributed in Europe, from southern Iceland and Norway south to the Canary Islands and throughout the Mediterranean. It is common close inshore and in estuaries. It feeds on rich mud, and browses the algae off rocks, usually in small pools. It breeds in spring; the silvery young form large schools in shore pools and lagoons.
Ⓑ 😛

The Sea Scorpion is a superb colour-change artist and is extremely difficult to spot even in a small rock pool.

SANDEEL FAMILY

The sandeels (Family Ammodytidae) are small, elongate fishes, found most abundantly in the North Atlantic. They live in coastal waters, often swimming in huge schools in mid-water, but also burrowing into the sea bed.

Greater Sandeel
Hyperoplus lanceolatus
Up to 32cm length. The largest of all sandeels, it occurs in inshore waters from northern Norway and Iceland to northern Spain over sandy bottoms. It feeds on plankton and small fishes, and breeds in spring and summer, the eggs being buried in sand.
Ⓑ 😛

SAND-SMELT FAMILY

Three species of this family (Atherinidae) are found in Europe, one of which inhabits brackish water. They have two fins on the back, the first of which has slender spines, the second branched rays. All species have a silvery line along each side.

Sand-smelt
Atherina presbyter
Maximum length 21cm, but usually 10–15cm. This fish occurs in summer from Scottish and Danish coasts southwards to Gibraltar, but in winter it is rarely found north of Biscay. It lives in inshore waters and lagoons. Small crustaceans and small fishes are its main food. It breeds in summer.
Ⓑ 😛

BLENNY FAMILY

Blennies (Family Blenniidae) are small fishes found world-wide, chiefly in temperate and tropical seas although a few, including one European species, live in freshwater. They are scaleless, with two rays in each pelvic fin on the throat, which they use to raise themselves off the rocks. Many live in tidal pools and in very shallow water.

Shanny
Lipophrys pholis
Up to 20cm. This fish occurs along Atlantic and North Sea coasts as far north as Shetland, but is rare in the western Mediterranean. It is abundant on rocky shores, in pools, under stones or sea weed, and may also be found in pools with shelter on sandy shores. Barnacles, small crustaceans and green sea weed make up its diet. It spawns in spring and summer; the eggs are laid on the underside of a stone and guarded by the male.
Ⓑ 😛

Montagu's Blenny
Coryphoblennius galerita
Up to 8cm. This species occurs along the Mediterranean and Atlantic coasts as far north as southwestern Britain and southern Ireland. Particularly common in rock pools at mid-tide level and in shallow sheltered water, it feeds mainly on barnacles' appendages which it nips off with its sharp teeth. Its eggs are laid in summer in crevices in the rock, where the male guards them.
Ⓑ 😛

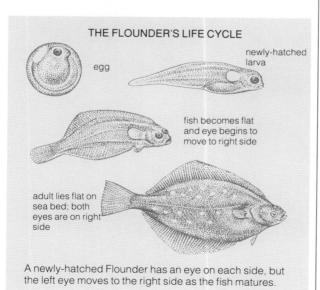

THE FLOUNDER'S LIFE CYCLE

egg

newly-hatched larva

fish becomes flat and eye begins to move to right side

adult lies flat on sea bed; both eyes are on right side

A newly-hatched Flounder has an eye on each side, but the left eye moves to the right side as the fish matures.

GUNNEL FAMILY

Gunnels (Family Pholidae) are small, shallow water fishes which live in the temperate North Atlantic and North Pacific. One species is found in Europe. All have a series of up to 100 sharp spines along the back, and are scaleless.

Butterfish
Pholis gunnellus
Up to 25cm. This fish lives along northern coasts as far south as Brittany. It hides under stones and clumps of seaweed on the shore and in shallow water down to depths of 50m. Its diet comprises worms, small crustaceans and molluscs. Spawning occurs from January to February. The eggs form clumps in crevices or empty mollusc shells and are guarded by one adult, which curls itself around them.
Ⓑ 🐟

GOBY FAMILY

There are up to 2000 species of goby (Family Gobiidae), most of which live in the shallow waters of temperate and tropical seas and estuaries, although a few inhabit freshwater. Their small bodies are scaly, they have two dorsal fins, and the pelvic fins are fused into a disc on the belly.

Common Goby
Pomatoschistus microps
Up to 6cm. This abundant fish occurs from the Baltic Sea to Spain in inshore waters, in intertidal pools, estuaries and brackish lagoons and ditches. It is common on muddy and sandy shores, where it feeds on small crustaceans and larvae. Spawning occurs from April to August; the eggs are laid in the hollow of a mollusc shell where they are guarded by the male.
Ⓑ 🐟

SCULPIN FAMILY

There are about 300 species of sculpin (Family Cottidae) known in the northern hemisphere, most of them marine. They are scaleless, although some have small prickles on their skin; their heads are large and have long spines which are not venomous.

Sea Scorpion
Taurulus bubalis
Up to 17cm. This species occurs from northern Norway to the northern coast of Spain. Abundant on rocky shores in pools and under seaweed, it feeds on crustaceans and small fishes. To help it ambush prey and avoid the attention of predators, it changes colour to blend into its background. Breeding begins in spring, the eggs being laid in clumps among seaweed.
Ⓑ 🐟

RIGHT-EYED FLATFISH FAMILY

Right-eyed flatfish (Family Pleuronectidae) are a large family of flatfishes which have both eyes on the right side of the head. They are widely distributed in cool temperate regions of the Atlantic, Pacific and Indian Oceans. Highly adapted to life on the sea bed, they can even change colour to match their surroundings.

Flounder
Platichthys flesus
Up to 50cm. Distributed widely along all European coasts, this flatfish lives in shallow inshore waters. It is abundant in estuaries and may also occur in freshwater. Its diet is made up of bottom-living invertebrates. It spawns in the sea in spring; the young fish migrate upriver during summer.
Ⓑ 🐟

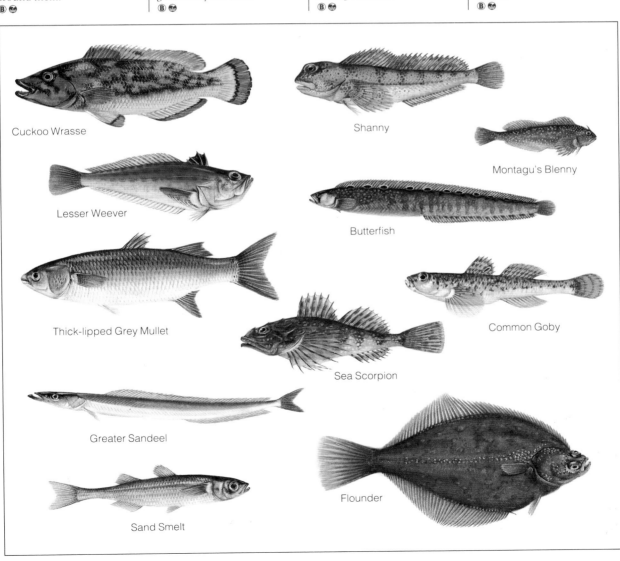

Cuckoo Wrasse

Shanny

Montagu's Blenny

Lesser Weever

Butterfish

Thick-lipped Grey Mullet

Common Goby

Sea Scorpion

Greater Sandeel

Flounder

Sand Smelt

INVERTEBRATES

Invertebrates are those animals that have no backbones. They belong to some 29 different phyla and far outnumber the vertebrates, or backboned animals, which belong to just one phylum – the Chordata. Invertebrates cannot compete in size with the largest vertebrates, but there is a vast range of size among them – from microscopic protozoans to squid measuring up to 15 metres long (including their tentacles) and giant clams weighing 275kg.

Invertebrate Structure
Many invertebrates have no skeleton and rely on the pressure of body fluids to maintain their shape. Others have external skeletons or shells, known as exoskeletons, which give them their shape and also provide protection.

Invertebrate Groups
The simplest invertebrates are the protozoans (Phylum Protozoa), with bodies consisting of just one cell. Within that cell, a protozoan conducts all the essential processes of life. The amoebae are the best known protozoans.

The many-celled invertebrates are much larger than the protozoans. Several phyla contain just a few kinds of rarely observed animals, and most of the animals you are likely to see belong to just five major phyla. The following pages are devoted to these five groups.

The largest phylum is the Arthropoda (see pp. 309–373). The name means 'jointed foot' and all adults have distinctly jointed limbs. Their bodies are divided into segments, and the animals are enclosed in exoskeletons. The main classes are the crustaceans, the insects, the arachnids, the centipedes and the millipedes. They total around a million species.

The Mollusca (pp. 300–308), which includes the slugs and snails, the squid, and the sea shells, has about 100,000 species. The animals are all soft-bodied creatures without any segmentation. Most of them have hard shells.

The Annelida (p. 374) includes a wide range of aquatic and terrestrial worms. They are slender animals with bodies clearly divided into segments. This separates them from several other groups of worm-like creatures, including the nematodes or round worms.

The Echinodermata (pp. 298–299) are confined to the sea. They include the starfishes. All have rough and often spiny skins and all are built on a radially symmetrical plan, meaning that cutting along any diameter will produce two identical halves. Most other animals are bilaterally symmetrical, with only one way of cutting to produce two similar halves.

The fifth major phylum, the Coelenterata (pp. 374–375), is another group of radially symmetrical animals. It includes the sea anemones and jellyfishes.

Times of Appearance and Measurements
Most aquatic invertebrates can be found at any time of the year. Many terrestrial species can also be found at all seasons, although some become dormant in the autumn. Many insects, however, are seasonal in their appearance and the times given are those at which the adults are most likely to be seen. In southern Europe they may appear earlier and continue later than indicated. If no dates are given for a species, it may be assumed that the adults can be found at any time.

The type of measurement used for each group is explained in the relevant introduction.

LEFT: *The Compass Jellyfish, named for its radiating stripes, occurs on the Mediterranean and Atlantic coasts of Europe. Up to 35cm across, it has a painful sting.*

ABOVE: *The Blood Starfish, an echinoderm, ranges from orange to purplish red and lives below low-tide level.*

BELOW: *The Brown-lipped Snail is a typical land-dwelling mollusc, with eyes at the tips of its longer tentacles.*

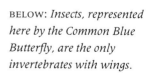

BELOW: *Insects, represented here by the Common Blue Butterfly, are the only invertebrates with wings.*

ECHINODERMS

These animals (Phylum Echinodermata) all live in the sea and many are found around the shore. They are built on a basically circular plan and the skin is rough and often spiny. Water-filled tubes run through the body and give off slender branches, known as tube-feet, which emerge through the body wall. These are used for feeding and for locomotion, and usually have disc-shaped suckers at their tips.

Reproduction is simple – most species release eggs and sperm into the water and leave fertilization to chance. Most echinoderms have planktonic larvae which bear little or no resemblance to the adults.

The Five Classes

The phylum contains five classes. The starfishes (Class Asteroidea) usually have five arms which are not clearly separated from the central disc. The mouth is on the underside, and there are rows of tube-feet under the arms. Many species are detritus-feeders but others are predators. These animals have amazing powers of regeneration. Not only can they regenerate lost arms, but a severed arm can grow a new body. The brittle stars (Class Ophiuroidea) resemble the starfishes, but their slender, brittle arms are sharply separated from the central disc. Although some species capture small items of prey, most feed on detritus. Many burrow in the sand or mud. Mostly globular in shape, the sea urchins (Class Echinoidea) are more spiny than the other echinoderms. Five bands of tube-feet run over the surface. The animals either sift detritus from the mud or scrape algae from the rocks. A chalky shell, called a test, lies just under the skin and is often washed up on the shore when the animal dies. The sea cucumbers (Class Holothuroidea) are sausage-shaped detritus-feeders with the mouth at one end. The skin is leathery. The Class Crinoidea (not illustrated) contains the sea lilies and feather stars, very few of which live in European waters.

Echinoderm means 'spiny skin', and this Common Sunstar clearly shows how this group of animals earned the name. This species is found in northern waters, often among mussel and oyster beds.

Starfishes

Sunstar
Solaster papposus
Family Solasteridae
Up to 25cm across although rarely more than 15cm. This common species ranges from purple to orange-red. It usually has 8–15 arms, although older specimens may have more. It lives on stony or sandy bottoms, down to 40 metres, and feeds on other echinoderms. It occurs in cool seas, from the English Channel northwards. *S. endeca* is very similar but has slightly longer arms.
Ⓑ 😎

Cushion Starlet
Asterina gibbosa
Family Asterinidae
Up to 7cm across. This relatively smooth species is usually yellow or green, but brick-red specimens are occasionally found. It lives in rocky areas down to depths of 100 metres, and can climb well with the aid of its tube-feet. Molluscs, worms, and various other echinoderms are its main prey. Unlike most starfishes, the female lays her eggs in clusters under stones, where they are fertilized by one or more attendant males. It is found from the English Channel southwards.
Ⓑ 😎

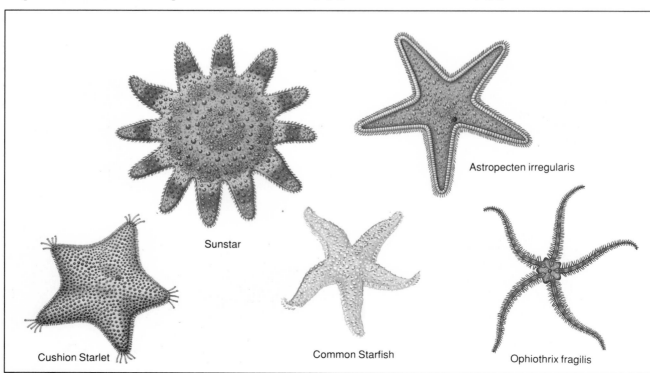

Sunstar

Astropecten irregularis

Cushion Starlet

Common Starfish

Ophiothrix fragilis

THE STARFISH'S POWERFUL SUCTION

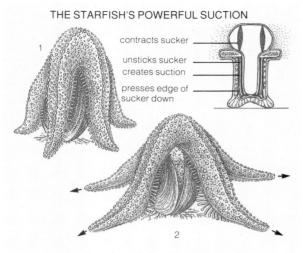

contracts sucker

unsticks sucker
creates suction

presses edge of
sucker down

1. Applying its suckers to both valves of a cockle, the starfish exerts a powerful pull. 2. As the valves gape, the starfish pours its digestive juices and ingests the cockle.

Astropecten irregularis
Family Astropectinidae
Up to 12cm across. Red to purplish brown, this species is often called a comb-star because of the spines on the edges of its arms. It burrows in sand and mud and eats a variety of small creatures, including small bivalves which it swallows whole. The tube-feet have no suckers. *A. aurantiacus* is similar, but grows to a diameter of about 60cm. It is red or orange and the spiny plates along the edge of the arms are often yellow. It lives in the Mediterranean and on the Atlantic coast of Portugal.
Ⓑ 😎

Common Starfish
Asterias rubens
Family Asteriidae
Up to 30cm across. Pale yellow or orange, through deep red to violet. It lives on stones and coarse sand and is commonly washed up on the shore. It feeds mainly on bivalves and is a serious pest on oyster farms.
Ⓑ 😎

Brittle Stars

Ophiothrix fragilis
Family Ophiotrichidae
Disc 2cm across; arms up to 7cm long. Its colouration varies, but this species is distinguished from most other brittle stars by its star-shaped disc. Its spiny arms are used to filter food particles from the water. One of the most common brittle stars, it is often abundant just below low-tide level and, in some places, large numbers may cover the sea bed.
Ⓑ 😎

Sea Urchins

Edible Sea Urchin
Echinus esculentus
Family Echinidae
Up to 16cm across, although usually much smaller. The living animal is pink, red or purple and densely spined. Long tube-feet, mostly with strong suckers, drag it along and also anchor it when necessary. It lives on rocky and gravelly bottoms and feeds on algae. Edible parts are the bulky reproductive organs. The test is deep pink with white spots and, being rather thick, is often washed on to the shore intact. This species is replaced in the Mediterranean by some very similar urchins.
Ⓑ 😎

Rock Urchin
Paracentrotus lividus
Up to 6cm across. This strongly spined species may be green, brown or violet. It lives in shallow water, usually on limestone rocks in which it excavates a small cavity. It often camouflages itself with fragments of shells and seaweeds, which are held in place by some of the tube-feet. It feeds on debris.
Ⓑ 😎

Violet Heart Urchin
Spatangus purpureus
Family Spatangidae
Up to 12cm long. This species is distinctly heart-shaped and the short, densely-packed, purplish spines give it a furry appearance. Its tube-feet have no suckers and the mouth lacks browsing teeth. The mouth is near the front, enabling the urchin to feed on detritus as it burrows through sand and mud with the aid of paddle-shaped spines on its underside. Its test is very thin.
Ⓑ 😎

Sea Cucumbers

Holothuria forskali
Family Holothuriidae
Up to 30cm long. This lethargic creature is dark brown to greenish black. It can be found on mud or sand, but more often wedges itself into rock crevices around low-tide level. It moves slowly by means of the rows of suckered tube-feet on its lower surface and scoops up detritus with the branching tube-feet around its mouth.
Ⓑ 😎

Edible Sea Urchin

test of Violet
Heart Urchin

Violet Heart Urchin

Rock Urchin

Holothuria forskali

MOLLUSCS

The molluscs (Phylum Mollusca) are soft-bodied invertebrates, most of which are protected by hard external shells. There are nearly 100,000 known species, ranging from the highly mobile oceanic squids to the slow-moving slugs and snails of our gardens and the completely sedentary oysters. Because the animals are so varied, it is not possible to give a simple definition of a mollusc, but one feature which is present in all the major groups is the mantle. This is a thick cloak of skin which envelops at least a part of the body. The space between the mantle and the rest of the body is called the mantle cavity and it is connected to the outside world by one or more openings.

In most aquatic molluscs the cavity contains gills: water is pumped in and out of the cavity and the gills absorb oxygen from it. The gills also play a major role in food collection in the bivalve molluscs (see p. 306). In land molluscs and many freshwater snails the mantle cavity acts as a lung: pond snails periodically come to the surface and expel bubbles of stale air from the lung before taking in fresh air.

Mollusc Shells

The mantle is also responsible for the formation of the shell, which has three layers. There is a horny outer layer, which gives the shell much of its colour, a middle layer composed of columnar crystals of calcium carbonate, and a smooth, often pearly, inner layer. The outer and middle layers are secreted by cells around the edge of the mantle; the inner layer is secreted by the whole mantle surface. The inner layer can thus be repaired if a shell is damaged, but the mollusc cannot restore the outer layers.

The Six Classes

Living molluscs are grouped into six classes, but this book concentrates on the three most important – the slugs and snails (Gastropoda), the bivalves (Lamellibranchia) and the squid, cuttlefish and octopus (Cephalopoda). The other three classes are all small groups, the members of which are entirely confined to the sea. They are the Scaphopoda, which includes the tusk shells; the Amphineura, which contains the chitons, or coat-of-mail shells; and the Monoplacophora, an ancient group represented today by just one deep-sea creature called *Neopilina*.

Bivalve molluscs (left) have two halves or valves to the shell, hinged at the top. They are usually measured by their width. Univalve molluscs (right), which have a single, usually coiled valve, are measured by their height. The opening of the univalve shell is nearly always on the right (dextral condition) as you look at the shell.

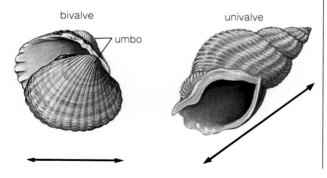

bivalve

umbo

univalve

SLUGS AND SNAILS

With about 60,000 species living on land, in the sea, and in fresh water, the Class Gastropoda is by far the largest group of molluscs. Gastropoda means 'belly-footed' and refers to the large muscular organ, known as the foot, on which the animals glide along. The head, with one or two pairs of retractile tentacles, is not clearly separated from the foot. Most of the snail's internal organs are contained within the visceral hump, which is coiled on top of the foot and enclosed in the mantle and shell. The snail can pull its foot into its shell as well, and many species close the shell with a horny disc known as the operculum. Most frequently found in sea snails, the operculum can be seen at the tip of the foot when the snail is active. Slugs are simply snails which have lost their shells during evolution. Their internal organs have been packed into the foot and the mantle has been much reduced or, as in the sea slugs, lost altogether.

The Great Black Slug, seen here in its orange form, lays its eggs at any time of the year. The opening through which the pearly white eggs emerge lies just in front of the lung opening, but is not normally visible. The eggs hatch in 4–6 weeks.

The Rasping Radula

All gastropods possess a rasp-like tongue called a radula. It is clothed with horny teeth and nibbles away at the animal's food rather like a cheesegrater. The front of the radula wears away quite quickly, especially in those species that rasp algae from rocks, but it grows continuously and new teeth are always moving forward from the back.

Reproduction

Most gastropods have separate sexes. Many marine species merely scatter their eggs and sperm into the water and leave fertilization to chance, but the more advanced species pair up and fertilization takes place internally. There is often a free-swimming larval stage which helps to scatter the species. Many land snails and slugs are hermaphrodite, with male and female organs in the same individual, but they still pair up and mate (see the photograph on p. 301). Their courtship and mating behaviour is often complex.

Land and Freshwater Species

These are herbivorous or carnivorous animals, nearly all belonging to the lung-breathing group known as pulmonates. Land species usually have two pairs of tentacles, with eyes at the tips of the longer ones. Water snails have only one pair of tentacles, with eyes at the base. Terrestrial species are active mainly at night or after daytime rain. They can be found throughout the year, although they hide away in very cold or dry weather. Snails often seal up their shells with slime which hardens into a parchment-like cap. Very few lands snails have opercula. All the species described here eat living or dead plant matter. Measurements given for the slugs are lengths when fully extended and, unless otherwise stated, those given for the snails are the shell heights, measured as shown in the diagram on page 300.

Great Black Slug
Arion ater
Family Arionidae
Up to 15cm. This is one of the round-back slugs, with no trace of a keel on the back. Usually black, it may also be grey, brown or orange, with the orange form particularly common in the south. Its lung opens near the front of the mantle on the right. When disturbed it contracts to a hemisphere and sways from side to side. Like all slugs, it is covered with slime, which helps to prevent desiccation and also gives some protection from enemies. In this species the slime is extremely sticky. It feeds on rotting vegetation.
Ⓑ Ⓞ ⏥

Great Grey Slug
Limax maximus
Family Limacidae
Up to 20cm. With a distinct keel on the rear quarter of the body, this is one of the largest slugs found in Britain. Its lung opens near the back of the mantle on the right. Often common in gardens, it feeds on fungi and decaying matter. The species has an amazing courtship – mating takes place while the animals are suspended in mid-air from a rope of slime. It is absent from the far north.
Ⓑ Ⓞ Ⓞ ⏥

Great Black Slugs mating – their genitalia are extruded to make contact and exchange sperm in the middle of the slimy coil. Like most land snails and slugs, this species is hermaphrodite.

Netted Slug
Deroceras reticulatum
Up to 5cm. This species has a keel on the hind end and its lung opening is near the back of the mantle on the right. It may be cream, brown or grey in colour, usually with some darker spots, and it exudes a milky slime when handled. It is one of the commonest slugs in Britain and a frequent pest of lettuces and other green vegetables. *D. agreste* of northern and upland areas is very similar, but never speckled.
Ⓑ Ⓞ ⏥

Budapest Slug
Milax budapestensis
Family Milacidae
Up to 6cm. This slug has an orange or yellow keel running back from the mantle and a sole with a dark central stripe. Its lung opening is near the back of the mantle on the right. The slug contracts into a 'C' when disturbed. A serious pest of potatoes and other root crops, it is rarely found far from human habitation. It is very common in Britain but rare elsewhere in western Europe.
Ⓑ Ⓞ

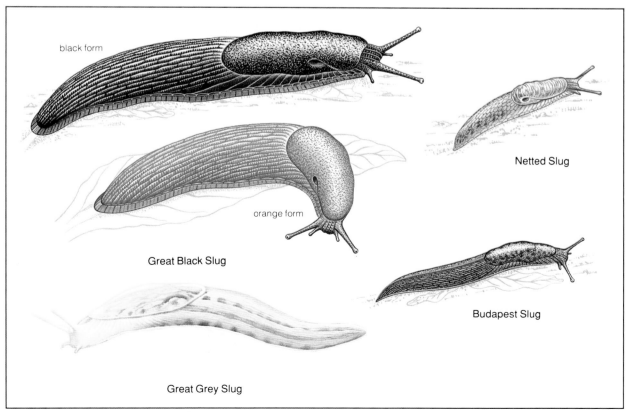

black form

orange form

Great Black Slug

Netted Slug

Budapest Slug

Great Grey Slug

Round-mouthed Snail
Pomatias elegans
Family Pomatiidae
Up to 1.3cm. This species has a rather thick shell with distinctly rounded whorls and a round opening. It is one of the very few land snails with an operculum and its eyes are at the base of the tentacles. It inhabits rough vegetation on lime-rich soils in southern and central Europe.
Ⓑ☻ⓜ

Two-toothed Door Snail
Clausilia bidentata
Family Clausiliidae
Up to 1.2cm. The spindle-shaped shell is sinistral – the opening is on the left. There are two prominent teeth inside the mouth of the shell. This snail is abundant on damp walls and rocks, where it grazes on mosses and algae. It is one of many similar species. All members of the family have sinistral shells.
Ⓑ☻✿ⓜ

Kentish Snail
Monacha cantiana
Family Helicidae
Up to 1.4cm high and 2cm across. This snail's shell is slightly flattened and creamy white with a reddish tinge near the opening, although it often looks steely grey with the snail inside it. It feeds on decaying vegetation in rough grassy places, mainly on lime-rich soils. It occurs in southern and central Europe, but mainly in the west. The similar *C. cartusiana* has a smaller shell with a dark brown lip.
Ⓑ✿☻ⓜ

Strawberry Snail
Trichia striolata
Up to 1.4cm across. The shell of this species is flattened, and sandy to purplish-brown, with a strong white ridge just inside the mouth when mature. Hairy when young, it likes damp, shady places in hedgerows, fields, waste ground and gardens, where it is a pest. It is found throughout central Europe. The closely related *T. hispida* is similar but a little smaller and its shell remains hairy throughout its life. The hairs are especially obvious in cool and damp habitats.
Ⓑ☻✿ⓜ

Sandhill Snail
Theba pisana
Up to 2cm. This snail has a dull, chalky white shell, often with a pink flush around the elliptical mouth and variable dark banding. It feeds on various plants and also on other snails. It lives in dry places, mainly near the sea, and congregates in dense clusters on dry plants in the summer, sealing its shell tightly against the drought. The snail keeps cooler here than it would if it stayed on the ground. Many other snails pass the summer in this way, but rarely in such large numbers. Uncommon in Britain, it is found in southern and central Europe and is especially common around the Mediterranean. *Cernuella virgata* is quite similar but has a much larger umbilicus - the dimple in the bottom of the shell. The shell is also a little more pointed.
Ⓑ☻ⓜ

Clusters of Sandhill Snails are a familiar sight in southern Europe in summer, when millions escape the hot ground by climbing vegetation.

Brown-lipped Snail
Cepaea nemoralis
Up to 20cm. This species sports a round, basically yellow, pink or brown shell with a dark brown lip. There are up to five spiral brown bands, some or all of which may fuse together or disappear completely. The snail lives in rough, grassy places and in woods. Woodland specimens are mostly pink or brown. Most grassland specimens are yellow and often have no bands at all. Hedgerow specimens usually have the strongest banding. The White-lipped snail (*C. hortensis*) is almost identical but its shell usually has a white lip.
Ⓑ☻✿☻ⓜ

Garden Snail
Helix aspersa
Up to 3.5cm. A familiar snail with a more or less globular shell that is yellowish brown with variable dark markings and a lightly wrinkled texture. Abundant in many well-vegetated habitats, it is a common garden pest which attacks the leaves of a wide range of plants. Found in southern and central Europe, but mainly in the west, it is eaten as a delicacy in many areas, especially in France. In the northern and eastern parts of its range it is confined on the whole to areas of human settlement.
Ⓑ☻✿ⓜ

Roman Snail
Helix pomatia
Up to 5cm. This snail has a very thick shell with coarse growth rings and spiral brown bands which are usually indistinct and sometimes absent. One of Europe's largest snails, it lives in woods and grassy places on lime-rich soils and is sometimes a pest in vineyards and gardens in the south. It is eaten in many areas, often after fattening on special diets, and is often called the edible snail. It is also known as the apple snail and the vine snail. It ranges through southern and central Europe but is very local in Britain.
Ⓑ☻✿ⓜ

THE LOVE-LIFE OF THE GARDEN SNAIL

1. The snails smear each other with mucus as they get acquainted. 2. Each shoots a stimulatory dart into the other. 3. They extrude their genitalia and exchange sperm.

Great Pond Snail
Limnaea stagnalis
Family Limnaeidae
Up to 6cm. The largest of several similar species, this snail has a long and very thin shell, non-retractable tentacles which are broad and flat, and no operculum. It is an air-breather, living in still and slow-moving water with plenty of plantlife. It feeds on both plant and animal matter, either living or dead, and lays its eggs in gelatinous masses on the stems and leaves of water plants. The related Wandering Snail *(L. peregra)* is similar but its shell is only 25mm high and it has a relatively short spire.
Ⓑ ☻

Great Ram's-horn Snail
Planorbarius corneus
Family Planorbidae
Up to 3cm across. The shell of this water snail is coiled in a flat spiral. The snail itself is deep brown or reddish, owing to its high haemoglobin content. The haemoglobin absorbs oxygen from the water and, although the snail is basically an air-breather, it comes to the surface much less often than the pond snails. The largest of several otherwise similar species, it lives in weedy ponds and feeds on the vegetation. It has no operculum.
Ⓑ ☻

River Limpet
Ancylastrum fluviatile
Family Ancylidae
Up to 0.8cm. The shell of this species resembles a small conical hat, with the point facing backwards and slightly to the right. Like the marine limpets, to which it is not closely related, the River Limpet clings tightly to stones and browses on the algae that grow on them. Although it belongs to the air-breathing group, it obtains all its oxygen from the water and never needs to come to the surface. It is very common in most clear streams and lakes, although its colours help to camouflage it well on the stones and it is not easily seen. The related Lake Limpet *(Ancylus lacustris)* is similar but has a flatter and narrower shell, with the point turning to the left. Restricted to still water, it is normally found clinging to water plants.
Ⓑ ☻

Round-mouthed Snail

Brown-lipped Snail

Garden Snail

Two-toothed Door Snail

Kentish Snail

Roman Snail

Strawberry Snail

Great Pond Snail

Great Ram's-horn Snail

Sandhill Snail

River Limpet

Sea Slugs and Snails

These resemble their terrestrial counterparts in having one or two pairs of tentacles, but the eyes, when present, are at the base of one pair of tentacles. The rasping radula (see p. 300) is used to obtain plant or animal food and can even be used to drill through the shells of other molluscs. All are basically gill-breathers. Many sea snails have long inlet siphons through which water is drawn into the mantle cavity. Sea slugs have lost both shell and mantle and breathe with the aid of false gills on their backs. Sea snails and sea slugs live mainly on rocky seabeds and shores. They shelter under seaweeds when the tide goes out in the daytime, although they often move about to feed in the damp air at night. Empty shells are washed up on beaches of all kinds. Unless stated otherwise, the following measurements given for the snails are shell heights (see p. 300).

Common Ormer
Haliotis tuberculata
Family Haliotidae
Up to 8cm long. The shell of this sea snail is coiled only at the apex and resembles half a bivalve shell, although the row of breathing holes readily identifies it as an ormer. It is greenish-brown to brick red, with a very pearly inside. The animal browses on algae growing on rocks and stones. It is found from the Channel Islands southwards.
😊

Common Limpet
Patella vulgaris
Family Patellidae
Up to 6cm across. The shell of this species is greenish-brown, conical and more or less circular at the base. It is almost uniformly pearly white inside. Shells that live high on the shore, where wave action is strongest, tend to be taller than those living in quieter waters further down. The animal attaches itself very firmly to a rock

with its circular foot, but wanders off to scrape algae from the surrounding rocks when the tide is in and also when the tide is out at night. After feeding it always returns to the same spot and the edge of the shell gradually wears a shallow groove, into which it fits perfectly. It lives on western and northern shores. Several similar species occur on the lower and middle shore.
Ⓑ😊

Blue-rayed Limpet
Patina pellucida
Up to 2cm across. The shell of this limpet is very thin and marked with brilliant blue lines when young. It becomes thicker with age and gradually loses the blue lines. It is normally found browsing on large seaweeds on northern and western shores.
Ⓑ😊

Painted Topshell
Calliostoma zizyphinum
Family Trochidae
Up to 4cm. The shell is orange, red or pink with darker spots. The outer layer often wears away to reveal the thick pearly layer in places. The animal browses on seaweeds on the lower shore, usually below low-tide level in northern regions, and is common in rock pools.
Ⓑ😊

Common Periwinkle
Littorina littorea
Family Littorinidae
Up to 3cm. Protected by a thick, greenish grey or almost black shell, this is the familiar fishmonger's winkle. It browses on seaweeds among rocks and stones near low tide level. Empty shells are often taken over by hermit crabs (see p. 312).
Ⓑ😊

Flat Periwinkle
Littorina littoralis
Up to 1.5cm. This species has a yellow, orange or pale brown shell, with or without darker bands. Flatter than other winkles and almost circular in outline, it feeds on seaweeds on the middle shore. The dark brown Small Periwinkle (*L. neritoides*), only 7mm high, lives just above high water mark. Its mantle cavity functions as a lung and it is well on the way to becoming a terrestrial species.
Ⓑ😊

The colourful shells of the Flat Periwinkle can often be found clinging to wracks and other seaweeds when the tide goes out.

Slipper Limpet
Crepidula fornicata
Family Calyptraeidae
Up to 6cm long. This species gets its name for the thick white plate extending halfway across the underside of the shell. It is a sedentary filter-feeder and a serious pest in mussel and oyster beds. It settles on the shells and intercepts their food supplies. Slipper limpets often occur in chains. The lowest animals in a chain are the oldest and they are all female, while those on the top are young males. The animals change their sex as they get older.
Ⓑ😊

Common Wentletrap
Clathrus clathrus
Family Epitoniidae
Up to 4.5cm. This shell is white to deep red and beautifully decorated with prominent ridges. The animal lives below low-tide level, ploughing through the sand and mud with its broad foot as it searches for worms and other small prey.
Ⓑ😊

Needle Shell
Bittium reticulatum
Family Cerithiidae
Up to 1.5cm. The tightly packed whorls on the shell each bear spiral rows of small tubercles. It is pale to dark brown, with a small siphon canal. The animal browses on seaweeds on mud and sand, usually below low-tide level.
Ⓑ😊

Pelican's Foot
Aporrhais pespelecani
Family Aporrhaidae
Up to 5cm. This species is named for the way in which the lip of the shell, which is mature yellow to dark brown, is drawn out into the shape of

a bird's foot. The animal burrows in sand and mud, usually in fairly deep water. It swallows detritus and digests any organic matter in it.
Ⓑ😊

European Cowrie
Trivia monacha
Family Cypraeidae
Up to 1.2cm long. The oval shell is ribbed, pink or greyish brown, and flattened on the lower side where there is a long, narrow opening. The mantle is extended and wrapped around the shell in life. The animal lives on rocky shores and is quite common in rock pools. It feeds on small sea squirts.
Ⓑ😊

Murex brandaris
Family Muricidae
Up to 9cm. The pale grey or yellowish shell of this animal has long spines and a very long siphon canal. It lives on muddy and stony bottoms in the Mediterranean, eating other molluscs as well as carrion. Its body contains a rich purple dye, known as tyrian purple, which the Ancient Romans used to dye their robes.
😊😊

Common Dog Whelk
Nucella lapillus
Up to 4.5cm. The shell of this snail is brown or yellow, often banded with white, and very thick. Abundant on rocks on the middle shore, it feeds on other molluscs and barnacles. It uses its radula, which is at the end of a slender proboscis, to drill through their shells and takes about two days to get through a mussel shell. This species is found on western and northern coasts.
Ⓑ😊

Sting Winkle
Ocinebra erinacea
Up to 6cm. A white or sand-coloured shell with prominent ribs protects this mollusc. It lives on stony bottoms and firm mud, where it drills holes in other mollusc shells with its radula, aided by chemical secretions.
Ⓑ 😎

Common Whelk
Buccinum undatum
Family Buccinidae
Up to 12cm. This whelk has a white to sandy grey shell, with a short, curved siphon canal. It lives on sand, mud, or stony bottoms, feeding on carrion. It also preys on bivalves, wedging their shells open with the lip of its own shell and then inserting its long proboscis. It lives on northern and western shores.
Ⓑ 😎

Sea Hare
Aplysia depilans
Family Aplysiidae
Up to 25cm long. This is halfway between a sea snail and a sea slug. It has a very thin, flexible shell which is completely covered by the folds of the green or brown mantle. The animal browses on seaweeds, usually below low-tide. It is found mainly in the Mediterranean, although there are similar species elsewhere. Sea hares eject purple dyes when alarmed.
😎

Grey Sea Slug
Aeolidia papillosa
Family Aeolidiidae
Up to 10cm long. This is the largest British sea slug. Grey to brown with many white-spotted, unbranched gills on its back, it feeds on sea anemones. It occurs on western shores to the north of the Bay of Biscay. There are many similar species and they include some of the most colourful and attractive of all marine animals.
Ⓑ 😎

Sea Slug
Dendronotus frondosus
Family Dendronotidae
Up to 6cm long. This slug may be cream, yellow or pale pink with numerous branched gills on its back. It browses on small coelenterates on rocky shores around northern and western coasts.
Ⓑ 😎

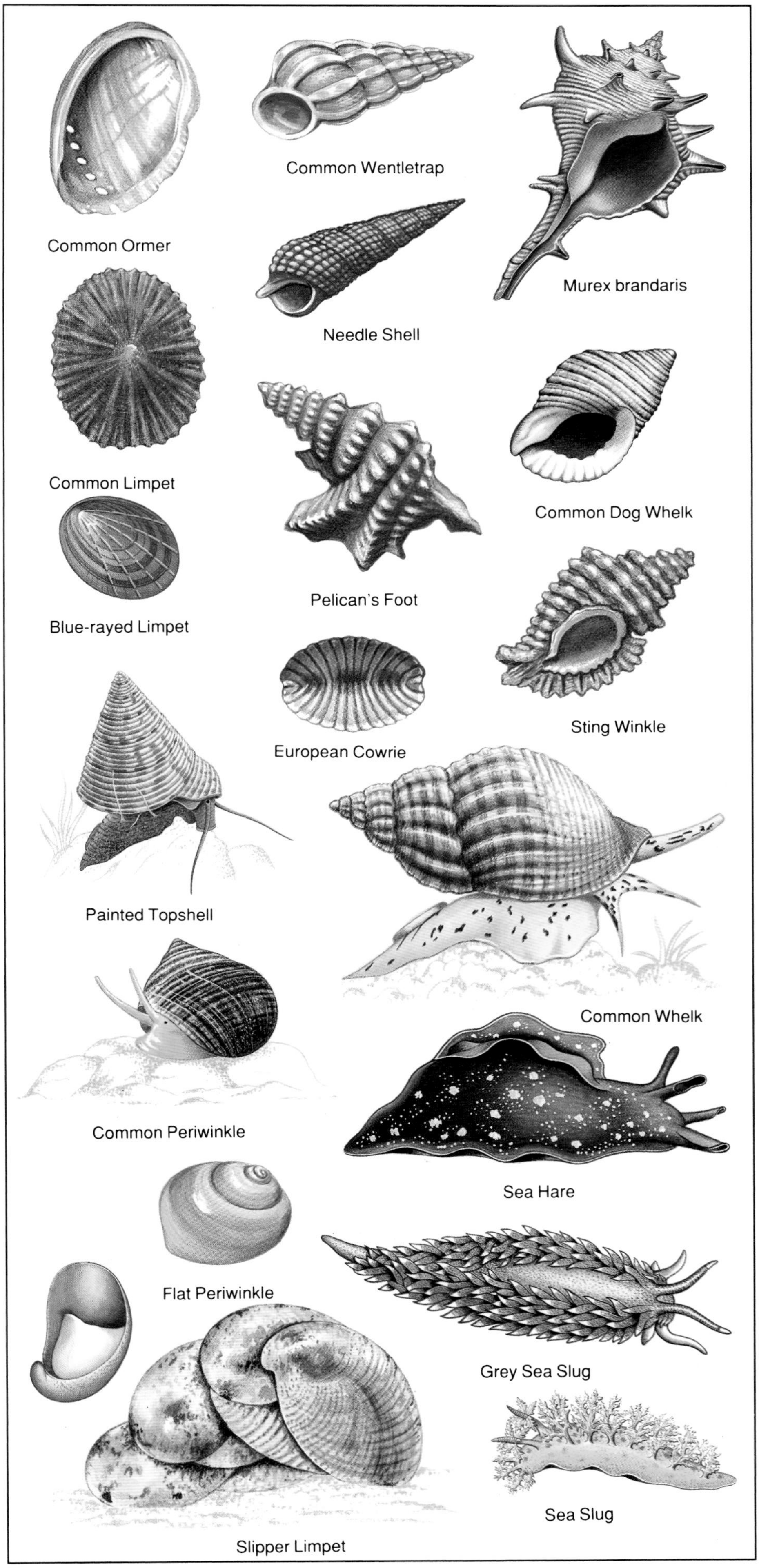

Common Ormer

Common Wentletrap

Needle Shell

Murex brandaris

Common Limpet

Blue-rayed Limpet

Pelican's Foot

Common Dog Whelk

European Cowrie

Sting Winkle

Painted Topshell

Common Whelk

Common Periwinkle

Sea Hare

Flat Periwinkle

Grey Sea Slug

Sea Slug

Slipper Limpet

305

BIVALVES

This is a group (Class Lamellibranchia) of 20,000 or so species whose shells are composed of two halves or valves. Each valve is asymmetrical and has a prominent point called the umbo. The valves are hinged around the umbo, usually with interlocking teeth and a tough, horny ligament. Strong muscles close the shell but, when they relax, the hinge ligament causes it to gape. The scars where the muscles were attached are visible in an empty shell. All bivalves live in water and all are filter-feeders. They use their large gills to strain food particles from a stream of water passing over them. The mantle is drawn out to form two tubular siphons – one to carry water to the gills and the other to carry it away again. Some bivalves have very long inlet siphons which they use to suck debris from the sea bed. Most have a muscular foot for burrowing into sand or mud, but there is no head. Most species have separate sexes, but a few are hermaphrodite. Eggs and sperm are usually just scattered into the water.

Bivalve Habitats

Some bivalves live in fresh water, but most live in the sea. Huge populations of bivalves live on the sea bed, usually burrowing in sand or mud. When they die, their empty shells are often cast up on the beach, sometimes forming huge banks. The hinges usually break as the shells are tossed about by the waves, and most of the shells on the beach are single valves. The habitats given in the descriptions below are those of the living animals. Measurements are taken across the width of the shell (see p. 300).

Swan Mussel
Anodonta cygnea
Family Unionidae
Up to 23cm. This is Europe's largest freshwater mussel. The shell is yellowish to greenish brown, depending on the amount of the horny outer layer remaining, and is very blunt at the rear where the frilly-edged siphons protrude. It has no hinge teeth. This species lives partly buried in the mud in still and slow-moving water.
Ⓑ☻

Common Mussel
Mytilus edulis
Family Mytilidae
Up to 15cm. The shell of this bivalve is brown, blue or black and hinged at the narrow, front end of the curved side. It attaches itself to rocks and stones with a cluster of tough, horny threads called the byssus. Valued as human food, the species is cultivated on a large scale in Europe, often in estuaries and tidal lagoons.
Ⓑ☻

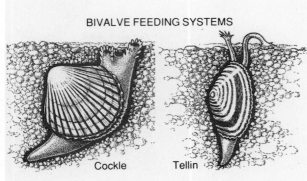

BIVALVE FEEDING SYSTEMS

Cockle   Tellin

The cockle draws water in through one siphon, extracts food particles from it, and pumps it out the other siphon. The tellin uses its siphon to suck debris off the sea bed.

Queen Scallop
Chlamys opercularis
Family Pectinidae
Up to 9cm. The strongly ribbed shell is almost circular with a straight, toothless hinge and slightly unequal 'ears'. It is usually pink or orange, but may also be yellow or brown. It lives on coarse sand and usually lies on its right valve, which is slightly flatter than the left one. It can swim jerkily by flapping its valves and forcing water out. It can also control its direction surprisingly well by bringing the edges of the mantle together at different points and shooting water out in different directions.
Ⓑ☻

Oyster
Ostrea edulis
Family Ostreidae
Up to 15cm. The shell is almost circular, but many are deformed as a result of growing in overcrowded conditions. The surface carries very rough concentric growth lines. The left valve is bowl-shaped and permanently fixed to rocks or stones, while the right valve is flat and forms a lid. Oysters live from low-tide level down to about 50m. They are widely cultivated for food. Tiles are placed in the water to provide suitable footholds for the free-swimming larvae (spat). In good feeding conditions the Oyster reaches adult size in about four years.
Ⓑ☻

Portuguese Oyster
Crassostrea angulata
Up to 10cm. The shell is longer and narrower than that of the common Oyster and the left valve is much deeper. It usually has deeply indented margins, into which the lid fits very neatly. There is just one purple muscle scar in each valve. The animal lives in the Atlantic and is edible. The Mediterranean Jewel-box (*Chama gryphoides*) is similar, but only about 6cm long and with two muscle scars in each valve.
Ⓑ☻

Common Cockle
Cardium edule
Family Cardiidae
Up to 5cm. This familiar species is protected by a white to mid-brown shell with 22–26 coarse ribs. The hinge

has two main teeth close to the umbo. It lives in sand and mud from the lower shore downwards and is often abundant in estuaries. Millions are taken each year for human food. It also supports huge populations of oystercatchers and other wading birds.
Ⓑ☻

Thin Tellin
Tellina tenuis
Family Tellinidae
Up to 3cm. The yellow, pink or red shell is very thin, but the hinge is strong and the valves commonly stay joined long after the animal's death. It lives vertically in sand from the lower shore downwards and sucks detritus from the sea bed with a long, mobile inlet siphon.
Ⓑ☻

Banded Wedge Shell
Donax vittatus
Family Donacidae
Up to 3cm. An oblong shell with the umbo towards the front typifies this creature. It is cream, yellow or brown on the outside, with or without dark bands, and purple or yellow on the inside. The animal lives in sand near low-tide level and feeds with long siphons like the Tellin.
Ⓑ☻

Banded Carpet Shell
Venerupis rhomboides
Family Veneridae
Up to 5cm. This species has a sandy brown shell with three or four slightly darker rays radiating from the umbo. When mature the shell often has zig-zag brown lines near the margin. There are three converging teeth below the umbo. The animal has short siphons and lives in a shallow burrow in mud or sand, usually below low-tide level.
Ⓑ☻

Rayed Trough Shell
Mactra corallina
Family Mactridae
Up to 7cm. The shell is thin, with a blunt umbo from which several white rays fan out across the surface. The inner surface varies from pink to violet. It lives just below the surface on sandy bottoms and feeds with short siphons. In some areas it exists at densities of 8,000 per square metre.
Ⓑ☻

Otter Shell
Lutraria lutraria
Family Lutrariidae
Up to 1.4cm. This mollusc has a distinctly elliptical, off-white to pink shell, with a brown outer skin which flakes off in patches. The valves gape slightly at each end. There is a spoon-shaped tooth under the umbo in each valve. The animal has long siphons, fused together to form a stout trunk, and burrows deeply in sand and mud.
Ⓑ 😕

Sand Gaper
Mya arenaria
Family Myidae
Up to 15cm. The shell is white to sand-coloured with peeling grey skin. It gapes at both ends. The left valve, smaller and more domed than the right one, contains a large, spoon-like tooth. The right valve has a deep groove to hold the tooth. The animal has huge siphons, fused together as in the Otter Shell. It lives in mud and sand, as much as 40cm below the surface. It cannot burrow again if dug up. The mollusc is known as the Soft-shelled Clam in America.
Ⓑ 😕

Large Razor Shell
Ensis siliqua
Family Solenidae
Up to 20cm. The shell is open at both ends, but with a short, toothed hinge at the front. The animal lives vertically in sand and feeds with short siphons. It can burrow at great speed by repeatedly extending and contracting its muscular foot. The related *E. ensis* is a smaller species with a curved shell.
Ⓑ 😕

Common Piddock
Pholas dactylus
Family Pholadidae
Up to 12cm. The shell is white and gapes at both ends. The thin valves have no hinge ligament, but there is a slender, curved tooth just under each umbo. The front end of the shell is very rough and rasp-like and is used to bore holes in soft rocks. The animal becomes completely and permanently enclosed in its self-made tomb and feeds by extending long siphons into the water.
Ⓑ 😕

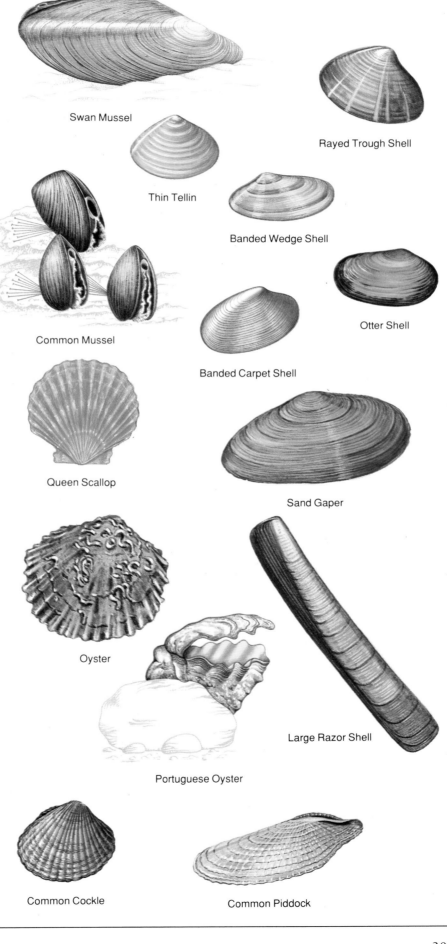

Swan Mussel

Rayed Trough Shell

Thin Tellin

Banded Wedge Shell

Common Mussel

Otter Shell

Banded Carpet Shell

Queen Scallop

Sand Gaper

Oyster

Large Razor Shell

Portuguese Oyster

Common Cockle

Common Piddock

CUTTLEFISH, OCTOPUS AND SQUID

These are highly mobile, predatory molluscs (Class Cephalopoda) in which the foot is divided into a number of sucker-covered tentacles surrounding the mouth. There are about 600 species and all are marine. There is no real shell, though the squid's body is supported by a horny plate embedded in the mantle and the cuttlefish is similarly supported by the familiar chalky 'cuttlebone', which is often found on beaches. The eyes are large and very efficient, and there is a horny, parrot-like beak in the centre of the arms. The salivary glands secrete a poison which quickly paralyzes prey.

Jet Propulsion

The body behind the head and tentacles is enclosed in a very thick, muscular mantle which opens to the outside by way of a tubular siphon or funnel and a number of other smaller openings. Rapid contraction of the mantle forces water out through the funnel and sends the animal speeding along by jet propulsion. It usually travels backwards, but can change direction by bending the siphon in different directions. When threatened or alarmed, most species can emit a dark fluid, usually known as ink, from a sac. This forms a cloud in the water and confuses an enemy while the cephalopod makes its escape. The animals also have an amazing ability to change colour to conceal themselves against different backgrounds. Under nervous control, the system works very rapidly and can produce quite complicated patterns. It is especially well developed in the cuttlefish. The sexes are always separate and courtship rituals are often complex. Cephalopods feed on a variety of fishes as well as crustaceans such as crabs and prawns. The group contains the largest of all invertebrates, but most members are quite small and, despite their sinister reputations, most are quite harmless to people.

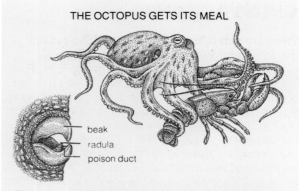

THE OCTOPUS GETS ITS MEAL

beak
radula
poison duct

The octopus's eight sucker-covered arms hold its prey tightly while its parrot-like beak injects a paralysing venom. The beak then bites the prey into small pieces.

Common Cuttlefish
Sepia officinalis
Family Sepiidae
Up to 30cm long. This animal's flat, oval body has eight short tentacles and two longer ones that can be shot out to catch shrimps and similar prey. It keeps close to the sea bed, over bare sand or vegetation. It swims by jet propulsion, or else more slowly by waving the fin surrounding the mantle. Its cuttlebone is often washed up on the beach. There are several similar species.
Ⓑ 🦑

Common Octopus
Octopus vulgaris
Family Octopodidae
Up to 3m across the extended arms, but usually much smaller; the arms are usually under 50cm long. The bag-like body has eight arms, each bearing two rows of suckers. A shy animal, it lurks in crevices on the sea bed and darts out to catch fish and crustaceans. It can inflict a painful bite if handled. It occurs no further north than the English Channel and is rare on British coasts.
Ⓑ 🦑

Common Squid
Loligo vulgaris
Family Loliginidae
Up to 50cm long. This animal has a cylindrical body with a diamond-shaped, stabilizing tail-fin. It has eight short arms and two long ones which are fired out to catch prey. This squid swims in shoals, often near the surface, and feeds mainly on fish. One of many similar species, it rarely occurs further north than the Dutch coast.
Ⓑ 🦑

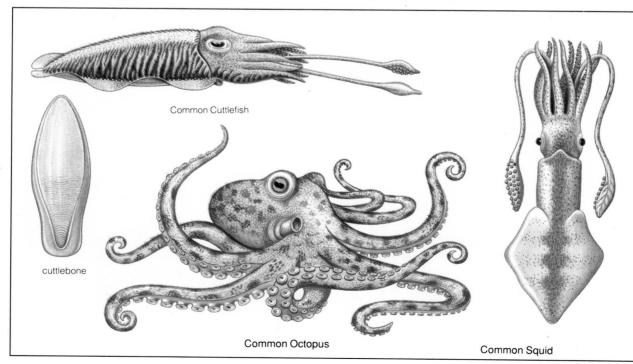

Common Cuttlefish

cuttlebone

Common Octopus

Common Squid

CRUSTACEANS

These animals (Class Crustacea), which nearly all live in water, form one of the major arthropod classes, with more than 25,000 known species. They are covered with a hard exoskeleton which is usually heavily impregnated with calcium carbonate. Its members range from minute floating creatures, such as the water fleas, to crabs and lobsters weighing several kilogrammes. Most of the animals are scavengers and many have complex life histories with several kinds of larvae. Apart from the barnacles, the crustaceans described below all belong to the largest and most advanced section of the class – the sub-class Malacostraca. Unless otherwise stated, the measurements are average adult lengths.

Barnacles

A group of marine crustaceans (Sub-class Cirripedia) whose adults are all completely sessile – permanently attached to a substratum – and normally comb food particles from the water with feathery limbs. The group also contains a few parasitic forms which attack crabs.

Acorn Barnacle
Semibalanus balanoides
Family Balanidae.
5–15mm diameter. The adult barnacle cements itself to inter-tidal rocks and looks nothing like any other crustaceans. It is surrounded by a tent-like wall composed of six chalky plates. It also has a lid formed from two more chalky plates. When submerged, the lid opens and out come six feathery limbs which rhythmically comb the water to gather food material. The larva is free-swimming and clearly shows its relationship to other crustaceans.
ⓑ☻

Woodlice

This is the only group of crustaceans (Order Isopoda) which has managed to invade the land, although they are still restricted to damp habitats and several species remain entirely aquatic. Most woodlice are flattened creatures and all have seven pairs of similar legs. Often known as slaters, they are all scavengers.

Sea Slater
Ligia oceanica
Family Ligiidae
10–25mm. Often black when young, the animal becomes greyish-green when mature. It feeds on the seashore at night, often around the strand line, and hides in rocky crevices by day – usually close to the high-tide level.
ⓑ☻

Oniscus asellus
Family Oniscidae
12–16mm. This shiny grey woodlouse has a pale yellowish margin. The long segment in the centre of the antenna is followed by three smaller segments. Abundant under stones and in rotting wood, it feeds on decaying matter of all kinds. It is often accompanied by *Porcellio scaber*, a much duller, steely grey woodlouse with only two antennal segments beyond the large central one.
ⓑⓄ④⊙⊚

Water Louse
Asellus aquaticus
Family Asellidae
18–25mm. The male of this species is much larger than the female and often carries her about, clasped to his belly. It is abundant in weedy ponds and streams, although it cannot swim. This louse feeds mainly on dead leaves and other vegetable debris and sometimes also on filamentous algae.
ⓑ☻

Amphipods

This order (Amphipoda) contains marine and freshwater crustaceans that have laterally compressed bodies. They usually have three pairs of swimming legs and three pairs of jumping legs on the abdomen. There are four pairs of walking and grasping legs at the front.

Freshwater Shrimp
Gammarus pulex
Family Gammaridae
15–30mm. The male of this species is larger than the female and often carries her about in the breeding season. Grey to reddish-brown, it is abundant in shallow streams, especially in limestone areas. It usually hides under stones and weeds with its body strongly curved, but it straightens out when swimming – usually on one side. It feeds mainly on detritus.
ⓑ☻

Sand Hopper
Orchestia gammarella
10–20mm. Greenish brown to chestnut, this amphipod burrows in the sand of the seashore, usually under the rotting seaweed and other debris on which it feeds. It leaps away when disturbed. Several similar species are called sand hoppers.
ⓑ☻

Acorn Barnacle

Oniscus asellus

Freshwater Shrimp

Sea Slater

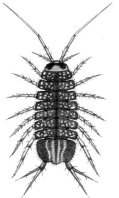

Water Louse

Sand Hopper

The COAST

The coast is a battleground where the land struggles to withstand the immense forces of the sea. In some places, such as England's east coast, the land is fast crumbling into the water and the sea is winning. But what the sea takes from one place it throws back elsewhere in the form of mud, sand, or shingle. The coast is thus an unstable habitat – especially on the shore, where wildlife must face the added problem of the twice daily rise and fall of the tides.

Flowers of the Seaside

Relatively few flowering plants can withstand the salty air of the coast, but they include some very colourful species. Thrift, for example, turns many cliffs pink in the summer and is often accompanied by Hottentot Fig. Shingle beaches seem unfavourable for plant life, but Sea Pea, Sea Kale and Yellow Horned-poppy grow above high tide level. They have long roots to anchor them in the shingle. Bright green mats of Sea Sandwort are common on the finer shingle and are often associated with red clumps of Sea Beet. The latter, found in most coastal habitats, is a member of the Goosefoot Family, which contains several salt-tolerant species.

Dunes develop where sand is blown inland from the shore. Bare and unstable at first, they are gradually colonized by Sand Couch and Lyme Grass, which bind the sand with their roots. Later invaders include Marram Grass, Sea Bindweed, Sea Holly and Sea Mayweed. The sand becomes covered with vegetation and grazing animals usually produce a dense turf. In the absence of grazing, the mature dunes develop into woodland, while young dunes continue to build up on the seaward side.

The eelgrasses are among the very few flowering plants living entirely under the sea. They form dense beds just below low-tide level – in estuaries and as well as on the open coast – and give shelter to many coastal fish. They also provide food for the Brent Goose.

The Seaweed Zones

Botanically speaking, the seashore really belongs to the seaweeds – members of the large group of flowerless plants known as algae. Seaweeds carpet many rocky shores, but are absent from stretches of sandy or muddy beach, where they are unable to establish a firm hold. Each of the many species of seaweeds grows in a particular zone,

ABOVE: *Rock pools are wonderful places for studying seashore life because the animals are active even when the tide is out.*
RIGHT: *The Sting Ray, readily identified by the sharp spine on its tail, frequently spends the daytime buried in the sand in shallow water.*

which is determined by its tolerance of air and fresh water. One of the most tolerant species in this respect is Channelled Wrack, and it grows higher on the shore than any other brown seaweed. Several green seaweeds grow high on the shore, especially in places where fresh water trickles over the rocks. Red seaweeds are the least tolerant of exposure and, apart from those occurring in rock pools, are rarely found growing above the low-water mark.

Animals at the Water's Edge

Despite the problems of the tides, the seashore is very rich in animal life. This is especially true of rocky shores, where crabs, winkles, and many other creatures can simply hide among the seaweeds to avoid desiccation until the tide returns. A rocky shore is even more fascinating if it has rock pools – natural aquaria in which one can watch shrimps, crabs, sea anemones, and small fishes going about their lives even when the tide is out. Sandy shores look

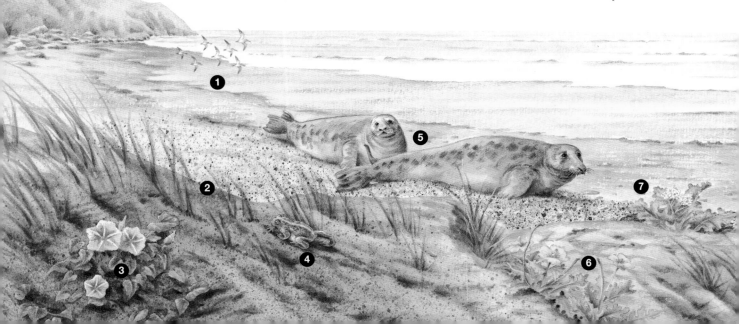

LEFT: *The bright blue flowers of Viper's-bugloss are found in many coastal habitats. They provide a welcome first feed of nectar for migrant butterflies and moths as they arrive in Britain.*
ABOVE: *A Great Cormorant displays its glossy greenish black plumage as it perches with its wings outstretched. This behaviour may be a display or it may help to dry the wings after diving.*
BELOW: *The Stoat, seen here among the sand dunes, occurs in almost every type of habitat, from mountain scree to the seashore.*

barren when the tide recedes, but under the surface they teem with lugworms, cockles and other bivalve molluscs waiting for the tide to return. The entrances to their burrows can often be seen on the surface of wet sand. The mud is equally rich, often containing thousands of small sea snails for each square metre of surface. These creatures provide food for many birds, such as the poorly-named Oystercatcher – which feeds largely on cockles – and other waders. The easiest place to find animals on a sandy shore – and the only place worth looking at on a shingle beach – is the strand line left by the receding tide. Many small creatures feed on the debris, and are themselves eaten by the scavenging gulls. Strand lines also yield plenty of seashells.

Mud Flats and Salt-marshes
The mud flats of sheltered bays and estuaries are the forerunners of the salt-marshes. The mud is initially colonized by various glassworts, which trap more mud around themselves and gradually raise its level. As the height of the mud approaches the average high-tide level, it begins to be colonized by typical salt-marsh plants,

including Sea Aster, Sea Purslane, and Annual Sea-blite. The salt-marsh is criss-crossed by numerous deep channels which carry the water away as the tide recedes, and there are also many small pools – often fringed with Sea Lavender. More mud is dumped by each tide and the level of the marsh rises until it reaches a level at which it is unaffected even by the highest spring tides. The salt-marsh flowers disappear and the marsh evolves into grassland.

Coastal Wildlife
 1 Dunlin
 2 Marram Grass
 3 Sea Bindweed
 4 Natterjack Toad
 5 Grey Seals
 6 Yellow Horned-poppy
 7 Sea-kale
 8 Curlews
 9 Common Terns
10 Mussels
11 Limpets
12 Oystercatchers
13 Herring Gull

Shrimps, Lobsters and Crabs

The members of this order (Decapoda) have five pairs of walking legs, of which one or more pairs may bear pincers for catching food. Most are flesh-eaters, although they eat carrion as readily as they take live prey. The thorax is covered by a sturdy shield known as the carapace, which often covers much of the head as well. The abdomen often bears five pairs of swimming limbs (also used by the female to carry her eggs), although the crab abdomen is usually very small and tucked under the thorax. Almost all the decapods are marine.

Common Shrimp
Crangon crangon
Family Crangonidae
4-7cm. The carapace of this species has a stout central spine and two lateral ones which, together with the claw-like front leg, distinguish it from several similar species. Abundant in coastal waters, it is active at night, when it eats all sorts of animals. By day it hides in sand or mud, often with just its eyes showing, and is very difficult to spot because it can change colour to match backgrounds ranging from yellow or pale grey to dark brown.
Ⓑ 😬

Common Prawn
Palaemon serratus
Family Palaemonidae
10cm. Common in coastal waters, generally over rocky bottoms, this prawn is easily distinguished from the Common Shrimp by the long, toothed rostrum on its head and by its slender front legs. It usually hunts for small animals at night. Almost transparent and very difficult to see in life, it becomes red when cooked.
Ⓑ 😬

Norway Lobster
Nephrops norvegicus
Family Nephropidae
10–20cm. The claws and carapace of this species bear sturdy spines. It lives on sandy and muddy bottoms, at depths of 30–200m. Large numbers are caught and marketed as scampi or Dublin Bay prawns.
Ⓑ 😬

Common Lobster
Homarus vulgaris
20–60cm. This is by far the largest European crustacean, easily recognised by its huge claws – which can cut through a finger – and blue or black colouration. It turns red only when cooked. The lobster inhabits rocky coasts below low-tide level, usually at depths between 20 and 30 metres. It hides in crevices by day and comes out to hunt at night. A scavenger, it is easily trapped in pots baited with dead fish. It is much in demand as a food delicacy and over-fishing has caused it to become rare in many areas.
Ⓑ 😬

Weighed down with a mass of eggs covering her abdomen, a female Common Prawn picks her way across a rock pool.

Spiny Lobster
Palinurus vulgaris
Family Palinuridae
20–40cm. This lobster has a heavily spined carapace. There are no pincers, but the thick antennae with their spiny bases are used as weapons. It lives in rocky areas, usually at depths of 50–100m, and feeds mainly on molluscs. In common with other lobsters and crayfish, it has a broad tail fan, a quick flick of which sends the animal zooming backwards through the water. Also known as the Crawfish, it is a popular food, especially around the Mediterranean. It is absent from northern Europe.
Ⓑ 😬

Crayfish
Potamobius pallipes
Family Potamobiidae
10cm. This is a freshwater species found in shallow, well-aerated streams with clean sandy or stony bottoms, usually in limestone and chalk districts. The claws have pale undersides. It hides under stones or in holes in the banks by day and feeds at night on a wide range of small animals. Young Crayfish also eat plant roots. The slightly larger *P. fluviatilis*, recognised by the red undersides of its claws, is reared for food on the continent and has been introduced to some British rivers.
Ⓑ 😬

Edible Crab
Cancer pagurus
Family Cancridae
12–30cm across, but only rarely over 20cm. It can be distinguished from most other crabs by the nine blunt lobes

on each side of its carapace. It lives in rocky places from the shore down to 50m. It feeds on all kinds of animals, alive and dead. Much sought after as food, it is caught in pots baited with dead fish.
Ⓑ 😬

Velvet Crab
Portunus puber
Family Portunidae
10cm across. Named for its hairy coat, this is one of the swimming crabs. Its hind legs are broad and flat and are used as oars to row the crab through the water. It can also crawl over the sea-bed like other crabs. It inhabits rocky and sandy coasts and is often found in rock pools.
Ⓑ 😬

Shore Crab
Carcinus maenas
8cm across. One of the commonest crabs in Britain, it is found on sandy and rocky shores and also in estuaries. Green or brown, it has five sharp teeth on each side of the carapace and three blunt ones between the eyes. The back legs are quite broad, but the crab is not a great swimmer and, like most other crabs, it scuttles over the sand with a sideways gait.
Ⓑ 😬

Hermit Crab
Eupagurus bernhardus
Family Paguridae
10cm long. Unlike true crabs, this species has a long, soft abdomen and it protects itself by taking up residence in an empty snail shell. It starts off in a tiny shell, but moves house many times as it grows. The large right claw is used to close the opening when the crab retires into the shell.
Ⓑ 😬

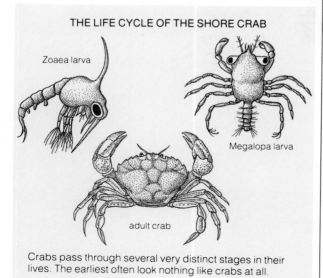

THE LIFE CYCLE OF THE SHORE CRAB

Zoaea larva

Megalopa larva

adult crab

Crabs pass through several very distinct stages in their lives. The earliest often look nothing like crabs at all.

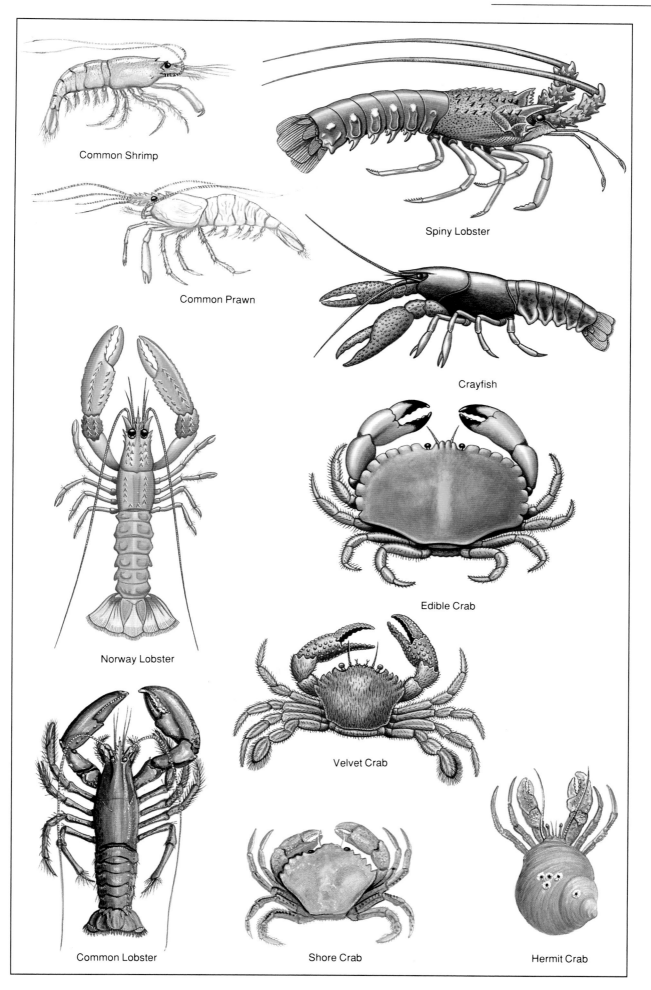

Common Shrimp

Spiny Lobster

Common Prawn

Crayfish

Norway Lobster

Edible Crab

Velvet Crab

Common Lobster

Shore Crab

Hermit Crab

SPIDERS AND THEIR RELATIVES

The Class Arachnida is an important group of arthropods that includes spiders, scorpions and ticks. Its members are distinguished from insects by their four pairs of legs and the lack of antennae, although a pair of palps just behind the mouth may resemble either legs or antennae. Arachnids lack real jaws, but all have a pair of claw-like limbs called chelicerae in front of the mouth. Most arachnids are carnivorous, but many mites eat plants. Spiders (Order Araneae) have two distinct body sections. The front part, or cephalothorax, carries the legs, and there are six or eight eyes around its front end. The palps are short and function like antennae, although in the males they have swollen tips and are also used in mating.

Poisonous Fangs

Some large spiders eat birds, lizards and even small mammals, but most of the European species feed on insects. Many spin elaborate webs to trap their prey, but others pursue or ambush their prey. A spider's chelicerae are in the form of poisonous fangs, which it uses to paralyse the victim before sucking it dry. All spiders make silk, even if they do not spin webs. The silk has many uses, including wrapping prey and protecting the eggs. Males are often smaller than females and perform courtship displays so that the females recognize them. Over 1000 species occur in Europe. The sizes given are body lengths.

Spiders

Amaurobius similis
Family Amaurobiidae
Male 6mm, female 12mm. This very common spider is found in crevices in bark and old walls, and often around window frames. It surrounds its retreat with an irregular, lace-like web. Insects are caught in the web and drawn into the spider's lair, usually being pulled in by one leg.
Ⓑ🌑🌕🌟

Daddy-long-legs Spider
Pholcus phalangioides
Family Pholcidae
8–10mm. This slender, long-legged spider frequents caves and buildings. When prey walks into its flimsy web, the spider throws more silk over it with its back legs. It feeds on other spiders and insects. This species can be seen all year, but becomes quiescent in winter. It is found in southern and central Europe.
Ⓑ🌟

SIGNALS FOR SURVIVAL

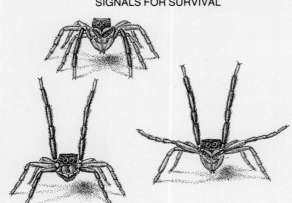

Mating is dangerous for male spiders. The jumping spider signals his intentions so that the female will not eat him.

A female wolf spider (Pardosa amentata) *covered with her young, which have just emerged from the egg-sac attached to her rear end.*

Dysdera crocata
Family Dysderidae
9–15mm. A slow-moving hunter, this species preys on woodlice, which it captures with its huge fangs. One fang pierces the underside of the prey and the other goes in through the top. It hunts at night, spending the daytime under stones and logs, often in a silk-lined cell.
Ⓑ🌕🌟

Nursery-web Spider
Pisaura mirabilis
Family Pisauridae
12–15mm. Abundant in dense vegetation, this is one of the wolf spiders which chase after their prey. It often basks on leaves with the two front pairs of legs held close together and pointing forward at an angle of about 30 degrees to the body. The egg cocoon is carried in the female's fangs. She fixes it to a plant when the eggs are about to hatch and covers it with a silken tent – hence the species' common name. She stands guard over the tent until the young have dispersed. The adult is found from May to July.
Ⓑ🌑🌕🌟🕸

Raft Spider
Dolomedes fimbriatus
Male 9–13mm, female 13–25mm. One of Europe's largest species, this wolf spider inhabits marshes and the edges of ponds and streams. It often sits on a floating leaf with its front legs resting on the water, and will skate towards any insect it senses on the surface nearby. It preys even on small fish. It is found from May to August.
Ⓑ🌑

Pardosa amentata
Family Lycosidae
5–7mm. One of several very similar wolf spiders, this common species hunts on the ground and is often seen sunbathing on stones. The female carries her egg cocoon attached to the spinnerets at her rear end, and when they hatch she carries the babies on her back for a few days. The adult is found from March to July.
Ⓑ🌑🌓🌕🌟🕸

Tarantula
Lycosa narbonensis
25mm. This is the famous tarantula of southern Europe – a large wolf spider whose bite was supposed to be fatal. In fact, the bite is rarely dangerous to people, although it is certainly painful. The spider lives in a burrow and darts out to catch passing insects.
🌑🌕🌟🌑🕸

Linyphia triangularis
Family Linyphiidae
5–6mm. One of Britain's commonest spiders, it forms hammock-like webs on almost every bush and clump of grass in late summer and autumn. The spider hangs below the web and waits for insects to collide with the superstructure and fall on to the sheet.
Ⓑ🌑🌕🌟🕸

Zebra Spider
Salticus scenicus
Family Salticidae.
5–7mm. This is one of the jumping spiders, with very large eyes on the front edge of the carapace. It creeps slowly towards its prey and then leaps on it. Prey is

pinned down by the spider's sturdy front legs and then bitten. The spider, which is common on house walls, can leap many times its own length. It is found from April to September.
Ⓑ☻♦Ⓧ☺

Enoplognatha ovata
Family Theridiidae
3–6mm. The upper side of this species' abdomen may be all cream, all red or have two red stripes. It is abundant in dense vegetation of all kinds and is often found in gardens. The web is a flimsy three-dimensional scaffold with sticky threads on the outside. Extra silk is thrown over trapped victims. The adult is found from June to August.
Ⓑ☻ⓄⓍ🕸

House Spider
Tegenaria gigantea
Family Agelenidae
11–15mm. A common inhabitant of houses and out-buildings, this species spins a roughly triangular sheet – the familiar cobweb – in a corner, with a tubular retreat at the angle. The web is not sticky, but small insects get their feet caught in the dense mat of silky threads and are then easily grabbed by the spider. Adults are most often seen in the autumn, but females can be found throughout the year. There are several similar species.
ⒷⓍ

Water Spider
Argyroneta aquatica
8–15mm, male often larger than female. This is the only spider living permanently under water. It builds a silken bell in still water and fills it with air brought from the surface among its body hairs. It sits in the bell during the day and goes out to hunt mainly at night.
Ⓑ☻

Agelena labyrinthica
8–12mm. This spider makes large funnel-shaped webs in low-growing vegetation. The spider itself can often be seen basking on the flat part of the web, but it hurries back to its central retreat when disturbed. Insects flying into the web's superstructure fall on to the sheet and are quickly caught. The adult is found from June to August.
Ⓑ☻Ⓧ🕸

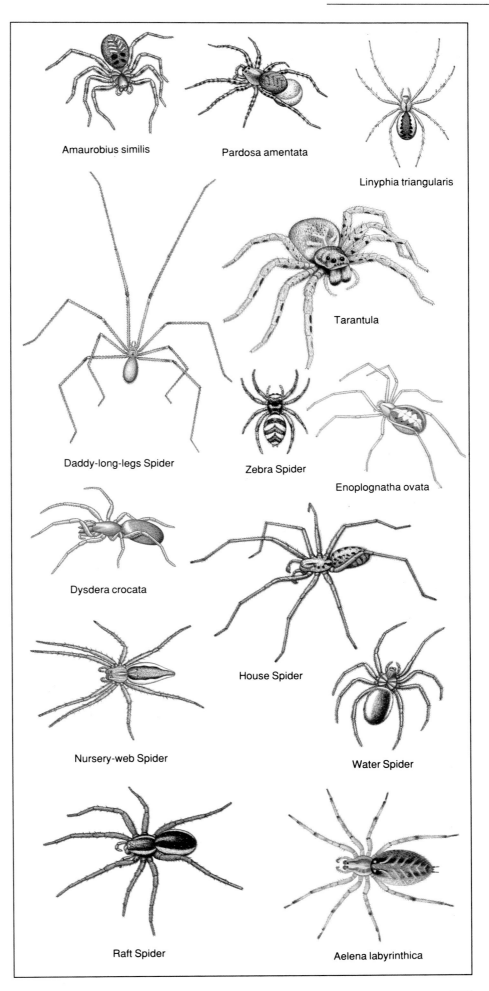

Amaurobius similis

Pardosa amentata

Linyphia triangularis

Tarantula

Daddy-long-legs Spider

Zebra Spider

Enoplognatha ovata

Dysdera crocata

House Spider

Nursery-web Spider

Water Spider

Raft Spider

Aelena labyrinthica

CRAB SPIDERS

These small spiders (Family Thomisidae) are mostly crab-like in appearance, with their front two pairs of legs usually longer than the rest. They often walk sideways. Crab spiders spin no webs and normally lie in ambush for their prey. They often catch butterflies and other insects much larger than themselves. They do not mutilate their prey as other spiders do: they simply drain out the body fluids.

Xysticus cristatus

4–7mm. A very common and variable crab spider found among low-growing herbage in spring and early summer. The male is darker than the female pictured here, but has similar markings.
ⓑ🐛◑✦🐝

Misumena vatia

Male 3–4mm, female 10–12mm. This spider usually lurks in flowers and catches insects that come to feed. The female may be white, yellow or pale green and can quickly change from one to the other to match different flowers. It is sometimes called the White Death Spider. The male is largely brown. It matures from May to August.
ⓑ🐛✦🐝

Thomisus onustus

Male 3mm, female 7mm. Identified by the two abdominal tubercles, the female of this species may be white, pink or yellow and can change colour to match different flowers. The male has an orange abdomen but is otherwise dark brown. Most common in the south, it is active from May to August.
ⓑ🐛🐝

ORB-WEB SPIDERS

These spiders (Family Argiopidae) spin the circular, sticky webs which are so beautiful when covered with dew or frost in the autumn. The spiders mature in the autumn and their webs are most noticeable at this time. The spider may rest at the centre of its web, but more often hides under a nearby leaf until an insect flies into the web. Most species pass the winter as eggs, wrapped in silken cocoons.

This crab spider (Misumena vatia) *is draining all the life from a hover-fly. It will leave an almost perfect, empty skeleton.*

Araneus quadratus

Male 6–8mm, female 9–15mm. This species may range from green to rich chestnut in colour but the female always has four large white spots. Its webs, up to 40cm across, are rarely more than 150cm above the ground. It is found from August to October and is especially common on heathland.
ⓑ🐛🐝

Garden Spider

Araneus diadematus
Male 4–8mm, female 10–12mm. Also known as the Cross Spider, because of the white cross on its orange to black abdomen, this is one of the commonest of Europe's orb-web spiders. Its webs, which may be up to 40cm across, can be seen on nearly every fence and hedge in the autumn.
ⓑ🐛◑✦🐝

Argiope bruennichi

Male 7mm; female 25mm. This striking spider usually makes a web with a zig-zag band of silk from top to bottom. The male has a slender brownish abdomen without the black bands of the female. This species is found from May to October in southern and central Europe but is rarely encountered in Britain.
ⓑ🐛✦🐝

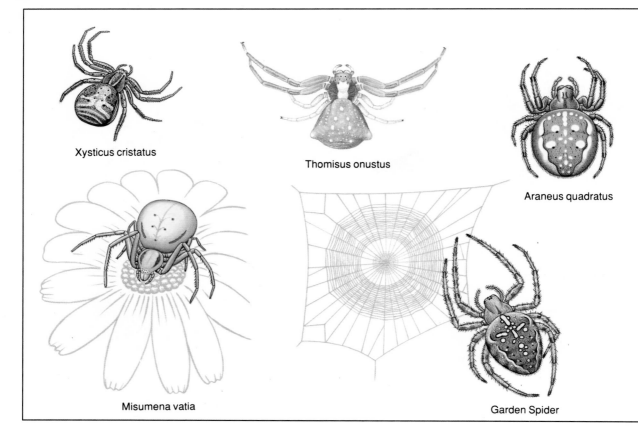

Xysticus cristatus

Thomisus onustus

Araneus quadratus

Misumena vatia

Garden Spider

Zygiella x-notata

4–7mm. The abdominal colour of this species varies, but there is usually a distinct leaf-like pattern, often with a silvery sheen. Its web, easily identified by the two missing segments near the top (see illustration), is particularly common on and around buildings – especially across doors and window frames. It is most often seen from July to October.
ⓑⓧ

Harvestmen

These arachnids (Order Opiliones) are commonly called harvest spiders but, unlike true spiders, their bodies are not divided into two sections, they have no poison fangs and produce no silk. There are just two eyes, perched on a turret near the middle of the back. They are mostly nocturnal and can be found resting on walls and vegetation by day. They eat a wide range of living and dead animal matter. Most species mature in late summer – hence their common name.

Phalangium opilio

Family Phalangiidae
4–9mm. This very common species of rough herbage, can be distinguished from most others by its unspotted white or pale grey underside. The male's chelicerae bear large, forward-pointing horns.
ⓑⓞⓧⓦ

Leiobunum rotundum

Family Leiobunidae
3–6mm. The male has an almost circular reddish brown body. The female is oval and mottled, with a dark central patch. The legs are extremely long and slender.
ⓑⓞⓧⓦ

Scorpions

The scorpions (Order Scorpiones) are easily identified by their large claws and long, sting-tipped tails, which usually arch forward over their bodies. Most species occur in the warmer parts of the world, but a few live in southern Europe. They are all nocturnal predators. Some scorpions have stings which may be very painful and potentially dangerous to people.

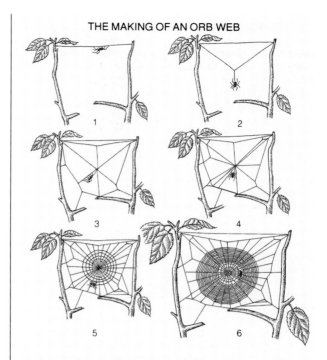

THE MAKING OF AN ORB WEB

1. The bridge thread is established. 2. The spider drops from a slack thread and pulls it tight. The junction of the Y will be the centre of the web. 3 and 4. More radial and frame threads are added. 5. A temporary, dry spiral is spun. 6. Working from the outside to the centre, the spider removes the dry spiral and lays down the sticky threads.

Euscorpius flavicaudis

Family Chactidae
35mm. One of the smallest scorpions, this species hides in crevices, especially in old walls, protruding its claws at night to capture any small animal that passes. The sting is rarely, if ever, used and the animal is not dangerous. It occurs mainly in southern Europe, but is established in a few other places.
ⓑⓧⓢ

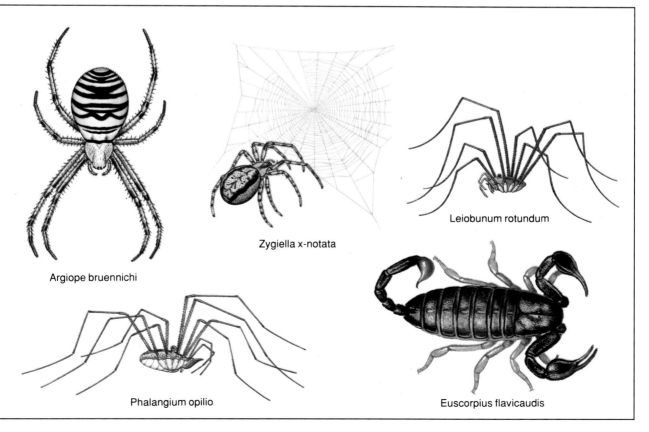

Argiope bruennichi

Zygiella x-notata

Leiobunum rotundum

Phalangium opilio

Euscorpius flavicaudis

THE INSECTS

With a million or so known species – and many more undoubtedly still to be discovered – the insects (Class Insecta) form by far the largest of the arthropod classes. Their extraordinary success is due in part to their size. Their average is rather less than that of a grain of rice, enabling them to occupy habitats denied to larger animals and to exist in immense numbers in small areas. Adult insects can almost all be recognized by their three pairs of legs, one pair of antennae, and a body clearly divided into three sections – head, thorax and abdomen. Most adults also have two pairs of wings, although some have only one pair and quite a number have no wings at all. There is considerable variation in the form of the wings.

Very few insects live in the sea, but they occur in almost every terrestrial and freshwater habitat and feed on just about everything from nectar to wood and from blood to dried dung and bones. To deal with such varied diets, they have an extraordinary variety of mouth-parts – from slender tubes for drinking blood and nectar to the powerful jaws needed for chewing solid wood.

Insect Life Cycles

Insects exhibit two main types of life history. In the first, exemplified by the grasshoppers, the youngster looks much like the adult except that it lacks functional wings. Such a youngster is called a nymph and it usually eats the same kind of food as the adult. It moults its skin periodically and the wing buds on its back get larger at each moult. At the final moult the adult insect, complete with fully developed wings, crawls out of the old nymphal skin. This type of life history, in which the young gradually assume the adult form, is called a partial metamorphosis. Dragonflies, bugs and earwigs all

The insect body is divided into three distinct parts – the head, thorax, and abdomen – each of which is composed of several segments. The legs and wings are always attached to the thorax. There is a great deal of variation in the form of the antennae.

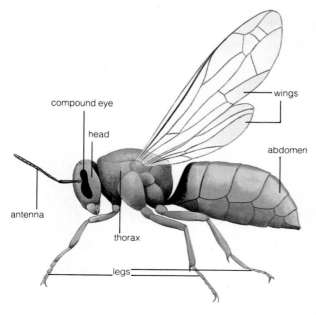

THE LIFE CYCLE OF THE GRASSHOPPER

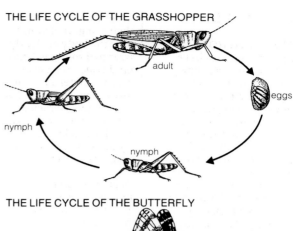

THE LIFE CYCLE OF THE BUTTERFLY

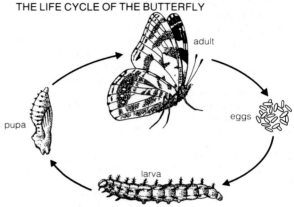

The grasshopper undergoes a partial metamorphosis, during which the nymph gradually assumes the adult form. The butterfly undergoes a complete metamorphosis. The change from the larval or caterpillar stage to the adult form takes place in the pupa or chrysalis.

have this kind of development. The second type of life history, typified by the butterflies and moths, involves a youngster which is very different from the adult. It is called a larva and it usually has totally different habits from the adult. The butterfly caterpillar, for example, is a leaf-feeder, while the adult sips nectar from flowers. The larva moults periodically, but does not gradually assume the adult form and shows no sign of wings. When fully grown, it turns into a pupa or chrysalis, and it is in this stage that the larval body is converted into that of the adult. This type of life history, shared by flies, bees and beetles as well as the butterflies and moths, is known as a complete metamorphosis. Many European insects get through just one brood or generation in a year, but some species have two or even three broods, especially in the warmer areas. A few species, notably those living in the far north, take over a year to complete their development. Many species that feed on wood also take several years to mature because of the low nutritional value of their food.

The Orders of Insects

Insects are arranged in about 28 orders, most of which are named according to the nature of their wings. Butterflies and moths, for example, belong to the Lepidoptera, which means 'scale-winged' and refers to the coating of tiny scales on their wings. Beetles, with their tough, horny forewings, belong to the Coleoptera, which means 'sheath-winged'. Several of the smaller orders, whose members are generally inconspicuous, have been omitted from the following pages.

Mayflies

These insects (Order Ephemeroptera) have two or four very flimsy wings and are weak flyers. Their hind wings, when present, are much smaller than the front ones and there are two or three slender tails. Adults are short-lived and do not feed. They are mostly nocturnal and rarely found far from the water in which they grow up. There is no chrysalis stage.

Isonychia ignota

Family Isonychidae
30mm wingspan. This species flies all summer around lakes and rivers in southern and central Europe. The female frequently has a large egg mass protruding from her rear end, ready to be dropped into the water.
☻

Stoneflies

Stoneflies are weak-flying insects (Order Plecoptera), which grow up in water without a chrysalis stage. Most species prefer cool, fast-flowing streams. Adults may nibble algae and pollen, but feed very little. They rest with their wings folded flat over the body or tightly wrapped round it. Their hind wings are usually much broader than their forewings. There are two slender tails, which are very short in some of the smaller species. The nymphs look much like wingless adults

Perlodes microcephala

Family Perlodidae
30–40mm span (female). This stonefly can be distinguished from most other large species by the uneven network of veins near its wing-tip. It is found around stony streams from March to July. The male usually has short wings and cannot fly.
Ⓑ☻

Caddis Flies

These are mostly brownish, moth-like insects (Order Trichoptera) whose wings are clothed with fine hairs. Generally nocturnal, they are often attracted to lights. They rest on waterside rocks or vegetation by day with wings folded roof-like over the body and antennae pointing forward. Some species lap nectar, but the mouthparts are poorly developed and most adults probably do not feed at all. The larvae almost all live in water and many make portable cases with sand grains or plant fragments. Each species has its own case pattern. The larvae pupate in their silken cocoons which they spin in their cases.

Phryganea grandis

Family Phryganeidae
35–40mm span. This species breeds in still and slow-moving water with plenty of vegetation. The male is smaller and lacks black streaks on its wings. It flies from May to August. It is absent from most of southern Europe. The larval case is up to 2.5cm long and is made of plant fragments.
Ⓑ☻

A freshly-emerged mayfly (right) is called a dun. It must change its skin once more to reach the final stage – the spinner (left).

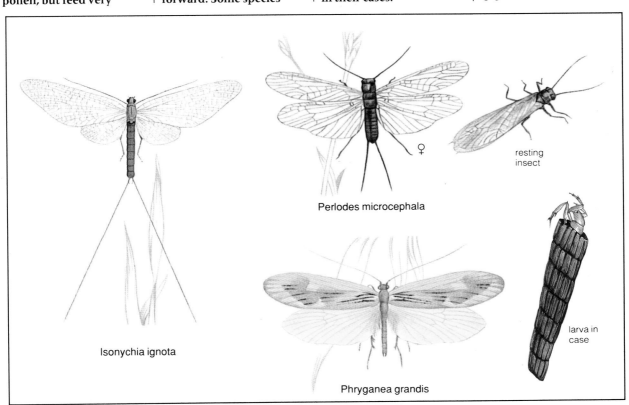

Isonychia ignota

Perlodes microcephala

♀

resting insect

Phryganea grandis

larva in case

Dragonflies

These insects (Order Odonata) have very short, bristle-like antennae and large eyes. There are two main groups: true dragonflies (Suborder Anisoptera) and the damselflies (Suborder Zygoptera). The true dragonflies, in which the hind wings are broader than the front ones, are divided into hawkers and darters. Hawkers spend most of their time on the wing, hawking to and fro over a stretch of territory as they search for flies and other insect prey. Darters spend much of their time resting on perches and dart out when prey approaches. The prey is scooped from the air by the spiky legs. The damselflies are more dainty than the hawkers and darters and have four wings of equal size and shape. They fly rather slowly and feed mainly by plucking insects from vegetation. All dragonflies have an aquatic nymphal stage. The nymphs are fierce carnivores, shooting out their spiky jaws to impale a variety of other creatures. There is no chrysalis stage and the nymphs simply climb emergent rocks or vegetation when it is time for the adults to emerge. Freshly emerged insects are very pale. The sizes given are wingspan measurements.

Emperor Dragonfly
Anax imperator
Family Aeshnidae
105mm. This hawker is the largest European dragonfly, and is seldom seen far from canals, ponds, and other still waters. Both sexes have a green thorax but the abdomen is bright blue in the male and green with a brown tip in the female. The nymph lives in weed beds and usually climbs on to floating leaves when ready to turn into an adult. It flies throughout southern and central Europe from May to September.
Ⓑ☻

Brown Aeshna
Aeshna grandis
100mm. It is the only large dragonfly with yellowish brown wings. Only the male has blue spots at the front of the abdomen. It breeds in still and slow-moving water and may be seen hawking along the water's edge from June to October. Although absent from Scotland, it is found far beyond the Arctic Circle.
Ⓑ☻

Gold-ringed Dragonfly
Cordulegaster boltonii
Family Cordulegasteridae
100mm. This species hawks low over streams, especially in heathland and moorland, from May to September. The female has a long ovipositor with which she pushes her eggs into the silt on the stream beds. The nymphs live partly buried in the silt. *C. bidentatus*, from southern and central Europe, is similar but the triangle behind the eyes is black instead of yellow.
Ⓑ◐☻

The Common Blue Damselfly is one of several species with blue and black males, but each species has its characteristic pattern.

Broad-bodied Chaser
Libellula depressa
Family Libellulidae
75mm. A very fast darter, this dragonfly usually perches more or less horizontally on bushes a metre or two above the ground. A dark patch at the base of each wing, together with yellow abdominal spots, distinguish this from a number of superficially similar species. The abdomen is blue only in mature males; females and young males are brown with yellow spots. It flies from May to September and breeds in still and slow-moving water. The Scarce Chaser (*L. fulva*) is similar, but has no yellow spots on the abdomen.
Ⓑ☻

Four-spotted Chaser
Libellula quadrimaculata
75mm. This fast-flying darter is easily recognized by the dark spot near the middle of the front edge of each wing. Dark smudges near the wing-tips are usually absent. One of the commonest dragonflies, it flies from April to October, sometimes migrating in huge swarms, especially in northern and upland areas. Particularly common around heathland pools in Britain, it frequently rests on the ground.
Ⓑ◐☻☻

Crocothemis erythraea
60mm. Reddish veins at the front of the wings usually identify this darter. Its body is yellow or brown at first, becoming red with age and especially vivid in the male. Unlike similar species, there is never any black on the top of the body. It breeds in still water and is common around Mediterranean rice fields from May to October.
☻☻

Ruddy Darter
Sympetrum sanguineum
55mm. The male is easily distinguished by the marked constriction near the front of its abdomen. The female is orange-brown. In both sexes the legs are black. Most similar species, such as the abundant Common Darter (*S. striolatum*), have yellow stripes on their legs. It flies from May to October, usually perching on plants with its wings drooping. It breeds in ponds and ditches with plenty of emergent plants.
Ⓑ☻

Banded Agrion
Calopteryx splendens
Family Calopterygidae
65mm. The male of this species is easily recognized by the dark blue patch on each wing. It has a metallic green body at first but gradually

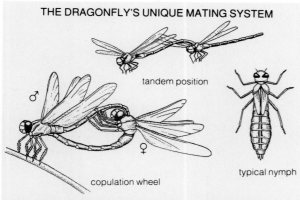

THE DRAGONFLY'S UNIQUE MATING SYSTEM

tandem position

copulation wheel

typical nymph

The male grips the female with his abdominal claspers. She curves round to complete the copulation wheel and collect sperm from his abdomen. The male may tow the female in the tandem position while she lays her eggs.

assumes a deep metallic blue. The female has a green body and uniformly yellowish green wings. Visible from April to September around canals and rivers, the males 'dance' over plants and the females prefer thicker vegetation. It is absent from Scotland and the far north. *C. virgo* is similar but the male's wings are mainly blue and this insect prefers faster streams. Both species are often called demoiselles.
Ⓑ☻

Emerald Damselfly
Lestes sponsa
Family Lestidae
50mm. This species breeds in still water, and rarely moves far from the fringing vegetation. Flying from June to October, it rests with wings half open. Only mature males have blue patches. The family contains several similar species, all with an elongated dark spot near the wing-tip. Other damselflies have squarer spots.
Ⓑ☻

Large Red Damselfly
Pyrrhosoma nymphula
Family Coenagriidae
40–50mm. A very common damselfly which breeds in still and slow-moving water and flies from April to September. The female has more black on the abdomen than the male. Black legs distinguish this species from the slightly smaller Small Red Damselfly (*Ceriagrion tenellum*), which also lacks red stripes on the thorax.
Ⓑ☻

Common Blue Damselfly
Enallagma cyathigerum
35–40mm. The male differs from the many similar blue and black damselflies in having a mushroom-shaped black spot at the front of its abdomen. The female is green and black and has a small spine under the eighth abdominal segment. It flies from April to September, by still and slow-moving water with floating vegetation.
Ⓑ☻

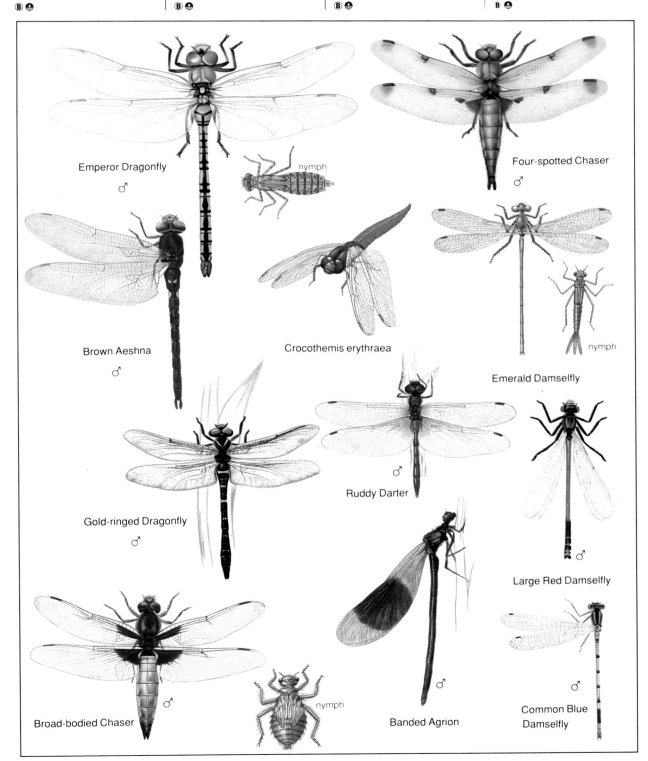

Emperor Dragonfly ♂

nymph

Four-spotted Chaser ♂

Brown Aeshna ♂

Crocothemis erythraea

Emerald Damselfly

nymph

Gold-ringed Dragonfly ♂

Ruddy Darter ♂

Large Red Damselfly ♂

Broad-bodied Chaser ♂

nymph

Banded Agrion ♂

Common Blue Damselfly ♂

Crickets and Grasshoppers

These long-legged jumping creatures (Order Orthoptera) are best known for their 'songs', which the males of most species perform by rubbing one part of the body against another – a process known as stridulation. Most species have their own characteristic song, although some are silent. The forewings are usually tough and the hind wings membranous, although the wings may be reduced to small flaps or lacking altogether. Flightless species are especially common in montane areas. There is no chrysalis stage. The measurements given are body lengths.

MOLE CRICKETS

These are sturdy insects (Family Gryllotalpidae) which spend most of their lives tunnelling through the soil with huge, mole-like front legs and feeding on roots and insect grubs. There are only three European species.

Common Mole Cricket

Gryllotalpa gryllotalpa
35–50mm. This cricket has short forewings but flies well, on warm evenings. The male produces a purring song at the burrow entrance. It lives in damp places and is dormant in winter. This is one of Britain's rarest insects.
Ⓑ ⊕

TRUE CRICKETS

These crickets (Family Gryllidae) have front wings which, when present, form a box-like cover for the body, distinctly flattened on top. The males sing by rubbing their front wings together. The females have a needle-like ovipositor (egg-layer).

Field Cricket

Gryllus campestris
20mm. A flightless, warmth-loving insect which lives in burrows in dry grassland and feeds mainly on grass. The male's shrill song is heard from May to July, mainly by day but also on warm nights. The adults die in autumn, when partly-grown nymphs dig hibernation burrows. It is found in southern and central Europe, but is extremely rare in Britain.
Ⓑ ⊕

House Cricket

Acheta domesticus
15mm. When folded, the hind wings of this insect project like tails from the rear of the body. Both sexes are fully winged and fly well. A scavenger, this species is found in and around buildings and rubbish dumps where there is continuous warmth. Active mainly at night, the male has a shrill and prolonged bird-like call.
Ⓑ ✪

Italian Cricket

Oecanthus pellucens
9–15mm. A delicate insect found on shrubs and other tall vegetation from July to October. It eats aphids and other small insects. The male has broad, almost transparent front wings, with which he produces a beautiful, soft warbling song at nightfall. The insect is difficult to track down because it alters the volume of its song, making it appear to come from different places. The female's front wings are narrow, giving her a much more slender look than the male. It occurs in southern and central Europe.
✪ ⊕

BUSH CRICKETS

This very large group (Family Tettigoniidae) resemble grasshoppers in shape but have much longer antennae. Males sing by rubbing their front wings together. Females have a broad, sabre-like ovipositor, with which they place eggs in the ground or in plant tissues. Generally active towards evening and through the first half of the night, they usually inhabit scrubby places and mature in the summer. The winter is passed in the egg stage. Most species eat both plant and animal material – usually other insects – although some of the larger species are purely carnivorous. Some fly readily but others, even if fully winged, are just as likely to leap or crawl away if disturbed.

Tylopsis liliifolia

13–23mm. This green or brown species is easily recognized by the antennae, which are up to five times as long as the body. The thoracic shield has distinctly rectangular side lobes. Found from July to October, it frequents grassy and bushy places. Its song is a series of faint chirps rather like the sound of striking matches. It occurs in southern and central Europe.
⊕

Oak Bush Cricket

Meconema thalassinum
15mm. This silent, nocturnal species lives mainly in trees and is often attracted to lights at night. The male has conspicuous claspers at the rear, used for holding the female during mating. It is largely carnivorous and eats a wide range of other insects. It is found from June to November.
Ⓑ ✪ ✪

Great Green Bush Cricket

Tettigonia viridissima
40–50mm. The top of the head and thorax of this species are brown, as is the stridulatory area at base of male's front wings. The female's ovipositor is more or less straight and just reaches the wing-tips. The song is a loud and rather harsh hissing sound produced in long bursts. It is active from June to October.
Ⓑ ✪ ⊕

Speckled Bush Cricket

Leptophyes punctatissima
9–18mm. This cricket is bright green with numerous small dark spots. The front wings are reduced to small flaps, forming a 'saddle' in the male. The song is a barely audible scratching sound. The ovipositor is very short and strongly curved. Adults are very well camouflaged on nettles and other herbage. The young nymph is easily mistaken for a greenfly.

Anonconotus alpinus is one of many flightless mountain bush crickets. The wings are just large enough to produce the song.

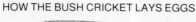

HOW THE BUSH CRICKET LAYS EGGS

The female *Ephippiger* uses her sword-like ovipositor to lay her eggs in the soil. The eggs will hatch in the spring.

Largely herbivorous, this species is found from June to November in southern and central Europe.
Ⓑ ⊗ ⊚

Dark Bush Cricket
Pholidoptera griseoaptera
13–20mm. One of the commonest bush crickets, this yellowish brown to black species inhabits hedgerows and other rough vegetation. The female is wingless and the male's wings are reduced to a little 'saddle'. Its song comprises short chirps – *psst-psst-psst* – produced at irregular intervals. It is found from July to November.
Ⓑ ⊗ ⊚

Anonconotus alpinus
20mm. A flightless brown or black bush cricket from the mountains of southern and central Europe. Its wings are reduced to tiny flaps. Found from July to October, it frequents stony ground or low-growing plants. Its song, which is produced only in sunshine, comes in short bursts and sounds rather like a sewing machine.
⊛

Ephippiger ephippiger
30mm. Green or brown, often with a clearly banded abdomen, this plump, flightless bush cricket is known in France as *le tizi* – a name which mimics the double chirp produced by the insect. Both sexes sing by rubbing their tiny yellowish wings together. The ovipositor is almost as long as the body and is used to lay eggs in the ground. The insect sings by night and day from July to November in scrubby habitats in southern and central Europe. It often damages vines.
⊗ ⊚

Saga pedo
100mm (including ovipositor). This voracious carnivore feeds mainly on other crickets and grasshoppers. Males are unknown in this species, although they do occur in related species in south-eastern Europe. The females lay fertile eggs without mating. It is found from June to October on grassy and shrubby habitats in the Mediterranean region.
⊜ ⊚

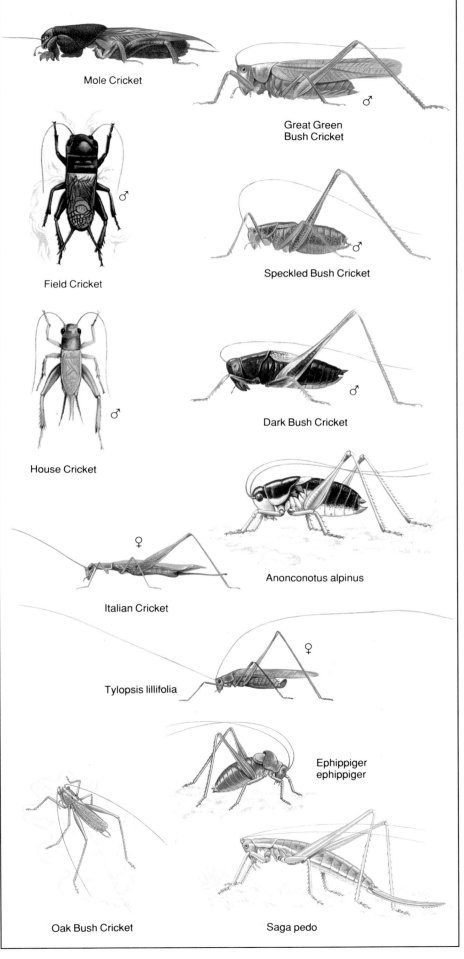

Mole Cricket

Great Green Bush Cricket ♂

Field Cricket ♂

Speckled Bush Cricket ♂

House Cricket ♂

Dark Bush Cricket ♂

Anonconotus alpinus

Italian Cricket ♀

Tylopsis lillifolia ♀

Ephippiger ephippiger

Oak Bush Cricket

Saga pedo

GRASSHOPPERS

Grasshoppers (Family Acrididae) are sturdy insects with antennae much shorter than the body. The forewings, when present, are quite narrow. The males sing by rubbing their back legs against their wings, although many species are silent. Completely vegetarian, they live mainly in grassland and are usually active only in sunshine.

Arcyptera fusca

22–40mm. A colourful insect of grassy slopes in the Alps and Pyrenees, the female, though much larger than the male, is short-winged and flightless. The song starts with a few croaky notes, develops into a loud rustle, and then dies away with a few more short notes. It is found from July to October.

Meadow Grasshopper
Chorthippus parallelus
10–24mm. This flightless species lacks hind wings in both sexes and the forewings of the female do not reach the middle of the abdomen. Its body may be green, brown or purple but the wings are normally brown. Found from June to November, it is especially common in damper areas. Its song is a hissing, produced in bursts of about three seconds with increasing volume.

Field Grasshopper
Chorthippus brunneus
15–25mm. This species may be brown, grey, purple or green, but is usually recognized by the hairy underside of the thorax. Only the mature male has a red-tipped abdomen. One of the commonest grasshoppers, it is found on dry, open grassland to from June to November. Its song comprises 6–10 short chirps, reminiscent of time signals, repeated at irregular intervals.

Oedipoda germanica

15–30mm. An inhabitant of dry, sparsely vegetated areas, this insect is well camouflaged on the ground but, if disturbed, it flies off, flashing its bright red hind wings. It quickly drops to the ground again and 'disappears', leaving a predator searching for something red. Its song is very quiet and produced only in the presence of a female. It is found from June to November in southern and central Europe. *O. coerulescens* has bright blue hind wings.

Migratory Locust
Locusta migratoria
30–50mm. This species forms huge swarms in Africa but most European specimens are of the solitary phase, recognized by the prominently domed thorax. The female is largely green, the male often brown. Found among vegetation of all kinds in southern and central Europe, it is a sporadic visitor to Britain. It is active from July to November; and all year in the far south. The male screeches loudly in the presence of a female.

Egyptian Grasshopper
Anacridium aegyptium
35–70mm. This silent species is distinguished from other large grasshoppers by its vertically striped eyes and a notched keel on its thorax. Found all year on trees and shrubs in southern Europe. Its nymphs are mostly bright green or orange.

Podisma pedestris

15–30mm. This flightless species is found on sparsely vegetated ground, usually above 1,000m. Its front wings are reduced to small flaps. A silent species, it is active from July to October. The female is much larger than the male.

Acrida ungarica

30–75mm. Easily identified by the pointed head and broad antennae, this silent grasshopper inhabits damp areas in the Mediterranean region from July to October. It may be brown or green and the female is often mottled. The female is so much longer and plumper than male that she is often taken for a different species.

Mantids and Cockroaches

These insects (Order Dictyoptera) have long, spiky legs and the forewings, when present, are tough and leathery. Cockroaches are mainly nocturnal scavengers, the native European species being mostly small, ground-living creatures. Mantids are predatory insects unrepresented in Britain, although several species live on the Continent. They stalk other insects or lie in wait with the spiny front legs held in front of the face. A lightning-fast strike impales the prey on the spines. There is no chrysalis stage in this order.

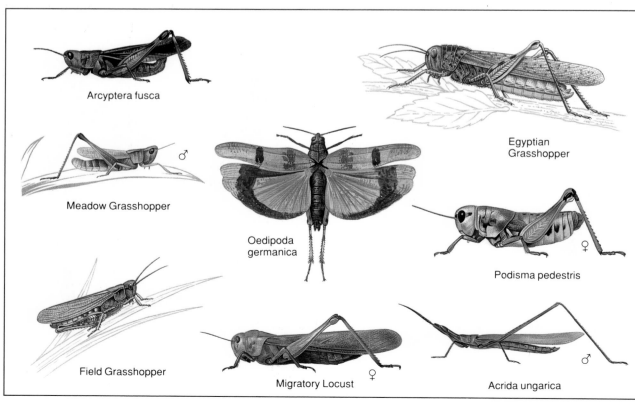

Arcyptera fusca

Meadow Grasshopper ♂

Oedipoda germanica

Field Grasshopper

Migratory Locust ♀

Egyptian Grasshopper

Podisma pedestris ♀

Acrida ungarica ♂

Praying Mantis

Mantis religiosa
Family Mantidae
40–80mm. This green or brown mantis lives in grassy places from June to November. The larger, stouter female may eat the male while mating. When alarmed this insect makes hissing sounds by rubbing the abdomen against the partly-raised wings. It is found in southern and central Europe.

Empusa pennata

Family Empusidae
45–70mm. This slender, long-necked mantis is green or brown. It inhabits rough grassy places from May to September and feeds mainly on small flies. The female does not attack the male. Its eggs hatch in summer, the nymphs feeding through autumn and winter and maturing late spring. It is found in southern Europe.

German Cockroach

Blatella germanica
Family Blatellidae
9–14mm. This pest is widely distributed in bakeries and other permanently heated buildings. It also occurs on rubbish dumps, where the heat of fermentation allows it to breed for much of the year. It flies well in warm weather.

The front legs of the Praying Mantis hold its grasshopper prey like a vice. Its tough jaws will quickly demolish the victim.

Stick Insects

Most stick insects (Order Phasmida) are tropical creatures, but half a dozen species – all wingless and uncannily twig-like – live in southern Europe. Males are very rare in most species, the females laying fertile eggs without mating. There is no chrysalis stage.

Clonopsis gallica

Family Phylliidae
50–75mm. This green or brown species has antennae hardly longer than its head. It feeds on leaves of various shrubs, mainly at night. It is found from May to October throughout southern and central Europe. The very similar *Bacillus rossius* has antennae much longer than its head.

Earwigs

These slender brown or black insects (Order Dermaptera) are easily recognized by the pincers at the rear – strongly curved in males, but straighter and thinner in females. The forewings, when present, are short and horny. The hind wings, when present, are thin and elaborately folded under the forewings, often protruding as small triangular flaps. Even fully winged species are usually reluctant to fly. Most are nocturnal scavengers. In all species the female protects the eggs and young. There is no chrysalis stage.

Labidura riparia

Family Labiduridae
25mm. Europe's largest earwig, this rather pale species lives mainly in sandy places, especially on river banks and by the sea. It can often be found under driftwood on the coasts of southern Europe. It is probably extinct in Britain.

Common Earwig

Forficula auricularia
9–17mm. This is Europe's most common earwig and the only one regularly seen in Britain. It is common all year in gardens, although it hides away in the coldest months, often entering houses. It may nibble flowers, but is otherwise harmless. Although fully winged it rarely flies. The male sometimes has much longer pincers than those shown.

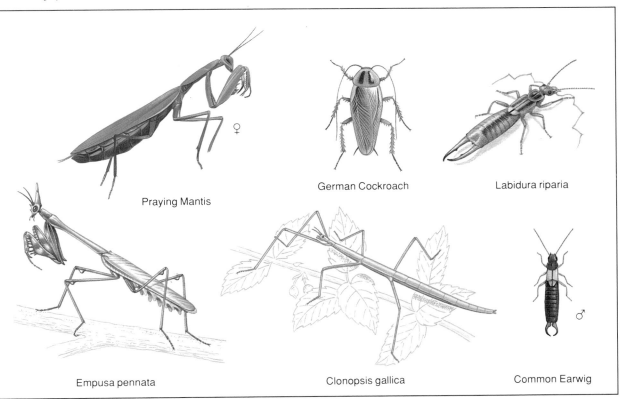

Praying Mantis

German Cockroach

Labidura riparia

Empusa pennata

Clonopsis gallica

Common Earwig

Bugs

This very large order (Hemiptera) is extremely varied, but all members have a hollow, needle-like beak for sucking up fluids. Most have four wings, but some are wingless. There are two major divisions in the order – the Heteroptera and the Homoptera. The forewings of the Heteroptera, when they are present, have a horny basal area and a membranous tip. The forewings of the Homoptera, when they are present, are either horny or membranous, but of uniform texture. Heteropterans include both plant and animal feeders and all the water bugs. Homopterans are all terrestrial plant-feeders and include the aphids and many other pests. There is no chrysalis stage.

Heteroptera

Hawthorn Shield Bug

Acanthosoma haemorrhoidale
Family Aconthosomatidae
14mm. One of many colourful shield-shaped bugs, this species feeds on the leaves and fruits of hawthorn and other trees. Common in woods and hedgerows, it overwinters in the adult state and is seen mainly in spring and autumn.
Ⓑ◐✿⊜

Graphosoma italicum

Family Pentatomidae
10mm. The bright colours of this shield bug warn of its most unpleasant taste. It feeds on a variety of plants, especially umbellifers, from June to October, and is found in southern and central Europe. *G. semipunctatum*, from southern Europe, has rows of red dots at the front instead of stripes.
⊜

Pied Shield Bug

Sehirus bicolor
Family Cydnidae
5–7mm. This common bug feeds on the sap of deadnettle and related plants, on which it can be found at most times of the year. Adults hibernate in the soil. The nymphs are creamy white with small black spots and, like other shield bug nymphs, more rounded than the adults. These bugs are often mistaken for beetles.
Ⓑ✿⊜

Common Pond Skater

Gerris lacustris
Family Gerridae
12mm. This bug lives on the surface of still or slow-moving water from April to November, skating around on the long second pair of legs and using its hind legs as a rudder. Water-repellent hairs on the feet prevent them from penetrating the surface film. Its front legs are used to catch small insects that fall onto the water surface. The male may ride on the female's back for days or even weeks

With its legs making little dimples in the water surface, the Common Pond Skater easily picks up the vibrations of potential prey.

after mating, giving rise to the country name of 'double insects'. Many individuals are fully winged and fly well, but most have reduced wings and cannot fly. Flying adults may hibernate far from the water.
Ⓑ😊

Water Boatman

Corixa punctata
Family Corixidae
13mm. Found in still and slow-moving water, this bug swims using its hairy back legs. It feeds on small algae or vegetable debris and, like most aquatic bugs, has hidden antennae and comes up tail-first for air. It flies well and often leaves the water to seek a new home. Males stridulate loudly during courtship by rubbing their front legs on their faces. This species is often called the Lesser Water Boatman to avoid confusion with the Backswimmer, which itself is often called a water boatman.
Ⓑ😊

Backswimmer

Notonecta glauca
Family Notonectidae
15mm. As its name suggests, this bug swims on its back. Its underside, which is uppermost when swimming, appears silvery because it carries a film of air trapped by fine hairs. The hind legs are much longer than the middle ones and row the insect jerkily through the water. It attacks any creature up to the size of a large tadpole, and will pierce unwary fingers if handled. Common in still and slow-moving water, it flies well and soon colonizes new ponds.
Ⓑ😊

Water Scorpion

Nepa cinerea
Family Nepidae
20mm. This species lives in shallow, muddy water, where it grabs other small animals with its strong front legs. It usually creeps slowly over the bottom, but may swim

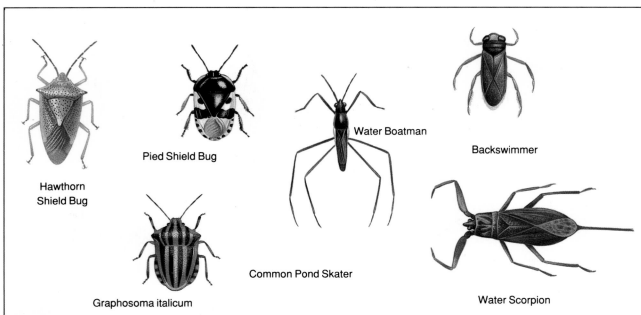

Hawthorn
Shield Bug

Pied Shield Bug

Graphosoma italicum

Common Pond Skater

Water Boatman

Backswimmer

Water Scorpion

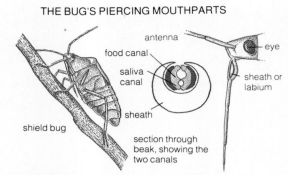

THE BUG'S PIERCING MOUTHPARTS

antenna
food canal
saliva canal
sheath
shield bug
eye
sheath or labium
section through beak, showing the two canals

Bug mouthparts fit together to form a needle-like beak with two canals. Food is sucked up one and saliva flows down the other. After use the beak folds under the body.

slowly. Periodically it draws air from the surface through the tube at the rear. A few individuals can fly. Harmless, despite its name, the bug generally feigns death when it is handled.
Ⓑ☻

Homoptera

Cicada orni
Family Cicadidae
25mm. Easily recognized by its spotted wings, this is one of Europe's largest cicadas. The males produce shrill calls, by the vibration of a tiny drum-skin on each side of the body and can be heard throughout the summer. It spends most of its time sucking sap from tree trunks through a sturdy beak, but its brown and grey coloration makes it hard to see. The nymphs spend several years feeding on roots. It occurs in southern and central Europe.
Ⓞ④

Cicadetta montana
15–25mm. Found on trees and shrubs from May to August, this small cicada can be recognized by the orange tinge at the base of the wings. The male makes a rather soft bubbling call which is not easily heard. It is widely distributed on the Continent, but confined to the New Forest in Britain.
Ⓑ◐④⬚

Common Froghopper
Philaenus spumarius
Family Cercopidae
6mm. Abundant on woody and herbaceous plants from May to September, this sap-sucking bug gets its name because it jumps away when disturbed. Its wing pattern varies a good deal and is sometimes almost black and white. Its nymphs are responsible for the 'cuckoo-spit' which covers plants in early summer. The froth protects them as they feed.
Ⓑ◐✹⬚

Cercopis vulnerata
10mm. This froghopper feeds on various plants, especially in wooded areas, from April to August. The nymphs feed on roots, protected by a mass of solidified froth. This species is found in southern and central Europe.
Ⓑ◐⬚

Thrips

These tiny black, brown or yellowish insects (Order Thysanoptera) are sometimes wingless but usually have four, minute feathery wings. They suck juices from a wide range of plants and fungi and are very common in flowers. Many species cause damage to crops because their feeding activities distort the leaves and fruits. Often called thunderflies, they swarm into the air in thundery weather. The females commonly hibernate in houses, often getting behind wallpaper and into picture frames. The life cycle is complex, but there is no real chrysalis stage. About 150 species occur in the British Isles.

Corn Thrips
Limothrips cerealium
Family Thripidae
2mm. This is one of the commonest thrips found in rural areas. It breeds in developing ears of cereals and causes shrivelling of the grain.

The adults emerge in swarms as the ears ripen and fly from June to September, after which the females hibernate. They fly again in spring and lay their eggs in the cereal flowers. The Pea Thrips (*Kakothrips pisivorus*) breeds in pea flowers and damages the young pods, which become silvery and fail to swell up properly.
Ⓑ✹⬚

Scorpion Flies

This small group (Order Mecoptera) is so-named because the males of most species have scorpion-like tails, although they are quite harmless. Their jaws are at the tip of a stout beak. Most are omnivorous scavengers with a strong liking for dead insects. The caterpillar-like larvae live in damp soil. There are about 30 European species.

Panorpa communis
Family Panorpidae
30mm wingspan. This insect is found from May to August in hedgerows, nettlebeds, gardens and other shady places. It often scavenges on the remains of prey trapped in spiders' webs. Its flight is very weak. One of a number of similarly-spotted species, it can be identified with certainty only by a detailed examination of the structure of the rear end.
Ⓑ◐✹⬚

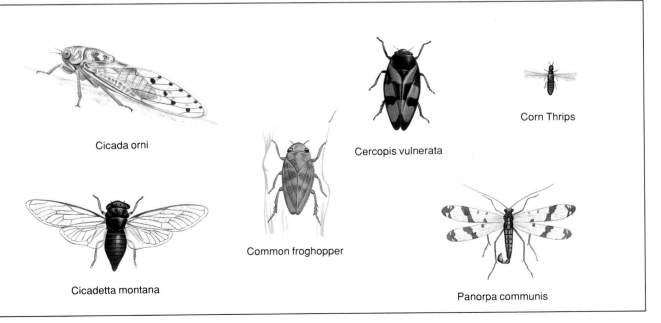

Cicada orni

Cicadetta montana

Common froghopper

Cercopis vulnerata

Corn Thrips

Panorpa communis

Lacewings and Relatives

This large and very varied group of carnivorous insects (Order Neuroptera) mostly have densely netted wings held roof-wise over the body at rest. They feed mainly on aphids and other small insects. The young stages are bristly, shuttle-shaped larvae. The measurements given are wingspans.

Alder Fly

Sialis lutaria
Family Sialidae
30mm. This weak-flying insect is generally seen resting on walls, fences, and vegetation close to still or slow-moving water from April to August. It rarely feeds. The eggs are laid in dense batches on reeds and other plants, and the feathery larvae fall into the water.
Ⓑ☻

Snake Fly

Raphidia notata
Family Raphidiidae
25mm. This species may be seen from May to August, mainly on trees and shrubs, where it rests with its long, snake-like neck raised. It feeds on aphids and other small insects. The female lays eggs in the bark of dead and dying trees with her long, needle-like ovipositor. When the larvae emerge, they feed under the bark.
☻Ⓞ⊕

Green Lacewing

Chrysopa septempunctata
Family Chrysopidae
30–40mm. Among the largest of many similar species, this lacewing can be distinguished by seven tiny black spots on the face. It is active from May to September in gardens, woods and hedgerows in southern and central Europe. Adults and larvae all feed on aphids and other small insects. *Chrysoperla carnea* is a smaller species that often comes into houses in autumn to hibernate, turning from green to flesh-coloured at this time of year.
Ⓑ○♁▥

Libelloides coccajus

Family Ascalaphidae
50mm. This fast-flying insect is often mistaken for a dragonfly, although easily distinguished by its long antennae. It snatches small insects in mid-air. It flies only in sunshine, resting at other times with wings pulled tightly back along its body to give a triangular appearance. It is commonly found in southern and central Europe from April to August.
▥

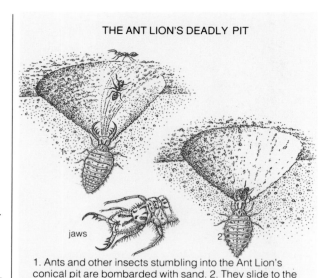

THE ANT LION'S DEADLY PIT

jaws

1. Ants and other insects stumbling into the Ant Lion's conical pit are bombarded with sand. 2. They slide to the bottom and are grabbed by the powerful jaws.

Ant Lion

Myrmeleon formicarius
Family Myrmeleonidae
80mm. A slow-flying nocturnal insect of dry, grassy places. On the wing from May to August, it plucks aphids and other small insects from vegetation. It gets its name because its larva catches ants in a pit. It occurs in most of Europe except the far north.
▥

Palpares libelluloides

100mm. This large ant lion flies by day in rough, grassy places from May to September. Often mistaken for a dragonfly, it flies much more slowly as it snatches small insects in flight or from vegetation. The larva buries itself in the soil, with its huge jaws at the surface to grab passing prey. It is found in southern Europe.
☻☻▥

Beetles

With 300,000 known species, the beetles (Order Coleoptera) are the largest of the insect orders. The forewings, known as elytra (singular elytron), are tough and horny and they usually conceal the membranous hind wings, although

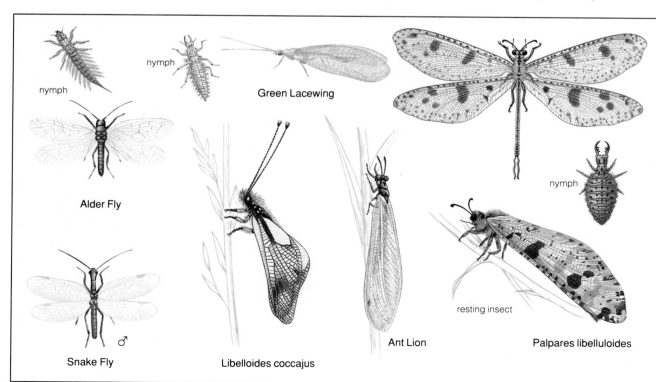

nymph

nymph

Green Lacewing

nymph

Alder Fly

Snake Fly ♂

Libelloides coccajus

Ant Lion

resting insect

Palpares libelluloides

A Great Diving Beetle puts its powerful jaws to work on a worm held firmly in its front legs. The oar-like hind legs, with which it propels itself in the water, are clearly visible.

many species have no hind wings. Water beetles carry their air supply under their elytra. All adult beetles have biting mouths and feed on every kind of food. The larvae are varied, but all have strong jaws and often feed on the same foods as the adults.

Green Tiger Beetle
Cicindela campestris
Family Carabidae
10–15mm. This beetle is seen on heathland and sandy places from May to August. Active only in sunshine, it chases ants and other small insects. It is among the fastest of all insects on the ground, with a top speed of about 60cm per second. It also flies well, with a loud buzzing sound. The larva lives in a vertical burrow.
Ⓑ ☻

Violet Ground Beetle
Carabus violaceus
20–30mm. This flightless beetle is named for its bright violet sheen. Often found under logs and stones by day, the beetle feeds on various invertebrates in woods, gardens and other habitats by night. Its shuttle-shaped larva is also an active hunter.
Ⓑ ◑ ✪ ⓦ

Calosoma sycophanta
17–30mm. Ranging from golden green to bronzy red, this beetle lives in trees and bushes, where both adult and larva feed voraciously on caterpillars. It is a valuable ally against the damaging gypsy moth caterpillars in many forests. This species is commonly found on the Continent, but it is only a rare visitor to Britain.
◑

Great Diving Beetle
Dytiscus marginalis
Family Dytiscidae
30mm. One of our largest water beetles, this predator lives in weedy ponds and streams, attacking a wide range of animals, including frogs and fishes. It swims well using its oar-like hind legs and often flies at night.
Ⓑ ☻

Whirligig Beetle
Gyrinus natator
Family Gyrinidae
5–7mm. This shiny black beetle whirls round and round on the surface of still and slow-moving water with the aid of short, paddle-like middle and hind legs. It catches small insects on or just beneath the surface. Each eye is divided into two parts – one looking across the surface and the other looking down into the water.
Ⓑ ☻

Burying Beetle
Nicrophorus vespillo
Family Silphidae
15–20mm. This beetle is distinguished from several similar species by its strongly curved hind legs and the two uninterrupted orange bands on its elytra. These beetles work in pairs to bury corpses of birds and small mammals and the female lays her eggs on the buried corpse. The adult beetles are active mainly in summer.
Ⓑ ✪ ⓦ

Devil's Coach-horse
Staphylinus olens
Family Staphylinidae
20–30mm. One of the rove beetles, with very short elytra, this nocturnal predator is commonly found under stones. When disturbed it raises its abdomen over the rest of the body in a threatening attitude – hence its other name of Cocktail.
Ⓑ ◑ ✪ ⓦ

Scarab Beetle
Scarabaeus sacer
Family Scarabaeidae
25mm. One of several Mediterranean dung beetles famed for their habit of rolling and burying balls of dung. Females lay eggs in the buried dung at certain times, or it is eaten by the adults, which often fight over the possession of the balls.
☻ ✪ ☻

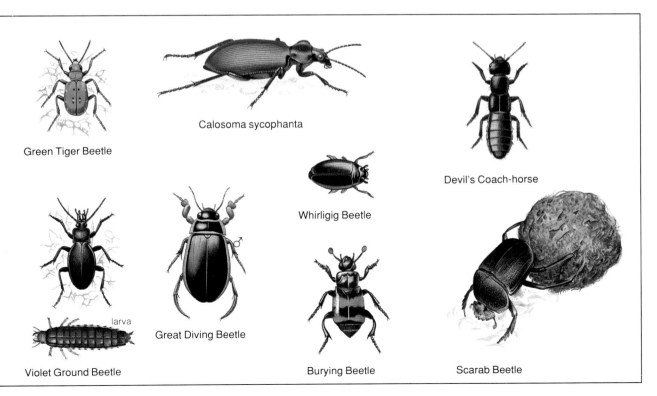

Green Tiger Beetle

Calosoma sycophanta

Whirligig Beetle

Devil's Coach-horse

larva

Great Diving Beetle

Violet Ground Beetle

Burying Beetle

Scarab Beetle

Stag Beetle
Lucanus cervus
Family Lucanidae
Male 50–70mm; female
20–40mm. Huge antler-like,
jaws give this beetle its name.
Found only in males, they are
used to wrestle over females.
The insect is found mainly in
and around woods. It flies
well in the evenings. The
larva resembles that of the
cockchafer but lives in tree
stumps and other decaying
wood. It is found in southern
and central Europe.
Ⓑ Ⓞ ✿

Cockchafer
Melolontha melolontha
Family Scarabaeidae
25mm. This beetle has an
antennal club that is clearly
split into flaps. The adult,
commonly called a May-bug,
flies from May to June. It
chews the leaves of trees and
shrubs, while the fat, white
C-shaped larva feeds on roots,
including those of cereals and
other crops.
Ⓑ Ⓞ ✿

Pine Chafer
Polyphylla fullo
35mm. The male has huge
scent-detecting antennae.
Found from June to August,
in and around pine woods in
southern and central Europe.
It screeches loudly when
handled. Adults chew pine
needles, while the larvae feed
on various roots.
Ⓞ ✤

Click Beetle
Athous haemorrhoidalis
Family Elateridae
12mm. Found in grassy places
in spring and summer, this is
one of the commonest click
beetles – so-called because,
when turned on their backs,
they leap into the air and
right themselves with a loud
click. The larva is one of the
notorious wireworms which
live in the soil and simply
chew their way right through
the roots and tubers of a wide
variety of crops.
Ⓑ Ⓞ 🕸

Ctenicera cuprea
11–16mm. Found on
grassland from May to
August, this click beetle
sometimes has a violet or
copper-coloured upper
surface. It occurs in northern
and central Europe.
Ⓑ 🍂 🕸

By clustering tightly together in this way, 7-spot Ladybirds are able to increase the effectiveness of their bold warning colours.

Rhagonycha fulva
Family Cantharidae
10–15mm. This soft-bodied
beetle frequents umbellifer
flowers from May to August
and it feeds on other insects.
The reddish body colour has
led to the beetle's common
name of Bloodsucker,
although it is quite harmless
to people. Together with
several more colourful
relatives, it is also known as a
Soldier Beetle.
Ⓑ ✿ 🕸

Glow-worm
Lampyris noctiluca
Family Lampyridae
10–18mm. The male has soft
brown elytra and looks like
many other beetles, but the
female is wingless and looks
more like a woodlouse. She is
the real Glow-worm, emitting
a pale greenish glow from her
rear end on warm summer
nights. Males flying overhead
detect the females' lights and
drop down to mate with
them. Adults rarely feed, but
the larvae, which resemble
the females, feed on small
snails. Glow-worms occur
mainly in chalk and limestone
areas, and are absent from
much of northern Europe.
Ⓑ 🕸

Firefly
Luciola lusitanica
10mm. Closely related to the
Glow-worm, this species has a
very different signalling
system. The males flash every
second or so as they fly and
the flightless females reply
with their own flashes. The
males then drop down to
mate. It is found from May to
July in southern Europe, but
only to the east of the Rhône.
✿ 🕸

Trichodes apiarius
Family Cleridae
15mm. Common on
umbellifers and other flowers
from May to July, this
colourful beetle feeds mainly
on pollen. It lays its eggs close
to the nests of various bees
and the young larvae enter
the nests and feed on the
bees' grubs.
✿ 🕸

Cardinal Beetle
Pyrochroa coccinea
Family Pyrochroidae
13–18mm. A rather flat
predatory beetle, commonly
found on flowers and tree
stumps from May to July. The
larvae prey on various small
animals under loose bark.
Ⓑ Ⓞ ✿

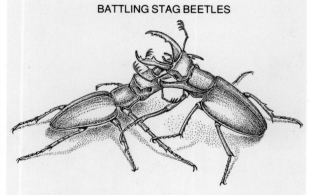

BATTLING STAG BEETLES

Male Stag Beetles wrestle with their antlers – which are really enlarged jaws – when competing for a female.

7-spot Ladybird
Coccinella 7-punctata
Family Coccinellidae
5–8mm. This is one of the
most common ladybirds. The
adult overwinters, often
among dead leaves and
sometimes in buildings. Both
the adult and the steely blue
larva are voracious predators
of aphids and are important
allies of the farmer and
gardener. The smaller 2-spot
Ladybird (*Adalia bipunctata*) is
equally common and often
overwinters in buildings in
dense swarms.
Ⓑ ✿ 🕸

22-spot Ladybird
Psyllobora 22-punctata
5mm. Eleven black spots on
each yellow elytron identify
this little ladybird. It is found
on shrubs and other low-
growing vegetation all year,
although it hides away in
debris during the coldest
times of year. It feeds mainly
on mildews.
Ⓑ ✿ 🕸

Cerambyx cerdo
Family Cerambycidae
25–60mm. One of Europe's
largest beetles, this species
belongs to the group known
as longhorns, so-named for
their long antennae. Mainly
nocturnal, it flies from May to
August in and around oak
woods. The larva tunnels in
oak trunks and destroys the
timber. The size of the adult
varies a great deal.
Ⓞ

Rosalia alpina
15–40mm. This very
beautiful and rare longhorn
flies in summer sunshine in
the montane beechwoods of
central and southern Europe.
The larva lives in dead and
dying beech trunks, and also
in ash and hornbeam in
southern areas. The species is
legally protected in many
regions.
Ⓑ 🍂 Ⓞ

Wasp Beetle
Clytus arietis
9–18mm. This day-flying
longhorn beetle is often seen
taking pollen and nectar from
hedgerow flowers from May
to August. Although
harmless, its wasp-like
colours and movements
afford it excellent protection
from birds. The larva develops
in dead wood.
Ⓑ Ⓞ ✿ 🕸

Green Tortoise Beetle
Cassida viridis
Family Chrysomelidae
7–10mm. One of several similar leaf-eating beetles in which the thoracic shield and elytra are expanded outwards and downwards. Their edges make contact with the leaf surface, eliminating any shadow and making the insect hard to see. Found from May to October, mainly on mint and other labiates.
Ⓑ🐝🌼🍄

Colorado Beetle
Leptinotarsa decemlineata
6–12mm. Alternating yellow and black stripes readily identify this notorious potato pest. A native of North America, this leaf beetle is now common in many parts of Europe. The adult and fleshy pink larva both eat potato stems and leaves from April to October.
🌼

Bloody-nosed Beetle
Timarcha tenebricosa
11–18mm. This flightless beetle is named for its habit of exuding bright red blood from its mouth when picked up or otherwise alarmed. It is commonly found from March to August in southern and central Europe.
Ⓑ🍄

Nettle Weevil
Phyllobius pomaceus
Family Curculionidae
9mm. This is one of the most common weevils, which are characterized by their angled antennae inserted on a snout or rostrum of varying length. It is an abundant species, feeding on nettles and many other plants from April to September. The larva feeds on the roots of nettles and various other plants.
Ⓑ🌼🌻🍄

Pea Weevil
Sitona lineatus
3–5mm. This is one of several short-snouted species with bulging eyes and striped elytra. It nibbles the leaves of clovers, peas and other legumes, producing conspicuously frilled margins from March to September. The adults overwinter in soil and debris. The larva feeds on the roots of legumes.
Ⓑ🌼🍄

Nut Weevil
Curculio nucum
6–9mm. The female of this species uses her long snout to drill into young hazel nuts, where she then lays her eggs. The adults are usually seen on hawthorn and other spring blossom.
Ⓑ🌼

Elm Bark Beetle
Scolytus scolytus
Family Scolytidae
3–6mm. This beetle is the carrier of Dutch elm disease, which has killed millions of elms in Europe. The female lays eggs under the bark of diseased trees and the larvae tunnel between the bark and the wood. The adults emerge from May to August.
Ⓑ🌼🌻🍄

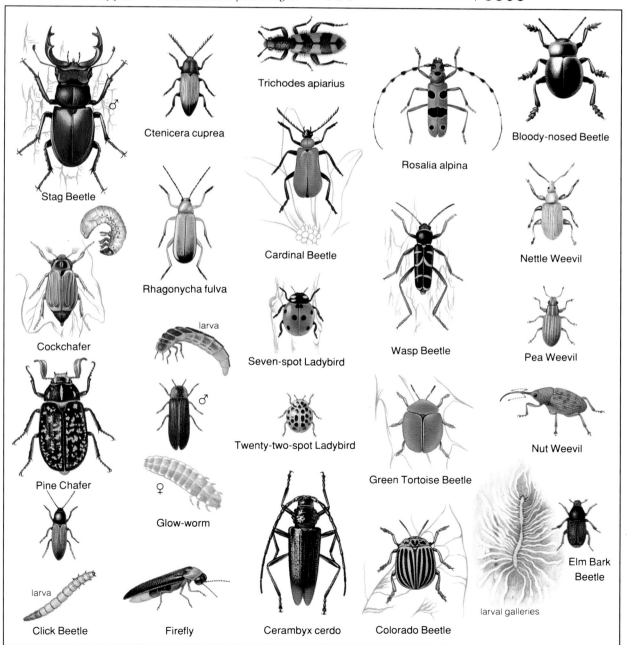

Stag Beetle

Ctenicera cuprea

Trichodes apiarius

Rosalia alpina

Bloody-nosed Beetle

Cockchafer

Rhagonycha fulva

Cardinal Beetle

Nettle Weevil

Pine Chafer

larva

Seven-spot Ladybird

Wasp Beetle

Pea Weevil

Twenty-two-spot Ladybird

Nut Weevil

Green Tortoise Beetle

Glow-worm

larva

Click Beetle

Firefly

Cerambyx cerdo

Colorado Beetle

Elm Bark Beetle

larval galleries

MEDITERRANEAN LANDS

The Mediterranean lands are those with long, hot summers and mild, wet winters. Most of the rain falls between October and April, and this is when most of the plant growth takes place. Defined thus, the Mediterranean lands cover much of Spain, peninsular Italy and Greece, but along the northern shores of the Mediterranean they form just a narrow band, rarely extending more than a few kilometres inland or over about 500m above sea level.

'Tough-leaved' Forests

Until about 8000 years ago the Mediterranean lands were clothed with evergreen forests dominated by tough-leaved oaks, including Cork Oak, and pines. Beneath the trees grew tough-leaved shrubs, all equipped with water-saving devices enabling them to withstand the long, hot summers. This was the sclerophyllous, meaning 'tough-leaved', forest. But then humans began to destroy the forests to make way for crops, sheep and goats. Centuries of over-grazing destroyed large areas of soil and made much agriculture impossible, although vineyards and olive groves remain in many places and cereals are grown where irrigation is possible. Where it has not been built on, most of the land is now covered with the scrubby vegetation known as maquis and garrigue. The original trees are now found mainly as scattered individuals or as small pockets of woodland. The maquis and garrigue could eventually pave the way for the return of the sclerophyllous forest, but frequent fires are likely to prevent anything more than local regeneration.

The Maquis

The typical maquis is an extremely dense vegetation covering huge areas of the Mediterranean region with an almost impenetrable green blanket. It develops mainly over acidic rocks and contains a wide variety of much-branched, evergreen shrubs reaching at least a metre in height and often exceeding two metres. These shrubs, which flourished under the original forest trees, include cistuses, Tree Heath, Strawberry Tree, Lentisc and also yellow-flowered spiny brooms. The flowers produce a riot of colour during the spring, but as they fade with the increasing heat of

RIGHT: *The lime-rich soils of the garrigue support a colourful array of Wild Thyme and other flowers.*
BELOW: *The shield bug* Graphosoma italicum *visits a number of Mediterranean flowers in the summer.*

summer the maquis returns to its monotonous green. Many shrubs contain aromatic oils which give the maquis its charateristic resinous smell. Corsica, famed for its extensive maquis, is often called the scented isle. Few herbaceous plants can survive under the dense maquis shrubs, but the ground under the cistus bushes may turn yellow in the spring with the flowers of *Cytinus hypocistis*.

As well as suffering frequent spontaneous fires, the maquis is often burnt deliberately to clear the ground for crops, but the thin soil soon degenerates and the maquis gradually returns, although in some places the soil disappears, exposing bare rock. The plant *Asphodelus microcarpus* is a conspicuous invader of the burnt ground.

Mediterranean Fauna

Plenty of birds inhabit the maquis and the garrigue but, apart from a few warblers, such as the Sardinian and Subalpine Warblers, they are not confined to or characteristic of these habitats. The same is true of the mammals that occur here, which include white-toothed shrews, rabbits, and several species of mice. As far as the vertebrates are concerned, the Mediterranean lands belong to the reptiles, many of which are confined to the region. Lizards bask on nearly every rock and bush, while snakes and tortoises enjoy the warmth of the ground below.

Insects are abundant in the Mediterranean, especially in the spring. They include some massive beetles, mantids, stick insects, and the handsome, fruit-loving Two-tailed Pasha Butterfly. Larval ant lions make their pits in sandy soil, while the adults drift silently over the vegetation at dusk. But the most conspicuous insects in the maquis and the garrigue are perhaps the numerous bush-crickets, which sing by night and day and can be quite deafening on summer nights.

The Garrigue

The classical garrigue is much more open than the maquis, and typically grows on limestone where the eroded soils are extremely shallow or even non-existent. The dominant plants are nearly all shrubby members of the Mint Family – including Rosemary, Thyme and Lavender – and they make the garrigue an even more aromatic habitat than the maquis. The plants are mostly about 50cm high – rarely more than a metre – and there is usually plenty of bare rock between them. It is therefore much easier to walk through the garrigue than through the maquis, but walking is not always painless because many garrigue plants carry sharp spines – a characteristic of many plants that grow in dry habitats. One of the worst offenders is the Kermes Oak, which usually grows as a holly-like bush. Numerous small bulbous plants and orchids flower on the garrigue in the spring, but most of these herbaceous species die down as the dry season sets in.

Although in their classical developments the maquis and garrigue are very different, it is possible to find all grades between the two extremes. Most ecologists believe that ungrazed garrigue, left to itself, will eventually develop into some kind of maquis. Conversely, regularly grazed or fired maquis may degenerate into some kind of garrigue. The Spanish word *matorral* is sometimes used to refer to these scrubby Mediterranean plant communities.

Wildlife of the Maquis
1 Lentisc
2 Mantis
3 Large Pink Cistus
4 Cytinus hypocistis
5 Scorpion
6 Ocellated Lizard
7 Ephippiger ephippiger
8 Strawberry-tree
9 Tree Heath
10 Spiny Broom
11 Hermann's Tortoise
12 Two-tailed Pasha
13 Asphodelus microcarpus

ABOVE: *Stone Pines, which are commonly known as Umbrella Pines, fringe many Mediterranean beaches, providing shade for both people and wildlife. Their cones yield a wealth of nutritious seeds.*

LEFT: *The Ladder Snake enjoys the warm, stony ground of the maquis, but is also at home basking on walls and even on roads.*

True Flies

The true flies (Order Diptera) have only one pair of functional wings. The hind wings are reduced to tiny pin-like bodies called halteres, which help maintain stability in flight. A few species, mostly parasitic ones, have reduced wings and some are completely wingless. All flies are liquid-feeders, either mopping up nectar and other liquids or biting other animals to suck their blood. Mosquitoes and horse-flies are the major blood-sucking flies in Europe. Fly larvae are all legless, but they are extremely varied in appearance and habits. Many live in water. This is a large order, with over 15,000 species in Europe. Many are commonly referred to as midges. The measurements given here are wingspans.

Crane-fly
Tipula oleracea
Family Tipulidae
40–50mm. This is one of the most abundant crane-flies, widely known as Daddy-long-legs. Most common from May to June, it inhabits fields and gardens, where its larvae, known as leatherjackets, damage crop roots. The male's abdomen is blunt at the end, but that of the female is pointed and used to push eggs into the soil. The very similar *T. paludosa* is more common in autumn.
Ⓑ❸🐝

Crane-fly
Tipula maxima
50–60mm. This species is easily recognized by its large size and spotted wings. It can be found throughout the summer, especially in wooded areas where its larvae live in damp soil and leaf litter. It flies mainly by night and is often attracted to lights.
Ⓑ🌑❸

Winter Gnat
Trichocera annulata
Family Trichoceridae
15mm. Resembling small crane-flies, this flimsy fly and its relatives can be distinguished by the short, sharply-bent vein at the rear of the wing. It can be found at most times of the year, but is especially noticeable on winter afternoons, when the males dance up and down in conspicuous mating swarms. The adults do not bite. The larvae live in decaying vegetable matter.
Ⓑ❸🐝

Mosquito
Culex pipiens
Family Culicidae
12mm. One of the most common mosquitoes, this species is active throughout the year and regularly occurs in buildings. The abdomen is clearly banded. Only the male has feathery antennae. Only the female sucks blood, as in all mosquitoes, but this species rarely attacks people. The larvae live in stagnant water. Mosquitoes can be distinguished from other similar flies by the scales on the veins and margins of the wings.
Ⓑ🌑❸

St. Mark's-fly
Bibio marci
Family Bibionidae
20mm. This species swarms over fields and gardens in spring, flying lethargically with its legs trailing below the body. It is frequently seen on hawthorn flowers and other blossom, and also basks on walls. The female has a much smaller head and eyes than the male. The larvae feed on roots and decaying matter in the soil.
Ⓑ❸🐝

Cleg-fly
Haematopota pluvialis
Family Tabanidae
15–20mm. This common, annoying horse-fly moves silently and bites before you realize you are under attack. Flying from May to October, it is especially common in and around damp woodlands. The abdomen varies from black to greyish yellow. The mottled wings are held roof-like over the body at rest.
Ⓑ🌑🌑🐝

Horse-fly
Chrysops relictus
15–20mm. Beautiful iridescent eyes characterize this and several similar species. As with all horse-flies, the females are blood-suckers and they often attack people. The male feeds on

The head of a Horse-fly showing the brilliant eye patterns characteristic of this family of flies.

nectar. These flies are active from May to September, mainly in light woodland and on heathland and rarely far from water. The larvae live in damp soil.
Ⓑ🌑🌑🐝

Robber-fly
Asilus crabroniformis
Family Asilidae
30–50mm. This fast-flying insect, one of the largest flies in Britain, catches other insects in mid-air and sucks them dry. Like most other robber-flies, it has a bristly 'beard' which protects its face from its struggling prey. It is found from June to October in open country. Its larvae live in cow dung.
Ⓑ🌑🐝

Bee-fly
Bombylius major
Family Bombyliidae
25mm. This easily recognized bee-like fly is harmless, despite its formidable appearance. The spear-like beak is used only for sucking nectar. Commonly seen feeding from low-growing flowers in the spring, the fly scatters its eggs on the soil. The larvae make their way into the nests of solitary bees where they feed on the bee grubs.
Ⓑ🌑❸🐝

Hover-fly
Syrphus ribesii
Family Syrphidae
20–25mm. This common hover-fly is abundant on hogweed and other umbelliferous flowers from April to November. Like many of its relatives, it is protected by its wasp-like appearance. Its maggot-like larva eats large numbers of aphids. The hover-flies make up a very large family, all of which have some of the posterior wing veins turning forward and running parallel to the hind edge of the wing to form a false margin.
Ⓑ❸🐝

Large Narcissus-fly
Merodon equestris
20–25mm. A common hover-fly with grey, tawny, or black hair and a bulge under the hind femur. On the wing from March to August. It is frequent in gardens, basking on the foliage of narcissi and other bulbous plants. The larvae feed on the bulbs and often destroy them.
Ⓑ🌑❸🐝

Drone-fly
Eristalis tenax
20–30mm. Named for its resemblance to a honey-bee, this common hover-fly can be seen feeding at flowers or sunning itself on walls and fences throughout the year. Its larva, known as the rat-tailed maggot, lives in muddy water and breathes with the aid of a telescopic tube.
Ⓑ❸🐝

Yellow Dung-fly
Scathophaga stercoraria
Family Scathophagidae
20mm. The golden-furred male of this species is conspicuous on fresh cow pats and other dung in all but the coldest months. The female is greyer, not so furry

and less conspicuous. These insects feed on smaller flies that visit the dung. The larvae develop in the dung.
Ⓑ🔄🐛

Flesh-fly
Sarcophaga carnaria
Family Sarcophagidae
25mm. Common around buildings, although seldom entering them, this fly can be seen on flowers or carrion or just sunning itself on walls throughout the year. Instead of laying eggs, the female gives birth to maggots which immediately start burrowing into the carrion on which they are laid.
Ⓑ✲

Greenbottle
Lucilia caesar
Family Calliphoridae
20mm. One of several rather similar, shiny green flies found in a wide range of habitats throughout the year. It is abundant on hedgerow flowers in the summer. The larvae feed mainly on carrion, but will attack living flesh when they get the chance. This species is one of several that cause sheep strike. It lays its eggs on the sheep, often in wounds, and the maggots burrow into the flesh.
Ⓑ✲🐛

Bluebottle
Calliphora vomitoria
20–25mm. This is the familiar blow-fly that enters the house and then makes a nuisance of itself as it buzzes noisily across the room in its search for a way out. It is often seen sunning itself on walls, even in the winter. Its maggots feed on dead flesh.
Ⓑ✲

House-fly
Musca domestica
Family Muscidae
15mm. Although less common than in the days of horse-drawn transport, this fly is still a nuisance in houses, where it samples all kinds of food and leaves germs on everything it touches. It is abundant around farms and stables, where there is plenty of manure in which its maggots can feed. It also breeds in rubbish dumps and wherever else it can find decaying matter. It is most common during the summer.
Ⓑ✲

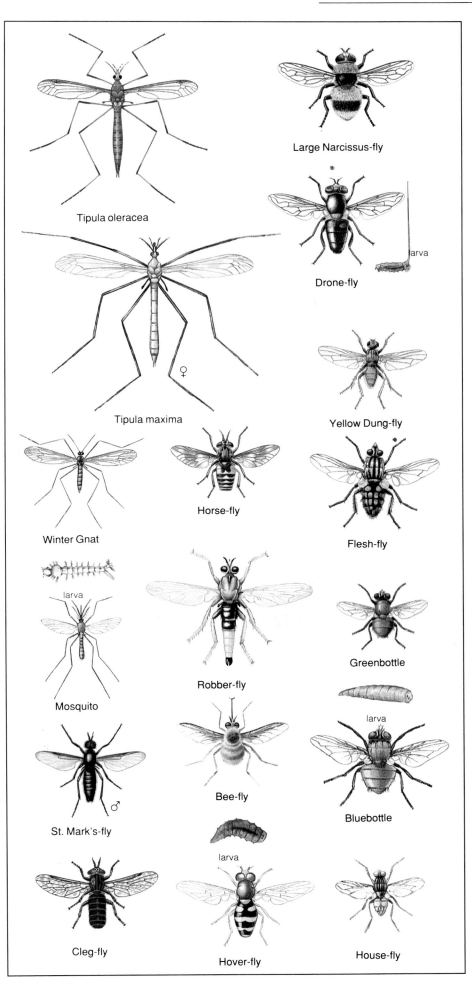

Tipula oleracea
Large Narcissus-fly
Drone-fly
larva
Tipula maxima
Yellow Dung-fly
Winter Gnat
Horse-fly
Flesh-fly
larva
Mosquito
Robber-fly
Greenbottle
larva
St. Mark's-fly
Bee-fly
Bluebottle
larva
larva
Cleg-fly
Hover-fly
House-fly

Butterflies

The butterflies belong to the Order Lepidoptera, which also contains the moths (see p. 356). The wings are clothed with minute scales, which give them their colours. Nearly 400 butterfly species live in Europe. All fly by day and drink nectar through a slender tongue or proboscis. All have clubbed antennae and rest with their wings held vertically above the body. All species pass through caterpillar and chrysalis stages before reaching maturity (see p. 318). The caterpillar has three pairs of true legs at the front and five pairs of stumpy prolegs on the abdomen. The sizes given are the approximate wingspans. Both sexes are shown only where they are significantly different. Unless otherwise stated, the insects have only one brood or generation in a year. The life cycle charts show the months during which each of the four stages can be found. Adults have shorter periods of activity in northern Europe than they do further south where there may be two or more broods in a year.

KEY TO LIFE CYCLE CHARTS

▬ egg	A dotted line shows a period of hibernation.
▬ larva	A paler tint of the main colour shows that a
▬ pupa	stage sometimes extends its life as indicated.
▬ adult	A thin line means that a stage may exist at that time but is not known for certain.

LIFE CYCLE

LIFE CYCLE	J F M A M J J A S O N D
Grizzled Skipper	
Dingy Skipper	
Lg Chequered Skipper	
Small Skipper	
Silver-spotted Skipper	
Large Skipper	
Swallowtail	
Scarce Swallowtail	
Apollo	
Spanish Festoon	

The key to this chart is on page 336.

SKIPPERS

About 40 skippers (Family Hesperiidae) are found in Europe. They are named for the short skipping flights they make from flower to flower. The males of the orange-coloured species – the golden skippers – have a scent brand on the forewing, which stimulates the females during courtship. Most skippers bask with their wings wide open, but the golden skippers sit with their hind wings flat and their forewings raised at an angle. The larvae have very short hair. They live in shelters made of leaves, and pupate in flimsy cocoons.

Grizzled Skipper

Pyrgus malvae
20–25mm. This species is distinguished from several similar skippers by the row of white spots close to the outer edge of the forewing. One or two broods fly in grassy places from April to August. The larva, which is brown above and green below, feeds mainly on wild strawberry.
Ⓑ 🐛

Dingy Skipper

Erynnis tages
25–30mm. This well-named butterfly has one or two broods in grassy habitats from May to August. The larva is green with a dark brown head and feeds on various leguminous plants.
Ⓑ 🐛

Large Chequered Skipper

Heteropterus morpheus
30–40mm. The spotted underside of the hindwing is unique. The insect flies from June to August in damp grassland. The larva is pale green with white and dark green stripes and it feeds on coarse grasses. It is found in southern and central Europe.
🔘 🐛

Small Skipper

Thymelicus sylvestris
25–30mm. This species flies from May to September in all kinds of grassy habitats. The larva is green with yellowish stripes and feeds on coarse grasses. It rests by day in a tubular retreat made of grass blades. The Essex Skipper (*T. lineola*) is similar but the underside of its antennal club is black instead of orange.
Ⓑ Ⓧ 🐛

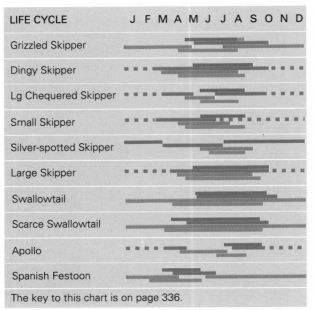

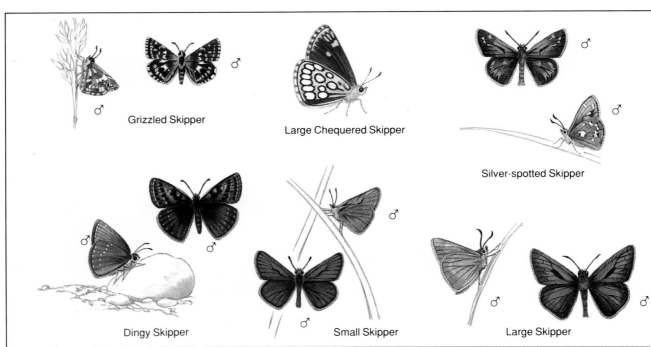

Grizzled Skipper

Large Chequered Skipper

Silver-spotted Skipper

Dingy Skipper

Small Skipper

Large Skipper

A freshly-emerged Swallowtail butterfly clings to its chrysalis skin while waiting for its wings to dry and harden, ready for flight. The chrysalis is usually attached to the species' foodplant.

SWALLOWTAILS AND APOLLOS

About 600 colourful butterflies comprise this largely tropical family (Papilionidae). Most of them have tailed hind wings. The caterpillar thrusts out a fleshy process behind the head when alarmed and this emits an odour which deters at least some of its enemies. The pupa is usually held upright on its support by a girdle of silk. There are 11 European species.

Swallowtail
Papilio machaon
60–100mm. This beautiful insect flies over flowery fields and hillsides from March to September. In Britain it is confined to the Norfolk Broads, where it flies in June and sometimes again from August to September. One to three broods are produced on the Continent. The larva feeds on Milk Parsley and other umbellifers. In its early stages the larva is black and white and resembles a bird dropping.

Scarce Swallowtail
Iphiclides podalirius
65–90mm. Actually more numerous than the Swallowtail in many areas, this insect frequents fields, gardens and woodland margins from March to September. The wing colour of the summer brood is much paler than that of the spring brood shown here. The larva is green with yellow lines and feeds mainly on blackthorn and other rosaceous trees, including cherries and other orchard species. It is found in southern and central Europe.

Apollo
Parnassius apollo
50–100mm. This rather variable butterfly is primarily a montane species, reaching altitudes of 3000m in the Alps and Pyrenees, although it flies at low levels in northern Europe. On the wing from May to September, it has a surprisingly slow flight and takes to the air only in bright sunshine. The larva is black with orange spots on the sides and feeds on stonecrops and saxifrages. It pupates in a flimsy cocoon on the ground.

Spanish Festoon
Zerynthia rumina
40–60mm. This species flies from February to June in rough, stony places in southern France and the Iberian Peninsula. The red spot near the base of the forewing distinguishes it from the Southern Festoon (*Z. polyxena*), which is found no further west than Provence. The brownish larva has rows of bristly tubercles, and feeds on birthworts.

Silver-spotted Skipper
Hesperia comma
28–32mm. Identified by the silvery spots on the underside, this skipper flies over rough grassland, mainly in chalk and limestone areas, from July to August. The female has a darker upperside than the male. The larva is dull green with a black head and feeds on fine-leaved grasses. It is very rare in Britain and confined almost entirely to chalk downs.

Large Skipper
Ochlodes venatus
25–35mm. This species flies from May to September, in grassy places of all kinds, including woodland rides. The female has a mottled orange and brown upperside and resembles the Silver-spotted Skipper. One to three broods are produced each year. The larva is mostly green with a black head. It lives in a silk tube on the coarse grasses that provide its food.

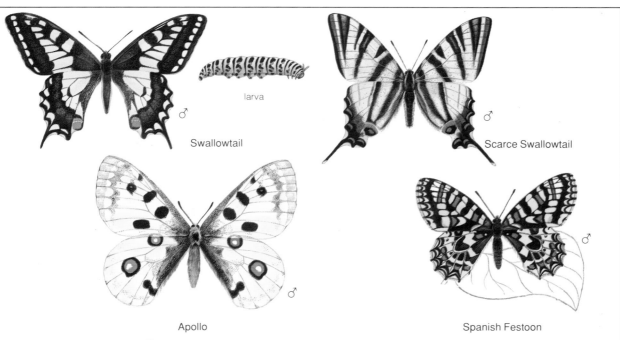

larva

Swallowtail

Scarce Swallowtail

Apollo

Spanish Festoon

The Orange-tip butterfly is a good example of sexual dimorphism, with only the male having the orange wing-tips.

WHITES AND YELLOWS

This family (Pieridae) contains about 2000 species, which are mostly of medium size and nearly all white or yellow. There are about 40 European species, although only six are resident in the British Isles. The sexes are usually quite similar although, among the whites, the males generally have fewer black spots than the females. The eggs resemble tiny skittles. The larvae are usually smooth and green and most feed on leguminous or cruciferous plants. Several species are serious pests. The pupa is attached to its support in an upright position and secured by a silken girdle. Unlike the pupae of other families, it has a single sharp point at the head end.

Small White
Pieris rapae
45–55mm. This is one of the most common butterflies in the world. It is on the wing from March to November and found almost wherever there are flowers. There are two broods in the north and three or four in the south. The larva is pale green with a yellow stripe along the back and another on each side. It feeds singly on brassicas and other crucifers and also on nasturtiums. It is a serious pest. The Southern Small White (*P. mannii*), found in southern Europe, is very similar but has a larger black patch at the wing-tip.
Ⓑ🐛🐾

Large White
Pieris brassicae
55–70mm. This common garden pest flies from April to October, with up to three broods in a year. It often migrates in large numbers, and can be found wherever there are flowers. The male has no spots on the upperside of the forewing, although those on the underside often show through. The larvae feed communally on brassicas and also on garden nasturtiums. Their bold colours and foul smell protect them from many enemies but huge numbers are destroyed by the little parasite *Apanteles glomeratus*.
Ⓑ🐛🐾

Green-veined White
Pieris napi
40–50mm. This species flies from March to November, with up to three broods, and occurs in a wide range of flower-rich habitats. The larva is like that of the Small White, but lacks the yellow stripe along the back. Although common in gardens, the larva feeds chiefly on charlock and other wild crucifers, and unlike the Small White it is not a pest of cultivated brassicas.
Ⓑ🐛🐾

Black-veined White
Aporia crataegi
55–65mm. This thinly-scaled species has wings which often become transparent with age, especially in the female. It flies from May to July in open country, visiting a wide range of flowers and often congregating to drink from damp patches on the ground. The larva is black with orange spots above and grey below. It feeds on blackthorn and other rosaceous trees and shrubs, including cultivated species, where it lives and hibernates communally in a silken tent. It has been extinct in Britain since the 1920s.
🐾🐛🐾

Bath White
Pontia daplidice
40–50mm. This species can be distinguished from several similar species by the central black spot which extends as a black smudge to reach the front edge of the underside of the forewing. Two to four broods fly from February to October in flowery places of all kinds. The larva is violet-grey with yellow lines and feeds on a wide range of crucifers. A great migrant, resident in southern Europe and moving northwards each spring to reach as far as Finland, it is only an infrequent visitor to Britain. The Dappled White (*Euchloe ausonia*) of the Alps and Pyrenees is similar, but the black spot on the upperside of the forewing extends forward to the wing margin.
🐛🐾

Orange-tip
Anthocharis cardamines
35–45mm. Only the male of this species has orange wing-tips. The female can be distinguished from similar species by her rather rounded wing-tip and the lack of white spots in the black patch. It flies from April to June in damp meadows, hedgerows, and woodland margins and is sometimes seen in gardens. The larva is green with a broad grey stripe on the side and very well camouflaged among the seed capsules of the Cuckoo Flower and other crucifers on which it feeds.
Ⓑ🐛🐾

Moroccan Orange-tip
Anthocharis belia
30–40mm. This butterfly flies from March to June over rough, uncultivated places in southern Europe. The males sometimes congregate and 'dance' on hill-tops or over prominent bushes. This behaviour, found in several butterfly species, is thought to attract unmated females. The larva is yellow and white with black spots and feeds on various crucifers. The Eastern Orange-tip (*A. damone*) is similar, but has more black on the underside and the female has no orange.
🐛🐾

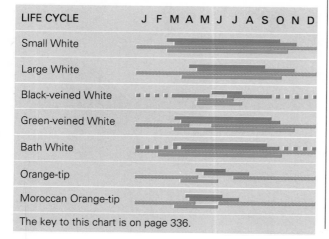

LIFE CYCLE	J	F	M	A	M	J	J	A	S	O	N	D
Small White												
Large White												
Black-veined White												
Green-veined White												
Bath White												
Orange-tip												
Moroccan Orange-tip												

The key to this chart is on page 336.

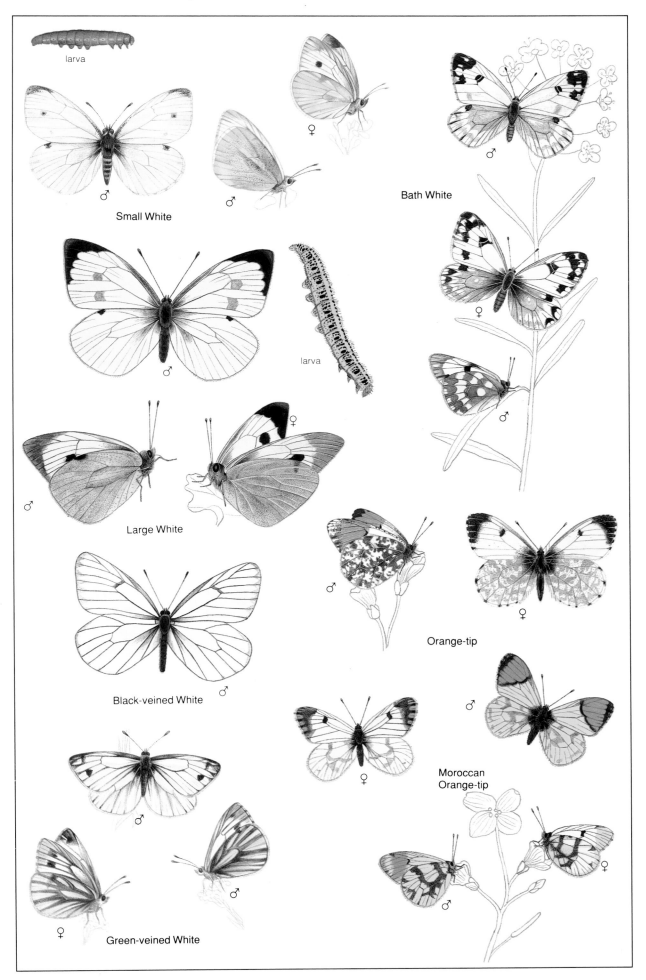

larva

Small White

Bath White

♂ ♀

Large White

larva

Black-veined White

Orange-tip

Moroccan Orange-tip

Green-veined White

Mountain Clouded Yellow

Colias phicomone

40–50mm. The dark scales on the wings of this butterfly help it to absorb the sun's warmth in its upland home. It flies from June to September on grassy slopes at altitudes between 1800 and 2400 metres in the Alps and Pyrenees. The larva is bluish green with a white stripe on each side and it feeds on various leguminous plants. ⬤

Moorland Clouded Yellow

Colias palaeno

45–60mm. Unlike most other clouded yellows, this species has solid black borders in the female as well as in the male. It flies from June to August over moors and meadows, usually at fairly low altitudes. It ranges from the Alps to the Arctic but is absent from most of western Europe. Specimens from the Alps are smaller and darker than northern specimens and have no black spot on the forewing. The larva is green with a yellow stripe on each side and feeds mainly on Bog Bilberry. ⬤⬤

Clouded Yellow

Colias crocea

45–60mm. Resident only in the south, this great migrant is a summer visitor to most parts of Europe, although the numbers reaching Britain vary a great deal from year to year. Several broods are on the wing from April to October, usually in flower-rich grassland, and are especially common in fields of clovers and Lucerne. The

species is a fast flyer and, like the other clouded yellows, it rarely opens its wings when settled. About ten per cent of females are of the very pale form known as *helice*. The larva feeds on clovers. ⬤⬤⬤

Northern Clouded Yellow

Colias hecla

40–45mm. The only deep yellow species in the far north, this butterfly flies from June to July over the low-growing tundra vegetation beyond the Arctic Circle. The green larva feeds on alpine milk-vetch and various *Vaccinium* species. Owing to the short summer, it probably takes two years to mature. ⬤

Pale Clouded Yellow

Colias hyale

45–55mm. Resident in the south, this species migrates northwards each spring, but is a rare visitor to Britain. Two or three broods are on the wing from May to September, frequenting flower-rich, grassy habitats. The female can be distinguished from the *helice* of the Clouded Yellow by its narrower black margins and brighter yellow underside. The larva feeds on various leguminous plants. Berger's Clouded Yellow (*C. australis*) has only recently been distinguished as a separate species. The adults of the two species are very similar in all respects, but the male Berger's Clouded Yellow usually has brighter yellow uppersides. The larva of Berger's Clouded Yellow has rows of heavy black dots. ⬤⬤

The Brimstone butterfly can be easily mistaken for a delicate leaf when resting with its wings closed.

Brimstone

Gonepteryx rhamni

50–60mm. Named for the brilliant colour of the male, this strong-flying butterfly occurs in many habitats, including gardens, which are often well away from its breeding grounds in hedgerows and the margins of deciduous woodland. The female's upperside is very pale green – often almost white – and she is frequently mistaken for a Large White in flight. Freshly-emerged butterflies fly from June to September and then hide away for the winter in ivy and holly bushes, where the leaf-like wings provide excellent camouflage. The butterflies reappear in spring, often as early as February in a mild year, and may remain on the wing until June, giving an adult life-span of about a year. They hardly ever open their wings when settled. The larva feeds on Buckthorn and Alder Buckthorn. ⬤⬤⬤⬤

Cleopatra

Gonepteryx cleopatra

50–70mm. The male of this species is easily identified, even in flight, by the orange flush on the forewing. The female is distinguished from the female Brimstone by a

narrow orange streak on the underside of the forewing. The species overwinters in the adult state and is on the wing from February to August, with the new generation appearing in early summer before the old one has died. The larva, very much like that of the Brimstone, feeds on Buckthorn. It is found throughout southern Europe. ⬤⬤

Wood White

Leptidea sinapis

35–45mm. This very delicate butterfly inhabits light woodland and surrounding grassland. It flies weakly, rarely far above the ground, from March to October. There are up to three broods; spring insects are greyer than the summer one shown here and have larger but less dense black spots. Summer females are almost unmarked. The larva is green with a yellow stripe on each side, and feeds on Meadow Vetchling, trefoils and other leguminous plants. The Eastern Wood White (*L. duponcheli*), inhabiting upland meadows in southern France and south-east Europe, is almost identical but its antennal clubs are dark underneath, instead of white as in the Wood White. ⬤⬤⬤

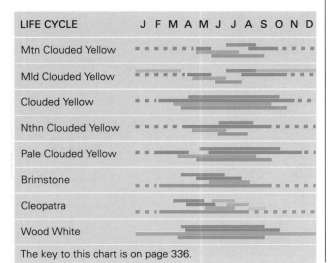

LIFE CYCLE	J F M A M J J A S O N D
Mtn Clouded Yellow	
Mld Clouded Yellow	
Clouded Yellow	
Nthn Clouded Yellow	
Pale Clouded Yellow	
Brimstone	
Cleopatra	
Wood White	

The key to this chart is on page 336.

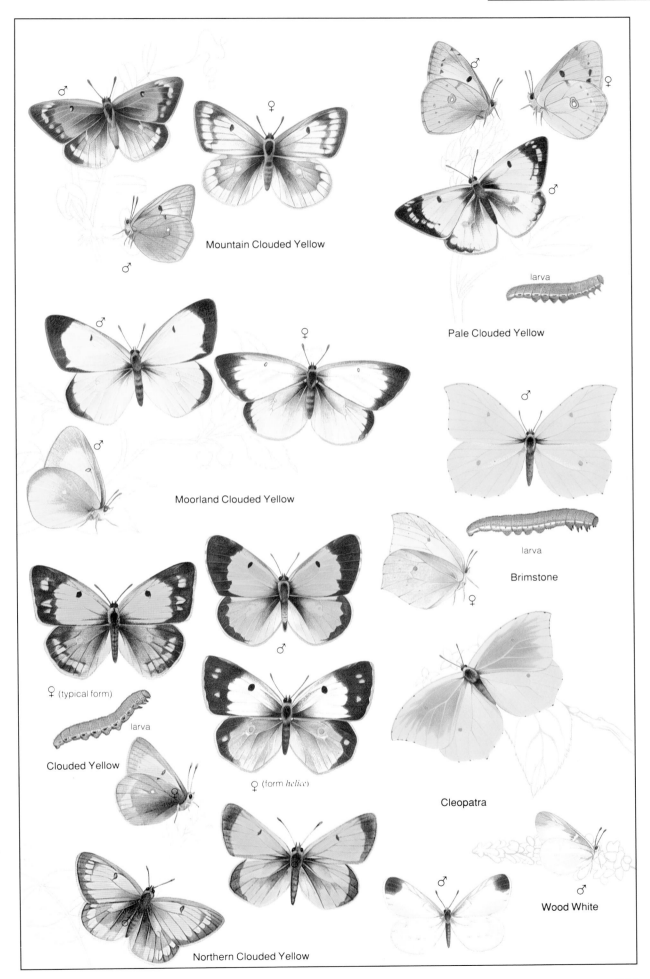

Mountain Clouded Yellow

Pale Clouded Yellow

larva

Moorland Clouded Yellow

Brimstone

larva

Clouded Yellow

♀ (typical form)

larva

♀ (form *helice*)

Cleopatra

Wood White

Northern Clouded Yellow

METALMARKS

The butterflies in this family (Riodinidae) are so-named because many have metallic wing markings. The front legs of the males are small and useless for walking, although those of the females are fully developed. The larvae are slug-shaped and hairy. There is one European species.

Duke of Burgundy

Hamearis lucina
25–35mm. This butterfly is on the wing from May to September in open woodland and scrubby places. It is fond of sunbathing but rarely takes much interest in flowers. There are one or two broods. The larvae feed on cowslips and primroses and pupate on the undersides of the leaves.
Ⓑ ○ ⊕

HAIRSTREAKS, COPPERS AND BLUES

This worldwide group (Family Lycaenidae) contains several thousand species, of which about 100 occur in Europe. Most are quite small, and brown, orange or blue. The sexes are usually quite different, especially among the coppers and blues. Most hairstreaks and many of the blues have slender, tail-like extensions on the hind wings.

Brown Hairstreak

Thecla betulae
34–36mm. This species flies from August to October in light woodland and over the surrounding fields and hedgerows. It keeps mainly to the tree-tops, where it feeds largely on honeydew. It occasionally descends to bask on low-growing vegetation, but rarely sits still for more than a few seconds. The male generally lacks the orange patch on the forewing found in the female. The larva is green with yellow stripes, and feeds mainly on Blackthorn.
Ⓑ ○ ⊛

Purple Hairstreak

Quercusia quercus
25–30mm. This butterfly is on the wing from June to September in oak woods, where it generally stays high in the trees and feeds on honeydew. The purple sheen, which is more extensive in the male, is visible only at certain angles. The larva feeds on oak leaves.
Ⓑ ○

White-Letter Hairstreak

Strymonidia w-album
25–38mm. This butterfly is like a male Black Hairstreak, but has little or no orange on the upperside. It is named for the W-shaped white line on the underside. It flies from June to August in and around light woodland in southern and central Europe. The slug-like green larva feeds on the buds, flowers and leaves of elms and limes.
Ⓑ ○

The Green Hairstreak butterfly blends in beautifully with the surrounding foliage. It rarely shows its brown upperside when at rest.

Blue-spot Hairstreak

Strymonidia spini
27–32mm. Named for the blue spot on the underside of the hind wing, this butterfly usually has a plain brown upperside. It flies over rough hillsides and other scrubby habitats from June to August. The larva is green with yellow and white stripes, and feeds mainly on Blackthorn but also on Buckthorn and hawthorns. It is found in southern and central Europe.
⊕

Black Hairstreak

Strymonidia pruni
28–33mm. The male of this species has just a few orange flecks on the upperside of the hind wing. The female has an orange band here and an orange patch on the front wing. It flies from June to August in old woodland. The slug-like larva is green with purplish stripes and feeds on Blackthorn. The insect is widely distributed, but rare in most regions.
Ⓑ ○

Green Hairstreak

Callophrys rubi
25–30mm. Leaf-green on the underside and dull brown above, this butterfly is hard to spot when resting on vegetation and is also difficult to follow in flight. It flies from March to July in a wide range of wooded and scrubby habitats, including heathland, and is one of Europe's most widely distributed butterflies. The larva is green and yellow and feeds on the flowers and leaves of gorse, broom, heather, and many other low-growing plants. It will also eat other small caterpillars.
Ⓑ ⊘ ○ ⊕

Small Copper

Lycaena phlaeas
20–30mm. This common and widely distributed butterfly flies from February to November. There are usually three broods. It prefers dry habitats, including fields and heathlands, but can be found in flower-rich places of all kinds, including gardens. The larva feeds on docks and sorrels.
Ⓑ ⊘ ⊛ ⊕

Purple-shot Copper

Heodes alciphron
30–35mm. Named for the male's beautiful purple sheen, this butterfly flies from June to August in flower-rich grassland, especially in the hills. The female lacks the purple sheen and is often dark brown with just an orange border to the hind wing. The larva is green with paler stripes and feeds on docks and sorrels. Found throughout southern and central Europe, in the south the male's purple sheen is poorly developed and both sexes appear orange with black spots.
⊕

Scarce Copper

Heodes virgaureae
30–35mm. Despite its name, this butterfly is not very scarce and is actually quite common in many flower-rich, upland meadows. It is on the wing from June to August, and the male is dazzling when basking in the sunshine. The greenish underside with black and white spots distinguishes it from other coppers. The larva is green with yellow stripes, and feeds on docks and sorrels.
⊕

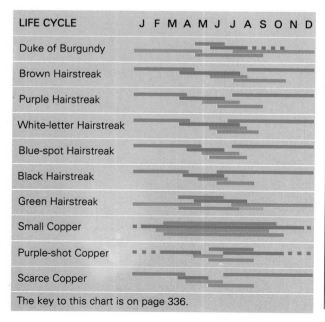

LIFE CYCLE	J F M A M J J A S O N D
Duke of Burgundy	
Brown Hairstreak	
Purple Hairstreak	
White-letter Hairstreak	
Blue-spot Hairstreak	
Black Hairstreak	
Green Hairstreak	
Small Copper	
Purple-shot Copper	
Scarce Copper	

The key to this chart is on page 336.

larva

Green Hairstreak

Duke of Burgundy

♀

♂

Brown Hairstreak

larva

Small Copper

♀

Purple Hairstreak

larva

♀ ♂

Purple-shot Copper

White-letter
Hairstreak

Blue-spot
Hairstreak

♂

♂

♂

♀

Black Hairsteak

Scarce Copper

Long-tailed Blue
Lampides boeticus
25–35mm. The two or three broods of this species fly in flowery places from May to October. The female is largely brown above, especially on the hind wing. The slender tails and dark spot at the rear of the wing give a good impression of a head when the wings are closed, especially when the butterfly moves its wings gently up and down, and distract at least some predators from the real head. The larva is green with yellow stripes, and lives in pods of legumes. Found in southern and central Europe, it is a great migrant and is distributed almost all over the world, although it is only a rare visitor to Britain and northern Europe.

Holly Blue
Celastrina argiolus
25–35mm. This is the only blue likely to be found in wooded areas and in towns and gardens. Two broods are on the wing from March to September but numbers fluctuate wildly from year to year. The black wing borders of summer brood females are much broader than those of the spring brood shown here. The butterflies feed mainly on honeydew. The larva is green with a white line on each side and often tinged with pink. It feeds on flowers and young fruits of the foodplant and also on young leaves. Spring

larvae feed on holly and a few other shrubs and trees, such as dogwood and snowberry, while summer larvae eat ivy. Very few other butterflies alternate their foodplants.

Green-underside Blue
Glaucopsyche alexis
25–35mm. This species flies from April to July in flowery meadows, especially in uplands. The female's upperside is brown. The underside spots of both sexes vary in size, as does the extent of the blue flush. The larva is yellowish-green with dark green and brown stripes. It feeds on various leguminous plants and is frequently attended by ants. Widely distributed in Europe, it is rare north of the Alps.

Large Blue
Maculinea arion
30–45mm. This butterfly is on the wing from June to July in rough grassland and heathland. The female is usually brighter than the male and often has larger spots. After feeding on wild thyme flowers for two or three weeks, the larva falls to the ground and is picked up by a red ant of the genus *Myrmica*, which is attracted by a sweet secretion produced by the larva. The ant carries the larva to its nest, where it spends the next few months feeding on ant grubs. Unharmed by the ants, it

Mating Silver-Studded Blue butterflies with the female, on the left, clearly showing the silvery-blue studs which give the species its name.

pupates there and emerges during the following summer. Found in southern and central Europe, the insect became extinct in Britain in 1979 – as a result of vegetational changes and the loss of the necessary ant colonies. It has now been re-introduced from the Continent to carefully monitored sites.

Silver-studded Blue
Plebejus argus
25–35mm. Named for the tiny silvery blue spots near the margin of the underside of the hind wing, this butterfly frequents heaths and dry grassland from May to September. The upperside of the male is largely blue, but the female is mostly brown with just a dusting of blue scales near the wing bases. There are one or two broods. The larva is green with dark brown and white stripes, and feeds on various plants including Gorse, Heather and Rock-rose.

Brown Argus
Aricia agestis
20–30mm. The upperside of this species is rich brown in both sexes. It flies over rough grassy places and heathland from April to September. There are one to three broods. The larva, which is green with a purplish brown and pink stripe, feeds on Rock-rose, Stork's-bill and other low-growing plants. It is found in southern and central Europe. In northern parts,

including the north of Britain, and in many mountainous regions it is frequently replaced by the Mountain Argus (*A. artaxerxes*), in which the red spots on the upperside of the forewing are very faint or absent. The British race also usually has a white spot in the middle of the forewing.

Cranberry Blue
Vacciniina optilete
20–30mm. A butterfly of mountains and moorlands, this species flies from June to August and can be recognized by the prominent red spot on the underside of the hind wing. The female is dark brown above with just a dusting of blue scales. The larva is green with a purple stripe on each side, and feeds mainly on Cranberry. It is found in northern and central Europe.

Damon Blue
Agrodiaetus damon
30–35mm. This species flies from June to August in the Alps and Pyrenees and other mountains of southern Europe. The female's upperside is dull brown with a pale fringe and her underside is coffee-coloured. The larva is green with yellow and red stripes, feeds on the flowers of sainfoins. In common with the larvae of many other blues, it is attended by ants which seek the sweet secretions of glands on various parts of its abdomen.

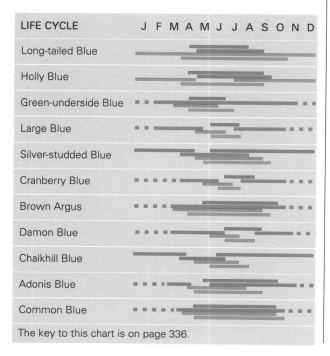

LIFE CYCLE	J	F	M	A	M	J	J	A	S	O	N	D
Long-tailed Blue												
Holly Blue												
Green-underside Blue												
Large Blue												
Silver-studded Blue												
Cranberry Blue												
Brown Argus												
Damon Blue												
Chalkhill Blue												
Adonis Blue												
Common Blue												

The key to this chart is on page 336.

Chalkhill Blue

Lysandra coridon
30–35mm. This common
butterfly of chalk and
limestone grassland flies from
June to August. The male is
easily identified by its silvery
blue upperside and lightly
chequered margins. The
female resembles a female
Adonis Blue but has white
scales, not blue ones, close to
the margin of its hind wing.
The larva is green with yellow
stripes and feeds on
Horseshoe Vetch and other
low-growing legumes where
it is permanently tended by
ants. The latter even bury the
pupa and guard it. It occurs in
southern and central Europe.
The Provence Chalkhill Blue
(*L. hispana*) from south-
western Europe is almost
identical but it is double-
brooded and, where the
ranges of the two species
overlap, it flies earlier and
later than the Chalkhill Blue.
Ⓑ ⓜ

Adonis Blue

Lysandra bellargus
25–35mm. Intense blue
wings with chequered fringes
distinguish the male of this
species from other blues. The
female resembles the female
Chalkhill Blue but is
distinguished from most other
blues of similar size by having
two black spots in the centre
of the underside of the
forewing. Two broods fly over
chalk and limestone hillsides
from May to September. The
larva is like that of the
Chalkhill Blue and feeds on
various low-growing
leguminous plants. The larvae
and pupae are always
guarded by ants. It is found in
southern and central Europe.
Ⓑ ⓜ

Common Blue

Polyommatus icarus
25–35mm. This is one of
Europe's most common
butterflies, and certainly the
most numerous blue, being
found in grassy places almost
everywhere from the Arctic to
the Mediterranean. One to
three broods fly from April to
October. The male has a slight
violet tinge, while the
female's upperside is brown
with varying amounts of blue
at the base of the wings. The
larva feeds on a wide range of
trefoils and other small
leguminous plants.
Ⓑ ⓜ

Cranberry Blue

Long-tailed Blue

Brown Argus

Damon Blue

Holly Blue

Green-underside Blue

Chalkhill Blue

Large Blue

Adonis Blue

Silver-studded Blue

larva

Common Blue

SNOUT BUTTERFLIES

Named for the long palps, which project snout-like in front of the head, these butterflies (Family Libytheidae) are found mainly in tropical areas. The front legs of the males are much reduced, although those of the females are fully developed. There is only one European species.

Nettle-tree Butterfly
Libythea celtis
35–45mm. Easily recognized by the prominent 'beak' near the wing-tip, this species flies from June to September in light woodland and around villages and then goes into hibernation. At rest, the dark, jagged wings look just like dead leaves. The butterflies fly again from March to May, when they lay their eggs. The larva is green with a pinkish stripe on each side and feeds on the Nettle-tree. The pupa is suspended by its rear end. It occurs in southern and eastern Europe.
○ ✪

VANESSIDS AND FRITILLARIES

This world-wide family (Nymphalidae) contains several thousand species of mostly rather colourful, fast-flying butterflies of which about 70 occur in Europe. The sexes are generally quite similar. All members of the family have only four fully developed legs: the front legs are short and brush-like, especially in the males. The larvae of most species are covered with elaborate spines and the pupae, which are generally suspended from the tail end, are often ornamented with gold or silver markings.

Two-tailed Pasha
Charaxes jasius
70–85mm. This striking butterfly flies from May to October in scrubby habitats in the Mediterranean region and is rarely seen far from the coast. It is fond of ripe figs and other fruit. The larva feeds on the leaves of the Strawberry Tree, among which it is very well camouflaged.
☺ ○ ✪

Purple Emperor
Apatura iris
65–80mm. Only the male has the purple sheen which gives this species its name. On the wing in deciduous woodlands from July to August, it spends most of its time high in the trees – especially oaks – where it feeds largely on honeydew exuded by aphids. The males sometimes come down to drink from damp soil and also from dung and carrion, but the females rarely descend other than to lay their eggs on sallow leaves. The larva is brown when young and spends the winter on sallow twigs, protected by its excellent camouflage – it turns green in spring. It has two horns on its head but none of the spines typical of the family. It is absent from Scandinavia and most of the Mediterranean region.
Ⓑ ○

The Camberwell Beauty is so-named because the first British specimen was caught near Camberwell in London in 1748.

White Admiral
Limenitis camilla
50–60mm. On the wing with a graceful, gliding flight from June to July, this species frequents wooded areas with plenty of open spaces and bramble flowers. It is surprisingly difficult to see when basking on leaves in dappled sunlight. The larva feeds on honeysuckle and hibernates in a folded leaf attached to a twig. It is absent from extreme north and south. Populations of this species fluctuate markedly with summer temperatures and are at their highest in years with the hottest Junes.
Ⓑ ○

Southern White Admiral
Limenitis reducta
45–55mm. This species is similar to the White Admiral but has a clear white spot in the middle of its forewing and only one row of black dots on the underside of its hindwing. It frequents light woodland and surrounding grassland, flying from May to October. There are two or three broods. The larva resembles that of the White Admiral and feeds on honeysuckle. It occurs in southern and central Europe.
○ ▥

Camberwell Beauty
Nymphalis antiopa
60–75mm. This strong-flying butterfly of open woodland is a migratory species, and so can be seen in almost any habitat. It feeds mainly on sap oozing from wounded trees. It flies from June to September and again from March to April after hibernating in hollow trees and log-piles. The spiny larva is black with red spots. It feeds communally under a large web on sallow and birch. It is a rare visitor to Britain.
○ ✪

Large Tortoiseshell
Nymphalis polychloros
50–65mm. Distinguished from the far more common Small Tortoiseshell by its size and by having much less black on the hind wing, this butterfly frequents lightly wooded areas, including orchards. Flying from June to September and again from March to April after hibernation, it feeds largely on sap oozing from trees. The larva is black with yellowish spines and feeds gregariously – usually on elms and willows. It is very rare in Britain and possibly extinct as a resident, although occasional migrants arrive from the Continent. The Yellow-legged Tortoiseshell (*N. xanttomelas*)) from eastern Europe is similar but has yellowish-brown middle and hind legs instead of black.
○ ✪

Small Tortoiseshell
Aglais urticae
45–50mm. One of Europe's most common butterflies, this species is often abundant in gardens, especially in the autumn when it is feeding up for the winter. It frequently hibernates in sheds and houses. It flies from March to October, and there are three broods. The larva lives communally on stinging nettles. Migrants occasionally reach Iceland.
Ⓑ ✪ ▥

LIFE CYCLE	J F M A M J J A S O N D
Nettle-tree Butterfly	
Two-tailed Pasha	
Purple Emperor	
White Admiral	
Sthn White Admiral	
Camberwell Beauty	
Large Tortoiseshell	
Small Tortoiseshell	

The key to this chart is on page 336.

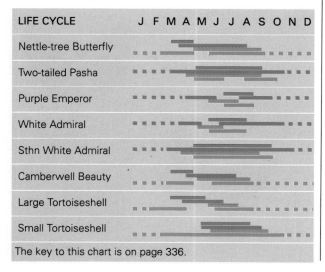

Nettle-tree Butterfly

Southern White Admiral ♂ ♂

Two-tailed Pasha

Camberwell Beauty

Purple Emperor ♂ ♂ ♀

Large Tortoiseshell ♂ ♂

White Admiral ♂ ♂

larva

Small Tortoiseshell ♂ ♂

larva

larva

347

The pale underside of this Comma butterfly, feeding on mint, shows it to belong to the summer brood, which is known as form hutchinsoni. *The distinctive comma mark is clearly visible.*

Peacock
Inachis io
55–70mm. An unmistakable butterfly, common in most of Europe except the far north in gardens and wherever else it can find flowers such as buddleias. It flies from July to October and again in spring after hibernating in hollow trees, sheds and other secluded places. Spring insects are often rather ragged and dull in colour, but they often survive well into May. Up to 400 eggs are laid in an untidy heap on Stinging Nettles and the larvae feed gregariously on the leaves. Migrants occasionally reach Iceland.
Ⓑ✪▥

Red Admiral
Vanessa atalanta
55–70mm. This species flies from March to October in all kinds of flower-rich habitats, including gardens. It is also very fond of ripe fruit in the autumn. In southern Europe, it overwinters as an adult, usually in hollow trees and out-buildings but occasionally in rabbit burrows and similar holes. It cannot normally survive the winter further north and new butterflies move up from the south each spring. A great migrant, it is one of the few butterflies which regularly appear in Iceland. There are two broods. The larva of this species is dark and spiky with a yellow band on each side and feeds on Stinging Nettles, usually concealing itself in a folded leaf.
Ⓑ✪▥

Painted Lady
Cynthia cardui
55–65mm. This great migrant occurs nearly all over the world. It is an annual visitor to Europe from North Africa, where it breeds throughout the year. Two or three broods are produced in Europe from February to October, and the butterfly usually reaches Britain in June. By July, it can be as far north as the North Cape and Iceland. It flies in gardens and any other flower-rich habitat. There is some return migration in the autumn. The larva is black with yellow spines and feeds mainly on thistles, protected in a tent of leaves. It also eats Mallow and Stinging Nettles.
Ⓑ✪▥

Comma
Polygonia c-album
45–55mm. Named for the white, comma-shaped mark on the underside of its hind wing, two broods of this butterfly frequent gardens, woodland margins, and other flower-rich places from March to October. The summer generation is paler than the autumn one. The latter overwinters in dense vegetation and flies again in spring. The spiky larva is black with orange bands and has a large white patch on the rear, giving it a vague resemblance to a bird dropping – especially when young. It feeds mainly on Stinging Nettle. The Southern Comma (*P. egea*) has a white 'V' instead of a comma mark.
Ⓑ❍✪

Map Butterfly
Araschnia levana
30–40mm. Named for the complex pattern on its underside, this butterfly exists in two very different forms. The spring brood (April to June) resembles a small fritillary, while the summer brood (July to September) is like a small White Admiral. Both generations fly in and near woodland. The larva is black with yellowish spines and feeds on Stinging Nettle. The eggs are laid in chains which resemble the nettle catkins. It is found in central Europe and the Pyrenees.
❍✪▥

Silver-washed Fritillary
Argynnis paphia
55–75mm. Silver streaks, as opposed to spots, distinguish this butterfly from most other fritillaries. It is on the wing in wooded areas from June to September and it is often seen at brambles and thistles. Black streaks on the male's wings consist of scent-producing scales which stimulate the female during courtship. The larva feeds on violets. Up to 15 per cent of the females in some areas are dusted with green scales.
Ⓑ❍

Dark Green Fritillary
Mesoacidalia aglaja
45–65mm. A butterfly of rough grasslands and heaths as well as light woodland. On the wing from June to August, it is very fond of knapweeds and thistles. Distinguished from other fritillaries by the greenish underside of its hind wing, on which all the spots are silver. The larva is black with red spots on the sides and feeds on violets. This species is one of Europe's widest-ranging butterflies and is found from Sicily to the North Cape.
Ⓑ➤▥

Queen of Spain Fritillary
Issoria lathonia
35–45mm. This fritillary can be identified by the very large silver spots on its underside and the slightly concave outer margin to the forewing. It flies in flowery habitats from February to October, and there are up to three broods. The larva has black with white spots and a double white line along the back, and feeds on violets. In southern Europe the species is believed to spend the winter in any of the four life stages.
▥

Pearl-bordered Fritillary
Clossiana euphrosyne
35–45mm. A butterfly of light woodland and rough grassland, it is on the wing from April to August during which time there are usually one or two broods. It is particularly fond of bugle flowers in woodland rides and clearings. The larva is black with white spots and yellow spines and feeds on violets. Northern specimens are smaller and darker. The Small Pearl-bordered Fritillary (*C. selene*) is very similar but has more silver spots on its underside.
Ⓑ❍④▥

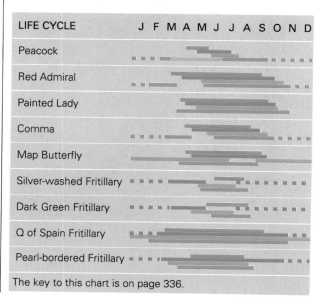

LIFE CYCLE	J F M A M J J A S O N D
Peacock	
Red Admiral	
Painted Lady	
Comma	
Map Butterfly	
Silver-washed Fritillary	
Dark Green Fritillary	
Q of Spain Fritillary	
Pearl-bordered Fritillary	

The key to this chart is on page 336.

Peacock

larva

Red Admiral

Painted Lady

Dark Green Fritillary

Silver-washed Fritillary

larva

♂ (first generation)

♂ (first generation

♂ (second generation)

Queen of Spain Fritillary

Pearl-bordered
Fritillary

Comma

Map Butterfly

349

This male Glanville Fritillary is drinking from damp ground, enabling it to obtain vital sodium from the soil.

Arctic Fritillary
Clossiana chariclea
30–35mm. One of the world's most northerly butterflies, flying from June to August over the Scandinavian tundra well beyond the Arctic Circle. It has even been seen in Greenland within about 1000km of the North Pole. Little is known of this hardy butterfly's early stages, but the larva probably feeds on violets and cassiope.

Weaver's Fritillary
Clossiana dia
30–35mm. Also known as the Violet Fritillary, this very small fritillary is easily identified by the sharp angle at the front of the hind wing. It flies on grassy slopes and in woodland clearings from April to October. There are two or three broods. The larva is black with yellow and orange stripes and feeds on violets and brambles. It is widely distributed and often very common in southern and central Europe.

Glanville Fritillary
Melitaea cinxia
30–45mm. Five black spots in the outer part of the upperside of each hind wing distinguish this species from several similar fritillaries. It flies in grassy places from April to September, and has one or two broods. The larvae

are black with a chestnut head and feed on plantains. They hibernate together in silken nests. It is widespread and often very common in southern and central Europe, but is confined to the Isle of Wight in Britain.

Knapweed Fritillary
Melitaea phoebe
35–50mm. This species is very similar to the Glanville Fritillary, but lacks the black dots in its hind wing. One to three broods fly from April to September in grassy places, especially in hilly districts. The larva is greyish with black and white stripes and yellowish spines and feeds gregariously on knapweeds and plantains. It occurs in southern and central Europe.

Spotted Fritillary
Melitaea didyma
30–45mm. An attractive but very variable species, with marked regional and seasonal variation. It can usually be identified by the bright, unspotted orange band near the outer edge of the underside of its hind wing, and the row of black dots outside it. One to three broods fly from May to September in grassy places. The female is often dusted with grey in the mountains. The larva is like that of the Knapweed Fritillary, but paler and its head is brown instead of black. It lives gregariously on plantains, speedwells and toadflaxes in southern and central Europe.

Heath Fritillary
Mellicta athalia
35–45mm. This species is very variable and not easily distinguished from similar fritillaries, although the zig-zag black line near the outer edge of the underside of its forewing is often heavier than in other species. One to three broods fly from May to September over grassland and open woodland, but the species is not often associated with typical heathland. The larva is black with many small white spots and it feeds communally on Common Cow-wheat and plantains. Although one of the commonest fritillaries on the continent, it is one of Britain's rarest butterflies.

Cynthia's Fritillary
Hypodryas cynthia
30–45mm. A montane species, it flies from May to August at altitudes up to 3000m in the Alps and Bulgarian mountains. The male is easily identified by its white patches, but these areas are yellowish in the female. At the highest levels, especially on the south-western Alps, the male's upperside is almost entirely black and white. The larvae are black with yellow bands and they feed gregariously on plantains and lady's mantles.

Lapland Fritillary
Hypodryas iduna
35–40mm. This butterfly flies from June to July over the boggy moorland near the tree line in the far north, where it is the only species with this colouration. The larvae are very dark and feed gregariously on plantains, speedwells and bilberries.

Marsh Fritillary
Eurodryas aurinia
30–45mm. Although most at home on bogs and moors, this butterfly is also found on dry grassland. The prominent dots near the outer edge of its hind wing and the lack of dark markings on the underside of its forewing help to identify it. The spiky black larvae feed gregariously, mainly on plantains and Devil's-bit Scabious and sunbathe in dense masses in the spring.

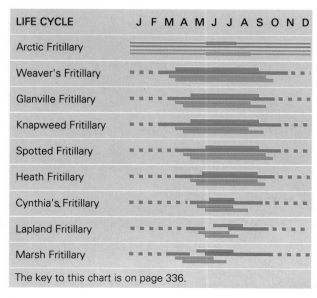

LIFE CYCLE	J F M A M J J A S O N D
Arctic Fritillary	
Weaver's Fritillary	
Glanville Fritillary	
Knapweed Fritillary	
Spotted Fritillary	
Heath Fritillary	
Cynthia's Fritillary	
Lapland Fritillary	
Marsh Fritillary	

The key to this chart is on page 336.

Arctic Fritillary

Spotted Fritillary

Weaver's Fritillary

Heath Fritillary

Glanville Fritillary

Cynthia's Fritillary

Lapland Fritillary

Knapweed Fritillary

Marsh Fritillary

THE BROWNS

Almost all of the 3000 or so species in this family (Satyridae) are brown and nearly all have eye-spots on the wings. The front legs are reduced to small brush-like appendages, as in the Nymphalidae. Several of the veins near the base of the forewing are distinctly swollen. The males of many species have a dark patch on the forewing known as a scent brand or sex brand. It consists of slender scent-emitting scales used during courtship. The caterpillars are usually green or brown, clothed with fine hairs, and have a short, forked tail. They are largely nocturnal and feed on grasses. The pupae either hang upside-down on food-plants or lie in flimsy cocoons among leaf litter. Just over 100 species live in Europe.

Marbled White

Melanargia galathea
45–55mm. This species flies in rough, grassy places from June to August and the female scatters her eggs as she flies. The larva is brown or green. It is found in southern and central Europe. Several similar species, with slightly different patterns, also live in southern Europe.
Ⓑ 🏵

Woodland Grayling

Hipparchia fagi
65–75mm. This species flies from June to September in light woodland and scrubby places, often settling on tree trunks where its mottled underside blends beautifully with the bark. The larva is pale brown with darker stripes, and feeds on various coarse grasses. It is found in southern and central Europe.
🏵 ✤ 🏵

Grayling

Hipparchia semele
45–60mm. This butterfly flies from May to September over heathland and rough, grassy places, often resting on the ground with its wings angled towards the sun so that little shadow is cast. In this position, its mottled undersides make it very difficult to spot. The larva is pale brown with darker stripes and feeds on various fine-leaved grasses. It is absent from the far north.
Ⓑ 🏵 🏵

The Hermit

Chazara briseis
40–65mm. Two eye-spots on the forewing and none on its hind wing distinguish this species from others with a similar pattern. The female is often very much larger than the male. It flies from May to September in dry, grassy places. The larva is greyish with darker spots. It occurs in southern and central Europe.
🏵

The Mountain Ringlet varies a good deal and tends to have much less orange on its wings in the far north and at high altitudes.

Arctic Grayling

Oeneis bore
45–50mm. This thinly scaled butterfly flies from June to July on stony hillsides and coastal areas in the far north. The larva is pale brown with darker stripes, and takes two years to mature.
⊖

Mountain Ringlet

Erebia epiphron
35–45mm. The upper and lower surfaces are very similar, although the number of spots varies in different areas. It flies from June to August in the mountains of southern and central Europe and also in upland Britain, usually on damp grassland or moorland. The larva is green with pale stripes.
Ⓑ 🏵 🏵

Baltic Grayling

Oeneis jutta
45–55mm. The eye-spots usually lack white centres and sit on a much yellower band than in other similar species. The insect flies from May to July on moorland and damp woodland in northern Europe. The larva is brown with darker stripes and takes two years to mature.
🏵 🏵

The Dryad

Minois dryas
55–70mm. Blue-centred eye-spots separate this butterfly from several otherwise similar species. It flies from June to September in light woodland and rough grassland, meadows and fens. The larva

is grey with darker spots and stripes and feeds on purple moor grass and other coarse grasses. It is found in southern and central Europe.
🏵 🏵 🏵

Great Banded Grayling

Brintesia circe
65–80mm. A single blind eye-spot on the upperside usually distinguishes this butterfly from others with a similar pattern. It flies from June to August in light woodland and nearby grassland. The larva is greyish-brown with darker stripes. It is found in southern and central Europe.
🏵 🏵

Arctic Ringlet

Erebia disa
45–50mm. A complete lack of spots on the hind wing separates this species from all other browns in the far north. It flies from June to July over bogs and moors beyond the Arctic Circle. The larva takes two years to mature.
⊖

Scotch Argus

Erebia aethiops
40–55mm. A pale band on the underside of the hind wing, containing three or four tiny dots, distinguishes this species. It flies from July to September, usually in damp upland grassland and open woodland. The larva is yellowish-brown with darker stripes. It is found in central and south-eastern Europe and in northern Britain.
Ⓑ 🏵 🏵 🏵 🏵

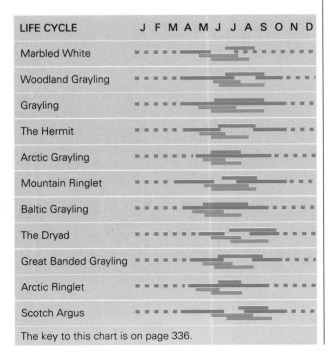

LIFE CYCLE	J	F	M	A	M	J	J	A	S	O	N	D
Marbled White												
Woodland Grayling												
Grayling												
The Hermit												
Arctic Grayling												
Mountain Ringlet												
Baltic Grayling												
The Dryad												
Great Banded Grayling												
Arctic Ringlet												
Scotch Argus												

The key to this chart is on page 336.

Baltic Grayling

The Hermit

Marbled White

larva

Arctic Grayling

The Dryad

Woodland Grayling

Great Banded Grayling

Mountain Ringlet

Arctic Ringlet

Grayling

Scotch Argus

This Gatekeeper in flight clearly shows the double pupil in the eyespot that identifies this species.

Almond-eyed Ringlet
Erebia alberganus
35–45mm. Easily recognized by its oval or almond-shaped wing spots, this species flies from June to August in the Alps and other mountains of southern Europe. The larva is green with yellowish stripes and brown dots.
⊙

Dewy Ringlet
Erebia pandrose
35–50mm. This butterfly is distinguished from all other browns by the greyish underside of its hind wing combined with the four black spots on its forewing. It flies from June to August in Scandinavia and on the mountains of southern and central Europe. The larva is green with dark stripes and a black head.
⊙⊙⊘

Meadow Brown
Maniola jurtina
45–60mm. One of Europe's commonest butterflies, this species flies in grassy places almost everywhere from May to September. The male has less orange on its upperside than the female, and is sometimes completely brown. The larva is green with a pale stripe on each side.
Ⓑ◐⊕

Gatekeeper
Pyronia tithonus
35–40mm. This species flies from July to September in lightly-wooded habitats, including hedgerows, and the surrounding grassland. It is especially fond of bramble blossom and marjoram flowers. Two white pupils in its eye-spot distinguish it from the Meadow Brown. The larva is pale brown with darker markings and a white stripe on each side. It occurs in southern and central Europe. The Spanish Gatekeeper (*P. bathseba*) has a yellowish stripe on the underside of its hind wing. The Southern Gatekeeper (*P. cecilia*) has no eye-spots on underside of its hind wing.
Ⓑ◐✦⊕

Ringlet
Aphantopus hyperantus
40–50mm. Yellow-ringed eye-spots on the underside identify this butterfly. It flies from June to August in woodland rides and along old hedgerows, especially in slightly damp situations, and is very fond of bramble blossom. The larva is pale brown with darker stripes. It is absent from the far north and from much of Iberia.
Ⓑ◐⊕

Small Heath
Coenonympha pamphilus
25–35mm. A very common butterfly, this species flies in all kinds of grassy places from April to October. There are one to three broods. The larva is green with light and dark stripes. The Large Heath (*C. tullia*) is larger and greyer, with white streaks on the underside of its forewing. It flies over damp grassland, usually in the uplands.
Ⓑ◐⊘⊕

Dusky Heath
Coenonympha dorus
30–35mm. The eye-spots on the hind wing curve inwards instead of running more or less parallel to the wing margin as in related species. The female's upperside is mainly orange. It flies from June to July over rough grassland in southern Europe. The larva is bluish-green with darker stripes.
⊕

Pearly Heath
Coenonympha arcania
35–40mm. An orange forewing and brown hind wing distinguish this butterfly from most of its relatives. One or two broods fly in light woodland and grassy places from June to September. The larva is green with pale and dark stripes. It is found in southern and central Europe.
◐⊕

LIFE CYCLE	J	F	M	A	M	J	J	A	S	O	N	D
Almond-eyed Ringlet												
Dewy Ringlet												
Meadow Brown												
Gatekeeper												
Ringlet												
Small Heath												
Dusky Heath												
Pearly Heath												
False Ringlet												
Wall Brown												
Speckled Wood												
Woodland Brown												

The key to this chart is on page 336.

False Ringlet
Coenonympha oedippus
35–45mm. Similar to the Ringlet, this species has a paler underside and a clear silvery line outside the row of eye-spots. The latter are larger and brighter in the female than in the male, which has few or no spots on the underside of its forewing. The larva is bright green. It flies from June to July over damp grassland throughout southern and central Europe. Although common locally, this is regarded as the most seriously threatened of Europe's butterflies.

Wall Brown
Lasiommata megera
35–50mm. On the wing from March to October, in two or three broods, this is a butterfly of dry, sunny places. It often basks on walls and bare ground, but is hard to spot when it closes its wings. The larva is bluish-green with white stripes. It is absent from most of northern Europe. The Large Wall Brown (*L. maera*) is similar but usually a little larger and less brightly coloured.

Speckled Wood
Pararge aegeria
35–45mm. Butterflies from south-western Europe have orange spots, but those from elsewhere have an unmistakable pattern of cream spots on a brown background. Southern insects are like the Wall Brown, but can be distinguished by the scalloped wing margin. One to three broods fly from March to October in woodland rides and clearings and other lightly-wooded areas, rarely visiting flowers and feeding mainly on honeydew. The larva is bright green with white stripes. It is absent from the far north.

Woodland Brown
Lopinga achine
45–55mm. The large eye-spots on its upperside make this species unmistakable. It flies from June to August in and near woodland. The larva is green with pale stripes. It is found in northern and central Europe, excluding Britain and north-western Germany.

Almond-eyed Ringlet

larva

Ringlet

False Ringlet

Dewy Ringlet

larva

Small Heath

Wall Brown

Meadow Brown

Dusky Heath

Speckled Wood

Gatekeeper

Pearly Heath

Woodland Brown

Moths

Moths share the Order Lepidoptera with the butterflies. No single feature distinguishes all the butterflies from all the moths although, with the exception of the day-flying burnet moths, our European moths do not have clubbed antennae. Most moths fly at night and rest with their wings folded flat or roof-like over the body. There are nearly 5000 species in Europe, with wingspans ranging from about 3mm to 15cm. Many have reduced mouth-parts and do not feed at all in the adult state. Moth life histories are just like those of the butterflies (see p. 318), although the chrysalis is often formed in the soil or in a silken cocoon spun by the fully grown caterpillar. See p. 336 for information on the life cycle charts and the measurements given.

SWIFT MOTHS

The moths in this family (Hepialidae) are fast-flyers with very short antennae. The adults do not feed. The larvae all feed on roots. There are about ten European species.

Ghost Moth
Hepialus humuli
45–50mm. This moth is named for the ghost-like rising and falling flight of the male over grassy places at dusk. His wings are dull brown below and the rhythmic flashing of the white uppersides attracts the yellowish female. The moths fly from June to July. The larva is white with brown spots and a brown head.
Ⓑ ✿ ▥

BURNETS AND FORESTERS

This is a large family (Zygaenidae) of mostly brightly coloured, day-flying moths. Burnets, which are generally black and red with clubbed antennae, are often mistaken for butterflies, but their slow, drifting flight is quite unmistakable. Their bold colours advertise the poisonous nature of these moths. Foresters have metallic green wings and lightly toothed antennae. Burnets usually pupate in papery cocoons attached to plant stems, while foresters generally pupate on the ground. The family contains about 60 European species, which are often seen feeding at flowers.

The striking Six-spot Burnet moth is a common visitor to the purple flowers of thistles and knapweeds in grassland.

Six-spot Burnet
Zygaena filipendulae
30mm. The deep metallic green of this moth's forewing often appears bluish or black. The moth flies by day in open flowery habitats from June to August. The squat larva is cream with black spots and feeds on trefoils and related plants. There are about 30 similar species in Europe, although the proportion of red and black varies. Some species have cream rings around the spots.
Ⓑ ▥

CLEARWING MOTHS

The clearwings (Family Sesiidae) are fast-flying diurnal moths which, because their wings largely lack scales, bear striking resemblances to various bees and wasps, especially when in flight. The caterpillars are white or cream and they all feed inside their food-plants, mostly in the roots and trunks of trees. They spend the day sun-bathing on the foliage. Many take two years to mature. There are about 50 European species.

Hornet Clearwing
Sesia apiformis
30–40mm. One of the largest of the clearwings, this species resembles a wasp except that it lacks the characteristically narrow waist of the wasp. It flies from May to July, mainly in damp woodlands where the larva feeds in roots and trunks of poplars.
Ⓑ ○

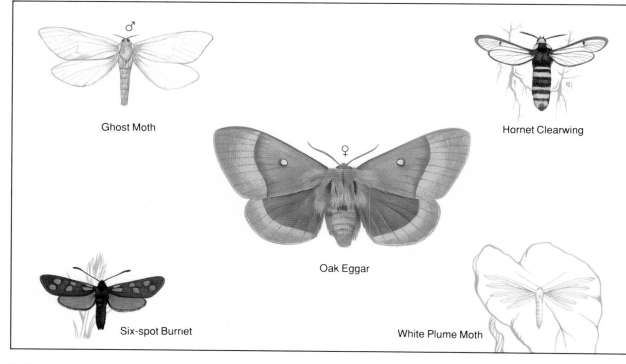

Ghost Moth ♂

Oak Eggar ♀

Hornet Clearwing

Six-spot Burnet

White Plume Moth

PLUME MOTHS

The members of this family (Pterophoridae) are easily recognized because their wings are usually split into feather-like plumes. At rest, the two wings of each side are wrapped together and held at right angles to the body to form a slender 'T'.

White Plume Moth

Pterophorus pentadactyla
20–30mm. A common visitor to lighted windows at night, this pure white moth has two plumes in the forewing and three in the hind wing. Hedgerows and disturbed land are its main habitats, where the hairy green larva feeds on bindweeds. It flies from May to August, and is absent from the far north.

Ⓑ✪㊉

EGGARS AND LACKEYS

Eggars and Lackeys (Family Lasiocampidae) are stout and furry brown moths. The females are usually a good deal larger than the males. There is no proboscis and the adults do not feed. The larvae are generally hairy and often brightly coloured. They pupate in sturdy silk cocoons.

Oak Eggar

Lasiocampa quercus
60–90mm. This moth flies from May to August in most open habitats. The yellowish-brown female is nocturnal and scatters her eggs freely as she flies. The dark-brown male flies rapidly by day in search of a resting female. The larva is velvety black with bands of brown hair and white spots on the sides. It feeds on bramble, heather, and many other species of tree and shrub.

Ⓑ🖰㊉㊉

Drinker Moth

Philudoria potatoria
50–70mm. Named for the larval habit of drinking dew, this moth flies in all kinds of grassy habitats from May to August. The male is usually brick-red, often with yellow patches, while the female is largely yellow. Both sexes have two white spots on the forewing. The larva feeds on coarse grasses and pupates in a long yellowish cocoon fixed to the grass stems.

Ⓑ㊉

Lackey Moth

Malacosoma neustria
30–45mm. This moth flies from June to August wherever there are trees and hedgerows and is often common in towns. Its wings, longer and more pointed in females than in males, range from buff to brick red. The larva is steely blue with red, white and black lines; its head is bluish with two large black spots. It feeds gregariously in a silken tent on deciduous trees and is often a pest.

Ⓑ🖰㊉㊉

Fox Moth

Macrothylacia rubi
45–70mm. Two pale lines on the forewings distinguish this moth from several similar species. The male is usually reddish brown, while the female is greyish brown. It frequents light woodland and open country from May to July. The female is nocturnal and the male diurnal. The larva is velvety black with narrow orange bands. It feeds on bramble and heather.

Ⓑ🖰㊉㊉

Lappet Moth

Gastropacha quercifolia
55–90mm. Identified by its serrated wing margins, this moth is a deep purplish brown in the north of Europe, and yellowish brown in the south. It inhabits light woodland and hedgerows and flies from May to September in one or two broods. At rest, the forewings are held roof-like but the hind wings are held more or less flat giving the moth a remarkable resemblance to a dead leaf. The larva is dark grey with fine black hair. It feeds on blackthorn and many other trees. Numerous fleshy flaps on the sides help to conceal it when resting by day.

Ⓑ㊉㊉

LIFE CYCLE	J F M A M J J A S O N D
Ghost Moth	
Six-spot Burnet	
Oak Eggar	
Hornet Clearwing	
White Plume Moth	
Drinker Moth	
Lackey Moth	
Fox Moth	
Lappet Moth	

The key to this chart is on page 336.

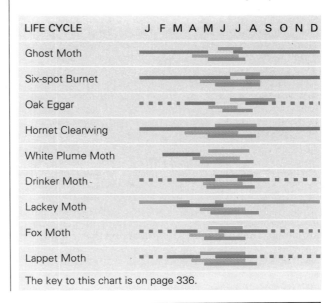

larva

Lackey Moth

Drinker Moth

larva

Lappet Moth

Fox Moth

EMPEROR MOTHS

This family (Saturniidae) contains some of the world's largest moths, including the giant silkmoths whose larvae produce huge cocoons of silk. Most are tropical species and only four live in Europe, including the Giant Peacock Moth which, with a wingspan of about 15cm, is Europe's largest moth. The adults do not feed. Only the Common Emperor Moth is found in Britain.

Common Emperor Moth

Saturnia pavonia
50–80mm. This species is on the wing from April to June over heathland and other open habitats. The male is much brighter than the female, with orange hind wings. He flies by day and picks up the scent of the resting female with his large, feathery antennae. She flies by night. The larva is orange and black when young, but becomes green and black later. It feeds on a wide range of shrubs and pupates in a tough brown cocoon. The Giant Peacock Moth (*S. pyri*) of southern Europe is similar but much larger.
Ⓑ 🗭 🗑

GEOMETER MOTHS

Collectively known as geometers, the moths in this large family (Geometridae) are mostly rather flimsy and slender-bodied. Most of them rest with their wings held flat – either covering the body or held well out to the sides. The thorn moths and a few others rest with their wings held vertically like butterflies. The larvae, often known as loopers or inchworms, have only two pairs of legs on the abdomen, including the claspers right at the back. Many are amazingly twig-like and well camouflaged when at rest, often bearing bumps which resemble buds. They move by alternately stretching the front end forward and then bringing the hind end up to it, throwing the body into a high loop. This habit is also responsible for the name geometer, which means ground-measurer. Many species pupate in cocoons on the vegetation, but others pupate under the ground. The family contains over 800 European species.

The eye-like markings of the Common Emperor Moth are highly effective in frightening predatory birds away.

Yellow Shell

Camptogramma bilineata
20–30mm. A very common moth of hedgerows and other scrubby habitats, including gardens. It flies from May to August, usually at dusk. Its wings are sometimes dark brown with black lines. The slender green or brown larva feeds on grasses and various low-growing herbs.
Ⓑ ○ ❁ 🗑

Brimstone Moth

Opisthograptis luteolata
30–40mm. Two broods of this easily recognized moth fly from April to October virtually anywhere trees and shrubs are found. It is very common in gardens and a frequent visitor to lights. The brown, twig-like larva, with a distinct hump in the centre, feeds on hawthorn and many other trees.
Ⓑ ○ ❁ 🗑

Magpie Moth

Abraxas grossulariata
35–40mm. Abundant in and around hedgerows from May to August, this attractive, yet distasteful moth is well protected by warning colours, although the exact wing pattern is very variable. The larva, with much the same pattern as the adult, feeds on Blackthorn, gooseberries, and many other shrubs and turns into a black and yellow pupa inside a flimsy cocoon. The Clouded Magpie (*A. sylvata*) has fewer and paler black

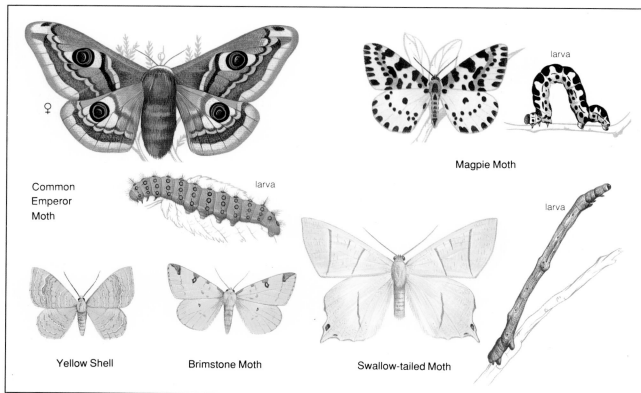

♀ Common Emperor Moth

larva

Yellow Shell

Brimstone Moth

Swallow-tailed Moth

larva

Magpie Moth

larva

spots and the orange stripe in the middle of the forewing is reduced to a small patch near the hind edge. The moth flies in deciduous woodland in the summer.

Ⓑ ✪ ⓜ

Swallowtailed Moth

Ourapteryx sambucaria
50–60mm. Named for the little tail on each hind wing, this moth flies from June to July, drifting ghost-like over hedgerows, gardens, and lightly wooded areas at dusk. The long, slender larva is extremely twig-like and feeds on a wide variety of shrubs at night. Ivy is one of its favourite food-plants and it is particularly well camouflaged when clinging to the older twigs of this plant.

Ⓑ ◐ ✪ ⓜ

Speckled Yellow

Pseudopanthera maculata
20–30mm. This is an unmistakable day-flying species which is on the wing from April to July in open woodland and scrubby habitats. An extremely variable species, its dark spots are sometimes joined into bands and sometimes almost absent. The fairly stout larva is green with white lines along it, and its favourite food-plants include wood sage and various other herbs.

Ⓑ ◐ ✪ ⓜ

Purple Thorn

Selenia tetralunaria
30–45mm. This is one of the few moths whose undersides are virtually the same as its uppersides. One or two broods fly from April to September, the summer brood being much paler and yellower than the spring brood pictured here. It frequents lightly wooded areas and rests with its wings held vertically above its body. The knobbly, brown larva is very twig-like and feeds on a wide range of deciduous trees. The Lunar Thorn (*S. lunularia*) is similar, but has much more jagged wing margins and is usually somewhat paler.

Ⓑ ◐ ✪ ⓜ

Peppered Moth

Biston betularia
45–65mm. On the wing from May to August, this common moth exists in two main forms – the normal speckled form and the black melanic form known as *carbonaria*. The latter was first recorded in northern England in 1848, after which it rapidly spread to many industrial areas and largely replaced the normal form because it was well camouflaged on smoke-blackened trees and buildings. The normal form is becoming more common again now that pollution is being

controlled and trees and buildings are cleaner. The speckled form has remained common in rural areas, although the melanic form is common there too. It is believed that the larvae of melanic moths are in some way more tolerant of low levels of pollution than those of normal moths, so the melanic forms survive in rural areas even though the adults are conspicuous and many are taken by birds. The twig-like brown or green larva has a clear notch on its head and feeds on a wide variety of trees and shrubs.

Ⓑ ◐ ✪ ⓜ

Winter Moth

Operophtera brumata
25–35mm. Only the male of this species is winged and it regularly comes to lighted windows during the winter months. The wingless female sits in the trees waiting for a male to arrive. It is an abundant species, whose slender greenish larvae cause much damage to cultivated fruit trees by feeding on the blossom. They also feed on the leaves and flowers of many other trees before dropping down to pupate in the surrounding soil. Its wide range includes Iceland.

Ⓑ ◐ ✪ ⓜ

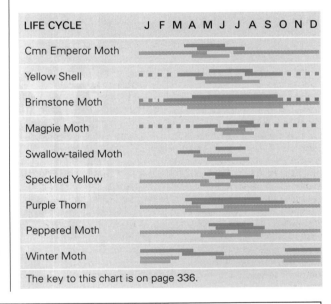

LIFE CYCLE	J F M A M J J A S O N D
Cmn Emperor Moth	
Yellow Shell	
Brimstone Moth	
Magpie Moth	
Swallow-tailed Moth	
Speckled Yellow	
Purple Thorn	
Peppered Moth	
Winter Moth	

The key to this chart is on page 336.

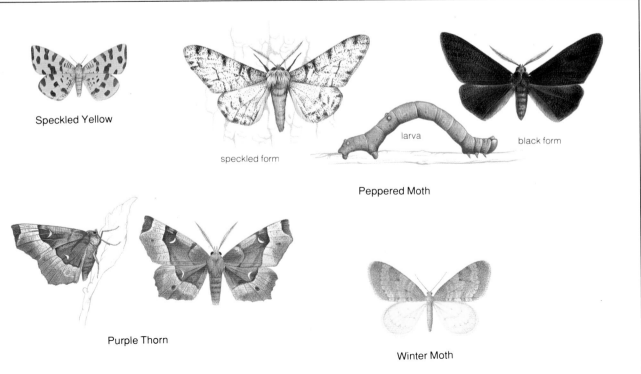

Speckled Yellow

speckled form

larva

black form

Peppered Moth

Purple Thorn

Winter Moth

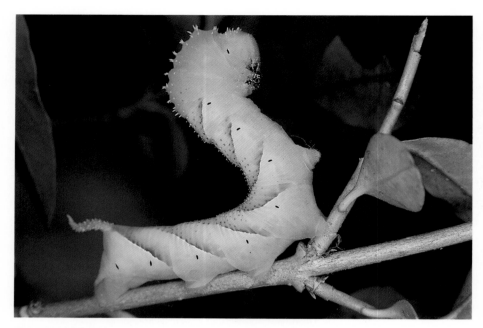

The caterpillar of the Death's Head Hawkmoth in the sphinx-like attitude that is responsible for the family name Sphingidae.

HAWKMOTHS

These fast-flying moths (Family Sphingidae) live mainly in the tropics. There are over 1000 species, but only 23 occur in Europe. Some have no proboscis and do not feed as adults, but others have enormously long tongues which they plunge deep into flowers while hovering in front of them. The larvae are hairless, often with diagonal stripes and a curved horn at the rear. They pupate in the soil.

Convolvulus Hawkmoth
Agrius convolvuli
90–120mm. Completely grey wings distinguish this moth from the Privet Hawkmoth. A strong-flying migrant, it arrives in Europe each spring from North Africa and two or three broods are on the wing until October. Although regularly reaching Iceland and other parts of northern Europe, the moth does not usually breed in northern areas. The larva is bright green or deep brown with diagonal yellow stripes and it feeds on bindweeds.

Death's Head Hawkmoth
Acherontia atropos
100–135mm. Named for the skull-like pattern on its thorax, this African moth arrives in Europe each spring, sometimes in large numbers, and breeds on potatoes and nightshades. A few European-bred moths turn up in Britain each summer and they occasionally reach as far north as Iceland. The moth does not visit flowers, but invades bee hives to take honey with its short tongue. The larva is usually yellow with diagonal blue or purplish stripes and a curly yellow horn. It feeds on potato plants and nightshades.

Privet Hawkmoth
Sphinx ligustri
100–120mm. This is the largest resident British moth. It can be distinguished from the superficially similar Convolvulus Hawkmoth by its brownish thorax and forewings and by the pink stripes on its hind wings. It flies from June to August wherever privet grows and is common in gardens and towns. At rest, the wings are pulled tightly back along the body and the insect resembles a broken twig. The larva, which can measure up to 75mm long, feeds mainly on privet, ash and lilac.

Lime Hawkmoth
Mimas tiliae
70–80mm. The wings of this species vary from pinkish brown to green and grey, and the outer edge of the forewing is indented. It is on the wing from May to July, mainly in wooded areas, but it is not uncommon in towns in some years. The adult does not feed. The larva is pale green with diagonal yellow stripes, red spiracles and a largely blue horn. It feeds on lime, elm and many other deciduous trees.

Poplar Hawkmoth
Laothoe populi
70–90mm. When resting in its characteristic position with the hind wings projecting slightly in front of the forewings, this moth looks very like a bunch of dead leaves. When disturbed, the forewings are raised to expose a brick-coloured spot on the hind wings. This is one of the commonest hawkmoths, frequently found in towns and gardens and is regularly attracted to lights at night. It flies from May to September in one or two broods, and does not feed. The larva is green with yellow dots and diagonal yellow stripes and feeds on poplars and willows.

Eyed Hawkmoth
Smerinthus ocellata
75–95mm. When disturbed, this common moth reveals large eye-spots on the hind wings and sways menacingly backwards and forwards, frightening birds and other predators. It flies from May to September in one or two broods and does not feed. The larva is pale green with dense white dots and pale diagonal stripes. It feeds on sallow, apple and plum, and usually rests upside down.

Pine Hawkmoth
Hyloicus pinastri
70–80mm. This moth flies from May to August. The young larva is green with white stripes and is well camouflaged on pine needles, but it becomes mottled with brown as it grows and then rests on the twigs. Widely distributed in coniferous woodlands on the Continent, this moth is confined to the southern parts of Britain.

Oak Hawkmoth
Marumba quercus
120mm. This species resembles a large, yellowish Poplar Hawkmoth, although it rests in a very different position. Its hind wings are orange-brown. It flies from May to July in the Mediterranean region, in cork oak forests. The larva is bluish green with diagonal yellow stripes. It feeds mainly on cork oak.

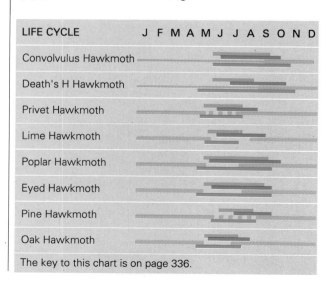

LIFE CYCLE	J F M A M J J A S O N D
Convolvulus Hawkmoth	
Death's H Hawkmoth	
Privet Hawkmoth	
Lime Hawkmoth	
Poplar Hawkmoth	
Eyed Hawkmoth	
Pine Hawkmoth	
Oak Hawkmoth	

The key to this chart is on page 336.

Convolvulus Hawkmoth

Poplar Hawkmoth

Death's Head Hawkmoth

Eyed Hawkmoth

Privet Hawkmoth

larva

Pine Hawkmoth

Lime Hawkmoth

Oak Hawkmoth

Narrow-bordered Bee Hawkmoth

Hemaris tityus

40–50mm. This moth is on the wing from May to June, and it flies by day in woodland glades and over rough grassland. Most of the scales are lost during the first flight, leaving just a narrow border to each wing. Very similar to a bumble bee in appearance, it flies faster than a bumble-bee and hovers at flowers at feeding time. Bugle is one of its favourite flowers. The larva is pale green with red spots and a red horn. It feeds on scabious. The Broad-bordered Bee Hawkmoth (*H. fuciformis*) is similar but has broader wing margins and its abdominal band is chestnut instead of black. It often has a second generation in August in southern Europe and may visit garden buddleias. Its larvae eat honeysuckle and bedstraws. Ⓑ◕Ⓞ◍

Hummingbird Hawkmoth

Macroglossum stellatarum

50–60mm. This day-flying moth is most often seen as a brown blur as it darts from flower to flower or hovers in front of a bloom to feed. The rapidly beating wings produce an audible hum which gives the insect its name. A permanent resident of southern Europe, up to four broods are on the wing throughout the year, although they hide in crevices in the coldest weather. There is a northward migration each spring and this insect reaches all parts of Europe, including Iceland on rare occasions. A summer brood is produced in most central and northern areas and flies until October, but the species rarely survives the winter north of the Alps. The larva is green or reddish brown with light and dark lines and a yellow-tipped blue horn. It feeds on bedstraws and wild madder. Ⓑ◔◍

Spurge Hawkmoth

Hyles euphorbiae

65–80mm. This hawkmoth has pinkish or yellowish green forewings, with heavy brown markings. Resident in southern and central Europe, it flies from May to August in one or two broods, and is a sporadic visitor to Britain and the north in summer. The larva, extremely poisonous and vividly adorned in warning colours, feeds on various spurges from which it obtains its poisonous properties. A similar species is the Bedstraw Hawkmoth (*H. gallii*) but this has a broader and more regular brown stripe along the front edge of its forewing and its hind wing has a narrow, brownish border instead of pink. Its larva is brown with large white spots and feeds on bedstraws. ◔◍

Elephant Hawkmoth

Deilephila elpenor

60–75mm. This moth flies in a wide range of habitats, mainly from May to July, although a second brood may appear from August to September. On the wing at dusk, it is very fond of honeysuckle blossom. At rest, its wings are swept back like an arrowhead – a feature which it shares with several other hawkmoths. The larva feeds on willowherbs and bedstraws and, when alarmed, it pulls its head and thorax back into the abdomen, causing the eye-spots to swell and give the creature a frightening appearance. Ⓑ◔◔◍

Small Elephant Hawkmoth

Deilephila porcellus

45–55mm. Smaller and much yellower than the Elephant Hawkmoth, this species flies from May to September in one or two broods. It frequents grassy

LIFE CYCLE	J	F	M	A	M	J	J	A	S	O	N	D
N-brd Bee Hawkmoth					▬	▬						
H Hawkmoth				▬	▬	▬	▬	▬	▬			
Spurge Hawkmoth				▬	▬	▬	▬	▬				
Elephant Hawkmoth					▬	▬	▬	▬				
Small E Hawkmoth					▬	▬	▬					
Proserpinus proserpina					▬	▬						
Puss Moth					▬	▬	▬					
Buff-tip					▬	▬	▬					
Pebble Prominent				▬	▬	▬	▬	▬				

The key to this chart is on page 336.

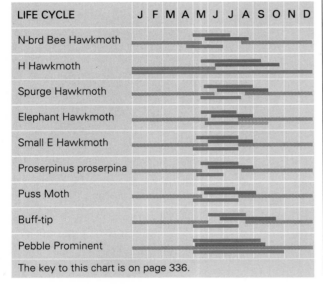

Narrow-bordered Bee Hawkmoth

larva

Spurge Hawkmoth

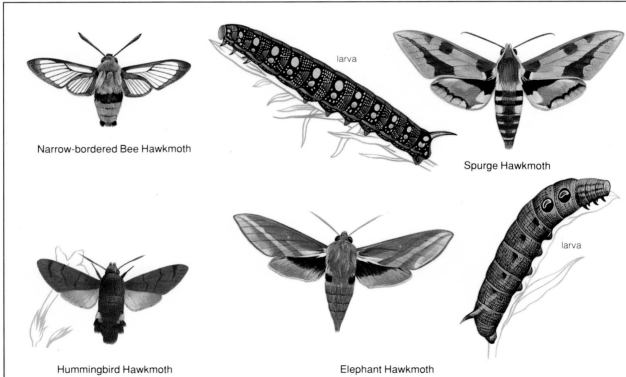

Hummingbird Hawkmoth

Elephant Hawkmoth

larva

At rest on trees or on the ground, the Buff-tip moth is very difficult to distinguish from a broken twig.

habitats, including mountain slopes and woodland glades, where the larva feeds on bedstraws. The larva is like that of the Elephant Hawkmoth but has no horn and is occasionally green.
Ⓑ ◐ ✪ ⊞

Proserpinus proserpina
35–60mm. The forewings of this species are usually green, but may be brown or grey and always have a dark central band and wavy outer margins. It flies from May to July, mainly near water but also over waste ground and in light woodland. It is a rare species and seems to be becoming even rarer. The

larva is dark brown with diagonal black and white stripes low down on the sides. It has no horn but there is a prominent eye-spot in its place. It occurs in southern and central Europe.
◐ ✪ ⊞

PUSS MOTHS AND PROMINENTS

This group (Family Notodontidae) contains mostly rather large, stout-bodied moths with relatively long forewings capable of fast flight. They resemble the noctuid moths (p. 366) in their generally sombre colours, but differ in their wing venation. **Many are known as prominents because the forewings bear tufts of scales at the rear and these project above the body when the insects are at rest. The caterpillars are generally hairless, but many bear fleshy outgrowths on the back and the claspers – the last pair of legs – are sometimes drawn out to form slender tails. Many raise both ends of the body when resting, gripping the twigs with just four pairs of legs.**

Puss Moth
Cerura vinula
60–80mm. Sometimes almost white, this furry moth flies from May to July wherever poplars and willows grow. It is also common in towns, where it is attracted to street lights at night. The larva rests with front and rear ends raised. The last pair of legs are tail-like and, when the larva is alarmed, they wave retractable red filaments. At the same time, the larva pulls its head into the front of the thorax, which swells up and takes on a threatening appearance. It also fires an acidic spray from thoracic glands. It feeds mainly on

willows and poplars and is remarkably difficult to see when resting on the leaves. It forms a very tough and well camouflaged cocoon in a bark crevice.
Ⓑ ◐ ✪

Buff-tip
Phalera bucephala
50–70mm. Named for its pale wing-tips and the yellowish hairs on the thorax, this moth looks just like a broken twig when resting on a branch or on the ground with its wings wrapped tightly round its body. It flies from May to July in many habitats, including towns, and is commonly attracted to lights. The larvae feed gregariously on a wide range of deciduous trees and often denude whole branches.
Ⓑ ◐ ✪ ⊞

Pebble Prominent
Eligmodonta ziczac
40–50mm. Named for the pebble-like mark at the wing-tip, this moth clearly reveals the tuft of scales characteristic of the prominent moths when seen from the side. On the wing in wooded areas from May to October. The larva is pinkish grey, with a large rust-coloured patch towards the rear and two fleshy horns near the middle. It feeds on willows and poplars.
Ⓑ ◐

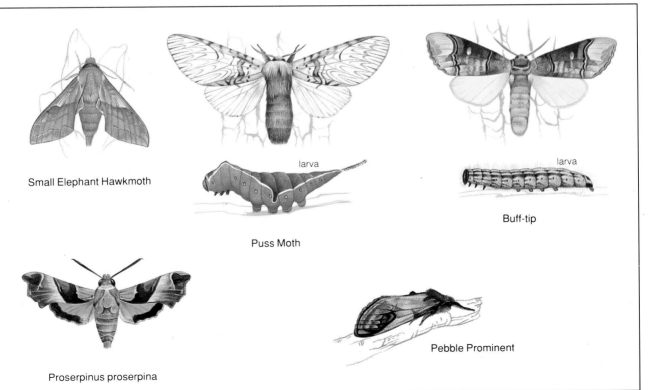

Small Elephant Hawkmoth

larva

Puss Moth

larva

Buff-tip

Proserpinus proserpina

Pebble Prominent

PROCESSIONARY MOTHS

This small family (Thaumetopoeidae), closely related to the Notodontidae, is named for the larval habit of marching in long columns. The three European species are all very similar.

Pine Processionary Moth

Thaumetopoea pityocampa
30–50mm. This species flies from June to July in the pinewoods of southern and central Europe. The female has longer, narrower wings than the male. The larvae live communally in silken nests on the pine trees and go out to feed at night, marching in single file with each one nuzzling the rear of the one in front. They are largely black, with tufts of brownish hairs. They overwinter in the nests and pupate in the spring, when they march over the ground by day, looking for pupation sites. The larvae cause damage to pine forests. The Oak Processionary Moth (*T. processionea*) is similar but its larvae make their nests on oak trunks.
✦

LIFE CYCLE	J	F	M	A	M	J	J	A	S	O	N	D
P Processionary Moth												
Vapourer Moth												
Yellow-tail												
Gypsy Moth												
Garden Tiger												
Cinnabar Moth												
Jersey Tiger												
White Ermine												
Buff Ermine												
Scarce Footman												

The key to this chart is on page 336.

TUSSOCK MOTHS

A family (Lymantriidae) of rather hairy moths, they are generally grey or brown and the female is usually larger than the male and often has a dense tuft of hair at the tip of her abdomen. She uses some of the hairs to cover her eggs. The antennae are strongly feathered in the male, but there is no proboscis and the moths do not feed. The larvae are very hairy and many bear dense tufts or tussocks which give the group its name. The hairs can cause severe irritation if the larvae are handled. Pupation takes place in a cocoon which usually incorporates many of the larval hairs.

Vapourer Moth

Orgyia antiqua
35–40mm. Only the male of this species is winged, flying rapidly by day, from May to October, wherever there are trees and shrubs. The plump female never moves further than the surface of her cocoon, where she mates and lays her eggs. There are one to three broods. The larva, identified by its dark plumes fore and aft and its four cream tufts, feeds on a wide range of deciduous trees.
Ⓑ Ⓞ ✿ ⓜ

Yellow-tail

Euproctis similis
35–45mm. This moth flies from June to August, frequenting wooded areas and hedgerows. The female has a much larger yellow tuft at the rear than the male and lacks the black spot on the forewing, but many males also lack this spot. The larva feeds on hawthorn and many other deciduous trees and shrubs. The Brown-tail (*E. chrysorrhoea*) is similar, but has a brown abdominal tuft.
Ⓑ Ⓞ ✿ ⓜ

Gypsy Moth

Lymantria dispar
45–70mm. The sexes of this species are very different. On the wing from July to September, the male flies in wooded areas by day, the female does not fly, although she is fully winged. She remains close to her cocoon and, after mating, lays a large batch of eggs and covers them with a thick layer of yellowish hairs from her abdomen. The larva is mottled grey with blue and red spots and feeds on a wide range of deciduous trees. This species is a serious forest and orchard pest in many parts of Europe and North America. It has been extinct in Britain since the middle of the 19th century, although migrant males occasionally arrive from the Continent.
Ⓞ ✿ ⓜ

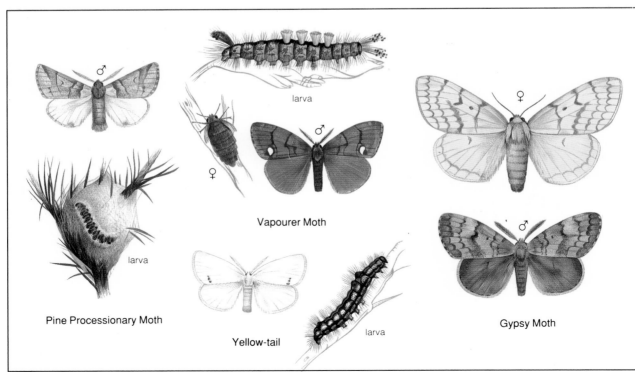

larva

Pine Processionary Moth

larva

Vapourer Moth

Yellow-tail

larva

Gypsy Moth

The male Buff Ermine at rest on the woodland floor. The dark markings help to break up its outline.

TIGERS AND ERMINES

Most of these moths (Family Arctiidae) are brightly coloured and very hairy, warning birds that they are unpleasant to eat. The adults commonly do not feed. The larvae of most species are also very hairy and they pupate in cocoons made largely from the larval hairs. The family also contains a number of much smaller and duller species known as footmen. The larvae of the footmen all feed on lichens.

Garden Tiger
Arctia caja
50–80mm. On the wing from June to August, this common moth has a very variable pattern, with the dark spots sometimes all joined together. The larva, known as a woolly bear because of its hairy coat, feeds on a wide range of low-growing plants.
Ⓑ Ⓞ ⓜ

Cinnabar Moth
Tyria jacobaeae
35–45mm. On the wing from May to August in grassy habitats, this moth is basically nocturnal, although often seen fluttering weakly in the daytime when it has been disturbed. The red colouration is occasionally replaced by yellow. The larva, displaying classic warning colouration, feeds openly on ragworts. It has been used in some places to control this weed. Although widely distributed, it tends to be restricted to coastal areas in the north. It is rare on heavy soils where the larvae seem unable to bury themselves for pupation.
Ⓑ ⓜ

Jersey Tiger
Euplagia quadripunctaria
50–65mm. This tiger moth flies by night and day from May to September, usually in open country but often in light woodland. Huge numbers gather in certain areas. The Valley of Butterflies on the Island of Rhodes is a well-known site. The larva is like that of the Garden Tiger but has a yellow stripe along its back. Found in southern and central Europe, including the Channel Islands, it occurs in Devon on the British mainland.
Ⓑ Ⓞ ⓜ

White Ermine
Spilosoma lubricipeda
35–50cm. The moth flies almost everywhere from May to August and commonly comes to light. The black dots vary in size and are occasionally absent. The wings may even be yellowish in Scotland and Ireland. The larva, clothed with tufts of dark brown hair, has a red stripe along the back. It feeds on a wide range of low-growing plants.
Ⓑ Ⓞ Ⓧ ⓜ

Buff Ermine
Spilosoma luteum
35–45mm. The markings on this moth are very variable, with the female usually much paler than the male. On the wing nearly everywhere from May to August, it is a common visitor to light. The larva is like that of White Ermine but slightly paler and without the red stripe.
Ⓑ Ⓞ Ⓧ ⓜ

Scarce Footman
Eilema complana
30–35mm. Quite common, despite its name, this moth flies from June to August in lightly wooded areas and a range of more open habitats. The pale streak at the front edge of its forewing is of constant width. At rest, the wings are rolled tightly around the body. The larva, not easy to distinguish from those of other footmen, is brownish with rows of orange and white spots. It feeds on various lichens. The Common Footman (*E. lurideola*) is similar, but rests with its wings almost flat. The pale streak on its forewing tapers towards the tip.
Ⓑ ⬭ Ⓞ Ⓧ ⓜ

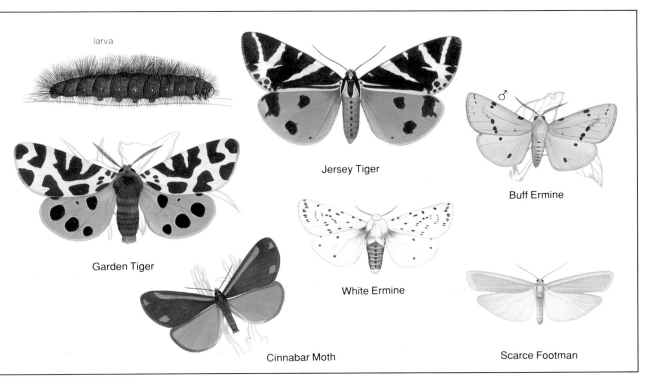

larva

Jersey Tiger

Buff Ermine

Garden Tiger

White Ermine

Cinnabar Moth

Scarce Footman

SYNTOMID MOTHS

A family (Ctenuchidae) consisting largely of day-flying and often very colourful moths, many of which taste and smell quite awful. With their slow, drifting flight, many species resemble burnet moths, (see p. 356) but their antennae are not clubbed and they are actually more closely related to the tigers and ermines. There are about half a dozen European species, all with either black and white or brown and white colouration.

Nine-spotted Moth
Syntomis phegea
35–40mm. This day-flying moth is on the wing from May to August with a slow, drifting motion. It frequents flowery places including gardens. The hairy larva is greyish brown with a chestnut head and lives gregariously on a wide range of herbaceous plants. It is found in southern and central Europe, but is rare north of the Alps.
🌣 🐛

NOCTUID MOTHS

Sometimes known as owlet moths, or simply as noctuids, the members of this large family (Noctuidae) are mostly nocturnal. There are over 1200 species in Europe.

With a few exceptions, they have fairly stout bodies and sombre forewings which provide good camouflage when at rest during the day. Most also have dull hind wings, although the yellow underwings are familiar exceptions. The larvae are mostly without conspicuous hairs and nearly all of them pupate in the soil. The pupae are normally shiny and bullet-shaped.

Heart and Dart
Agrotis exclamationis
35–45mm. The forewings of this moth range from pale to very dark brown, but usually show clearly the dark dart near the middle and the heart-shaped mark just beyond it which give the moth its name. At rest, the wings lie more or less flat over the body and not roof-like as in most noctuids. One or two broods fly from April to September and it is very common in cultivated areas. The larva is reddish brown above and greyish below and feeds on a range of herbaceous plants, attacking both roots and aerial parts.
Ⓑ 🌣 🐛

Large Yellow Underwing
Noctua pronuba
50–60mm. This is one of several species with bright yellow hind wings. The forewings of the male are mid-brown to almost black, while those of the female are

The Angle Shades moth resting in its characteristic attitude with its wings crumpled up and strongly resembling a leaf.

pale brown. The wings are laid flat over the body at rest. When disturbed, the moth flies rapidly off on an erratic course and flashes its hind wings. It then drops suddenly to the ground, leaving any pursuing bird searching unsuccessfully for something yellow. It is on the wing from June to September almost everywhere and is even resident in Iceland. The plump larva is brown with black dashes on the sides and is one of the infamous cutworms, feeding more or less at ground level and cutting through the stems of a wide range of herbaceous plants – causing damage which is commonly attributed to slugs.
Ⓑ 🌣 🐛

Grey Dagger
Acronicta psi
35–45mm. Named for the little dagger-like markings on the forewings, this common moth is extremely well camouflaged when resting on lichen-covered rocks and tree trunks. The hind wings are pale grey. It is on the wing from June to August more or less wherever there are trees and shrubs; it is commonly found in gardens and is often attracted to lights. The forewings of this moth are often much darker in when it occurs in industrial areas. The handsome larva feeds on a wide range of trees and shrubs. The closely related Dark Dagger (*A.tridens*) is almost identical in the adult stage and the two species

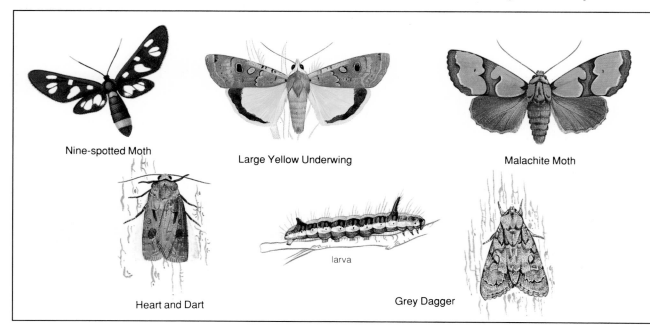

Nine-spotted Moth

Large Yellow Underwing

Malachite Moth

Heart and Dart

larva

Grey Dagger

cannot be distinguished with certainty without dissection. But their larvae are quite different, that of the Dark Dagger having a shorter horn and a white back.

Ⓑ◐✿🐛

Malachite Moth
Celotaenia celsia
50mm. On the wing from August to October, this beautiful moth flies in open pine forests. It is named after the green mineral malachite, and its colouration provides good camouflage when it rests on lichen-covered trees by day. The larva is yellowish-green with black spots and a brown head and feeds on grasses. Found in northern and central Europe, the moth is to be found mainly in eastern areas.

✤

Mullein Moth
Cucullia verbasci
50mm. The streaked brown forewings and the tuft of pale hairs on the thorax give this moth a strong resemblance to a broken twig or sliver of bark when it is resting on the ground or on low-growing vegetation. It flies from April to June in most habitats, although it is absent from the far north. The larva, well protected by warning colours, feeds openly on various kinds of mullein and often completely destroys the flower spikes – much to the annoyance of gardeners. The Shark Moth (*C. umbratica*) has a similar shape but is greyer.

Ⓑ✿🐛

Angle Shades
Phlogophora meticulosa
40–50mm. The forewings of this noctuid are a beautiful mixture of pink, green and brown with a bold olive-green 'V' across the centre. The colours fade with age and the greens quickly change to brown in dead specimens. The curious way in which the wings crumple at rest makes the moth remarkably like a dead leaf. Two overlapping broods fly throughout the year, but the moth is most common from May to September. The larva is brown or green with dark diagonal dashes on the back and a white line on each side. It feeds on herbaceous plants and is often a garden pest. A great migrant, the moth is a regular visitor to Iceland.

Ⓑ◐✿🐛

Herald Moth
Scoliopteryx libatrix
40–50mm. The attractive forewings of this moth conceal dull greyish brown hind wings. In the northern half of Europe it flies from August to October and then goes into hibernation in hollow trees and out-houses. It reappears to fly from March to June, and thus has a very long adult life. The bright green larva is relatively long and slender and it feeds on willows and poplars during the summer. In southern regions, including parts of southern England, some of the larvae mature quickly to give new adults in June.

Ⓑ◐✿🐛

Silver-Y
Autographa gamma
30–45mm. Named for the silvery mark in the middle of the forewing, this moth is a great migrant. Resident in southern Europe, where it flies more or less throughout the year, it spreads to all regions during the summer and regularly reaches Iceland. It can be seen hovering at flowers by day and night. One or two broods develop in northern and central Europe during the summer. The larva is green with faint white markings and it tapers markedly towards the front. Like many related species, it has only two pairs of prolegs in front of the claspers. It feeds on low-growing herbs.

Ⓑ✿😟🐛

Antler Moth
Cerapteryx graminis
25–40mm. This moth is named for the pale, branching streaks on the forewings. The wings range from greyish-brown to rich chestnut. The moth flies over grassland from June to September, and can be seen by night and day. It is common on the rough grazings of upland regions. The female is much larger than the male and has paler wings. The larva is dark brown and rather plump, with pale lines on the back and a broader white stripe along each side. It feeds on grasses and can destroy upland pasture. It is resident throughout Europe, including Iceland.

🐛

LIFE CYCLE	J	F	M	A	M	J	J	A	S	O	N	D
Nine-spotted Moth												
Heart and Dart												
Lg Yellow Underwing												
Grey Dagger												
Malachite Moth												
Mullein Moth												
Angle Shades												
Herald Moth												
Silver-Y												
Antler Moth												

The key to this chart is on page 336.

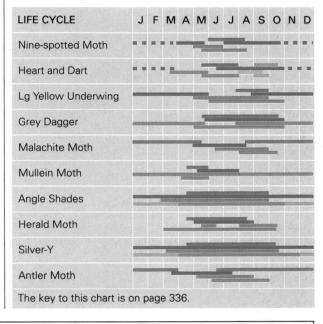

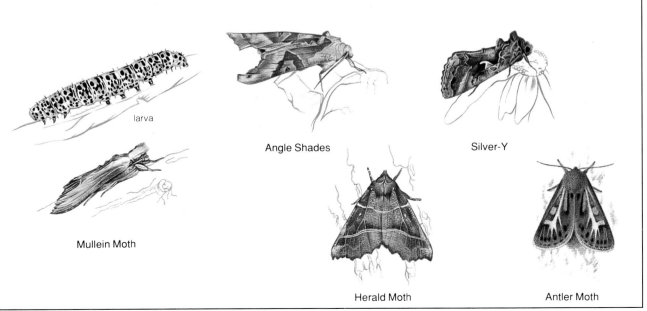

larva

Angle Shades

Silver-Y

Mullein Moth

Herald Moth

Antler Moth

Bees, Wasps, Ants, and Relatives

This large and variable order (Hymenoptera) contains over 100,000 known species. The hind wings are generally much smaller than the front wings and are linked to them by a row of microscopic hooks. Two distinct sub-orders exist: the Symphyta and the Apocrita. The Symphyta contains the sawflies, in which the thorax and abdomen are broadly joined without any 'waist', while all the other hymenopterans belong to the Apocrita and all have the characteristic 'wasp waist'. The females of the bees and wasps and many of the ants have powerful stings, which are modified ovipositors. Many wasps use their stings to paralyze prey for their young, but otherwise the stings are used for defence. Social behaviour is displayed by some bees and wasps and by all the ants. These insects live in colonies founded by females known as queens. All the other members of the colony are the queen's offspring. Most of them are sterile females called workers and they do all the building and food-gathering chores as well as tending their younger sisters. Unless otherwise stated the measurements given in the descriptions are wingspans.

SAWFLIES

These insects get their name from the tiny saw-like ovipositors with which most of the females cut slits in plants before laying their eggs there. Most of the larvae feed on leaves and look like caterpillars except that sawfly larvae have more legs on the abdomen. Some live inside the stems of their food-plants. Adult sawflies feed mainly on pollen.

Horntail

Urocerus gigas
Family Siricidae
10–60mm. The female of this species has a drill-like ovipositor with which she lays eggs in the trunks of weak and dying pine trees. The larva feeds on the timber and takes two or three years to mature. It frequently survives the sawmill and causes great alarm when the adult emerges from building timbers in new houses. Also known as the Wood Wasp, it flies from May to October.
Ⓑ Ⓐ ⊗

Gooseberry Sawfly

Nematus ribesii
Family Tenthredinidae
10–15mm. The male of this species is more slender than the female and has a lot of black on the abdomen. Found from April to September on gooseberries and currants, both wild and cultivated, its gregarious larvae often completely strip the bushes.
Ⓑ Ⓞ ⊗

BEES

This family (Apidae) contains several hundred European species. Most are clothed with hairs which play a vital role in collecting and carrying pollen. Most bees are solitary insects, with each female making her own nest and stocking it with nectar and pollen. When the nest is complete the female generally takes no further interest in it. The social bees include the honey bees and the bumble bees, all of which make their nests with wax from their own bodies. Honey bee colonies are perennial, but bumble bee colonies last for just one season. The social bees all carry pollen home on their hind legs, held in place by rows of stiff hairs known as the pollen baskets. Adult bees feed mainly on nectar. The family also contains a number of social parasites often called cuckoo bees, which make no nests of their own and lay their eggs in the nests of other bees.

This Honey Bee is reaping a rich harvest from a dandelion flower. Its pollen baskets are bulging with the bright orange pollen.

Tawny Mining Bee

Andrena fulva
20-25mm. This is one of several relatively flat, solitary bees which excavate nest burrows in lawns and similar places. The female is bright reddish brown, but the male is much duller. This bee is abundant in spring, especially on Blackthorn blossom and on garden currants and gooseberries.
Ⓑ ⊗ ⊕

Leaf-cutter Bee

Megachile centuncularis
15-20mm. This is the bee responsible for cutting neat, semi-circular pieces from the leaves of roses and other plants. The female uses the pieces to construct sausage-shaped cells in hollow stems or other suitable crevices. Each cell then receives an egg and a store of food. The adult resembles a small honey bee, but the female has bright orange hairs under her abdomen. It flies from May to August in northern and central Europe.
Ⓑ ⊗ ⊕

Long-horned Bee

Eucera longicornis
20–25mm. The male of this species has very long antennae and a bright yellow face. The female has normal-length antennae and, apart from her wing veins, she looks very much like a honey

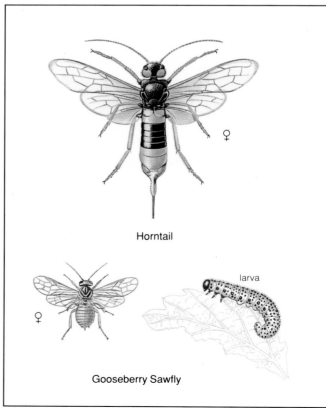

Horntail

♀

Gooseberry Sawfly

larva

THE NEST OF THE LEAF-CUTTER BEE

1. The female Leaf-cutter Bee cuts discs from a leaf with her jaws. 2. She carries them to her nest-site. 3. She uses the fragments to construct the cells of the nest.

bee drone. She makes her nest in the ground. This bee is on the wing from April to July, and is found mainly in dry, grassy areas.

Ⓑ ⊛ ⓜ

Carpenter Bee
Xylocopa violacea
40–50mm. This is the most common of four very similar bees in southern and central Europe. This fast-flying insect appears in late summer and feeds on a wide range of flowers before hibernating in various holes and crevices. It reappears and mates in the spring, after which the female excavates a nest in a dead tree or other timber.

◯ ⊛ ⓜ

Honey Bee
Apis mellifera
20–25mm (worker). There are many races of honey bee, some with orange patches on the front of the abdomen, but all can be recognized by the very long, narrow cell reaching almost to the wing-tip. The nest consists of several vertical wax combs, each made of six-sided cells. The young bees are reared in the cells, which are also used to store honey and pollen. Honey bees spend the winter huddled in the centre of the nest. The much larger queen leaves the hive only to mate or to move off with a swarm to a new home.

Ⓑ ◯ ⊛ ⓜ

White-tailed Bumble Bee
Bombus lucorum
20–40mm. This bee may be distinguished from several similar species by its lemon yellow bands. It is among the first of the bumble bees to appear in the spring. The queens often wake from hibernation in February, when they visit sallow blossom and any other available flowers. They nest under the ground, usually in deserted mouse-holes, when nectar supplies build up later in the spring. A brood of small workers is reared and they take over the foraging work. Later workers are larger, and those reared in late summer are almost as large as the queens. New queens and males are reared in late summer and, once they have mated, the new queens begin to look for hibernation sites. The other members of the colony die in the autumn.

Ⓑ ◯ ⊛ ⓜ

Red-tailed Bumble Bee
Bombus lapidarius
20–40mm. This striking bee flies in all kinds of open country, but is often confined to coastal grassland in northern regions. The male of the species, which is seen only in late summer, has a

yellow collar just behind the head. Its life cycle is similar to that of the White-tailed Bumble Bee, although the nest is frequently built under a stone. The closely related *Bombus ruderarius* is very similar, but has reddish brown pollen baskets instead of black.

Ⓑ ◗ ⊛ ⓜ

Carder Bee
Bombus pascuorum
20–32mm. This very common bumble bee is usually tawny brown but it often has a lot of black on it, especially in northern regions. However, in southern Europe it is often quite red. The coat is always rather thin. The queens are very fond of deadnettle flowers in the spring. Its life cycle is similar to that of the other bumble bee species, but the nest is usually built on the ground rather than under it. It is sometimes built in old birds' nests. The name Carder Bee comes from its habit of collecting fibrous material for the nest and combing it out with its legs in much the same way that wool from sheep is carded before spinning. This bee has a very long season and remains on the wing well into the autumn.

Ⓑ ◗ ⊛ ⓜ

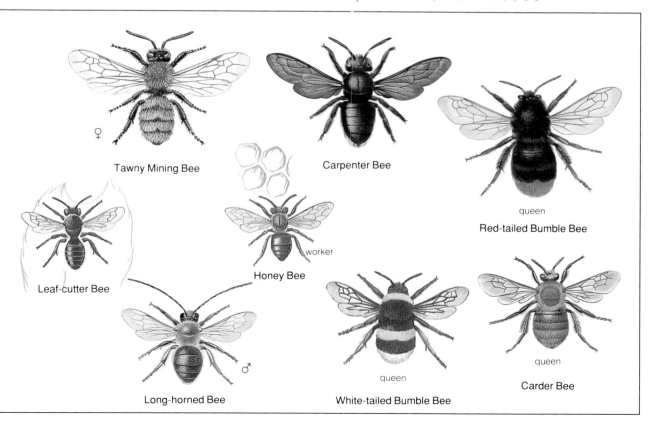

Tawny Mining Bee

Carpenter Bee

queen
Red-tailed Bumble Bee

Leaf-cutter Bee

Honey Bee
worker

♂
Long-horned Bee

queen
White-tailed Bumble Bee

queen
Carder Bee

SOCIAL WASPS

The members of this family (Vespidae) form annual colonies like those of the bumble bees (see p. 369). The nests consist of horizontal tiers, each with numerous six-sided cells, and all are built with paper that the wasps make by chewing old wood. The grubs live in the cells and are fed mainly with chewed insects. No food is stored in the cells. The queens are usually much larger than the workers. Social wasps are distinguished from most of the solitary species by the way they fold their wings longitudinally along the sides of the body. Most solitary species lay their wings flat over the backs.

Hornet
Vespa crabro
30–50mm. This is the largest European social wasp and is easily distinguished by its brown and yellow colours. It usually nests in hollow trees. There are no more than a few hundred colony members. On the wing from April to October, it is often attracted to lights at night. Its population fluctuates markedly from year to year, especially in Britain.
ⒷⓄⒶⓄ

Common Wasp
Vespula vulgaris
25–45mm. This is one of several common black and yellow species. Its face usually has an anchor-shaped mark and the yellow thoracic stripes are parallel-sided. There are four yellow spots at the rear of the thorax. This species usually nests under the ground or in roof cavities, building a yellowish football-sized nest covered with overlapping 'shells'. It flies from April to October.
ⒷⓄⒶⒶ

Paper Wasp
Polistes dominulus
20–25mm. The abdomen of this species tapers at the front instead of being squared off as in other social wasps. It lives in colonies of just a few dozen insects. The queens are no larger than the workers. The nest is a small paper umbrella with just a few dozen cells, often fixed to buildings. It is on the wing from March to October in southern and central Europe.
ⒶⒶⒶ

SOLITARY WASPS

Potter Wasp
Eumenes coarctatus
Family Eumenidae
20–25mm. The first abdominal segment of this wasp is more or less bell-shaped and much narrower than the following segments. It is named for the little clay pots which the female makes on heathers and other plants. After laying an egg in each one, she fills it with paralyzed caterpillars and seals it. On the wing from June to September it is widespread on the continent, but confined to southern parts of Britain.
ⒷⒶ

Spiny Mason Wasp
Odynerus spinipes
15–20mm. This is one of several similar species, distinguished from most social wasps by the anterior tapering of the abdomen, and from most other solitary species by the lengthwise folding of the wings at rest – a feature shared by all members of the Eumenidae. It nests in vertical sandy banks and in the mortar of old walls, stocking the nest with weevil larvae. It flies from May to August.
ⒷⒶⒶⓄ

Ectemnius cephalotes
Family Sphecidae
15–30mm. This is one of several very similar wasps that nest in rotten tree stumps and other dead wood. Its nests are stocked with flies, which are paralyzed and brought in slung under the wasp's body. It remains on the wing from June to September.
ⒷⒶⓄⒶⒶ

Bembix rostrata
25–35mm. This wasp is very similar to some of the social wasps, but it holds its wings flat over its body at rest. It nests in sandy soil and the female has a prominent brush of hairs on her front legs for sweeping the sand. The nest is stocked with flies and, unlike most other solitary wasps, the female brings further supplies from time to time as her larvae make inroads into the store. It is on the wing from May to August.
ⒶⓄⒶ

Ammophila sabulosa
25–30mm. This is one of a number of slender species known as sand wasps. They all nest in sandy soil and stock their nests with small, hairless caterpillars. The female has strong bristles on her front legs for sweeping away the sand.
ⒷⒶⒶⒶ

Bee-killer Wasp
Philanthus triangulum
5–35mm. The female of this species is much bigger than the male. Its abdomen is largely yellow, usually with two or three black triangles on it. The nest is often dug deep in a sandy bank and the female has a strong comb of bristles on her front legs to help with the digging. The nest is stocked with honey bees, which the wasp catches on flowers and paralyzes with

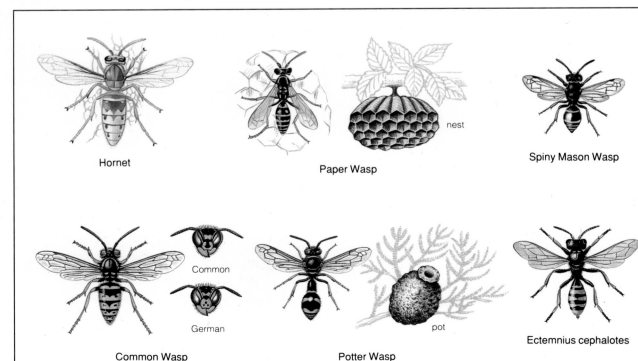

Hornet

Paper Wasp

nest

Spiny Mason Wasp

Common Wasp

Common

German

Potter Wasp

pot

Ectemnius cephalotes

her sting. She flies back to her nest with the victims clasped upside-down to her belly. Found in southern and central Europe, it is rare in Britain.

Ⓑ 🪱 😊 🗓

Anoplius viaticus

Family Pompilidae
20–30mm. This is one of several similar species which, in common with the rest of the family, stock their nests with spiders. Its legs are relatively long, especially the hind ones, and the female is usually much larger than the male. Its nest is usually excavated in the ground and, unlike most members of the Sphecidae, this insect catches its prey before digging its nest. It is active all summer in southern and central Europe.

Ⓑ 🪱 🕷 🗓

ANTS

In this family of social insects (Formicidae) the workers are always wingless and generally much smaller than the queens. Males and queens are winged for their mating flights, but the queens lose their wings before beginning their nests or, as often happens, before entering an existing nest and joining forces with the resident queen. The nests

Wood Ants rub their antennae together to exchange information, usually about the location and quality of food sources.

have no elaborate cells of wax or paper – just simple chambers excavated in the soil or in timber. There are carnivorous, herbivorous, and omnivorous species and they are active in all but the coldest months of the year, at which time they retire to the innermost parts of the nest and become dormant.

Wood Ant

Formica rufa
5–11mm long. This is a large black and reddish brown ant (males and queens are blacker than workers) whose thread-like waist carries a slender, leaf-like scale. Its nest, often built around a tree stump, consists of a maze of underground tunnels topped by a large mound covered

with leaves and other debris. The ant has no sting, but can squirt formic acid from its rear when alarmed and it also has a fierce bite. Basically omnivorous, it has a preference for animal food and is a protected species in some European countries because of its value in removing insect pests from the forests. Its mating flights take place in May and June.

Ⓑ 🔾 ④

Black Garden Ant

Lasius niger
3–5mm long. This very common ant generally nests under stones but is quite happy under paths and houses and even under town pavements. Its waist has a small upright scale on it. It has no sting. This ant is omnivorous but has a strong liking for the honeydew

produced by aphids. Huge mating swarms emerge from the nests between June and August. The Yellow Meadow Ant (*L. flavus*) is very similar apart from its colour and builds the familiar ant hills in rough grassland.

Ⓑ 🪱 🕷 🗓

Harvester Ant

Messor barbara
4–12mm long. This dark ant has a chestnut or black head and a clearly two-segmented waist. It has a sting. It lives in dry places in southern and central Europe and feeds almost exclusively on seeds. Long lines of workers can be seen carrying or dragging seeds to their nests, where large-headed workers, mistakenly called soldiers, crack them open with their large jaws. The discarded husks often form prominent mounds around the nest entrances.

🪱 🕷 😊 🗓

Red Garden Ant

Myrmica ruginodis
5–10mm long. This very common stinging ant has a two-segmented waist. It is mainly carnivorous, although it enjoys honeydew. It commonly nests under stones in gardens, with up to 300 workers in each colony. It also nests in tree stumps. Its mating flights take place from July to August.

Ⓑ 🪱 🔾 ④ 🕷 🗓

Bembix rostrata

Bee-killer Wasp

Wood Ant

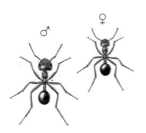

♂ ♀

Harvester Ant

Ammophila sabulosa

Anoplius viaticus

Black Garden Ant

Red Garden Ant

371

Parasitic Hymenoptera

These insects nearly all spend their early lives inside other insects, although some merely attach themselves to the outsides of their hosts. Adult females usually track down suitable hosts by scent and then lay their eggs in or on them. The parasitic grubs gradually destroy their hosts, but not until the parasites themselves are fully grown and ready to pupate. The females of some species have ovipositors longer than the rest of the body. The ichneumons are the best known of the parasites, but there are many other families.

Chrysis ignita
Family Chrysididae
15mm. This is one of a group of colourful parasites known as ruby-tailed wasps or jewel wasps. They are also known as cuckoo wasps because they lay their eggs in the nests of solitary bees and wasps. The grubs then consume the host larvae and may also take some of the stored food. Adults can be seen searching for their hosts' nests on walls and tree trunks from April to September.
Ⓑ ⦿ ◯ ✪ ⬚

Scolia hirta
Family Scoliidae
35mm. Common on flowers from June to October, this sturdy insect has a deep violet sheen to its wings. Its larvae parasitize various chafer grubs. Found in central and southern Europe, it is often abundant on sand dunes. It is not found in Britain. The related *S. flavifrons*, from the Mediterranean area, is similar but measures up to 60mm.
⦿ ⬚

Apanteles glomeratus
Family Braconidae
4mm. This insect grows up inside the caterpillars of the Large White butterfly and plays a major role in controlling the population of this pest. A single caterpillar may support 150 *Apanteles* grubs. Fully-grown grubs leave the host and pupate in little yellow cocoons around its shrivelled skin. Adults fly from April to September.
Ⓑ ✪

Ophion luteus
Family Ichneumonidae
30mm. This is one of several similar ichneumons which develop in or on moth caterpillars. Its ovipositor is very short, but can cause a pricking sensation if the insect is handled. Adults fly by night in summer and autumn and are commonly attracted to lights.
Ⓑ ◯ ✪ ⬚

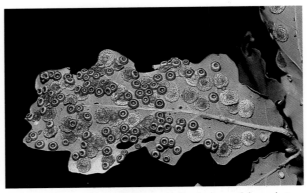

Spangle galls, caused by gall wasps, are abundant on oak leaves but do not harm the trees. Two separate species have invaded this leaf.

Rhyssa persuasoria
50–60mm. This large ichneumon is parasitic on horntail grubs tunnelling in pine trunks. Having located a suitable host by scent – a considerable achievement in itself – the female uses her long ovipositor to drill accurately into the trunk and to lay an egg on the grub.
Ⓑ ⬆

GALL WASPS

These small insects (Family Cynipidae) are responsible for the development of oak apples, robin's pincushions, and many other strange plant growths known as galls. The adults are rather ant-like, with or without wings, and are always somewhat flattened from side to side. Females lay their eggs in the plants and the presence of the young larvae causes the plant tissues to swell and form the galls, with the larvae feeding on the nutritious tissues inside them. Each species induces the formation of its own characteristic gall.

Biorhiza pallida
10mm. This gall wasp induces the formation of oak apples on oaks in summer. Adults emerge from the galls in June and July and mated females lay eggs on fine oak roots. The new larvae cause small spherical galls to develop on the roots. Wingless females emerge in the spring and lay eggs on the twigs without mating. These lead to a new generation of oak apples.
Ⓑ ◯

Ruby-tailed Wasp

Apanteles glomeratus

Ichneumon Fly

oak gall

Gall Wasp

Scolia hirta

Rhyssa persuasoria

Diplolepis rosae

HOW THE MILLIPEDE WALKS

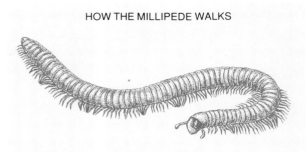

The millipede moves its numerous legs forward in groups, although each leg swings forward slightly after the one behind it, so waves move rhythmically along the body and carry it smoothly forward.

Diplolepis rosae

10mm. This common gall wasp is responsible for the growth of robin's pincushion or bedeguar galls on wild roses. Adult wasps emerge from the woody galls from April to June and lay their eggs on the fresh leaves and twigs. Males are extremely rare in this species and the females produce fertile eggs without mating.

Ⓑ 🐞 💮

MYRIAPODS

This section comprises the centipedes and millipedes. These are superficially similar arthropods with long, many-segmented bodies and many legs. As a result they have often been placed together in a single section known as the Myriapoda (many feet). But there are many significant differences between the two groups and they are now usually placed in two separate classes. The centipedes (Class Chilopoda) are fast-moving carnivores which catch and kill other animals with a pair of poison claws surrounding the head. Mostly nocturnal, they have rather flat bodies and one pair of legs per segment. The millipedes (Class Diplopoda) are relatively slow-moving herbivores, cylindrical in shape, with two pairs of short legs on most of the body segments. Several species are pests of cultivated plants.

Centipedes

Lithobius forficatus

Family Lithobiidae
18–30mm. Like all members of the family, this very common species has 15 pairs of legs, including the hind legs which trail behind and act as extra antennae. It spends the daytime under logs, stones, or loose bark.

Ⓑ 🐛 🅾 ➍ 🐞 💮

Haplophilus subterraneus

Family Himantariidae
50–70mm. This centipede inhabits soil and leaf litter, and has between 77 and 83 pairs of legs. This is one of the few centipedes which occasionally damage plant roots.

Ⓑ 🅾 🐞 💮

Scolopendra cingulatus

Family Scolopendridae
8–12cm. Europe's largest centipede, this species is most likely to be found lurking under stones on rough ground. It has 21 pairs of legs and varies from yellowish brown to deep green. It has a painful and potentially dangerous bite.

😊 🐛 💮

Scutigera coleoptrata

Family Scuterigidae
30mm. This species has 15 pairs of legs. The last pair are so much like the antennae that it is hard to know which end of the animal is which. It is an extremely fast runner and inhabits caves, old walls, and other rocky places in the Mediterranean region. It occurs in buildings further north but is very rare in Britain.

Ⓑ 🐞

Millipedes

Polydesmus angustus

Family Polydesmidae
25mm. This is one of the flat-backed millipedes, with broad flanges on each segment giving it a distinctly flat appearance. It lives in leaf litter and other decaying vegetable matter.

Ⓑ 🅾 ➍ 🐞 💮

Tachypodiulus niger

Family Iulidae
50mm. This is one of several very similar shiny, cylindrical species which coil up when disturbed. It regularly climbs trees and is often found under loose bark.

Ⓑ 🅾 🐞 💮

Pill Millipede

Glomeris marginata
Family Glomeridae
20mm. Named for its ability to roll into a ball, this millipede is often confused with woodlice, but it has 17–19 pairs of legs. Woodlice have 7 pairs. It lives in turf or leaf litter on lime-rich soils.

Ⓑ 🅾 🐞 💮

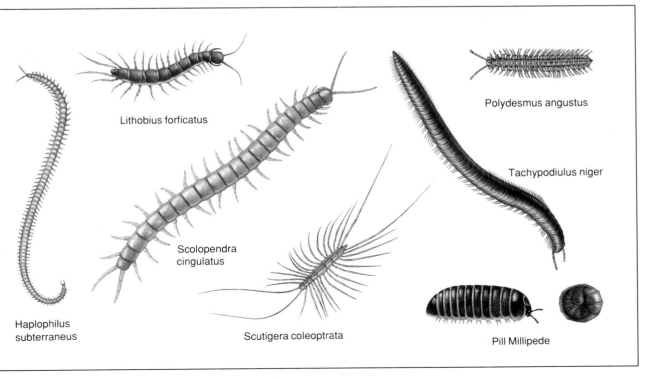

Lithobius forficatus

Scolopendra cingulatus

Haplophilus subterraneus

Scutigera coleoptrata

Polydesmus angustus

Tachypodiulus niger

Pill Millipede

The Peacock Worm's colourful fan of tentacles waves in the ocean currents, filtering planktonic food from the water.

SEGMENTED WORMS

The segmented worms or annelids (Phylum Annelida) have bodies that are divided into many rings or segments. There are three classes. In the Oligochaeta, each segment has just a few bristles. The leeches, which belong to the Hirudinea, have suckers fore and aft but no bristles. Most are aquatic. The Polychaeta contains the marine bristleworms.

Common Earthworm
Lumbricus terrestris
Family Lumbricidae
9–30cm, with 110–160 segments. This worm is reddish-brown above and yellowish below. The swollen region or clitellum produces cases for the eggs, and covers segments 32–37 in the adult. Like all earthworms, it feeds by swallowing soil and digesting organic matter in it.
Ⓑ ◐ ✦ ⓶

Horse Leech
Haemopis sanguisuga
Family Hirudidae
30cm long when extended, but can contract to a blob. This leech is green, brown or black. It can swim, but spends much of its time hunting worms in soil. Prey is crushed with blunt teeth and ingested whole. It cannot pierce human skin to suck blood and has no connection with horses.
Ⓑ ☻

Polychaeta

Ragworm
Nereis diversicolor
Family Nereidae
10cm with 90–120 segments. This worm varies from green to red, but is usually yellowish with a red line on its back. A weak swimmer, it lives in muddy or sandy shores. It grabs small prey in its strong jaws and also strains food particles from the water.
Ⓑ ☻

Lugworm
Arenicola marina
Family Arenicolidae
Up to 35cm. This worm is green to black with feathery red gills. It lives in a U-shaped burrow in mud and sand, sucking in sediment and digesting its organic content before voiding the remainder in coils on the surface. Immense numbers of lugworms live around the coast and in estuaries.
Ⓑ ☻

Peacock Worm
Sabella pavonina
Family Sabellidae
Up to 25cm. This worm lives in a slender tube constructed with sand grains. It filters food from the water with the fan of tentacles around its mouth. Large numbers live below low-tide level, but if uncovered they withdraw their tentacles and leave the tubes sticking up like pencils.
Ⓑ ☻

COELENTERATES

The coelenterates (Phylum Coelenterata) have no true skeleton, no head, and no real sense organs, although a simple network of nerves runs through the body. There is just one body opening, through which food is taken in and waste passed out. It is usually surrounded by food-catching tentacles. These are carnivorous animals and usually well-endowed with stinging cells which are fired into the prey like tiny harpoons. There are two main types of body: the polyp, which is fixed and roughly cup-shaped, and the free-swimming medusa or jellyfish type. Sea anemones and corals form the Class Anthozoa, which is entirely marine. Jellyfishes of the Class Scyphozoa are also confined to the sea, but the Class Hydrozoa contains several freshwater animals, such as Hydra, as well as many marine ones. Many of the latter form branching colonies.

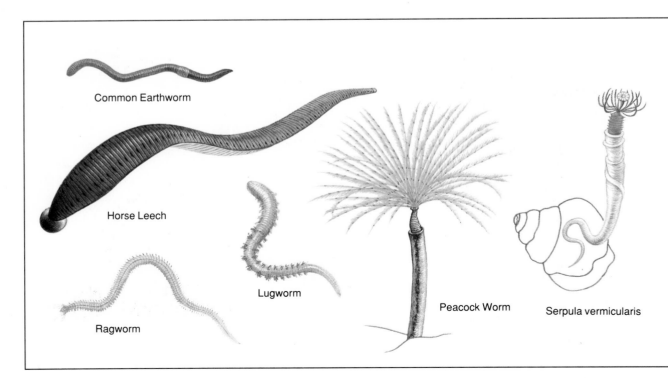

Common Earthworm

Horse Leech

Ragworm

Lugworm

Peacock Worm

Serpula vermicularis

Serpula vermicularis
Family Serpulidae
5cm. This worm secretes a limestone tube around itself and attaches it to stones and shells in shallow water. It filters food particles from the water with its tentacles, withdrawing into the tube when the tide recedes and closing the entrance with a cone-shaped lid.
Ⓑ 😊

Anthozoa

Beadlet Anemone
Actinia equina
Family Actiniidae
Up to 6cm across and 7cm high, this is Europe's most common shore-dwelling sea anemone. Usually reddish-brown, often with green spots, it abounds in rocky crevices in the inter-tidal zone. Out of water, it withdraws its tentacles and contracts to a blob of jelly.
Ⓑ 😊

Dahlia Anemone
Urticina felina
Up to 7cm across and 15cm high when fully expanded, although usually much shorter. Often found with the beadlet anemone, this species can usually be distinguished by its paler, banded tentacles. The body is often decorated with small stones and shell fragments, which adhere to the sticky surface.
Ⓑ 😊

Snakelocks Anemone
Anemonia viridis
Up to 12cm across and 5cm high, with relatively long tentacles. The colour of this species ranges from white to green or brown. Its tentacles cannot be withdrawn into the body and, unlike the Beadlet and Dahlia anemones, this anemone can stand only a very short exposure to the air. It normally lives in rock pools or below low-tide level. It often occurs in clusters because it can reproduce simply by splitting in two and the two new individuals frequently stay close together. Splitting can be accomplished in just two or three hours. This species is one of the largest and most common sea anemones occurring in the Mediterranean.
Ⓑ 😊

Scyphozoa

Common Jellyfish
Aurelia aurita
Family Aureliidae
Up to 40cm across. This largely colourless jellyfish is easily recognized by its four circular, violet reproductive organs. It is probably the world's most common jellyfish and drifts in large shoals, which are often washed up on our beaches. Although it has stinging cells, these have a negligible effect on people. The adult jellyfish feeds on planktonic organisms, which become caught up in its sticky coat and are then wiped off and carried to the mouth by the four frilly arms.
Ⓑ 😊

Hydrozoa

Portuguese Man o'War
Physalia physalis
Family Physalidae
This colonial animal consists of hundreds of small polyps clustered under a gas-filled blue or pink float. Its name derives from the fanciful resemblance of its float to old Portuguese warships. The colony drifts with the winds and currents, trailing its long tentacles in the water. The tentacles, armed with stinging cells powerful enough to cause severe injury to people, capture small fish and pull them up to the feeding polyps under the float for digestion. The food is then distributed to the whole colony. It is usually seen offshore in the Atlantic and Mediterranean.
Ⓑ 😊

Brown Hydra
Hydra oligactis
Family Hydridae
Up to 10mm long when extended. This animal hangs from plants in ponds and streams. Its tentacles catch water fleas and other small animals and push them into the mouth, making the body bulge until they are digested. Small buds often sprout from the body and grow into new individuals which eventually fall and become independent. It can also reproduce sexually and passes the winter as an egg surrounded by a tough coat. There are several similar green or brown species.
Ⓑ 😊

COMB JELLIES

These marine animals (Phylum Ctenophora) were once grouped with the coelenterates because of their similar body structures, but they have no stinging cells and they are now placed in a separate phylum.

Sea Gooseberry
Pleurobrachia pileus
Family Pleurobrachiidae
2–3cm in diameter. This creature drifts through the water by beating the iridescent cilia which form eight vertical rows on its body. It eats small animals which are caught with sticky lasso-like threads on the retractile tentacles. It resembles a soft glass marble when washed up on the beach, but very soon shrivels in the air.

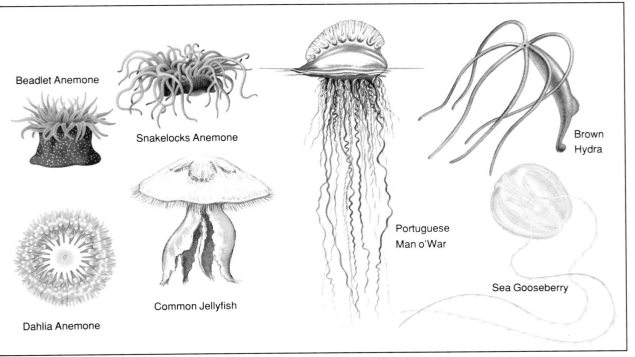

Beadlet Anemone

Snakelocks Anemone

Dahlia Anemone

Common Jellyfish

Portuguese Man o'War

Brown Hydra

Sea Gooseberry

INDEX

ACKNOWLEDGEMENTS

The publishers would like to thank the following artists for their contribution to this book:

Main Chapters Introduction (pages 6–9); Wild Flowers: (11–89) Peter Chesterton, John Davis, Colin Emberson, George Thompson ; Trees and Shrubs (91–129) Norma Birgin, Richard Bonson, Terry Callcut, Wendy Bramall; Ferns and Mosses (132–39) Richard Bonson, Wendy Bramall; Fungi (142–160) Sean Milne, Bernard Robinson; Seaweeds (161–3) Wendy Bramall; Mammals (165–93) William Oliver, Guy Troughton; Birds (195–265) Alan Harris; Reptiles and Amphibians (269–79) Denys Ovenden; Fishes (282–95) Alan Male, Denys Ovenden, Norman Weever; Invertebrates (297–375) Sophie Allington, Terry Callcut, Richard Lewington, Denys Ovenden, Gordon Riley, Bernard Robinson, George Thompson, David Wright.

Habitat Landscapes Heaths and Moors (pages 46–7) Richard Bonson; The Grassland Scene (84–5) Anne Winterbotham; The Coniferous Forests (98–9) Guy Troughton; The Deciduous Forests (126–7) Gill Tomblin; Man-made Habitats (148–9) Guy Troughton; Life in the Mountains (188–9) Guy Troughton; The Northern Tundra (246–7) Guy Troughton; Freshwater Habitats (286–7) Mick Loates; The Coast (310–11) Mick Loates; Mediterranean Lands (332–3) Denys Ovenden.

We would also like to thank the following for supplying photographs for this book:

Page 3 Swift Picture Library; 6 B.Gibbons; 8 M.Chinery; 10 Swift Picture Library; 11 M.Chinery; 13 Natural Science Photos; 14 M.Chinery; 16 NHPA/R.Knightbridge; 19 NHPA/R.Tidman; 20 NHPA/D.Woodfall; 22 NHPA/E.A.Janes; 24 NHPA/M.Garwood; 26 NHPA/D.Woodfall; 28 NHPA/D.Woodfall; 30 NHPA/L.Campbell; 32 NHPA/J.Bain; 34 NHPA/ L.Campbell; 36 NHPA/M.Garwood; 38 NHPA/G.Bernard; 40 NHPA/S.Dalton; 42 NHPA/S.Dalton; 44 NHPA/ D.Woodfall; 47 M.Chinery; 49 NHPA/M.Garwood; 50 M.Chinery; 52 M.Chinery; 55 NHPA/N.Dennis; 56 NHPA/ G.Cambridge; 58 NHPA/M.Garwood; 60 NHPA/L.Campbell; 62 NHPA/L.Campbell; 64 M.Chinery; 66 NHPA/J.Bain; 68 C.Mattison; 70 NHPA/S.Dalton; 72 NHPA/M.Garwood; 77 M.Chinery; 78 M.Chinery; 80 C.Mattison; 82 NHPA/ S.Dalton; 86 NHPA/N.Callow; 88 NHPA/D.Woodfall; 90 NHPA/J.Meech; 91 ZEFA; 93 NHPA/G.Cambridge; 94 NHPA/ L.Campbell; 96 NHPA/N.Callow; 100 NHPA/D.Woodfall; 102 NHPA/E.A.Janes; 104 T.D.Timms; 106 Heather Angel; 108 Heather Angel; 110 NHPA/E.A.Janes; 112 NHPA/M.Garwood; 114 NHPA/L.Campbell; 116 NHPA/E.A.Janes; 118 NHPA/D.Woodfall; 120 NHPA/D.Woodfall; 122 C.Mattison; 124 NHPA/S.Dalton; 128 Heather Angel; 130 NHPA/ L.Campbell; 131 NHPA/D.Woodfall; 132 NHPA/D.Woodfall; 134 NHPA/L.Campbell; 136 M.Chinery; 138 NHPA/ S.Dalton; 140 Swift Picture Library; 141 NHPA/L.Campbell; 142 NHPA/M.Garwood; 143 NHPA/M.Garwood; 144 NHPA/J.&M.Bain; 146 NHPA/B.Paton; 148 NHPA/J.Blossom; 150 NHPA/B.Hawkes; 152 NHPA/M.Garwood; 154 NHPA/M.Garwood; 156 NHPA/S.Dalton; 158 NHPA/L.Campbell; 160 NHPA/L.Campbell; 162 NHPA/J.&M.Bain; 164 NHPA/M.Danegger; 165 ZEFA; 166 ZEFA; 167 B.Gibbons; 168 NHPA/S.Dalton; 170 NHPA/S.Dalton; 172 NHPA/ Silvestris; 174 NHPA/S.Dalton; 176 NHPA/S.Dalton; 178 NHPA/S.Dalton; 180 NHPA/H.Ausloos; 182 NHPA/ B.Hawkes; 184 NHPA/G.Laez; 186 NHPA/E.A.Janes; 188 NHPA/S.Dalton; 190 NHPA/M.Danegger; 192 NHPA/ Agence Nature; 194 Swan Photographic; 195 NHPA/S.Dalton; 196 NHPA/B.Hawkes 198 NHPA/Hellio & Van Ingen; 200 NHPA/L. Campbell; 203 NHPA/K.Ghani; 204 NHPA/P.Scott; 206 Swift Picture Library; 208 NHPA/S.Krasemann; 210 NHPA/J.Sauvanet; 212 NHPA/M.Danegger; 214 NHPA/D.Watts; 216 NHPA/L.Campbell; 218 NHPA/Hellio & Van Ingen; 220 NHPA/Hellio & Van Ingen; 222 NHPA/R.Tidman 224 Swift Picture Library; 226 NHPA/Hellio & Van Ingen; 228 NHPA/L.Campbell; 230 NHPA/M.Grey; 232 NHPA/M.Grey; 234 NHPA/S.Dalton; 236 NHPA/P.Petit; 238 NHPA/ S.Dalton; 240 NHPA/B.Hawkes; 242 NHPA/M.Danegger; 244 NHPA/L.Campbell; 247 NHPA/L.Campbell; 248 NHPA/ M.Grey; 250 NHPA/S.Dalton; 252 NHPA/R.Tidman; 254 NHPA/R.Tidman; 256 NHPA/S.Dalton; 258 NHPA/S.Dalton; 261 NHPA/M.Danegger; 262 NHPA/L.Campbell; 264 NHPA/R.Tidman; 266 B.Gibbons; 267 Heather Angel; 268 ZEFA; 269 NHPA/E.A.Janes; 270 NHPA/L.Campbell; 272 NHPA/Hellio & Van Ingen; 275 NHPA/Hellio & Van Ingen; 276 NHPA/S.Dalton; 278 NHPA/Lutra; 280 Heather Angel; 281 ZEFA; 282 ZEFA; 283 Heather Angel; 285 NHPA/ Agence Nature; 288 NHPA/Agence Nature; 290 Heather Angel; 292 Heather Angel; 294 NHPA/R.Waller; 296 B.Gibbons 297 Heather Angel (top) Swift Picture Library (bottom); 298 NHPA/M.Bain; 300 M.Chinery; 301 NHPA/ M.Tweedie; 302 M.Chinery; 304 NHPA/J.&M.Bain; 310 NHPA/E.A.Janes; 311 Swift Picture Library (top right and bottom) T.J.Smith (top left); 312 NHPA/J.Goodman; 314 M.Chinery; 316 NHPA/N.Callow; 319 NHPA/S.Dalton; 320 NHPA/S.Dalton; 322 M.Chinery; 325 Swift Picture Library; 326 NHPA/Lutra; 329 NHPA/S.Dalton; 330 NHPA/ S.Dalton; 334 M.Chinery; 337 NHPA/S.Dalton; 338 NHPA/E.A.Janes; 340 NHPA/S.Dalton; 342 NHPA/D.Woodfall; 344 NHPA/A.Barnes; 346 NHPA/S.Dalton; 348 NHPA/S.Dalton; 350 NHPA/M.Garwood; 352 NHPA/M.Garwood; 354 NHPA/S.Dalton; 356 NHPA/M.Garwood; 358 M.Chinery; 360 M.Chinery; 363 NHPA/N.Callow; 365 Swift Picture Library; 366 Swift Picture Library; 368 NHPA/J.Shaw; 371 NHPA/S.Dalton; 372 M.Chinery; 374 Heather Angel.